First Edition

ARITHMETIC

With an Introduction to Algebra

Ben Mayo

Cover Photo by David LaClair

Printed in the United States of America

CONTENTS

PREFACE

A Note to Instructors

This textbook was created to help students learn how to read, write, and think in terms of mathematics. Unlike most basic mathematics texts, this book introduces signed numbers right after whole numbers and then incorporates them into the chapters on fractions and decimals. This gives students extensive practice in working with negative numbers. Basic algebra concepts are introduced in each chapter including the topics of evaluating variable expressions and equation solving. This helps to reinforce arithmetic concepts that students are learning and it begins to prepare them to think abstractly. The exercises in this book cover a variety of levels of difficulty. However, all the exercises in this book are designed to be completed without the need for a calculator.

Acknowledgements

The author would like to thank the following people for their expertise in the areas of encouragement, grammar, inspiration, patience, proofreading, punctuation, and technical support:

Fellow instructors Julie Barker, Dodie Forest, Mike Jenck, Doug Lewis, Carolyn McCallum, Marty Meister, and Carolyn Schut at Yakima Valley Community College, as well as Jessica, Sean, and Sue Mayo.

This book is dedicated to the memory of Beverly Parnell (Bev), colleague, and friend. Bev always stood for what she believed in, even if it meant standing alone.

A Note to Students

This book was written with you in mind. The idea is to introduce you to the more challenging topics on a basic level so that when you encounter them in a future mathematics course they will be less intimidating. As you study the chapters on whole numbers, integers, fractions, and decimal numbers you will also be introduced to some basic algebraic concepts.

Unlike some textbooks that only work out a few examples of the easier problems and none of the more difficult ones, this book has an abundance of illustrations on several different levels. In addition, the examples show all the little in-between steps that are often left out. If you choose to read the explanations and the examples, you will find it a great help in gaining understanding of these topics. I hope your journey through this book will be an enjoyable one.

CHAPTER 1

WHOLE NUMBERS

Section 1: An Introduction to Whole Numbers

Counting Numbers or Natural Numbers
Whole Numbers
The Number Line
Inequalities
Place Value

Section 2: Rounding, Charts, Graphs, and an Introduction to Geometry

Rounding
Charts and Graphs
Geometric Terms

Section 3: Adding and Subtracting Whole Numbers

Addition
Addition Involving Carrying
Vocabulary of Addition
Variables
Evaluating Variable Expressions
Properties of Addition
Subtraction
Subtraction Involving Borrowing
Vocabulary of Subtraction

Section 4: More Adding and Subtracting of Whole Numbers

Applications with Charts or Graphs
Perimeter
Mixed Units
Angles

Section 5: Multiplying and Dividing Whole Numbers

Multiplication
Vocabulary of Multiplication
Properties of Multiplication
Exponents
Division
Vocabulary of Division
Properties of Division
Evaluating Variable Expressions

Section 6: More Multiplying and Dividing of Whole Numbers

Factors
Prime Numbers
Prime Factorization
Applications with Charts or Graphs
Perimeter of a Rectangle
Perimeter of a Square
Area of a Rectangle
Area of a Square
Other Formulas

Section 7: Order of Operations

Rules of Order of Operations
Evaluating Variable Expressions using Order of Operations
Formulas Involving Order of Operations

Section 8: Solving Equations

Equations
The Addition Property of Equality
The Subtraction Property of Equality
The Division Property of Equality
Solving Formulas using the Properties
Translating Words into Equations

Section 9: Estimating

Estimating

WHOLE NUMBERS

Section 1: An Introduction to Whole Numbers

Have you ever been at a railroad crossing and started to count the train cars as they passed by? Have you ever spotted a flock of birds overhead and started to count them as they flew by? What was the first number that you counted? I'll bet it wasn't zero. It was one, wasn't it? The point is this. When counting things, we do what is natural. We start with the number one. This leads to a set of numbers that are called the **counting numbers** or **natural numbers**. And as you might have guessed, they start with the number one.

The set of counting numbers, or natural numbers: 1, 2, 3, 4, 5, 6, 7, 8 . . .

The three dots after the number 8 are to imply that the list of numbers continues on forever.

Another important set of numbers is the **whole numbers**. This set includes all the natural numbers, along with the number zero.

The set of whole numbers: 0, 1, 2, 3, 4, 5, 6, 7, 8 . . .

Again, the three dots after the number 8 are to imply that the list of numbers continues on forever.

Note: A way to remember the whole numbers is to think of the number zero as a "hole". So, think of the set of whole numbers as starting with a hole.

One way of comparing or visualizing whole numbers is by use of a graph called a **number line**. Dots are placed on the number line, using a process called **graphing**. The number line has a **scale** at the bottom of it that indicates the value at that position on the number line. Where something begins is called its origin. The number line originates or begins with the number 0, so it should make sense that this point is known as the **origin**. A number line that is used to graph whole numbers has an arrowhead at its right end to imply the whole numbers continue to the right forever.

A number line

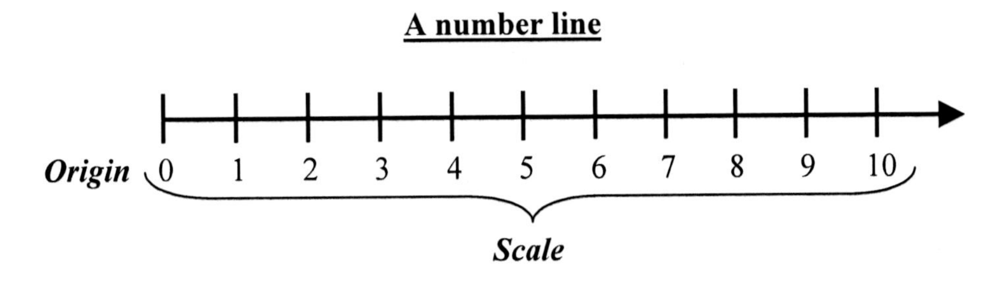

Example 1: Graph the whole numbers 3 and 7 on a number line.

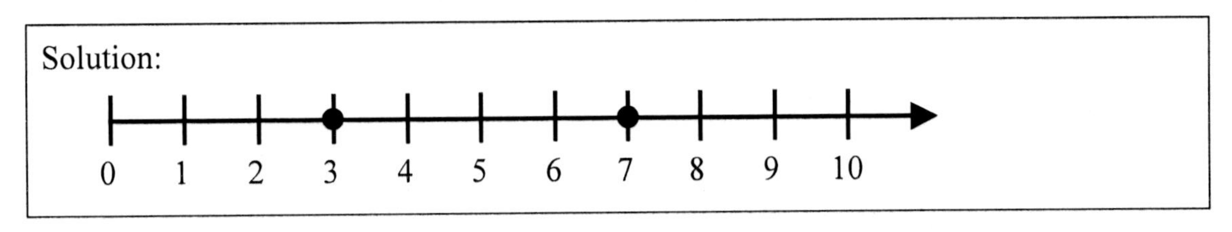

Moving from left to right on the number line, the numbers get larger. Moving from right to left on the number line, the numbers get smaller. Look at example 1 on the previous page. The number 7 is to the right of 3 on the number line because 7 is larger than 3. We can see this on the number line but there is another way to express the relationship between 7 and 3. To show that 7 is greater than 3, we use the symbol > (said, "**is greater than**") in the following manner: $7 > 3$. It also could be said that 3 is less than 7. We use the symbol < (said "**is less than**") in the following manner: $3 < 7$. The "is greater than" symbol > and the "is less than" symbol < are both called **inequality symbols**.

Example 2: Place the correct inequality symbol < or > between the two numbers. 7 2.

Solution: Since 7 is to the right of 2 on the number line,

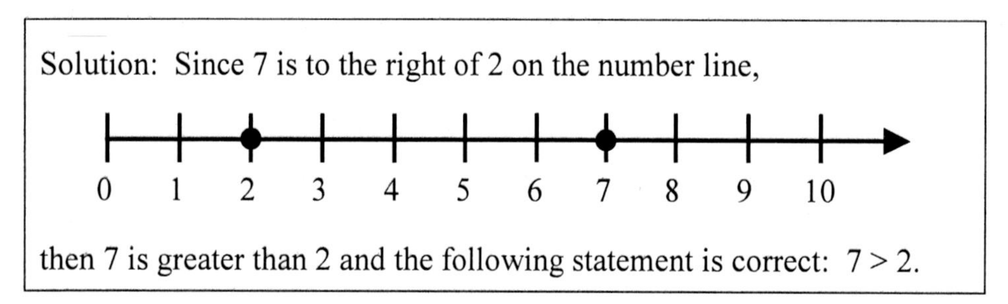

then 7 is greater than 2 and the following statement is correct: $7 > 2$.

Example 3: Place the correct inequality symbol < or > between the two numbers. 1 6.

Solution: Since 1 is to the left of 6 on the number line,

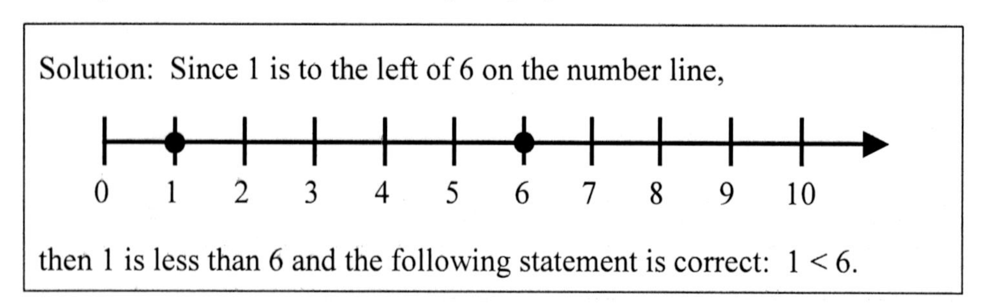

then 1 is less than 6 and the following statement is correct: $1 < 6$.

Note: Think of the > and < symbols as an alligator's open mouth. Since the alligator is hungry, its mouth always goes after the bigger meal (the bigger number).

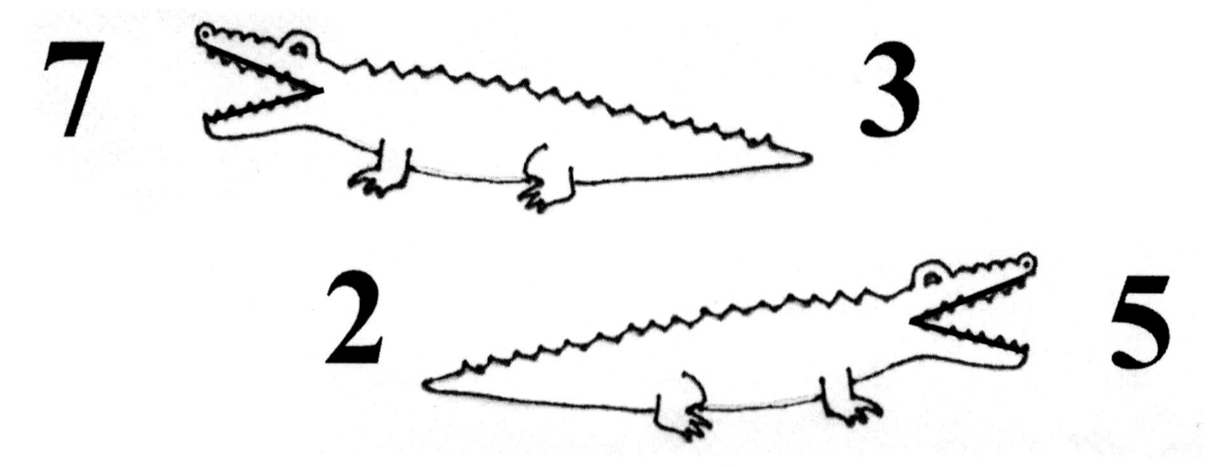

Example 4: The distance from Yakima to Spokane is 205 miles. The distance from Yakima to Portland is 188 miles. Using an inequality symbol, tell which distance is greater.

Solution: 205 miles > 188 miles. Therefore, the distance from Yakima to Spokane is greater than the distance from Yakima to Portland.

A whole number that is written using any combination of the digits 0 through 9 is said to be in standard form. For example, the number 2,375 is written in standard form. When a number is written in this form, the location of each digit in the number determines the digit's place value. In the number 2,375 the 2 is in the column that has a place value of *thousands*, the 3 is in the column that has a place value of *hundreds*, the 7 is in the column that has a place value of *tens*, and the 5 is in the column that has a place value of *ones*.

Thousands	*Hundreds*	*Tens*	*Ones*
2,	3	7	5

When a number is written in standard form, it is separated into groups of three digits. Each group is called a **period** and each period is separated by a comma. Each period has a name such as **ones**, **thousands**, **millions**, **billions**, etc.

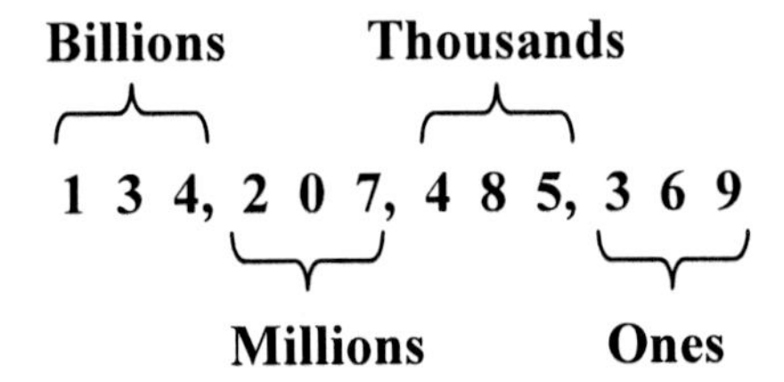

Let's look at this second number, but this time we will identify the place value of each digit.

Hundred-billions	*Ten-billions*	*Billions*	*Hundred-millions*	*Ten-millions*	*Millions*	*Hundred-thousands*	*Ten-thousands*	*Thousands*	*Hundreds*	*Tens*	*Ones*
1	3	4,	2	0	7,	4	8	5,	3	6	9

To translate a number into words, start at the left end. Identify the number in each period and replace each comma with the name of that period.

134,207,485,369 becomes "one hundred thirty-four billion, two hundred seven million, four hundred eighty-five thousand, three hundred sixty-nine."

Note: There are commas separating the periods when the number is written in words. There are hyphens separating the numbers in the tens columns from the numbers in the ones columns such as thirty-four and eighty-five. Although commonly used in conversation, the word "and" isn't needed to express whole numbers. This is because the word "and" is used to indicate the decimal point in a number. We will study this in a later chapter about decimal numbers.

Example 5: Write the following number in words: 2,054,317

> Solution: two million, fifty-four thousand, three hundred seventeen

Example 6: Write the following number in words: 608,005

> Solution: six hundred eight thousand, five

Example 7: Write three million, forty-five thousand, eighty in standard form.

> Solution: 3,045,080

A whole number can also be written in what is known as **expanded form**. In this form, each non-zero digit is expressed using its full value. The number 46,783 written in expanded form becomes: 40,000 + 6,000 + 700 + 80 + 3

Example 8: Write 4,078,902 in expanded form.

> Solution: 4,000,000 + 70,000 + 8,000 + 900 + 2

Note: When writing a number in expanded form it is not necessary to write "+ 0" for the digits that are zero in the whole number.

Example 9: Write 56,020 in expanded form.

> Solution: **Wrong way to write it**: 50,000 + 6,000 + 0 + 20 + 0
>
> **Correct way to write it**: 50,000 + 6,000 + 20

Section 1 exercises.

1. Are all natural numbers also whole numbers? Explain your answer.

2. Are all whole numbers also natural numbers? Explain your answer.

In each of the following problems, graph the given number.

3. 7

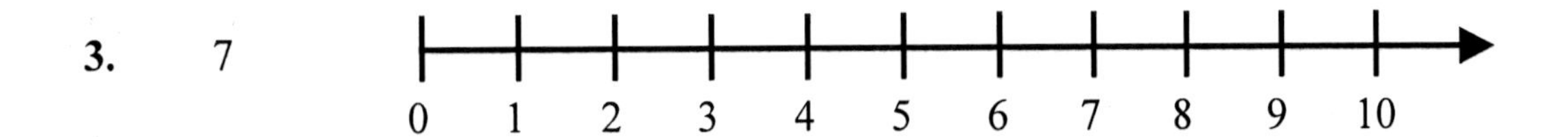

4. 5

5. 0

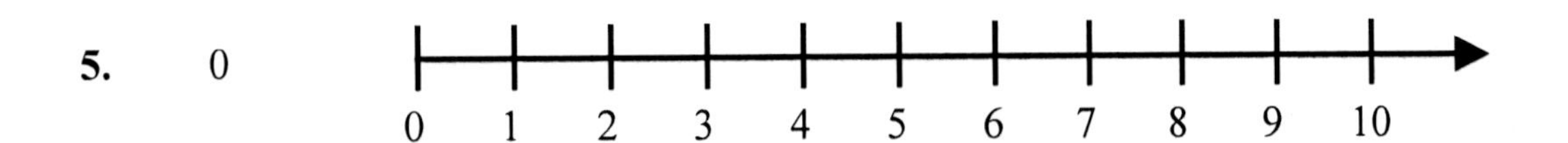

6. 8

In each of the following problems, graph the given numbers.

7. 3, 9

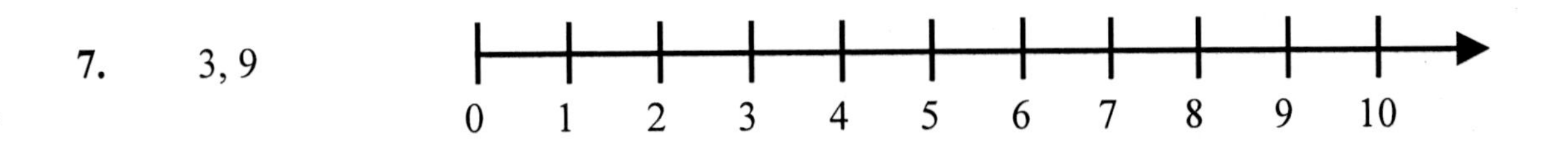

8. 1, 6

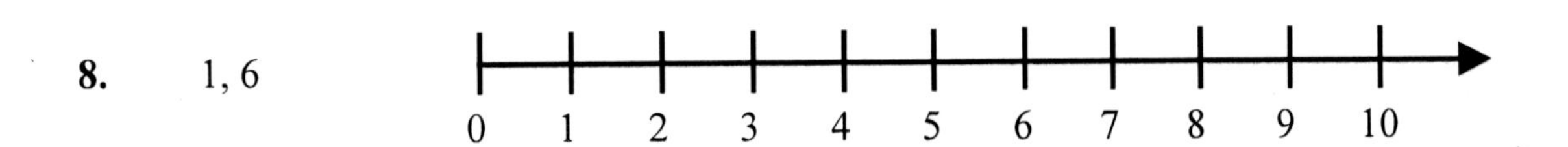

9. 0, 7

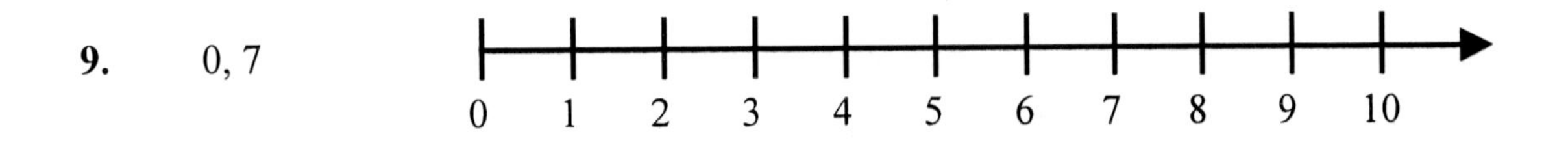

10. 2, 10

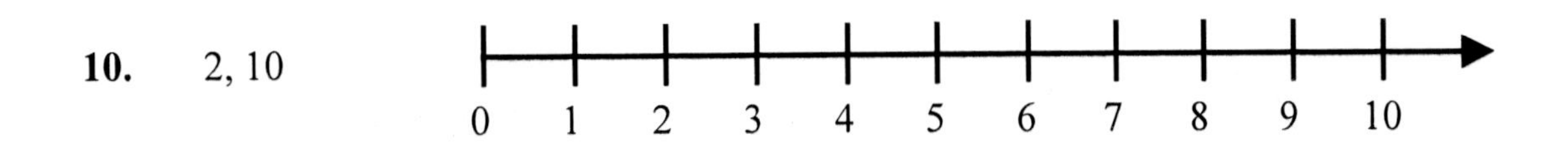

11. Graph the counting numbers that are less than 6.

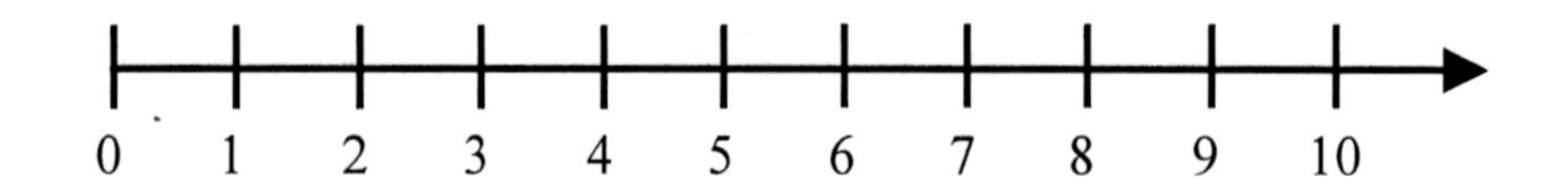

12. Graph the natural numbers that are less than 7.

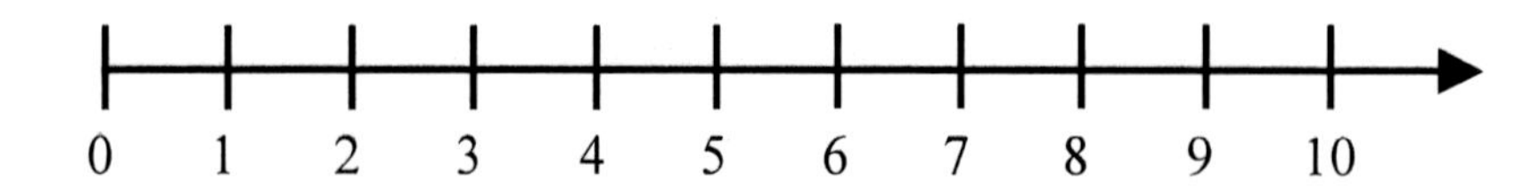

13. Graph the whole numbers that are 5 or less.

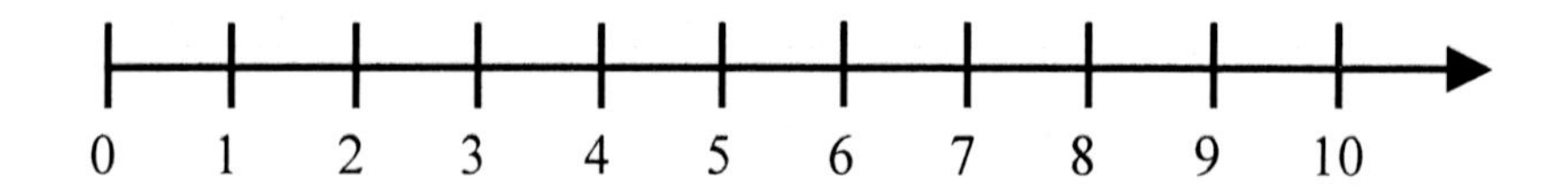

14. Graph the whole numbers that are 4 or less.

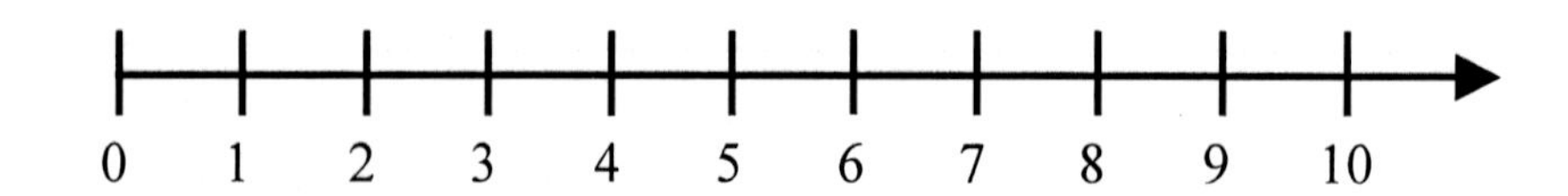

15. Graph the whole numbers that are larger than 2 and less than 6.

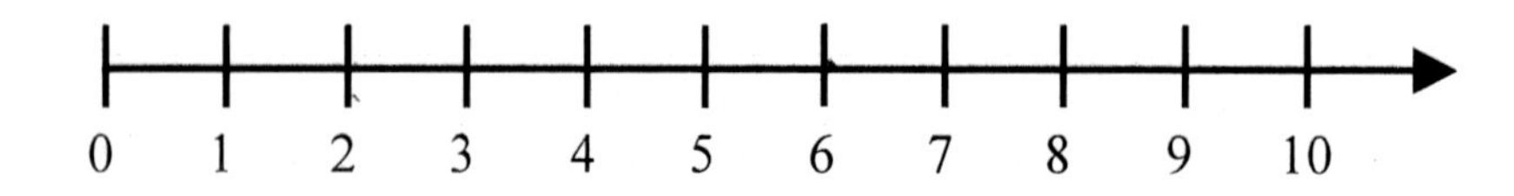

16. Graph the whole numbers that are larger than 4 and less than 9.

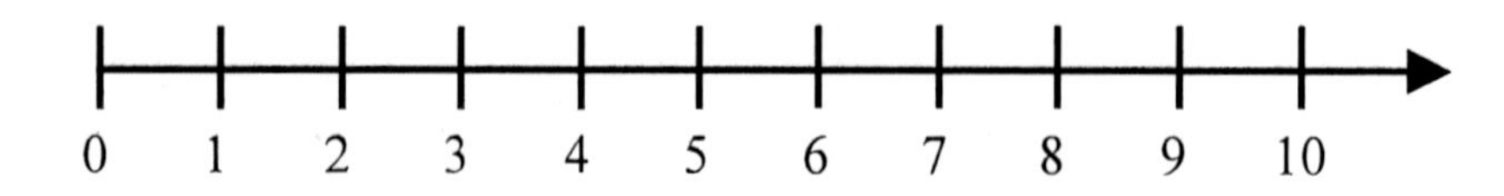

17. Graph the natural numbers that are between 4 and 9.

18. Graph the natural numbers that are between 2 and 6.

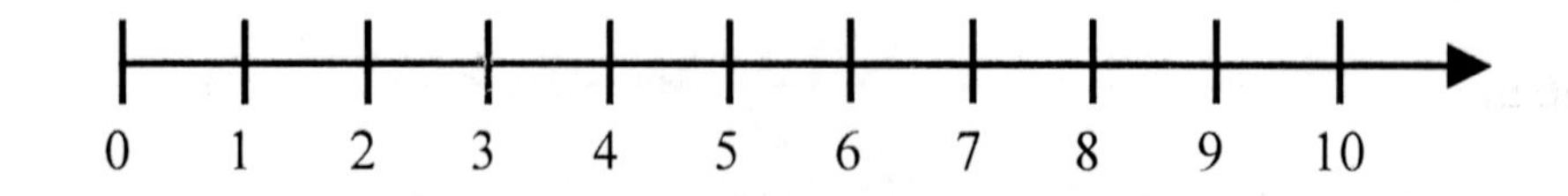

Place the correct inequality symbol < or > between each pair of numbers.

19. 81 18 **20.** 34 43 **21.** 415 451

22. 784 748 **23.** 4,305 3,450 **24.** 5,608 5,680

25. 0 49 **26.** 37 0 **27.** 48,000 4,800

28. 6,000 600 **29.** 7 4 **30.** 9 2

31. The average annual rainfall in Calabar, Nigeria is 118 inches, while the average annual rainfall in Seattle, Washington is 39 inches. Using an inequality symbol, tell which average annual rainfall is more.

32. The elevation of Mt. Hood is 11,245 feet, while the elevation of Mt. Rainier is 14,409 feet. Using an inequality symbol, tell which elevation is shorter.

33. In 2006, the population of Chesapeake, Virginia was 206,665, while the population of Fremont, California was 206,856. Using an inequality symbol, tell which population was smaller.

34. The attendance at Super Bowl XXXIV was 72,625, while the attendance at Super Bowl XXXV was 71,921. Using an inequality symbol, tell which attendance figure is greater.

35. For the number 23,543, what digit is in the hundreds column?

36. For the number 75,864, what digit is in the tens column?

37. For the number 10,076, what digit is in the thousands column?

38. For the number 98,463, what digit is in the ten-thousands column?

39. For the number 8,703, what digit is in the ones column?

40. For the number 5,068, what digit is in the hundreds column?

41. For the number 88,999, what digit is in the ten-thousands column?

42. For the number 99,888, what digit is in the ones column?

43. For the number 4,023, what digit is in the tens column?

44. For the number 2,021, what digit is in the thousands column?

Write each of the following numbers in words.

45. 49

46. 7,905

47. 637

48. 407,917

49. 11,516

50. 83

51. 3,047,010

52. 607,027,350,910

53. 806,713

54. 68,019,408,728

55. 4,203

56. 7,059,050

57. 10,403,017

58. 62,840,110

59. 263,002,162

60. 12,319

61. 34,000,319,007

62. 724

63. 746,091,028,080

64. 783,200,004

Write each of the following numbers in standard form.

65. thirteen

66. nineteen

67. one hundred seventeen

68. two hundred sixty-three

69. four thousand, seventy-two

70. eight thousand, twenty-one

71. eighty-six

72. ninety-nine

73. seven hundred ten

74. three hundred two

75. six thousand, four hundred two

76. nine thousand, two hundred seven

77. six hundred fifty-four

78. five hundred thirty

79. two hundred fifty thousand, twenty-six

80. one hundred forty thousand, sixteen

81. nineteen thousand, six hundred fifty-two

82. twenty-seven thousand, three hundred thirty-eight

83. seven million, eighteen thousand, fourteen

84. eight million, seventy-two thousand, three

Write each of the following numbers in expanded form.

85. 43

86. 17

87. 101

88. 202

89. 1,086

90. 2,093

91. 8,407

92. 9,605

93. 30,907

94. 50,608

95. 114,620

96. 283,940

97. 610,016

98. 830,038

99. 500,007

100. 700,001

101. 9,001,427

102. 8,030,814

103. 7,170,707

104. 6,260,606

WHOLE NUMBERS

Section 2: Rounding, Charts, Graphs, and an Introduction to Geometry

A rancher sent his hired man out to the pasture to bring in a herd of cattle. As the last cow entered the corral, the rancher asked the hired man how many cows he brought in. The hired man replied, "40." "That's strange," said the rancher, "I only own 37. How did you manage to count 40?" "I don't know," replied the hired man, "I just rounded them up."

We estimate numbers all the time in our daily lives. For instance, we might say, "It's about 150 miles to Seattle." Or, "There were roughly 500 people at the game last night." As the situation changes, the need for the degree of accuracy also changes. One of the ways to estimate or approximate a number is by **rounding**. To round a number we must first establish how accurate the answer needs to be. In other words, we decide at which place value we wish to round the number. After this is determined, the process is as follows.

Rounding: A number is rounded to a given place value by looking at the first digit to the right of the given place value. If this digit to the right is a 5 or greater, then round the given place value up (that is, increase its value by one). If this digit to the right is a 4 or less, then round the given place value down (that is, leave its value unchanged). When rounding a whole number at a certain place value, all digits to the right of that place value become zeros.

Example 1: Round 23,498 to the nearest thousand.

Solution: Place value to be rounded

↓

23,498

↑

First digit to the right

The first digit to the right of the thousands place value is a 4. Since 4 is less than 5, we will round down. Consequently, the 3 in the thousands place remains unchanged and all the digits to the right become zeros.

23,498 rounded to the nearest thousand becomes **23,000**.

We could also say $23{,}498 \approx 23{,}000$. The symbol "$\approx$" means "is approximately."

Example 2: Round 23,498 to the nearest hundred.

Solution: Place value to be rounded

23,498

First digit to the right

The first digit to the right of the hundreds place value is a 9. Since 9 is greater than 5, we will round up. Consequently, the 4 in the hundreds place will be increased in value by one (it becomes a 5) and all the digits to the right become zeros.

23,498 rounded to the nearest hundred becomes **23,500**. That is, $23{,}498 \approx 23{,}500$.

Example 3: Round 23,498 to the nearest ten.

Solution: Place value to be rounded

23,498

First digit to the right

The first digit to the right of the tens place value is a 8. Since 8 is greater than 5, we will round up. Consequently, the 9 in the tens place will be increased in value by one. However, this would create a 10 in the tens place, so we put a 0 in the tens place and carry a 1 over to the hundreds place. This makes the hundreds place a 5. Now, we have a 5 in the hundreds place, a 0 in the tens place and all remaining digits to the right become zeros.

23,498 rounded to the nearest ten becomes **23,500**. That is, $23{,}498 \approx 23{,}500$.

Example 4: Round 499 to the nearest thousand.

Solution: Place value to be rounded

499

First digit to the right

The first digit to the right of the thousand-place value is a 4. Since 4 is less than 5, we will round down. Consequently, the implied 0 in the thousands place remains unchanged and all the digits to the right become zeros.

499 rounded to the nearest thousand becomes **0**. That is, $499 \approx 0$.

Newspapers and magazines are full of charts and graphs used to compare data or look at trends. One of the more commonly used charts is called a **pie chart,** or a **circle graph**. A pie chart undoubtedly gets its name from the fact that it is shaped like a pie and is divided up in much the same way that a pie is cut into pieces.

Below is Janet's monthly budget in the form of a pie chart. Each sector or piece of the pie, as it is often called, is sized according to the quantity it represents in terms of the overall budget. For example, since the amount spent on housing is twice the amount spent on food, the sector that represents housing is twice the size as the one representing food costs. It is easy to tell at a glance that housing costs are a major part of Janet's budget, whereas items like electricity and the phone bill are a minimum part of her overall expenses.

Janet's Monthly Budget

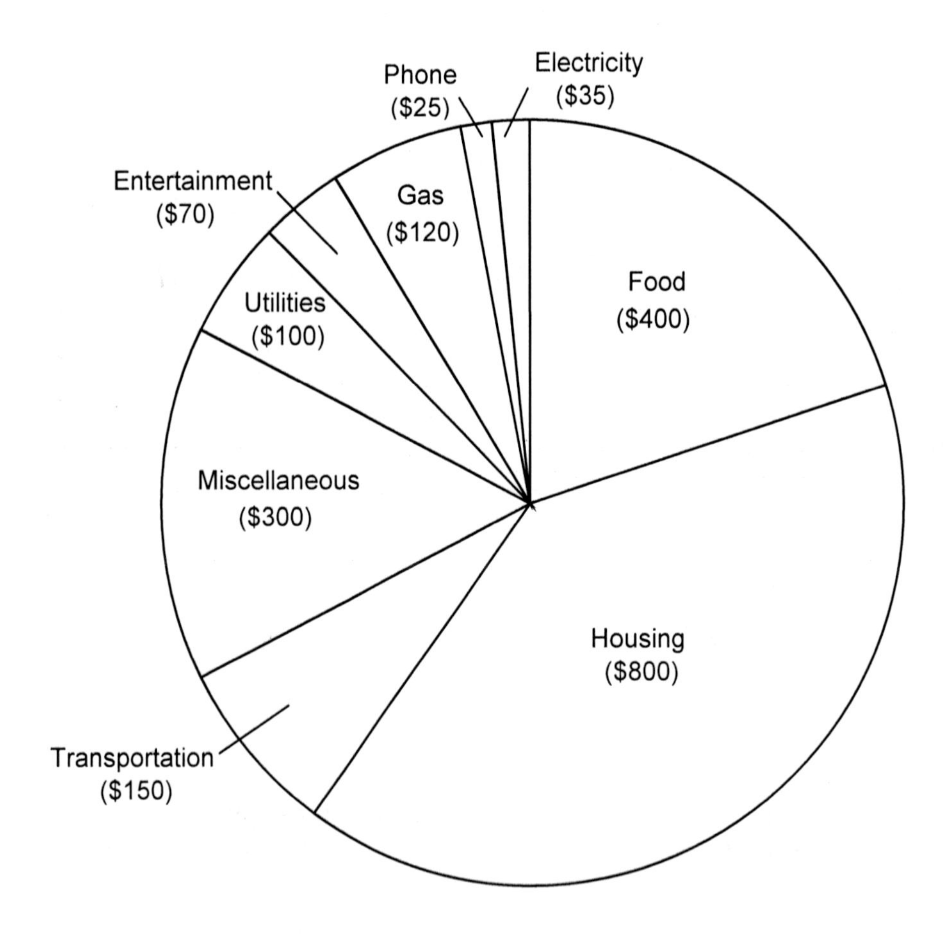

Example 5: Based on the pie chart of Janet's monthly budget, on what category does she spend the most money? On what category does she spend the least money?

Solution: The largest sector of the pie chart corresponds to housing, which is $800 per month. Therefore, she spends the most money on housing. The smallest sector of the pie chart corresponds to the phone, which is $25 per month. Consequently, she spends the least money for the phone.

Another kind of chart, or graph, is called a **bar graph**. We will look at three different kinds of bar graphs: a **vertical bar graph**, a **horizontal bar graph**, and a **double-bar graph**. First, we will consider the vertical bar graph.

Below is a bar graph providing information about the price of red delicious apples between the years 1996 and 2005. The horizontal axis lists the years and the vertical axis gives the price per box. For each year, the height of the bar corresponds to the price per box. The shortest bar corresponds to the lowest price, while the tallest bar corresponds to the highest price.

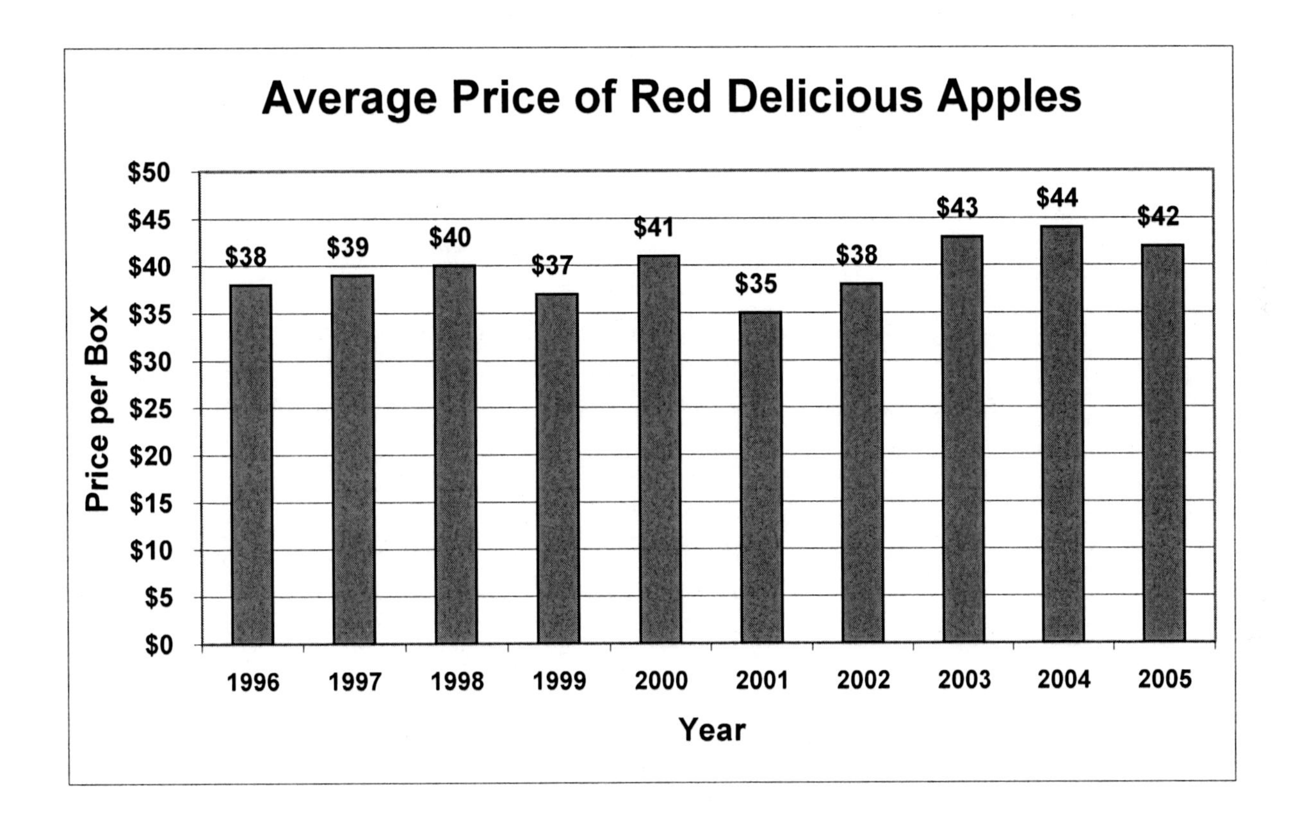

Example 6: Based on the bar graph of the average price of red delicious apples, in which year was the price lowest? In which year was the price highest? During what two years was the price the same amount?

Solution: The lowest price corresponds to the shortest bar, which was in 2001. The highest price corresponds to the tallest bar, which was in 2004. In both 1996 and 2002 the price was $38 per box.

A horizontal bar graph is much like a vertical bar graph, except the bars are horizontal instead of vertical.

Below is a bar graph providing information about the number of vehicles sold in the United States by certain companies during the month of January 2007. The horizontal axis lists the number of vehicles sold and the vertical axis gives the name of the company that sold the vehicles. The horizontal bars correspond to the number of vehicles sold by each company in January 2007. The shortest bar corresponds to the least amount of vehicles sold while the longest bar corresponds to the greatest amount of vehicles sold.

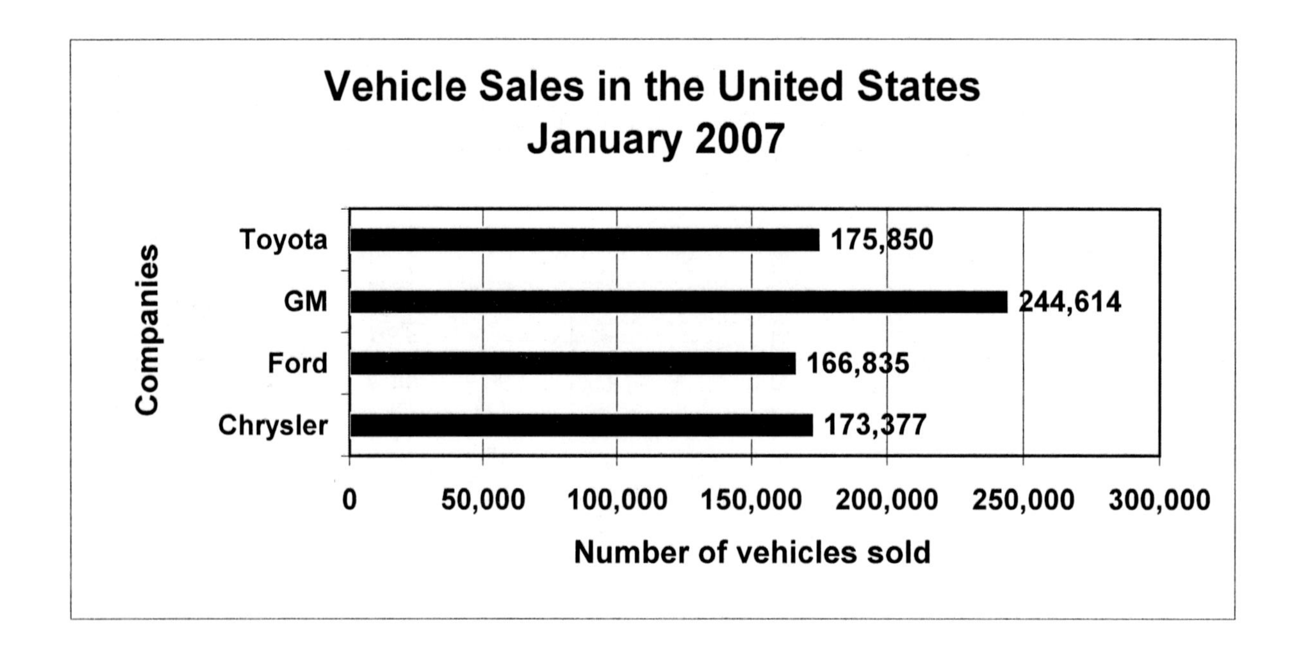

Example 7: Based on the bar graph of the number of vehicles sold in the United States by certain companies during the month of January 2007, rank the four companies in order from the one with the greatest amount of sales to the one with the least amount of sales.

Solution: Based on the length of each bar and the actual quantities given, GM ranks first, Toyota is second, Chrysler is third, and Ford is fourth in vehicle sales for the month of January 2007.

A double bar graph compares two different sets of data on the same graph.

Below is a double bar graph providing information about the high and low temperatures in degrees Fahrenheit. The horizontal axis lists the days of the week and the vertical axis gives the temperature. The black vertical bars correspond to the daily high temperature and the grey vertical bars correspond to the daily low temperature. The shortest bar corresponds to the lowest temperature and the tallest bar corresponds to the highest temperature.

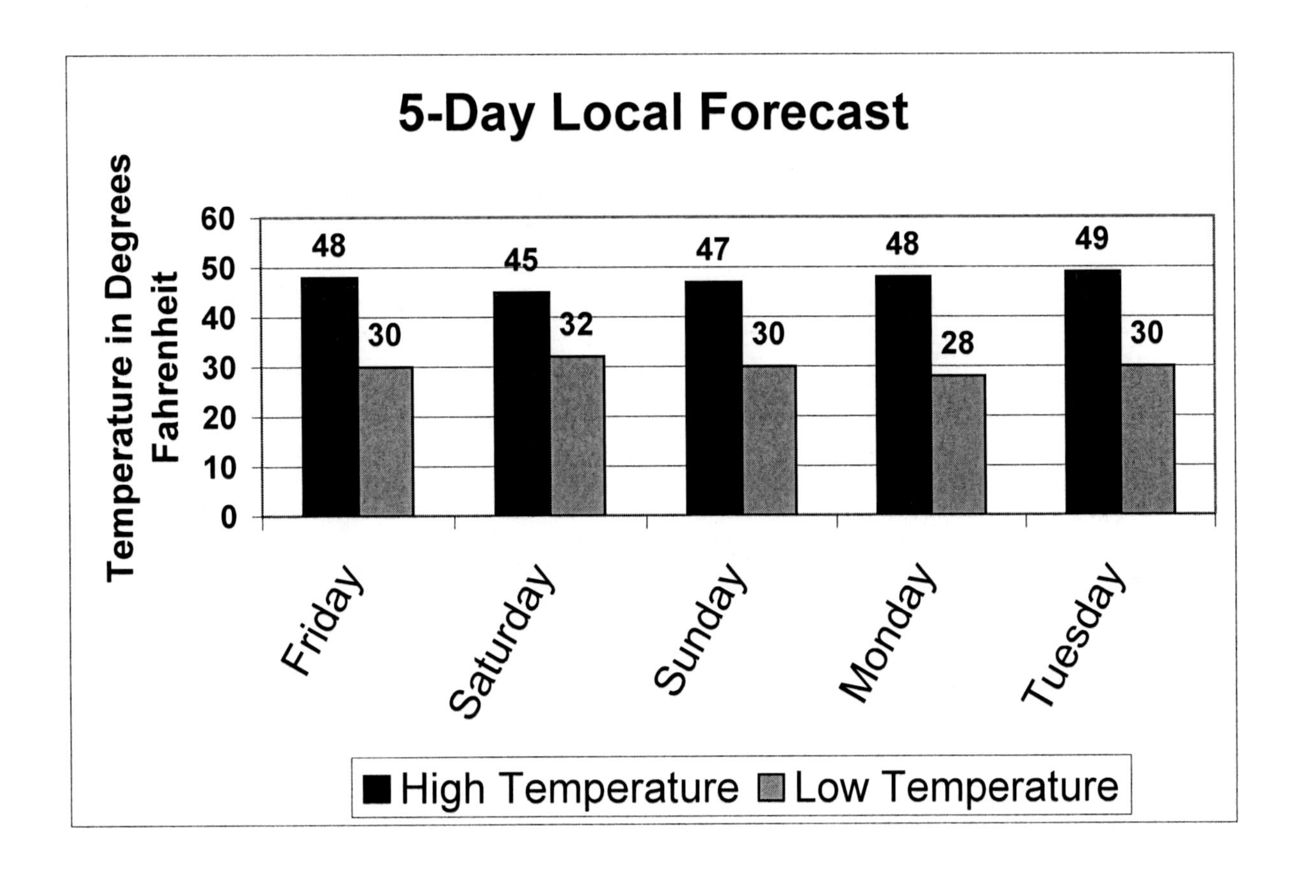

Example 8: Based on the double bar graph, what day had the highest temperature? What was the highest temperature? What day had the lowest temperature? What was the lowest temperature? On what day did both the high temperature decrease and the low temperature increase compared to the previous day?

Solution: The highest temperature occurred on Tuesday. That high temperature was 49° F. The lowest temperature occurred on Monday. That low temperature was 28° F. On Saturday the high temperature decreased and the low temperature increased.

The last kind of graph to be introduced at this point is called a **broken-line graph**. Points on a grid are used to represent information on a broken-line graph. These points are connected by line segments.

Below is a broken-line graph providing information about the average price of white bread between 1990 and 1998. The horizontal axis lists the years, and the vertical axis gives the price in cents per pound. The black dots correspond to the yearly average price per pound.

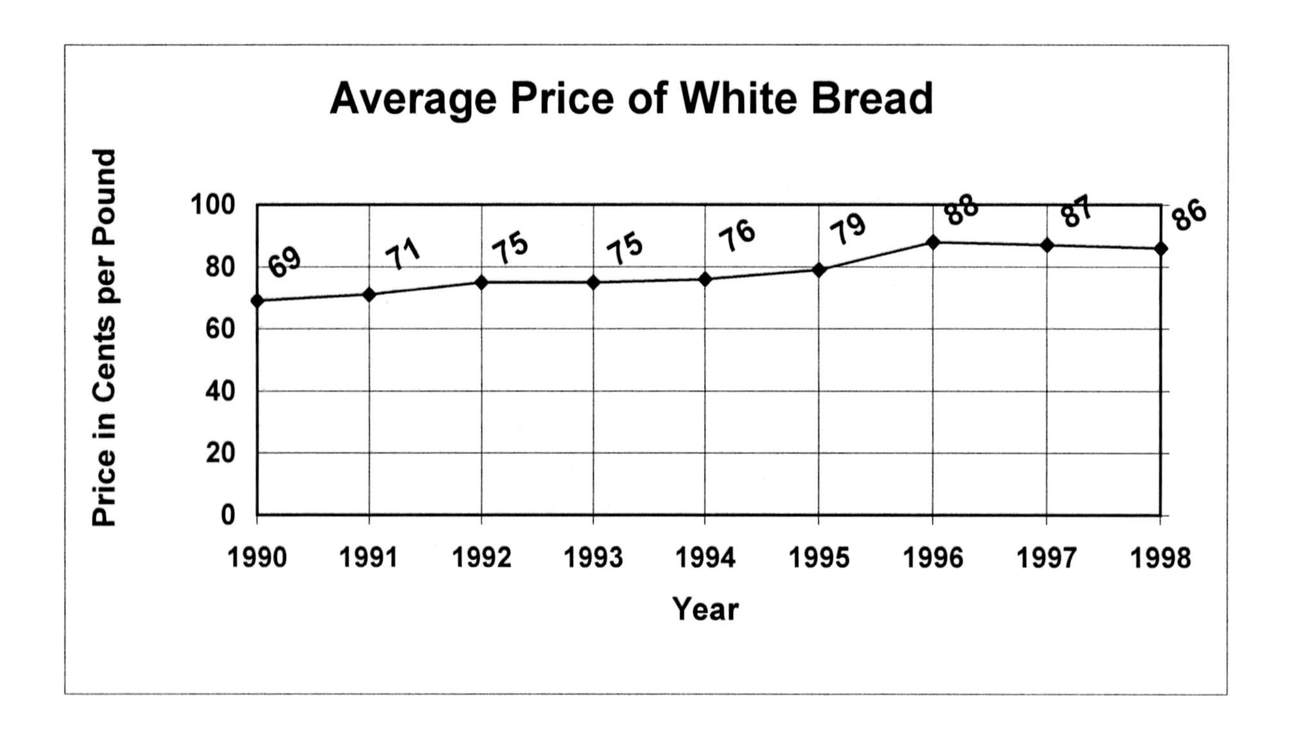

Example 9: During which year was the price of white bread the highest? What was that price? Describe the trend of white bread prices from 1994 to 1996.

Solution: The highest price occurred in 1996. That high price was 88¢ per pound. From 1994 to 1996 the price of white bread continued to increase every year.

Throughout the course of this book, problems involving **geometry** will be introduced. Here are some definitions of geometric terms that will be discussed.

Polygon: A polygon is a closed figure comprised of three or more connected line segments that lie in the same plane. Each of these line segments is a **side** of the polygon.

Examples of polygons

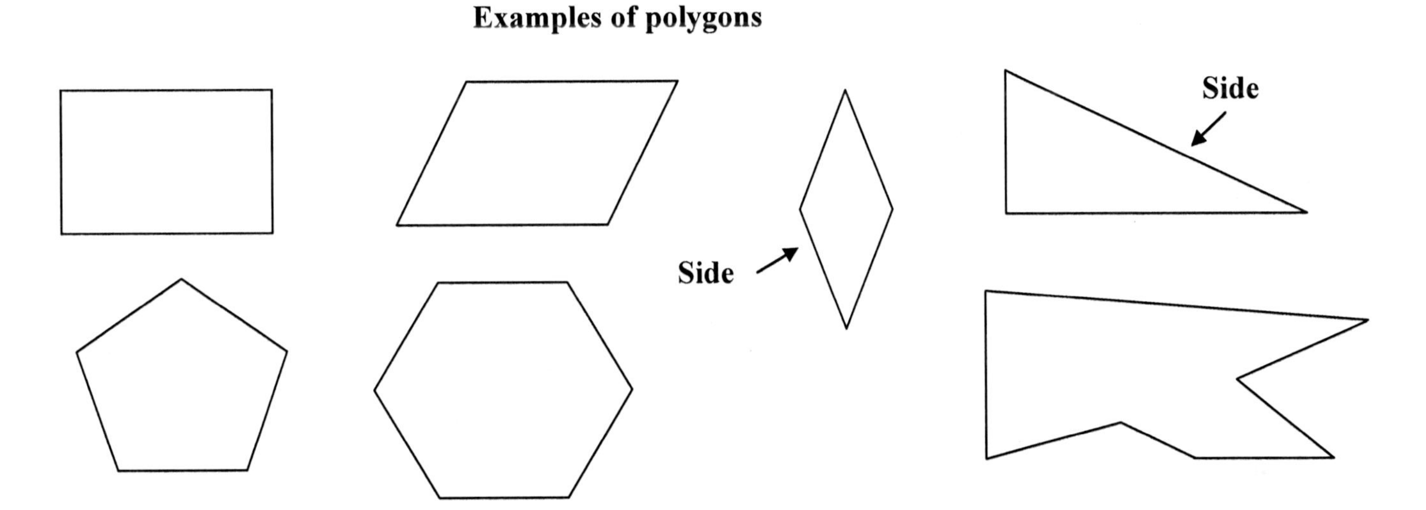

Triangle: A triangle is a polygon containing exactly three sides.

Examples of triangles

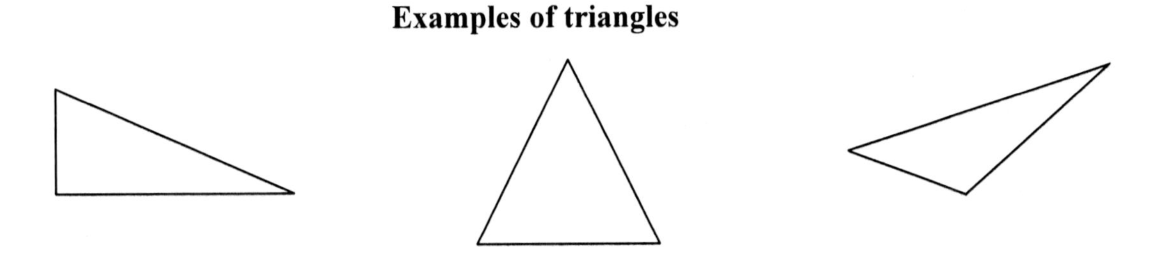

Rectangle: A rectangle is a polygon with exactly four sides. Opposite sides of a rectangle are parallel and have the same length. Each side connects with another side to form a 90°, or a right angle (we will talk more about angles later in the book). Connected sides are perpendicular to each other. A rectangle is a two-dimensional object. Like a plane, a rectangle has length and width, but no depth. Typically, the longer sides of a rectangle are called the lengths and the shorter sides are called the widths.

Examples of rectangles

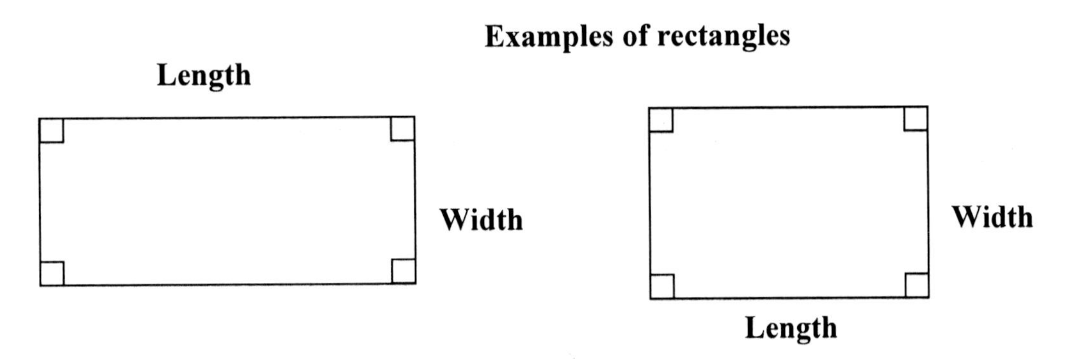

Note: The little boxes in the corners of each rectangle indicate that the sides meet at right angles.

Square: A square is a rectangle that has four sides of equal length.

Examples of squares

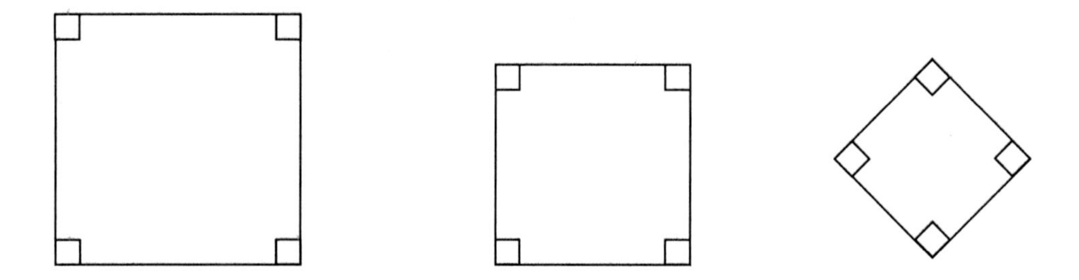

Example 10: Use the inequality symbol < to compare the lengths of the two line segments below.

Solution: Since the length of line segment B is less than the length of line segment A, the following statement is true. Line segment B < Line segment A. Or simply, B < A.

Example 11: Use the inequality symbol > to compare the length and the width of the rectangle below.

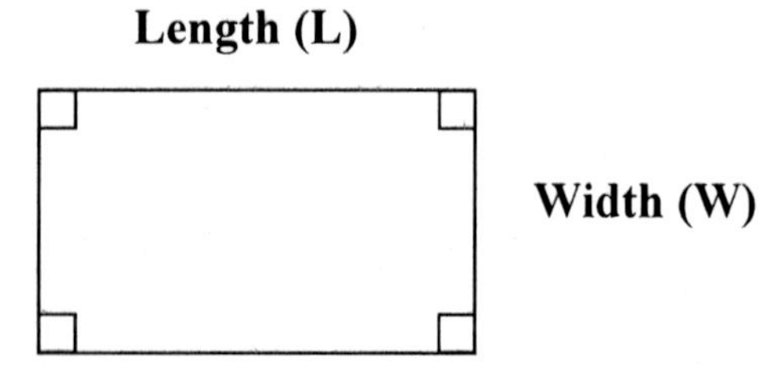

Solution: Since the length of the rectangle is greater that the width of the rectangle, the following statement is true. Length L > Width W. Or simply, L > W.

Example 12: Based on the number line below, place the correct inequality symbol, < or >, between each pair of letters.

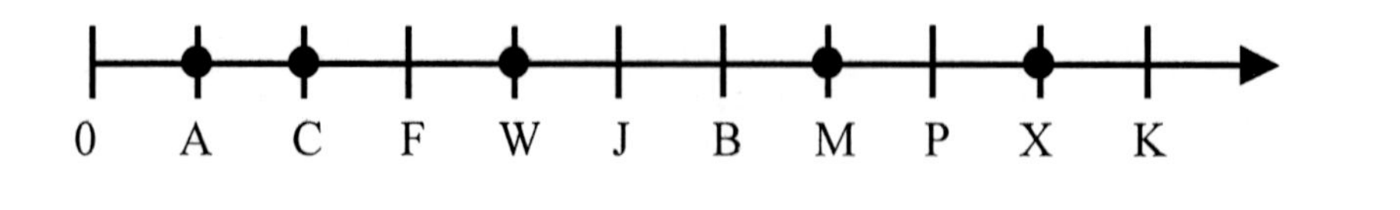

a) A W

b) M C

c) W X

Solution: a) Since A is to the left of W, then A < W. b) Since M is to the right of C, then M > C. c) Since W is to the left of X, then W < X.

Section 2 exercises. Round each number to the given place value.

1. 607 tens

2. 806 tens

3. 43,299 thousands

4. 61,703 thousands

5. 449 hundreds

6. 649 hundreds

7. 71,894 ten-thousands

8. 62,907 ten-thousands

9. 49 hundreds

10. 48 hundreds

11. 4,323 tens

12. 5,644 tens

13. 123,084 hundred-thousands

14. 649,987 hundred-thousands

15. 1,869,741 thousands

16. 2,879,516 thousands

17. 70,497 tens

18. 83,496 tens

19. 2,037 hundreds

20. 4,027 hundreds

21. 1,498,765 millions

22. 7,501,459 millions

23. 7,999,519 thousands

24. 3,999,827 thousands

25. 6,951 hundreds

26. 8,984 hundreds

27. 231,806 ten-thousands

28. 743,685 ten-thousands

29. 6,450 tens

30. 8,790 tens

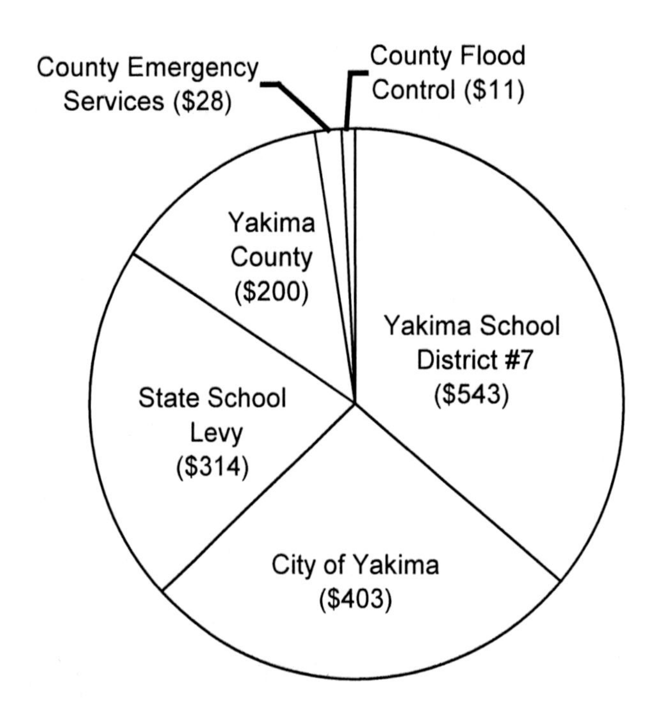

Use the pie chart above to answer the following questions.

31. What amount of John Doe's taxes goes to Yakima County?

32. What amount of John Doe's taxes goes to the city of Yakima?

33. Which category on the chart gets the most amount of money?

34. Which category on the chart gets the least amount of money?

35. Which is greater, the amount paid to the state school levy or the amount paid to the county emergency services?

36. Which is less, the amount paid to the county flood control or the amount paid to the county emergency services?

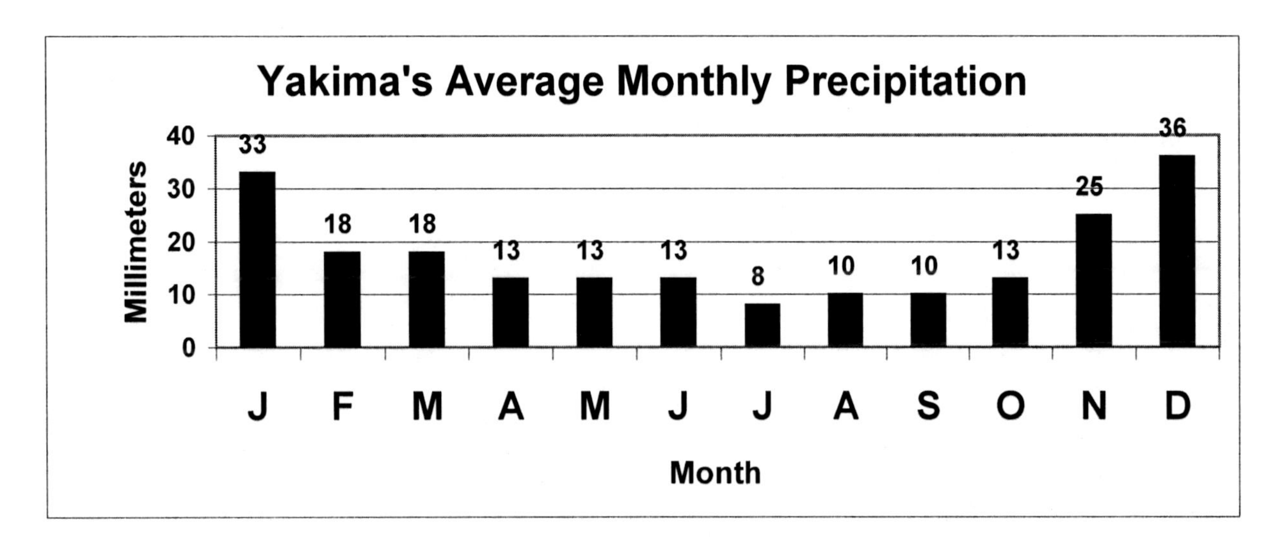

Use the bar graph above to answer the following questions.

37. Which month of the year usually gets the greatest amount of precipitation?

38. Which month of the year usually gets the least amount of precipitation?

39. Which month usually gets the greater amount of precipitation, April or October?

40. Which month usually gets the least amount of precipitation, August or September?

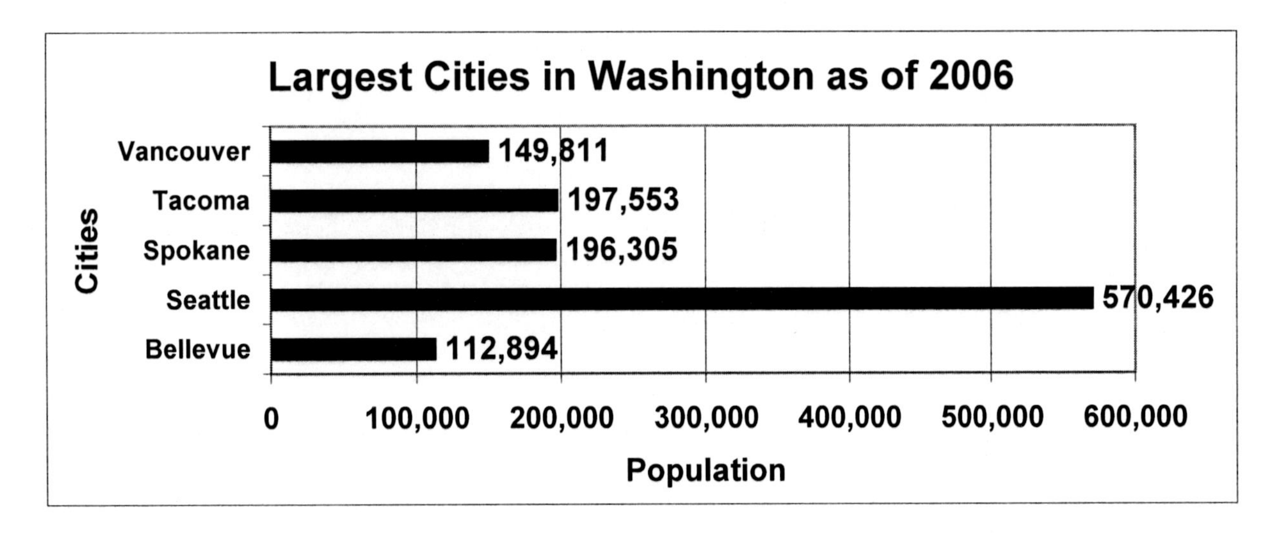

Use the bar graph above to give the following information.

41. Rank the five cities from largest to smallest, based on their population.

42. Rank the five cities from smallest to largest, based on their population.

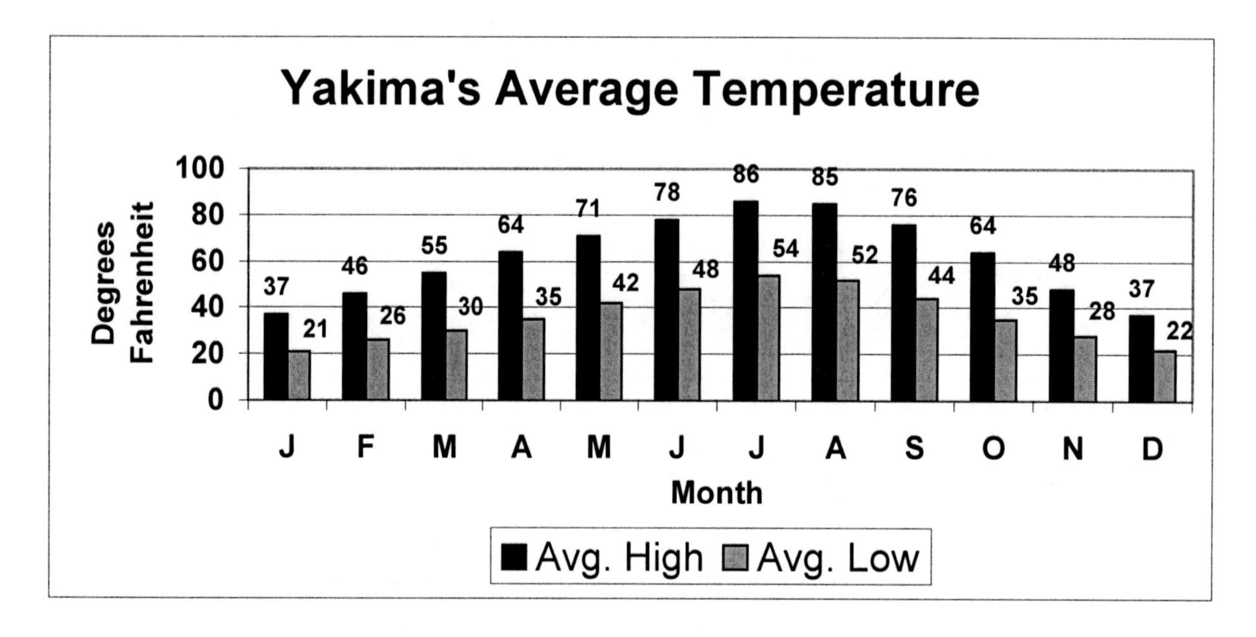

Use the double bar graph above to answer the following questions.

43. During which month(s) is Yakima's average high temperature the lowest?

44. During which month(s) is Yakima's average low temperature the highest?

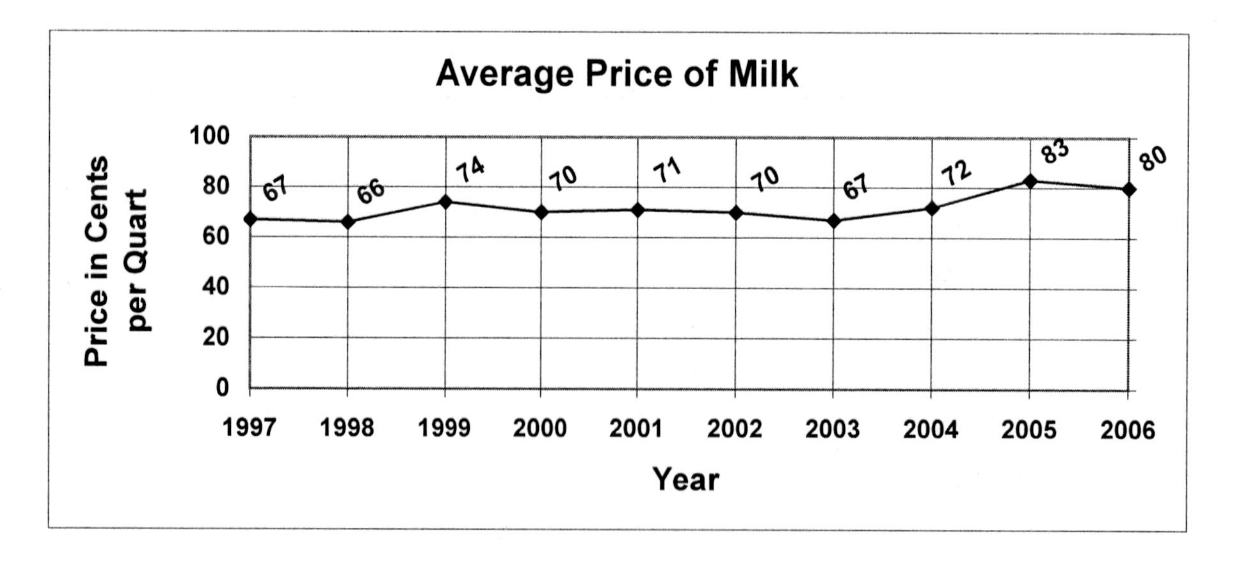

Use the broken-line graph above to answer the following questions.

45. During which two-year period did the price of milk decrease?

46. During which two-year period did the price of milk increase?

C D

47. Use the inequality symbol > to compare the lengths of the two line segments above.

48. Use the inequality symbol < to compare the lengths of the two line segments above.

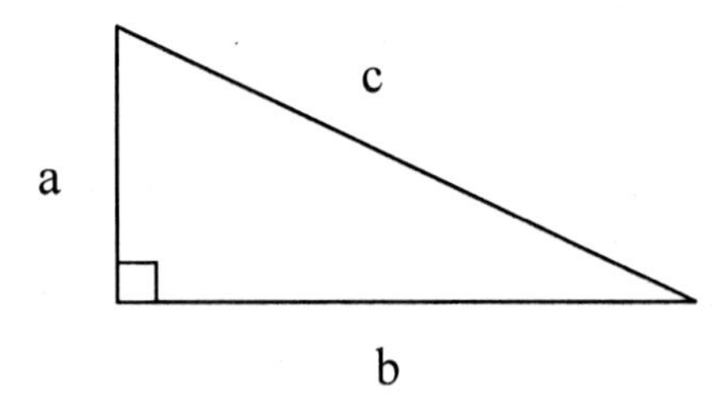

Use the triangle above to place the correct inequality symbol < or > between each pair of letters.

49. a b

50. c b

51. c a

52. a c

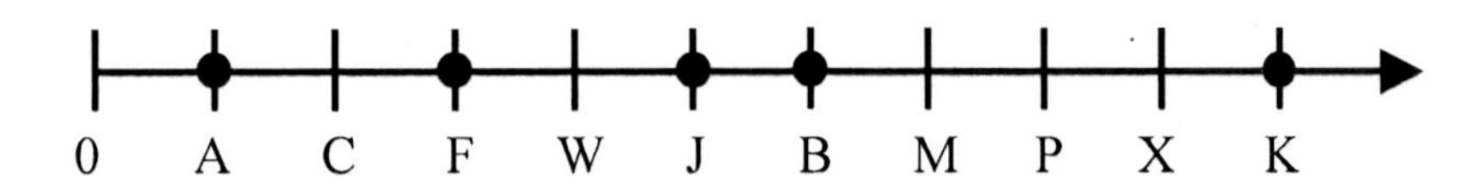

Use the number line above to place the correct inequality symbol < or > between each pair of letters.

53. F B

54. J A

55. K J

56. A F

Given that a < b and c > b, place the correct inequality symbol < or > between each pair of letters.

57. b a

58. b c

59. a c

60. c a

WHOLE NUMBERS

Section 3: Adding and Subtracting Whole Numbers

Joe ate 2 cookies on Monday and 4 cookies on Tuesday. What was the total number of cookies that Joe ate? In order to determine this amount we need to add together the numbers 2 and 4.

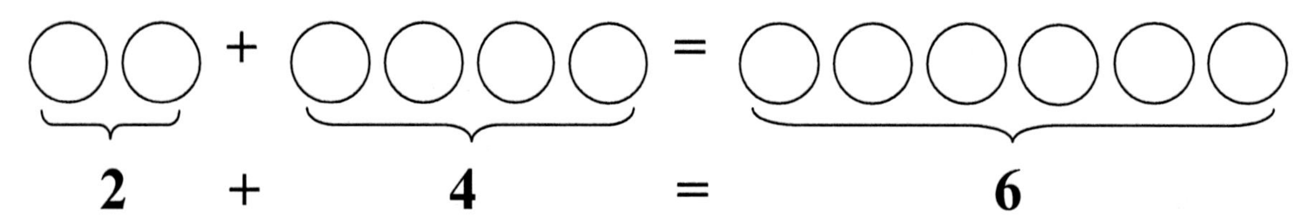

2 + 4 = 6

So, Joe ate a total of 6 cookies. The numbers that are added together are called **addends** and the result of adding is called the **sum** or the **total**.

2	+	**4**	=	**6**
↑		↑		↑
addend		**addend**		**sum**

When adding several numbers at a time, it is easiest to line up the numbers vertically. The numbers should line up in columns according to their place value. That is, the ones should line up, the tens should line up, etc.

421 + 35 + 502 becomes

$$\begin{array}{r} 421 \\ 35 \\ +\ 502 \\ \hline \end{array}$$

Starting with the ones column (at the right end), add the numbers in each column and write the result at the bottom of that column below the solid line.

$$\begin{array}{r} 421 \\ 35 \\ +\ 502 \\ \hline 958 \end{array}$$

Sometimes adding a column of numbers involves what is known as **carrying**. This happens when the sum of the numbers in any column is greater than 9.

Example 1: Add: 658 + 17

Solution: First, rewrite the problem vertically.

$$\begin{array}{r} 658 \\ +\ \ 17 \\ \hline \end{array}$$

Next, starting with the ones column, add the numbers in each column and write the result at the bottom of that column below the solid line. Note that 8 + 7 = 15. We can't put 15 at the bottom of the ones column because there is only room for one digit per column. Since 15 represents 1 ten + 5 ones, we put the 5 at the bottom of the ones column and carry the 1 ten to the top of the tens column. Then we proceed as usual.

$$\begin{array}{r} 1\ \ \\ 658 \\ +\ \ 17 \\ \hline 675 \end{array}$$

1 ← Carried from the 15

5 ↖ Left over from the 15

Example 2: Add: 286 + 455 + 193

Solution: First, rewrite the problem vertically.

```
  286
  455
+ 193
-----
```

Next, starting with the ones column, add the numbers in each column and write the result at the bottom of that column below the solid line. Note that 6 + 5 + 3 = 14. We can't put 14 at the bottom of the ones column because there is only room for one digit per column. Since 14 represents 1 ten and 4 ones, we put the 4 at the bottom of the ones column and carry the 1 ten to the top of the tens column. Then we proceed as usual.

```
   1 ← The 1 is carried from the 14
  286
  455
+ 193
-----
    4
     ↖ The 4 is left over from the 14
```

Now, adding the numbers in the tens column we get 1 + 8 + 5 + 9 = 23. We can't put 23 at the bottom of the tens column because there is only room for one digit per column. Since 23 represents 23 tens or 2 hundreds and 3 ten, we put the 3 at the bottom of the tens column and carry the 2 hundreds to the top of the hundreds column.

```
The 2 is carried from the 23 → 21
                              286
                              455
                            + 193
                            -----
                              ↗34
The 3 is left over from the 23
```

Finally, adding the numbers in the hundreds column we get 2 + 2 + 4 + 1 = 9.

```
                               21
                              286
                              455
Here is the final answer.   + 193
                            -----
                              934
```

There are several different words or word phrases that can be used to express addition. Here is a list of some of those phrases.

Word phrase	Used in an expression	Written as symbols
plus	three plus four	$3 + 4$
increased by	six increased by two	$6 + 2$
added to	nine added to seven	$7 + 9$
the sum of	the sum of one and five	$1 + 5$
more than	ten more than eight	$8 + 10$
total	the total of five and two	$5 + 2$

Example 3: Translate the following expression into mathematical symbols:
ten increased by five

Solution: Since "increased by" can imply addition, the expression becomes $10 + 5$.

Example 4: Translate the following expression into mathematical symbols:
six more than twelve

Solution: Since "more than" can imply addition, the expression becomes $12 + 6$.

Note: An important distinction should be made between the expressions “more than” and “is more than”. “Seven more than three” means 3 + 7, whereas “seven is more than three,” means 7 > 3.

Sometimes we talk about a quantity that is an unknown amount. A letter, called a **variable**, can be used to represent this quantity. It can be a capital or lower case letter. When numbers and variables are combined using operations such as multiplication, division, addition and/or subtraction, these combinations are called **algebraic expressions**. When we know the numerical value of the variables in these expressions we substitute the numbers in place of the variables. This allows us to determine the value of the algebraic expression. This process is called **evaluating algebraic expressions**.

Example 5: Evaluate the expression for the given value of the variable: $x+3$, where $x = 4$

Solution:

$x+3$	Substitute 4 in the place of x.
$4 + 3$	Add.
$4 + 3 = 7$	When $x = 4$, the value of $x+3$ is 7.

Example 6: Evaluate the expression for the given values of the variables: $x + y$, where $x = 647$ and $y = 551$

Solution:

$x + y$ Substitute 647 in the place of x and 551 in the place of y.

$647 + 551$ Add.

$$\begin{array}{r} 647 \\ +\ 551 \\ \hline 1{,}198 \end{array}$$

When $x = 647$ and $y = 551$, the value of $x + y$ is 1,198.

Variables can be used to describe number relationships. Following are several properties that tell about addition and how it works.

THE COMMUTATIVE PROPERTY OF ADDITION:

For any real numbers a and b,

$$a + b = b + a.$$

Two numbers can be added in any order and the sum will be the same.

Example 7: Use the fact that $4 + 5 = 9$ to show that addition is commutative.

Solution: $4 + 5 = 9$ and $5 + 4 = 9$. Therefore, $4 + 5 = 5 + 4$.

Conclusion: The order in which numbers are added does not change the resulting sum. This is an example showing that **addition is commutative**.

THE ASSOCIATIVE PROPERTY OF ADDITION:

For any real numbers a, b, and c,

$$(a+b)+c=a+(b+c).$$

When three or more numbers are added together, the way in which they are grouped does not change the resulting sum.

Example 8: Use the fact that $(2 + 3) + 4 = 5 + 4 = 9$ to show that addition is associative.

Solution: The numbers inside the grouping symbol (in this case, parentheses) are to be added first. The result is added to the remaining addend.

$(2+3)+4=5+4=9$ and $2+(3+4)=2+7=9$

Therefore, $(2+3)+4=2+(3+4)$.

Conclusion: When three or more numbers are added together, the way in which they are grouped does not change the resulting sum. This is an example showing that **addition is associative**.

THE IDENTITY PROPERTY OF ZERO:

For any real number a,

$$a+0=a \quad \text{and} \quad 0+a=a$$

If 0 is added to any real number a, the sum is a.

Note: The number 0 is called the additive identity.

Example 9: Use the number 6 to show an example of the identity property of zero.

Solution: $6+0=6$ and $0+6=6$.

Conclusion: **Adding 0 to a number does not change the number's original value.**

There are 6 cookies on a plate. If Joe eats 4 of the cookies, then how many cookies are left? In order to determine this amount we need to subtract 4 from 6.

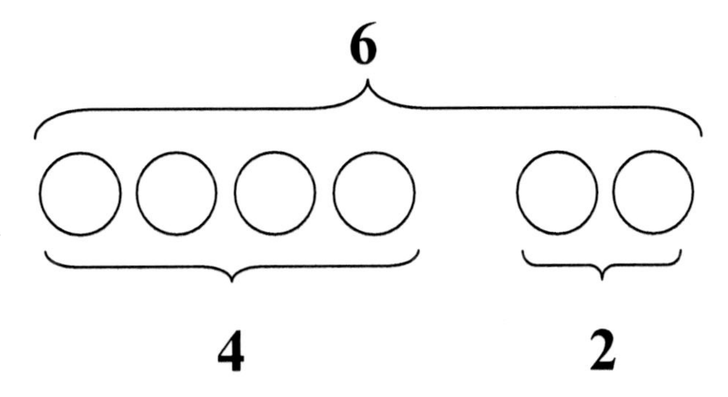

By looking at the cookies above we can see that there would be 2 left. So, 6 cookies minus 4 cookies equals 2 cookies. Or, simply put, $6-4=2$. Notice at the beginning of this section that $2+4=6$ and now we have $6-4=2$. That's because addition and subtraction are inverse operations. In a sense, they undo each other.

The numbers in a subtraction problem have special names. The first number is called the **minuend**, the number being subtracted is called the **subtrahend** and the result, or the answer, is called the **difference**.

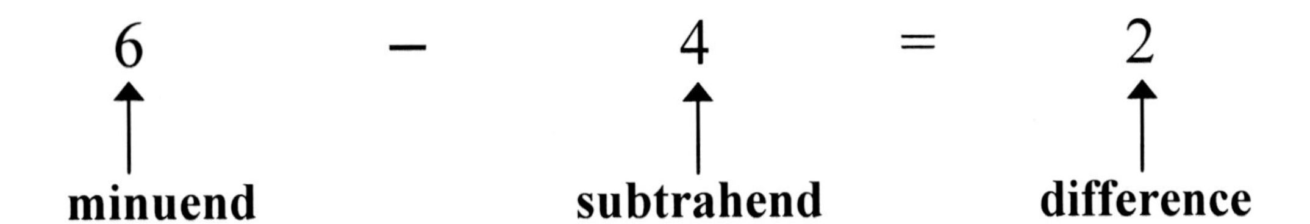

Unlike addition where several numbers can be added together at once, in subtraction only two numbers can be dealt with at a time. However, like addition, it is easiest to line up the numbers vertically and in columns according to their place value. That is, the ones should line up, the tens should line up, etc.

$765-34$ becomes $\begin{array}{r} 765 \\ -\ 34 \\ \hline \end{array}$

Starting with the ones column, subtract the numbers in each column and write the result at the bottom of that column below the solid line.

$$\begin{array}{r} 765 \\ -\ 34 \\ \hline 731 \end{array}$$

The answer can be checked by adding the subtrahend to the difference. The result should be the minuend.

$$\begin{array}{r} 731 \\ +\ 34 \\ \hline 765 \end{array}$$

The answer checks.

Sometimes subtracting numbers involves what is known as **borrowing**. This happens when the lower digit in a column is greater than the upper digit in the same column.

Example 10: Subtract: $683-346$

Solution: First, rewrite the problem vertically.

$$\begin{array}{r} 683 \\ -346 \\ \hline \end{array}$$

Next, starting with the ones column, subtract the numbers in each column and write the result at the bottom of that column below the solid line. Note that 6 can't be subtracted from 3 without creating a negative situation. What needs to happen now is to borrow 1 ten from the tens column. This creates a 7 in the tens column and a 13 in the ones column.

$$\begin{array}{r} {}^{7\,13} \\ 6\cancel{8}\cancel{3} \\ -346 \\ \hline \end{array}$$

Then we proceed as usual.

$$\begin{array}{r} {}^{7\,13} \\ 6\cancel{8}\cancel{3} \\ -346 \\ \hline 337 \end{array}$$

The answer can be checked by adding the subtrahend to the difference. The result should be the minuend.

$$\begin{array}{r} {}^{1} \\ 337 \\ +346 \\ \hline 683 \end{array}$$

The answer checks.

Example 11: Subtract: $925-654$

Solution: First, rewrite the problem vertically.

$$\begin{array}{r} 925 \\ -654 \\ \hline \end{array}$$

Next, starting with the ones column, subtract the numbers in each column and write the result at the bottom of that column below the solid line.

$$\begin{array}{r} 925 \\ -654 \\ \hline 1 \end{array}$$

Note that 5 can't be subtracted from 2 without creating a negative situation. What needs to happen now is to borrow 1 hundred from the hundreds column. This creates an 8 in the hundreds column and a 12 in the tens column.

$$\begin{array}{r} {}^{8\,12} \\ \cancel{9}\cancel{2}5 \\ -654 \\ \hline 1 \end{array}$$

Then we proceed as usual.

$$\begin{array}{r} {}^{8\,12} \\ \cancel{9}\cancel{2}5 \\ -654 \\ \hline 271 \end{array}$$

The answer can be checked by adding the subtrahend to the difference. The result should be the minuend.

$$\begin{array}{r} {}^{1} \\ 271 \\ +654 \\ \hline 925 \end{array}$$

The answer checks.

Example 12 A: Subtract: 6,003 – 468

Solution: First, rewrite the problem vertically.

$$\begin{array}{r} 6{,}003 \\ -\ 468 \\ \hline \end{array}$$

Next, starting with the ones column, subtract the numbers in each column and write the result at the bottom of that column below the solid line. We know that 8 can't be subtracted from 3 without creating a negative situation. So, we need to borrow a 1 from the tens column. However, there is only a 0 in the tens column, so we need to borrow from the hundreds column. However, there is only a 0 in the hundreds column, so we borrow a 1 from the thousands column. This creates a 5 in the thousands column and a 10 in the hundreds column.

$$\begin{array}{r} 5\ 10\ \ \ \ \\ \not{6},\not{0}03 \\ -\ 468 \\ \hline \end{array}$$

Now we can borrow a 1 from the hundreds column. This creates a 9 in the hundreds column and a 10 in the tens column.

$$\begin{array}{r} 9\ \ \ \ \ \\ 5\ \not{10}\ 10\ \ \\ \not{6},\not{0}\not{0}3 \\ -\ 468 \\ \hline \end{array}$$

Now we can borrow a 1 from the tens column. This creates a 9 in the tens column and a 13 in the ones column.

$$\begin{array}{r} 9\ 9\ \ \ \\ 5\ \not{10}\not{10}13 \\ \not{6},\not{0}\not{0}\not{3} \\ -\ 468 \\ \hline \end{array}$$

Then we proceed as usual.

$$\begin{array}{r} 9\ 9\ \ \ \\ 5\ \not{10}\not{10}13 \\ \not{6},\not{0}\not{0}\not{3} \\ -\ 468 \\ \hline 5{,}535 \end{array}$$

The answer can be checked by adding the subtrahend to the difference. The result should be the minuend.

$$\begin{array}{r} 1\,1\,1\ \\ 5{,}535 \\ +\ 468 \\ \hline 6{,}003 \end{array}$$

The answer checks.

Let's take another look at example 12, but this time use a slightly different approach.

Example 12 B: Subtract: 6,003 – 468

Solution: First, rewrite the problem vertically.

$$\begin{array}{r} 6{,}003 \\ -\ 468 \\ \hline \end{array}$$

Next, starting with the ones column, subtract the numbers in each column and write the result at the bottom of that column below the solid line. We know that 8 can't be subtracted from 3 without creating a negative situation. Notice that we have to go all the way over to the thousands column before we can borrow a 1. Think of 6,003 as having a 3 in the ones column and a 600 in the tens column. So, we borrow a 1 from the tens column which creates a 599 in the tens column and a 13 in the ones column.

$$\begin{array}{r} 599\ 13 \\ \not{6{,}00}\not{3} \\ -\ 468 \\ \hline \end{array}$$

Then we proceed as usual.

$$\begin{array}{r} 599\ 13 \\ \not{6{,}00}\not{3} \\ -\ 468 \\ \hline 5{,}535 \end{array}$$

We already checked the answer in example 12 A.

There are several different words or word phrases that can be used to express subtraction. Here is a list of some of those phrases.

Word phrase	Used in an expression	Written as symbols
minus	seven minus four	$7-4$
decreased by	six decreased by two	$6-2$
subtracted from	five subtracted from nine	$9-5$
the difference between	the difference between six and one	$6-1$
the difference of	the difference of ten and three	$10-3$
less than	six less than nine	$9-6$
less	eight less five	$8-5$

Example 13: Translate the following expression into mathematical symbols:
ten decreased by five

Solution: Since "decreased by" can imply subtraction, the expression becomes $10-5$.

Example 14: Translate the following expression into mathematical symbols:
four less than twelve

Solution: Since "less than" can imply subtraction, the expression becomes $12-4$.

Note: An important distinction should be made between the expressions "less than" and "is less than". "Three less than seven" means $7-3$, whereas "three is less than seven," means $3 < 7$.

Earlier in this section were some examples of evaluating variable expressions involving addition. Here is an example, but this time the problem involves subtraction.

Example 15: Evaluate the expression for the given values of the variables: $x-y$, where $x = 357$ and $y = 251$

Solution:

$x-y$ Substitute 357 in the place of x and 251 in the place of y.

$357-251$ Subtract.

$$\begin{array}{r} 357 \\ -251 \\ \hline 106 \end{array}$$

When $x = 357$ and $y = 251$, the value of $x-y$ is 106.

Section 3 exercises. Add each of the following.

1. 341 + 125

2. 476 + 323

3. 650 + 28

4. 740 + 16

5. 26 + 5,335

6. 18 + 2,445

7. 6,248 + 27 + 194

8. 735 + 92 + 1,726

9. 5,763 + 451 + 3,289

10. 6,812 + 34 + 5,790

11. 92,084 + 6,319

12. 1,816 + 46,405

13. 3,067 + 2,198

14. 1,638 + 4,275

15. 624,089 + 18

16. 356 + 873,849

17. 6,314 + 17,859 + 420

18. 4,214 + 28,603 + 576

19. 9 + 3,930 + 312

20. 3 + 6,728 + 814

21. 403 + 721,896 + 10,101

22. 214 + 311,657 + 29,306

23.
$$\begin{array}{r} 631{,}174 \\ +\ 877{,}350 \\ \hline \end{array}$$

24.
$$\begin{array}{r} 482{,}460 \\ +\ 753{,}298 \\ \hline \end{array}$$

25.
$$\begin{array}{r} 31{,}875 \\ 42{,}690 \\ 71{,}249 \\ +\ 86{,}053 \\ \hline \end{array}$$

26.
$$\begin{array}{r} 57{,}123 \\ 68{,}940 \\ 25{,}863 \\ +\ 91{,}407 \\ \hline \end{array}$$

27.
$$\begin{array}{r} 12{,}475 \\ 639 \\ 8{,}743 \\ 1 \\ +\quad 86 \\ \hline \end{array}$$

28.
$$\begin{array}{r} 36{,}217 \\ 945 \\ 8{,}146 \\ 3 \\ +\quad 72 \\ \hline \end{array}$$

29. Create a problem in which you add together three different 5-digit numbers to get a sum of 54,321.

30. Create a problem in which you add together three different 5-digit numbers to get a sum of 65,432.

Subtract each of the following.

31. $42-31$

32. $78-65$

33. $816-643$

34. $942-371$

35. $708-9$

36. $864-0$

37. $1{,}207-823$

38. $1{,}640-986$

39. $41{,}723-411$

40. $37{,}698-374$

41. $623-0$

42. $802-6$

43. $4{,}004 - 200$

44. $6{,}006 - 408$

45. $321 - 300$

46. $654 - 600$

47. $328 - 83$

48. $617 - 42$

49. $800{,}000 - 49{,}263$

50. $900{,}000 - 28{,}937$

51. $3{,}218 - 90$

52. $4{,}106 - 50$

53. $6{,}987 - 5{,}988$

54. $7{,}653 - 6{,}654$

55. $\begin{array}{r} 32{,}587 \\ -\ 6{,}949 \\ \hline \end{array}$

56. $\begin{array}{r} 28{,}716 \\ -\ 9{,}463 \\ \hline \end{array}$

57. $\begin{array}{r} 31{,}415 \\ -27{,}182 \\ \hline \end{array}$

58. $\begin{array}{r} 31{,}622 \\ -22{,}360 \\ \hline \end{array}$

59. Create a problem in which you subtract two 5-digit numbers to get a difference of 65,432.

60. Create a problem in which you subtract two 5-digit numbers to get a difference of 54,321.

Translate each phrase into mathematical symbols. Then determine the result in each case.

61. Find the total of seven and six.

62. What is thirty minus seventeen?

63. Find fifteen less six.

64. Find the sum of eight and four.

65. Find the difference between twelve and eight.

66. What is three more than twelve?

67. What is nine increased by fifteen?

68. What is five less than forty-two?

69. Find the difference of seventy-eight and sixty-nine.

70. What is two plus nineteen?

71. Find eighteen decreased by eleven.

72. What is ten added to fourteen?

73. What is the sum of fifty-nine and forty-six?

74. What is eight subtracted from twenty-seven?

Evaluate the expression $x + y$ for the given values of x and y.

75. $x = 15;\ y = 2$

76. $x = 4;\ y = 19$

77. $x = 16;\ y = 728$

78. $x = 37;\ y = 665$

79. $x = 0;\ y = 255$

80. $x = 827;\ y = 0$

81. $x = 2{,}873;\ y = 41$

82. $x = 3{,}419;\ y = 25$

83. $x = 7{,}842;\ y = 9{,}379$

84. $x = 8{,}219;\ y = 5{,}987$

85. $x = 42{,}816;\ y = 9{,}742$

86. $x = 6{,}378;\ y = 11{,}903$

Evaluate the expression $x - y$ for the given values of x and y.

87. $x = 86;\ y = 9$

88. $x = 53;\ y = 6$

89. $x = 682;\ y = 96$

90. $x = 703;\ y = 86$

91. $x = 802;\ y = 0$

92. $x = 563;\ y = 0$

93. $x = 6{,}313;\ y = 4{,}725$

94. $x = 7{,}842;\ y = 3{,}957$

95. $x = 30{,}000;\ y = 2$

96. $x = 40{,}000;\ y = 3$

97. $x = 75{,}014;\ y = 69{,}386$

98. $x = 83{,}018;\ y = 69{,}479$

Evaluate the expression $x + y + z$ for the given values of x, y, and z.

99. $x = 387;\ y = 59;\ z = 562$

100. $x = 269;\ y = 86;\ z = 371$

101. $x = 63;\ y = 6{,}910;\ z = 5{,}877$

102. $x = 37;\ y = 2{,}016;\ z = 7{,}809$

103. $x = 42{,}184;\ y = 716;\ z = 23{,}083$

104. $x = 28{,}179;\ y = 234;\ z = 47{,}102$

105. Which property states that if two numbers are added in any order, the sum will be the same?

106. Which property states that when three or more numbers are added together, the numbers can be grouped in any order and the sum will be the same?

Use only the commutative property of addition to rewrite each expression. Then, simplify the expression.

107. $8 + 5$

108. $2 + 11$

109. $9 + 3$

110. $6 + 7$

111. $27 + 0$

112. $79 + 18$

113. $62 + 29$

114. $34 + 0$

115. $216 + 77$

116. $319 + 88$

117. $412 + 319$

118. $218 + 563$

Use only the associative property of addition to rewrite each expression. Then, simplify the expression.

119. $(6 + 7) + 3$

120. $(4 + 3) + 7$

121. $9 + (1 + 4)$

122. $8 + (2 + 6)$

123. $7 + (13 + 6)$

124. $4 + (16 + 3)$

125. $(321 + 18) + 12$

126. $(637 + 19) + 21$

127. $(12 + 63) + 37$

128. $157 + (43 + 812)$

129. $376 + (24 + 419)$

130. $(39 +93) + 47$

WHOLE NUMBERS

Section 4: More Adding and Subtracting of Whole Numbers

Valuable information can be obtained from various charts or graphs by applying addition and/or subtraction to quantities given.

Janet's Monthly Budget

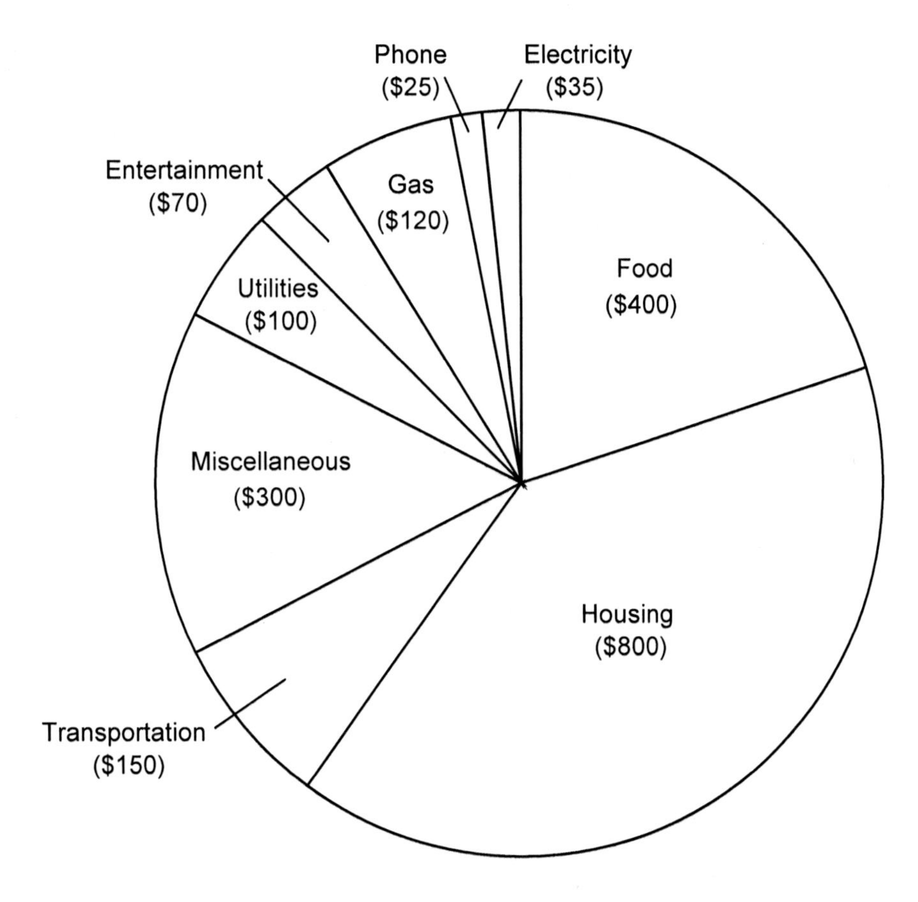

Example 1: Based on the pie chart above, what is Janet's total monthly budget?

Solution: To determine her total budget we must add the dollar amounts in all the sectors of the pie chart. Starting with housing and traveling clockwise around the chart we gather the following information:

```
  2 1
  $800
  $150
  $300
  $100
  $ 70
  $120
  $ 25
  $ 35
+ $400
------
$2,000  <------ Total monthly budget
```

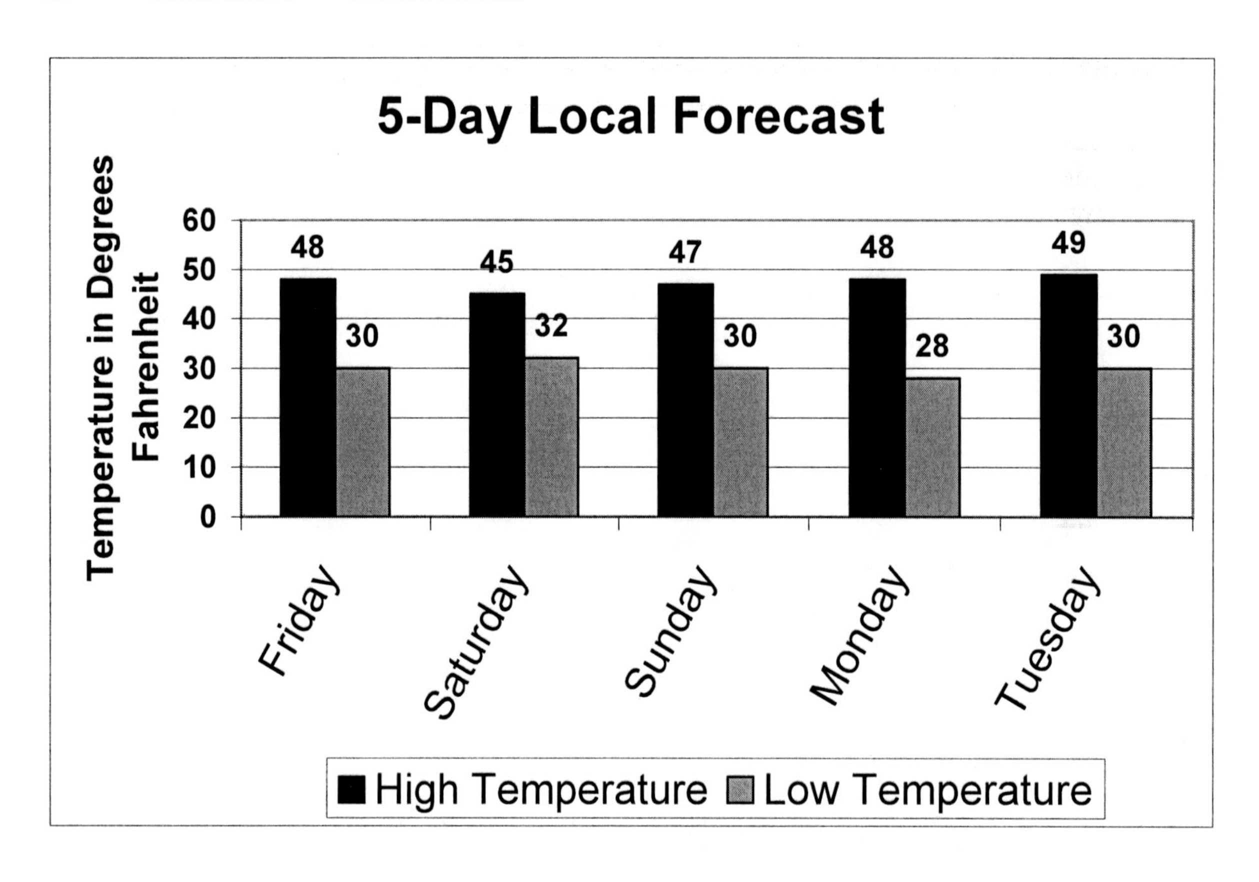

Example 2: Based on the double bar graph above, what day had the greatest difference between the high temperature and the low temperature?

Solution:

Friday	Saturday	Sunday	Monday	Tuesday
48	45	47	48	49
−30	−32	−30	−28	−30
18	13	17	20	19

The greatest difference between the high temperature and the low temperature occurred on Monday.

Suppose you were going to build a fence around a rectangular garden. To do this you need to know the dimensions of the garden, that is, the length and the width. By adding a length and a width, plus another length and width, you would get the total distance around the rectangular garden. This distance is called the **perimeter** of the rectangle. Basically, the perimeter of any object is the entire distance around it.

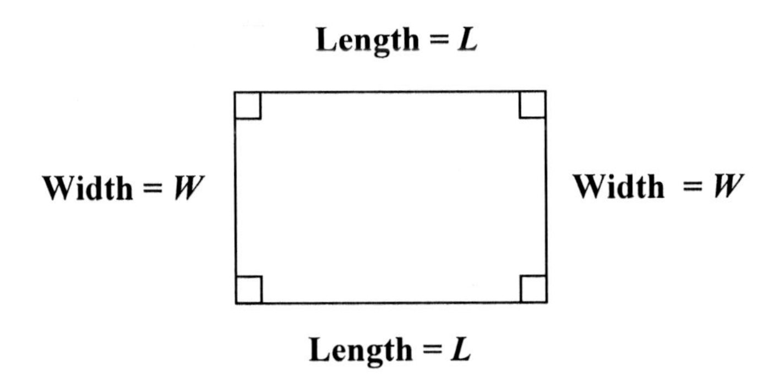

FORMULA FOR THE PERIMETER (P) OF A RECTANGLE:

$$P = L + W + L + W$$

Example 3: Find the perimeter of a rectangle with a length of 8 feet and a width of 5 feet.

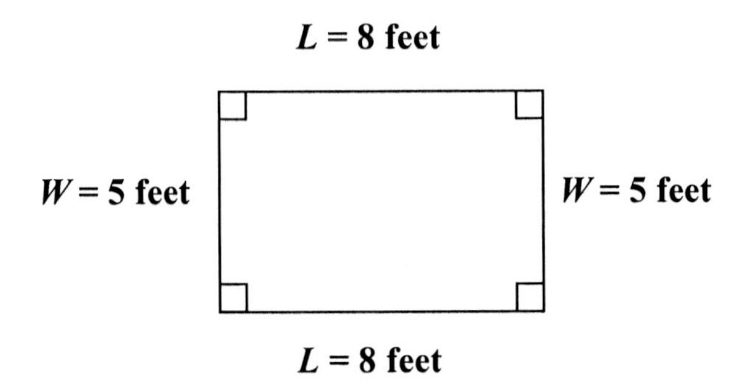

Solution: The length is 8 feet and the width is 5 feet. Using the formula for the perimeter of a rectangle, $P = L + W + L + W$ gives us

$$P = 8 \text{ feet} + 5 \text{ feet} + 8 \text{ feet} + 5 \text{ feet}.$$

$$\begin{array}{r} 8 \text{ feet} \\ 5 \text{ feet} \\ 8 \text{ feet} \\ + \; 5 \text{ feet} \\ \hline 26 \text{ feet} \end{array}$$

The perimeter of the rectangle is 26 feet.

In a previous section we discussed three specific polygons: A triangle, a rectangle and a square. Now that we know the formula for the perimeter of a rectangle, here are the formulas for the perimeter of a triangle and of a square.

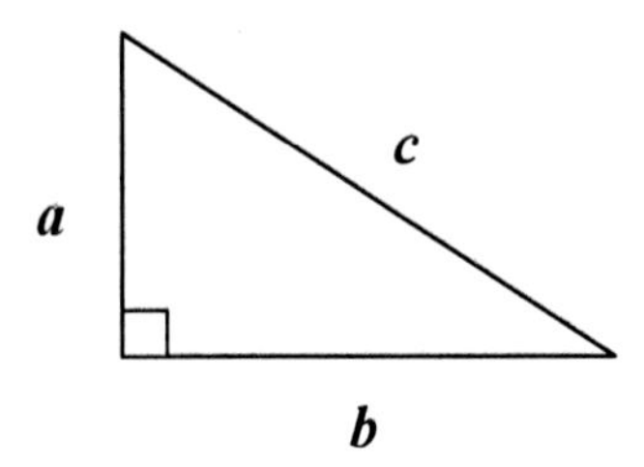

Given a triangle with sides a, b and c, we have the following formula:

FORMULA FOR THE PERIMETER OF A TRIANGLE:

$$P = a + b + c$$

Example 4: Find the perimeter of the following triangle:

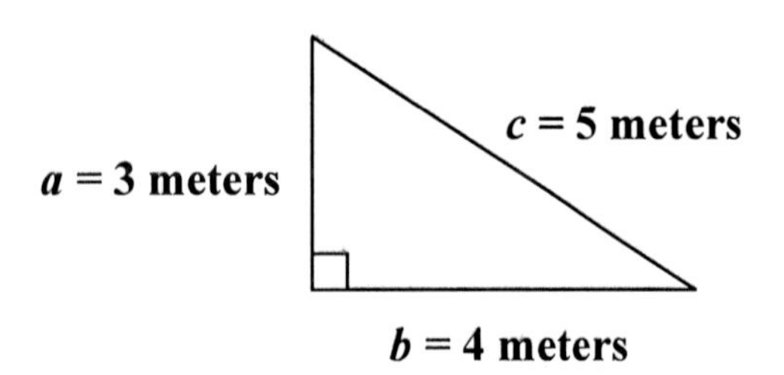

Solution: $a = 3$ meters, $b = 4$ meters and $c = 5$ meters. Using the formula for the perimeter of a triangle, $P = a + b + c$ gives us

$$P = 3 \text{ meters} + 4 \text{ meters} + 5 \text{ meters}.$$

$$\begin{array}{r} 3 \text{ meters} \\ 4 \text{ meters} \\ +\ 5 \text{ meters} \\ \hline 12 \text{ meters} \end{array}$$

The perimeter of the triangle is 12 meters.

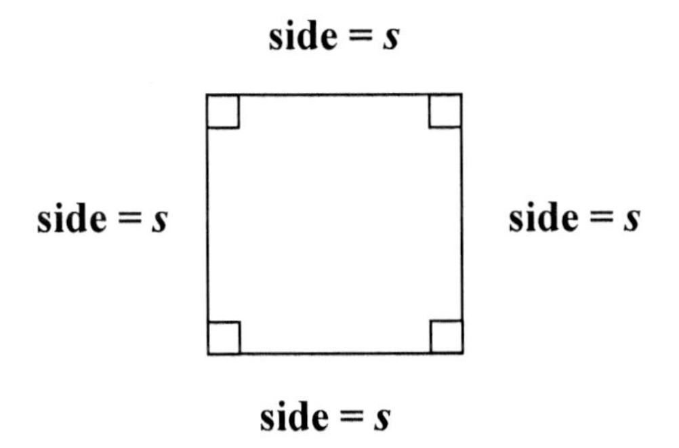

Given a square with four equal sides s, we have the following formula:

FORMULA FOR THE PERIMETER OF A SQUARE:

$$P = s + s + s + s$$

Example 5: Find the perimeter of a square with a side of 7 inches.

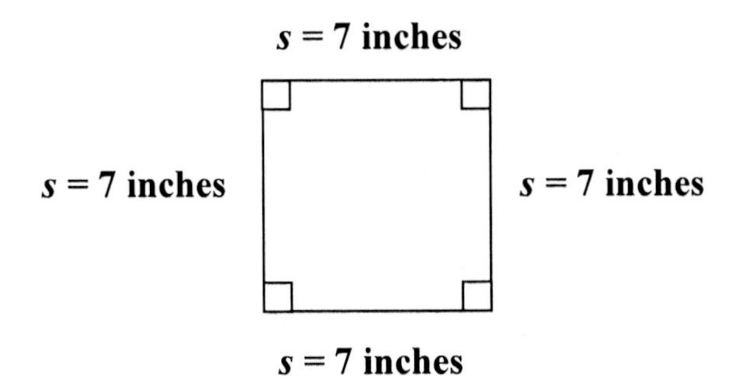

Solution: $s = 7$ inches. Using the formula for the perimeter of a square,

$P = s + s + s + s$ gives us

$P = 7$ inches + 7 inches + 7 inches + 7 inches.

```
   7 inches
   7 inches
   7 inches
+  7 inches
  28 inches
```

The perimeter of the square is 28 inches.

Sometimes dimensions of a polygon, such as the length and width of a rectangle, are given in what are called **mixed units**. Consider the rectangle below.

L = 6 feet 4 inches

W = 2 feet 5 inches

Example 6: Find the perimeter of the rectangle shown above.

Solution:

To determine the perimeter of this rectangle, use the formula $P = L + W + L + W$. This gives us P = 6 feet 4 inches + 2 feet 5 inches + 6 feet 4 inches + 2 feet 5 inches. Now, adding up these distances we get the following:

```
   6 feet  4 inches
   2 feet  5 inches
   6 feet  4 inches
 + 2 feet  5 inches
 ------------------
  16 feet 18 inches
```

Since there are 12 inches in 1 foot, we can take 12 inches from the 18 inches we have and change it into 1 foot. This gives us 6 inches left over. So in effect, the 18 inches becomes 1 foot 6 inches. Now, we can add the unit of 1 foot to the other 16 feet to get 17 feet. And, we still have the 6 inches from before to give us a total of 17 feet 6 inches. The whole process looks like this:

```
   6 feet  4 inches
   2 feet  5 inches
   6 feet  4 inches
 + 2 feet  5 inches
  16 feet 18 inches
```

16 feet + 18 inches

= 16 feet + 12 inches + 6 inches

= 16 feet + 1 foot + 6 inches

= 17 feet + 6 inches or 17 feet 6 inches.

Note: Think of the process of carrying used in basic addition. In this case, 12 inches in the inches column gets carried and becomes 1 foot in the feet column.

Let's look at another example involving mixed units. Only, this time we will subtract.

Example 7: A carpenter has a board that is 8 feet 4 inches long. If she saws off a piece of board that is 3 feet 7 inches long, what will be the length of the remaining board?

Solution:

The whole process looks like this:

$$\begin{array}{r} 8\text{ feet } 4\text{ inches} \\ -3\text{ feet } 7\text{ inches} \\ \hline \end{array}$$

Since we can't take 7 inches away from 4 inches, we must borrow 1 foot from the feet column.

$$\begin{aligned} & \overbrace{8\text{ feet}} + 4\text{ inches} \\ &= 7\text{ feet} + 1\text{ foot} + 4\text{ inches} \\ &= 7\text{ feet} + \underbrace{12\text{ inches} + 4\text{ inches}} \\ &= 7\text{ feet} + 16\text{ inches} \end{aligned}$$

Now the subtraction problem becomes the following:

$$\begin{array}{r} 7\text{ feet } 16\text{ inches} \\ -3\text{ feet } 7\text{ inches} \\ \hline 4\text{ feet } 9\text{ inches} \end{array}$$

The remaining board is 4 feet 9 inches in length.

Note: Think of the process of borrowing used in basic addition. In this case, 1 foot in the feet column gets borrowed and becomes 12 inches in the inches column.

Warning!! Be careful that a foot borrowed becomes 12 inches and not just 10 inches.

Example 8: A carpenter worked for 3 hours and 43 minutes before lunch and then another 2 hours and 36 minutes after lunch. What was the total time that the carpenter worked?

Solution: Add 3 hours 48 minutes to 2 hours 36 minutes.

$$\begin{array}{r} 3\text{ hours } 43\text{ minutes} \\ +\ 2\text{ hours } 36\text{ minutes} \\ \hline 5\text{ hours } 79\text{ minutes} \end{array}$$

Since 60 minutes = 1 hour, we get the following:

$$\begin{aligned} & 5\text{ hours} + \overbrace{79\text{ minutes}} \\ &= 5\text{ hours} + 60\text{ minutes} + 19\text{ minutes} \\ &= \underbrace{5\text{ hours} + 1\text{ hour}} + 19\text{ minutes} \\ &= 6\text{ hours} + 19\text{ minutes} \end{aligned}$$

or 6 hours 19 minutes.

As was mentioned previously, each side of a rectangle or each side of a square connects with another side to form a 90° or right angle.

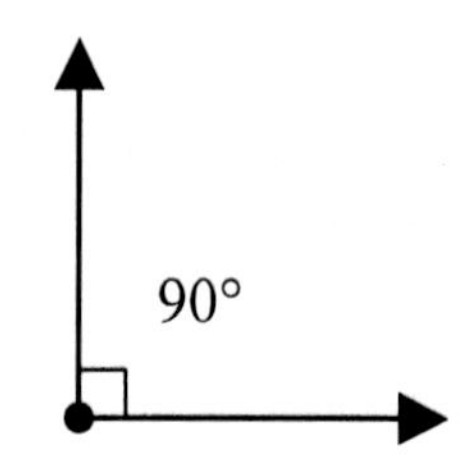

The size of an angle is measured in units called **degrees**. The symbol " ° " is used to indicate degrees. For instance, a **right angle** measures 90 degrees or 90°. Here are some other common angles and their measures given in degrees.

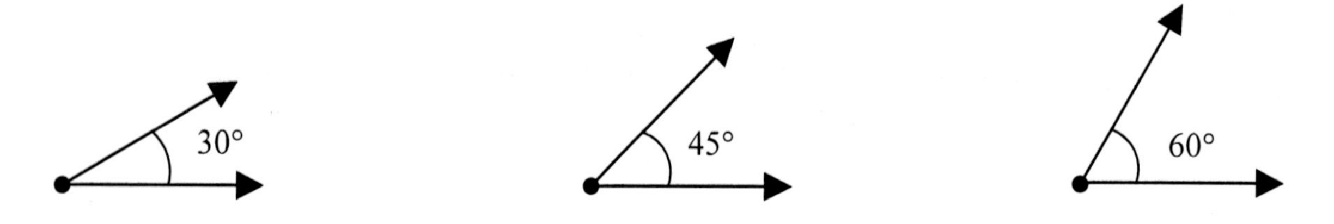

Another important angle is called a **straight angle**. A straight angle appears as a line with a point highlighted. Its measure is 180°.

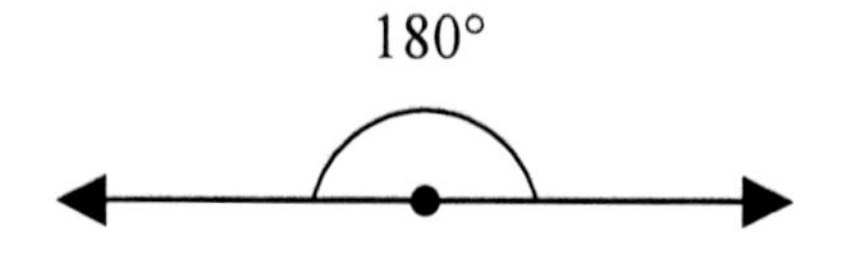

The measure of angles can be added or subtracted. For instance, a 30° angle and a 60° angle can be added together to form a 90° angle. Or, a 20° angle can be subtracted from a 70° angle to form a 50° angle.

When the sum of the measure of two angles is 90°, the angles are said to be a pair of **complementary angles**.

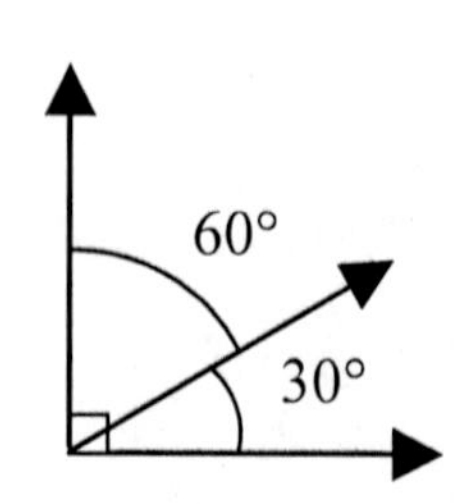

When the sum of the measure of two angles is 180°, the angles are said to be a pair of **supplementary angles**.

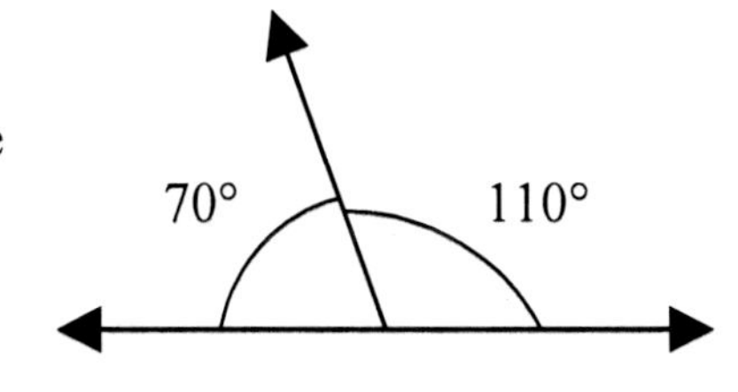

The notation used to refer to an angle and its measure is as follows:

Given,

A 30°

we say, "the measure of angle A is 30 degrees."

Using notation, we write $m(\angle A) = 30°$ or simply $\angle A = 30°$.

Example 9: Given $\angle A = 43°$ and $\angle B = 47°$, are $\angle A$ and $\angle B$ a pair of complementary angles?

Solution: Since 43° + 47° = 90°, then $\angle A$ and $\angle B$ are a pair of complementary angles.

Example 10: Given $\angle C = 139°$ and $\angle D = 31°$, are $\angle C$ and $\angle D$ a pair of supplementary angles?

Solution: Since 139° + 31° = 170°, then $\angle C$ and $\angle D$ are not a pair of supplementary angles.

Example 11: Given $\angle W = 24°$, find $\angle X$ such that $\angle W$ and $\angle X$ are a pair of complementary angles.

Solution: If $\angle W$ and $\angle X$ are a pair of complementary angles, then

$\angle W + \angle X = 90°$. Since $\angle W = 24°$, then

$24° + \angle X = 90°$. By subtracting 24° from both sides of the equation it becomes

$24° - 24° + \angle X = \underbrace{90° - 24°}$. Finally,

$\angle X = 66°$.

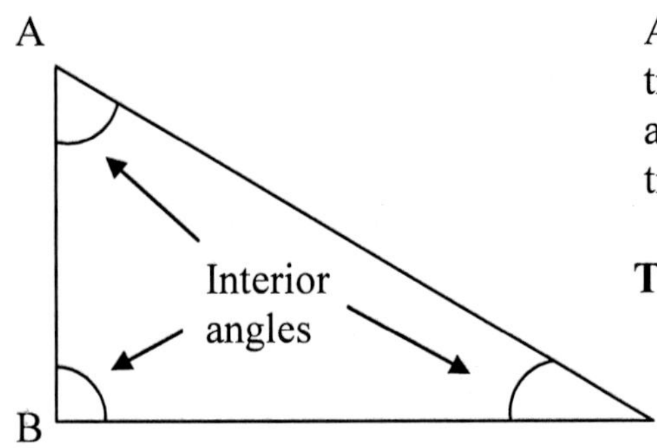

A triangle has what are called **interior angles**. Just like a tricycle has three wheels, a triangle has three interior angles. One of the things that is always true about a triangle is the following:

The sum of the three interior angles of a triangle is 180°.

So, for the triangle above, $\angle A + \angle B + \angle C = 180°$.

Example 12: A given triangle contains interior angles $\angle D$, $\angle E$ and $\angle F$. If $\angle D = 46°$ and $\angle E = 64°$, then find $\angle F$.

Solution: Since $\angle D$, $\angle E$ and $\angle F$ are the three interior angles of a triangle, then their sum is 180°. That is,

$\angle D + \angle E + \angle F = 180°$. Since $\angle D = 46°$ and $\angle E = 64°$, then

$46° + 64° + \angle F = 180°$. Adding together 46° + 64° the equation becomes

$110° + \angle F = 180°$. By subtracting 110° from both sides of the equation it becomes

$110° - 110° + \angle F = \underbrace{180° - 110°}$. Finally,

$\angle F = 70°$.

Here is a review of word phrases that indicate addition:

Plus, increased by, added to, the sum of, more than, total

Other expressions that may imply addition include:

How many are included? Find the complete amount. How many altogether?

Here is a review of word phrases that indicate subtraction:

Minus, decreased by, subtracted from, the difference between, the difference of, less than, less

Other expressions that may imply subtraction include:

How much longer (or shorter)? How much more (or less)? How much higher (or lower)?

Caution!! Be careful of the word "**and**." Sometimes people think that it always means addition because of expressions like "Tom and I went to the store." Or, "the sum of 3 and 7." However, it could just as easily be used in an expression like "the difference of 7 and 3" which is a subtraction problem.

Section 4 exercises. Use Figure 1 for questions 1-4.

Figure 1

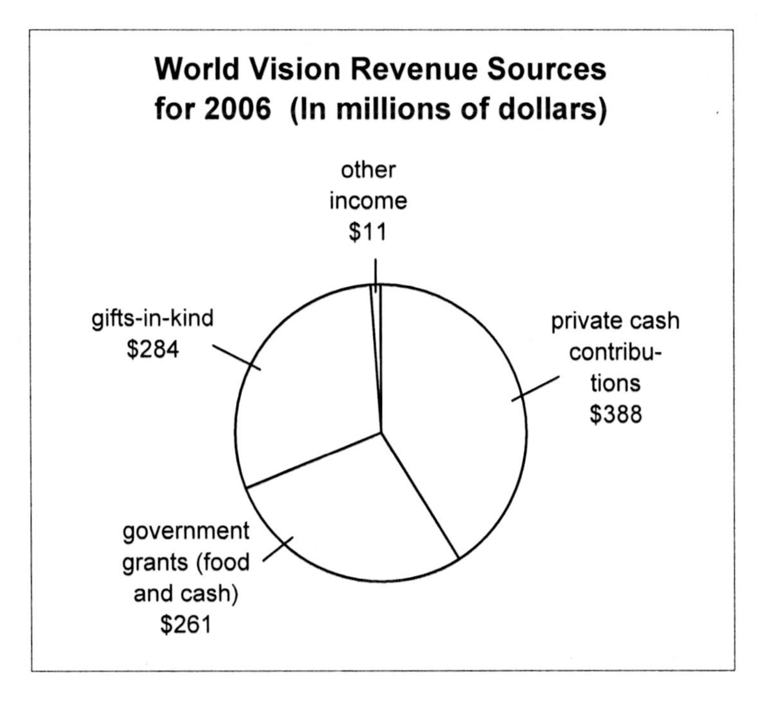

1. What was the total amount of revenue for World Vision in 2006?

2. How much more revenue was generated from private cash contributions than from government grants?

3. How much less revenue was generated from gifts-in-kind than from private cash contributions?

4. Which source generated the least amount of revenue?

Use Figure 2 for questions 5-6.

Figure 2

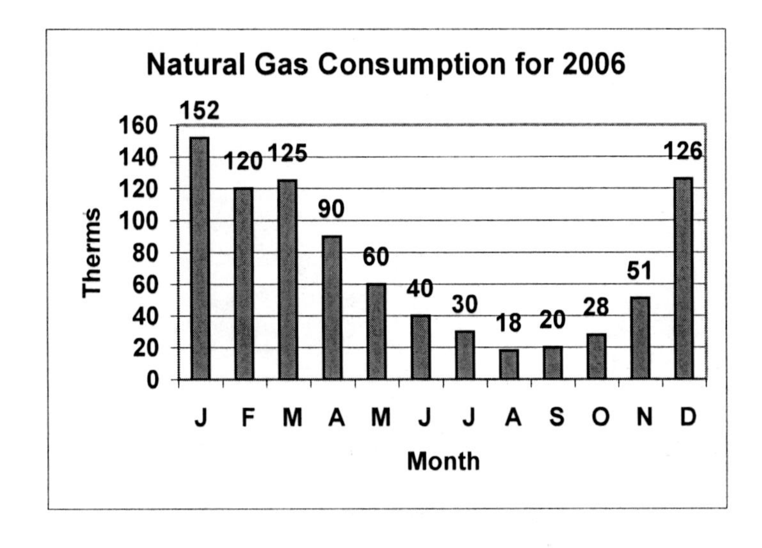

5. How many therms of natural gas were consumed altogether in October, November and December?

6. How many therms of natural gas were consumed altogether in March, April and May?

Figure 3

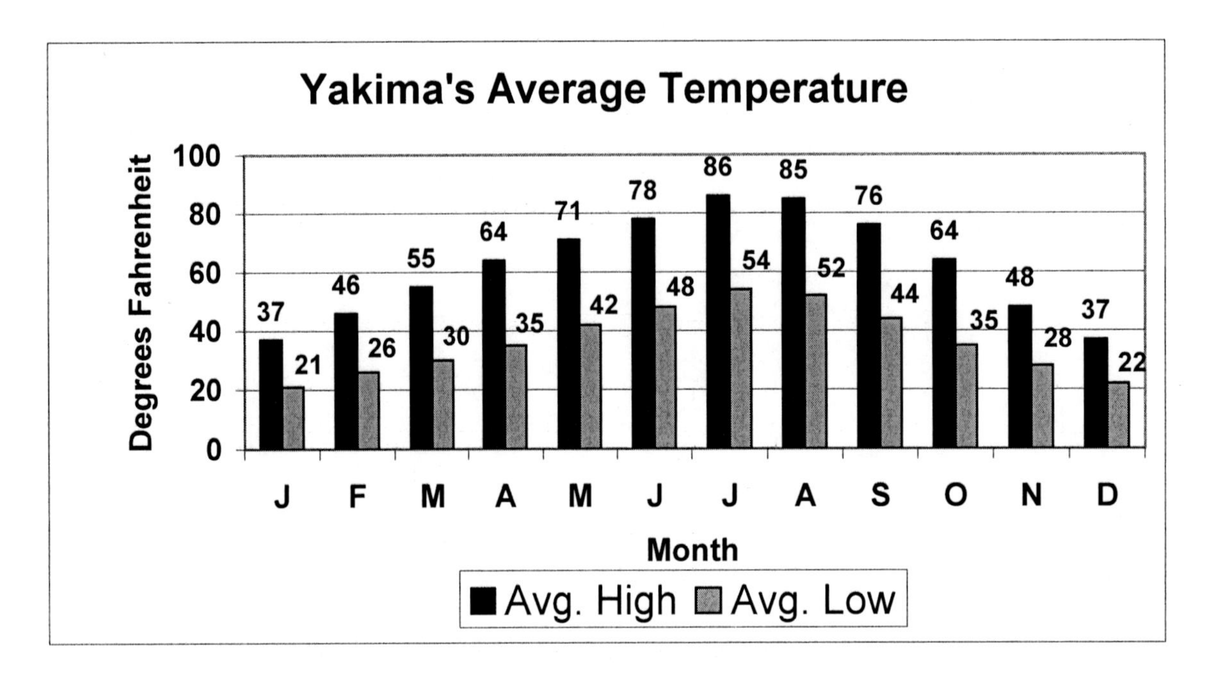

Use Figure 3 for questions 7-12.

7. What's the difference between the high temperature and the low temperature in April?

8. What's the difference between the high temperature and the low temperature in May?

9. How much lower is the average high in December than in June?

10. How much lower is the average high in November than in July?

11. How much higher is the average low in July than in November?

12. How much higher is the average low in June than in December?

Find the perimeter of each polygon. Note: 12 in. = 1 ft.

13.

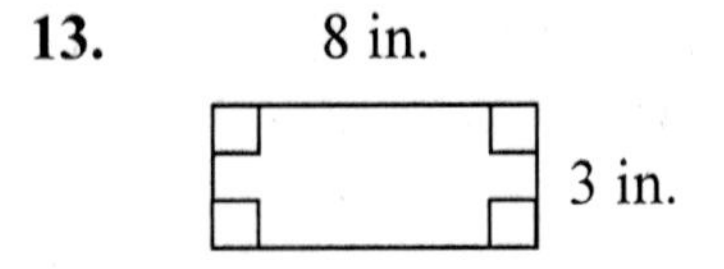

14.

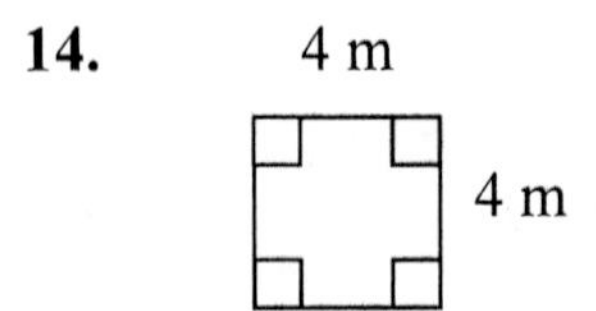

15.

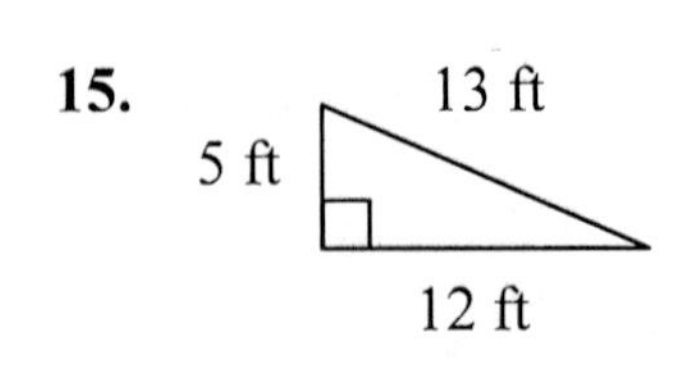

16.

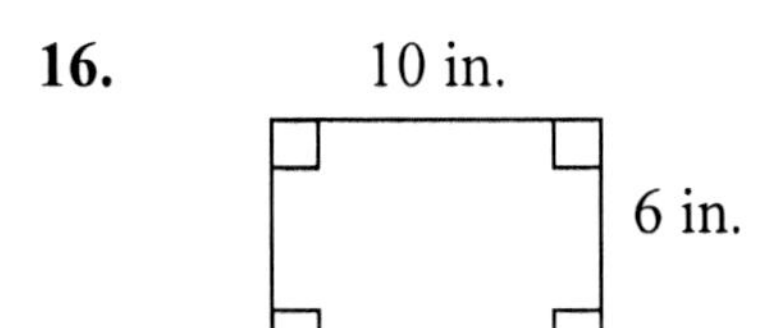

17.

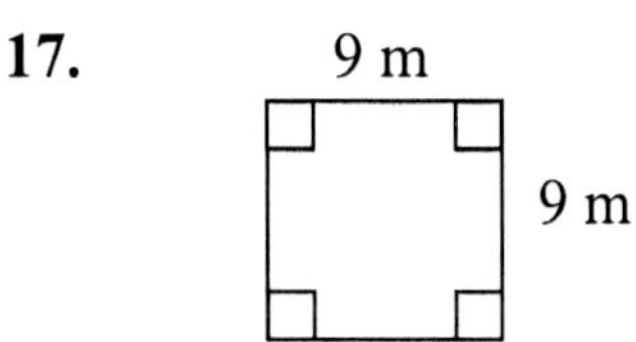

18.

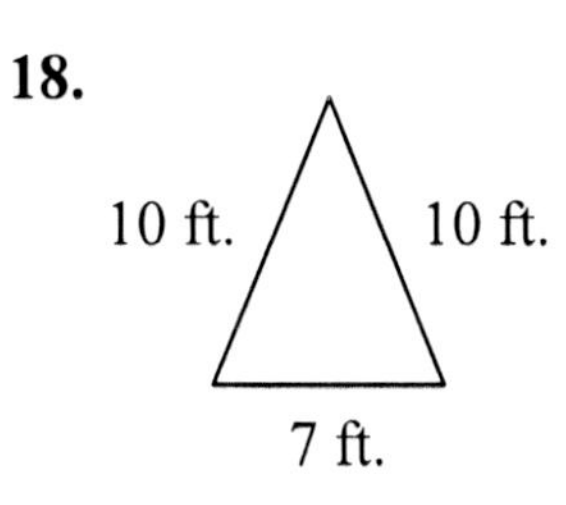

19.

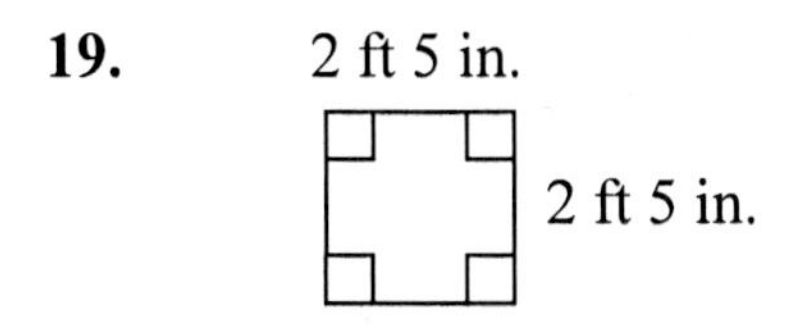

20.

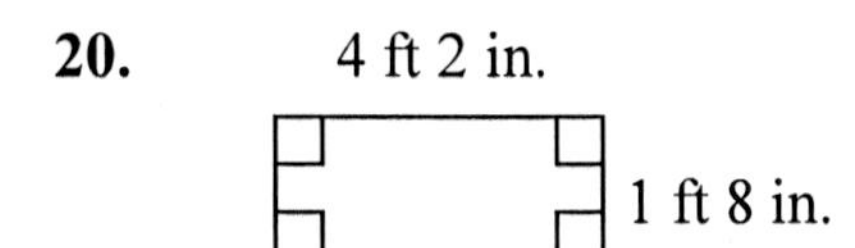

21.

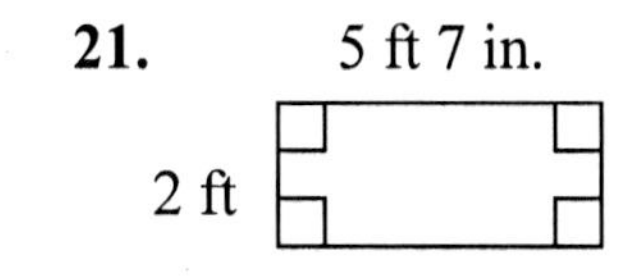

22.

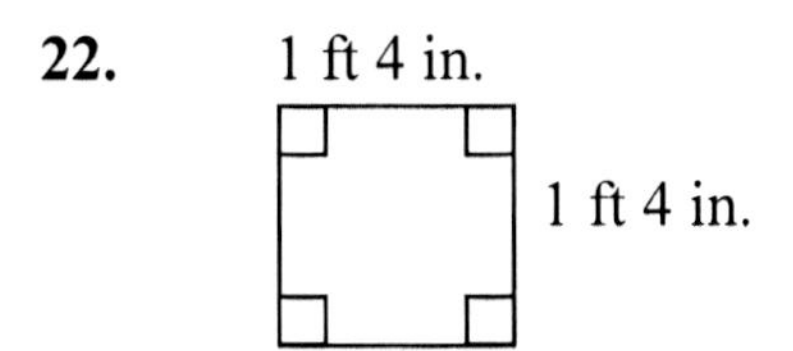

23.

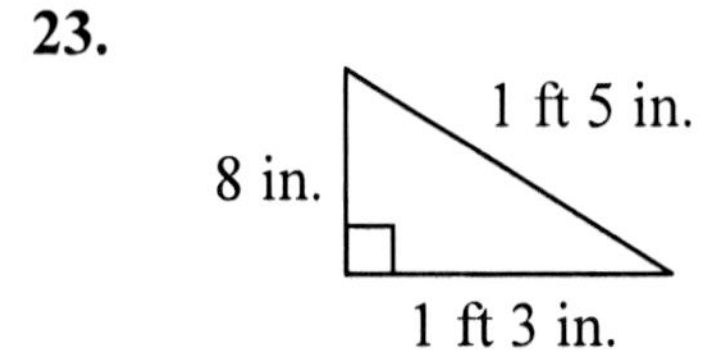

24.

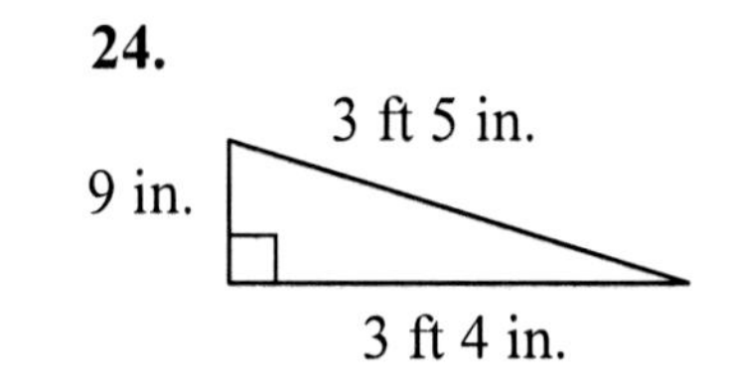

25. A farmer wants to build a rectangular pen to hold cattle. If the dimensions of the pen are to be 24 ft 6 in. by 8 ft 6 in., what is the complete amount of fencing needed to build the pen?

26. A mason wants to build a stone wall around a rectangular shaped garden. If the dimensions of the garden are 18 ft 4 in. by 15 ft 6 in., what is the complete amount of stone wall needing to be built around the garden?

27. John needs to work a total of 3 hours and 20 minutes in order to pay back his grandfather for a loan. If John has already worked 1 hour and 45 minutes, how much longer does he need to work to finish paying off the loan?

28. It will take Jennifer 2 hours and 15 minutes to run a certain distance. If she has already run for 1 hour and 27 minutes, how much longer must she run to complete the distance?

29. Carl purchased three packages of hamburger from the butcher. The first package weighed 3 lb 5 oz, the second package weighed 2 lb 9 oz and the third package weighed 3 lb 6 oz. What was the total weight of the three packages? Note: 16 oz = 1 lb.

30. Julie purchased three packages of lamb chops from the grocery store. The first package weighed 4 lb 7 oz, the second package weighed 3 lb 10 oz and the third package weighed 2 lb 8 oz. What was the total weight of the three packages? Note: 16 oz = 1 lb.

31. Ben wants to take 10 lb of chocolate on a trip. If he already has chocolate bars weighing 2 lb 10 oz and 4 lb 9 oz, how much more chocolate does he need to take?

32. Sue wants to take 8 lb of rice on a camping trip. If she already has packages of rice weighing 2 lb 12 oz and 3 lb 6 oz, how much more rice does she need to take?

For each pair of angles, tell whether they are complementary, supplementary or neither one.

33. $\angle A = 38°$, $\angle B = 62°$

34. $\angle C = 164°$, $\angle D = 16°$

35. $\angle E = 95°$, $\angle F = 85°$

36. $\angle G = 38°$, $\angle H = 52°$

37. $\angle J = 44°$, $\angle K = 46°$

38. $\angle M = 22°$, $\angle N = 68°$

39. $\angle P = 90°$, $\angle R = 60°$

40. $\angle S = 48°$, $\angle T = 62°$

41. $\angle U = 14°$, $\angle V = 76°$

42. $\angle W = 90°$, $\angle X = 90°$

43. Given that $\angle X = 29°$, find $\angle Y$ such that $\angle X$ and $\angle Y$ are complementary angles.

44. Given that $\angle A = 38°$, find $\angle B$ such that $\angle A$ and $\angle B$ are complementary angles.

45. Given that $\angle C = 118°$, find $\angle D$ such that $\angle C$ and $\angle D$ are supplementary angles.

46. Given that $\angle E = 74°$, find $\angle F$ such that $\angle E$ and $\angle F$ are supplementary angles.

47. Given that $\angle G = 39°$, find $\angle H$ such that $\angle G$ and $\angle H$ are supplementary angles.

48. Given that $\angle M = 28°$, find $\angle N$ such that $\angle M$ and $\angle N$ are supplementary angles.

49. Given that $\angle P = 3°$, find $\angle R$ such that $\angle P$ and $\angle R$ are complementary angles.

50. Given that $\angle W = 11°$, find $\angle Z$ such that $\angle W$ and $\angle Z$ are complementary angles.

51. A given triangle contains interior angles $\angle D$, $\angle E$ and $\angle F$. If $\angle D = 29°$ and $\angle E = 51°$, then find $\angle F$.

52. A given triangle contains interior angles $\angle M$, $\angle N$ and $\angle P$. If $\angle M = 127°$ and $\angle N = 35°$, then find $\angle P$.

53. A given triangle contains interior angles $\angle X$, $\angle Y$ and $\angle Z$. If $\angle X = 148°$ and $\angle Y = 15°$, then find $\angle Z$.

54. A given triangle contains interior angles $\angle R$, $\angle K$ and $\angle W$. If $\angle R = 40°$ and $\angle K = 33°$, then find $\angle W$.

55. If one of the interior angles of a triangle is a right angle, then the remaining angles are a pair of _____________ angles.

56. If $\angle D$, $\angle E$ and $\angle F$ are the three interior angles of a triangle and $\angle D + \angle E = \angle G$, then $\angle F$ and $\angle G$ are a pair of _____________ angles.

WHOLE NUMBERS

Section 5: Multiplying and Dividing Whole Numbers

Joe baked a batch of cookies. When he put them on the cookie sheet, they formed 3 rows of 4 cookies each.

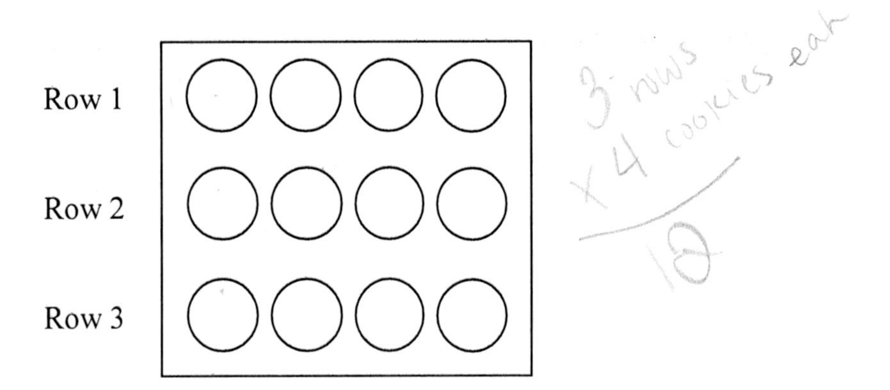

What was the total number of cookies baked? 3 rows of 4 cookies each would be 4 + 4 + 4 =12.

Another way of looking at it is, 3 rows of 4 cookies each would be 3 times 4 = 12 or $3 \times 4 = 12$.

Notice that **multiplication** is the same as repeated addition of the same number. That is,

$3 \times 4 = 4 + 4 + 4 = 12$

Numbers that are to be multiplied together are called **factors**. The result of multiplication or the answer, is called the **product**.

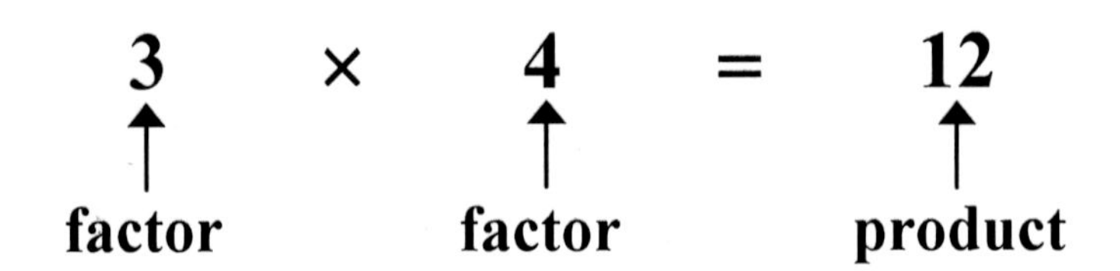

There are several different symbols that are used to indicate multiplication. The $\times$ in the above example is one of them. Other ways of indicating multiplication include using a dot between factors or parentheses around one or both of the factors. The statement "three times four equals twelve" could be written in all of the following ways:

$3 \times 4 = 12$ $\quad 3 \cdot 4 = 12$ $\quad (3)(4) = 12$ $\quad 3(4) = 12$ $\quad (3)4 = 12$

Note: When a number is being multiplied by a variable, the number is written next to the variable such as 3*a* or 5*x*. (No multiplication symbol is needed). When two variables are being multiplied together, they are written next to each other such as *xy* or *ab*. (Again, no multiplication symbol is needed).

Multiplying any one-digit number by any other one-digit number produces a set of products that should be memorized. For example, $7\cdot 3=21$, $9\cdot 7=63$ and $4\cdot 8=32$. This set of factors and their resulting products are often referred to as "the times tables." We will use this information when multiplying numbers together that are larger than one digit.

Example 1: Multiply 46 and 3.

Solution: Write the problem vertically

$$\begin{array}{r} 46 \\ \times\ 3 \\ \hline \end{array}$$

Multiply the 6 by 3. The result is 18.
Put the 8 in the ones column below the solid line and carry the 1 to the tens column above the 4.

$$\begin{array}{r} 1 \\ 46 \\ \times\ 3 \\ \hline 8 \end{array}$$

Multiply the 4 in the tens column by 3. The result is 12.
Add the 12 to the 1 that was previously carried to the tens column. The result is 13. Put the 13 below the solid line in the tens column. Actually, the 3 goes in the tens column and the 1 is carried over to the hundreds column.

$$\begin{array}{r} 1 \\ 46 \\ \times\ 3 \\ \hline 138 \end{array}$$

Therefore, the product of 46 and 3 is 138.

The product of any whole number and 10 is called a **multiple of 10**. A multiple of 10 is any whole number that ends in zero. For example, 10 is 1×10; 20 is 2×10; 50 is 5×10; 100 is 10×10; or 350 is 35×10.

Notice a pattern using multiples of 10.

$34\times 1\underline{0}=34\underline{0}$ $34\times 1\underline{00}=3{,}4\underline{00}$ $34\times 1{,}\underline{000}=34{,}\underline{000}$

You can multiply a whole number by 10, 100, or 1,000 by attaching one, two, or three zeros to the right of the original whole number.

This pattern also works when multiplying two numbers that are multiples of ten

To multiply 30 by 20, multiply 3 by 2 and then attach two zeros.

$3\times 2=6$

$3\underline{0}\times 2\underline{0}=6\underline{00}$

Example 2: Multiply 87 and 26.

Solution:

First multiply 87 by 6.

```
   4
  87
×  6
----
 522
```

Next multiply 87 by 20.

```
    1
   87
×  20
-----
1,740
```

Now add the results.

```
    87
×   26
------
   522
+1,740
------
 2,262
```

Therefore, the product of 87 and 26 is 2,262.

Example 3: Multiply 427 and 35.

Solution:

First multiply 427 by 5.

```
   13
  427
×   5
-----
2,135
```

Next multiply 427 by 30.

```
     2
   427
×   30
------
12,810
```

Now add the results.

```
    427
×    35
-------
  2,135
+12,810
-------
 14,945
```

Therefore, the product of 427 and 35 is 14,945.

Note: As a general rule we do not write out a separate multiplication problem for each digit. Instead, we write the product formed by each digit in a column below the multiplication problem. The results are then added together to achieve the final product.

Example 4: Multiply 371 and 23.

Solution:

First multiply 371 by 3.

```
    2
  371
×  23
-----
1,113
```

Next multiply 371 by 20.

```
    1
  371
×  23
-----
1,113
7,420
```

Now add the results.

```
    371
×    23
-------
  1,113
+ 7,420
-------
  8,533
```

Therefore, the product of 371 and 23 is 8,533.

Example 5: Multiply 298 and 207.

Solution:

First multiply 298 by 7.

$$\begin{array}{r} {}^{6\,5} \\ 298 \\ \times\ 207 \\ \hline 2{,}086 \end{array}$$

Next multiply 298 by 200.

$$\begin{array}{r} {}^{1\,1} \\ 298 \\ \times\ 207 \\ \hline 2{,}086 \\ 59{,}600 \end{array}$$

Now add the results.

$$\begin{array}{r} 298 \\ \times\ 207 \\ \hline 2{,}086 \\ +\,59{,}600 \\ \hline 61{,}686 \end{array}$$

Therefore, the product of 298 and 207 is 61,686.

There are several different words or word phrases that can be used to express multiplication. Here is a list of some of those phrases.

Word phrase	Used in an expression	Written as symbols
times	three times four	$3\cdot4$ or $3(4)$
the product of	the product of six and two	$6\cdot2$ or $6(2)$
multiplied by	nine multiplied by seven	$9\cdot7$ or $9(7)$
twice	twice the number five	$5\cdot2$ or $5(2)$
double	double the number eight	$8\cdot2$ or $8(2)$
triple	triple the number ten	$10\cdot3$ or $10(3)$

Example 6: Translate the following expression into mathematical symbols: the product of seven and three

Solution: Since "the product of" means to multiply, the expression becomes $7\cdot3$.

Example 7: Translate the following expression into mathematical symbols: six times twelve

Solution: Since "times" means to multiply, the expression becomes $6\cdot12$.

As with addition, there are several properties of multiplication that hold true for any real number.

THE COMMUTATIVE PROPERTY OF MULTIPLICATION:

For any real numbers a and b,

$$a \cdot b = b \cdot a.$$

Two numbers can be multiplied in any order and the product will be the same.

Example 8: Use the fact that $3 \cdot 7 = 21$ to show an example of the commutative property of multiplication.

Solution: $3 \cdot 7 = 21$ and $7 \cdot 3 = 21$. Therefore, $3 \cdot 7 = 7 \cdot 3$.

Conclusion: The order in which numbers are multiplied does not change the resulting product. This is an example showing that **multiplication is commutative**.

THE ASSOCIATIVE PROPERTY OF MULTIPLICATION:

For any real numbers a, b, and c,

$$(a \cdot b) \cdot c = a \cdot (b \cdot c).$$

When three or more numbers are multiplied together, the way in which they are grouped does not change the resulting product.

Example 9: Use the fact that $(3 \cdot 4) \cdot 5 = 12 \cdot 5 = 60$ to show an example of the associative property of multiplication.

Solution: Following order of operations,

$(3 \cdot 4) \cdot 5 = 12 \cdot 5 = 60$ and $3 \cdot (4 \cdot 5) = 3 \cdot 20 = 60$.

Therefore, $(3 \cdot 4) \cdot 5 = 3 \cdot (4 \cdot 5)$.

Conclusion: When three or more numbers are multiplied together, the way in which they are grouped does not change the resulting product. This is an example showing that **multiplication is associative**.

Note: The numbers inside the grouping symbol (in this case, parentheses) are to be multiplied first. The result is multiplied by the remaining factor.

THE IDENTITY PROPERTY OF ONE:

For any real number a,

$a \cdot 1 = a$ and $1 \cdot a = a$.

If 1 is multiplied by any real number a, the product is a.

Note: The number 1 is called the multiplicative identity.

Example 10: Use the number 4 to show an example of the identity property of one.

Solution: $4 \cdot 1 = 4$ and $1 \cdot 4 = 4$.

Conclusion: **Multiplying 1 by a number does not change the number's original value.**

THE MULTIPLICATION PROPERTY OF ZERO:

For any real number a,

$a \cdot 0 = 0$ and $0 \cdot a = 0$.

If 0 is multiplied by any real number a, the product is 0.

Example 11: Use the number 7 to show an example of the multiplication property of zero.

Solution: $7 \cdot 0 = 0$ and $0 \cdot 7 = 0$.

Conclusion: **Multiplying 0 by a number or multiplying a number by 0 produces a product that is 0.**

Exponents

When a number is to be multiplied by itself several times, such as $2\cdot2\cdot2\cdot2\cdot2$, there is a shortcut notation used to indicate this repeated multiplication of the same factor.

$2\cdot2\cdot2\cdot2\cdot2$ can be written as 2^5. In this case, the 2 is called the **base** and the 5 is called the **exponent**. Writing $2\cdot2\cdot2\cdot2\cdot2$ as 2^5 is called writing the expression in **exponential form**. 2^5 is called an **exponential expression**. 2^5 is read as "2 raised to the fifth power," or just "2 to the fifth power." Writing 2^5 as $2\cdot2\cdot2\cdot2\cdot2$ is called writing an exponential expression in **expanded form**.

$$\underbrace{2^5}_{\text{exponential form}} = \underbrace{2\cdot2\cdot2\cdot2\cdot2}_{\text{expanded form}}$$

Note: Be careful not to confuse 2^5, which is $2\cdot2\cdot2\cdot2\cdot2$ or 32, with $2\cdot5$ which equals 10.

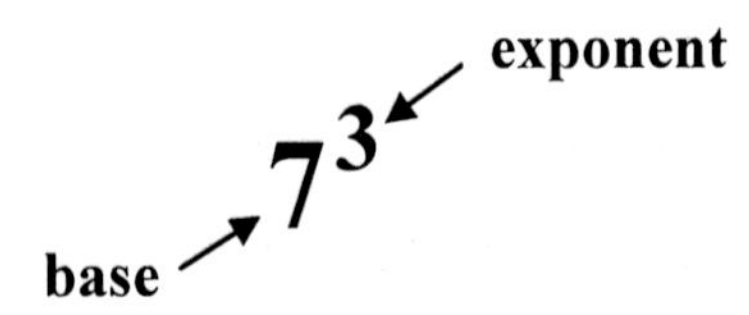

The exponential expression 7^3 means $7\cdot7\cdot7$ which when multiplied together equals 343. That is, $7^3=7\cdot7\cdot7=343$. The exponent "3" tells how many factors of the base "7" are to be multiplied together.

In general an exponential expression b^n is read as "b raised to the nth power."

For example, 6^4 is read as "6 to the fourth power," or 8^6 is read as "8 to the sixth power."

However, in the cases of second and third powers there are alternative names given.

5^2 can be read as "5 to the **second power**" or "5 **squared**."

4^3 can be read as "4 to the **third power**" or "4 **cubed**."

Note: A number raised to the first power can be written with a 1 as an exponent or with no exponent at all. 8^1 means the same thing as just 8, that is, $8^1 = 8$.

Example 12: Evaluate the expression: 2^7

Solution:	
2^7	Expand the exponent.
$2\cdot2\cdot2\cdot2\cdot2\cdot2\cdot2$	Then, multiply the factors.
128	

Example 13: Write the expression in exponential form: $3 \cdot 3 \cdot 7 \cdot 7 \cdot 7 \cdot 7 \cdot x \cdot x \cdot x$

Solution:

Since there are 2 factors of the number 3, 4 factors of the number 7, and 3 factors of the variable x the expression

$$\underbrace{3 \cdot 3}_{3^2} \cdot \underbrace{7 \cdot 7 \cdot 7 \cdot 7}_{7^4} \cdot \underbrace{x \cdot x \cdot x}_{x^3}$$

becomes

or

$3^2 \cdot 7^4 \cdot x^3$.

Powers of 10 When the number 10 is raised to a power, the exponent on the 10 is the same number as the amount of zeros contained in the number when it is written in expanded form.

For example:

$10^1 = 10$ The exponent is a 1. There is 1 zero in the number 10.

$10^2 = 10 \cdot 10 = 100$ The exponent is a 2. There are 2 zeros in the number 100.

$10^3 = 10 \cdot 10 \cdot 10 = 1{,}000$ The exponent is a 3. There are 3 zeros in the number 1,000.

$10^4 = 10 \cdot 10 \cdot 10 \cdot 10 = 10{,}000$ The exponent is a 4. There are 4 zeros in the number 10,000.

$10^5 = 10 \cdot 10 \cdot 10 \cdot 10 \cdot 10 = 100{,}000$ The exponent is a 5. There are 5 zeros in the number 100,000.

Example 14: Evaluate the expression: 10^9

Solution:

10^9 Expand the exponent.

$10 \cdot 10 \cdot 10 \cdot 10 \cdot 10 \cdot 10 \cdot 10 \cdot 10 \cdot 10$ Then, multiply the factors.

1,000,000,000 The exponent is a 9. There are 9 zeros in the number 1,000,000,000.

Joe pulled a batch of cookies out of the oven. Sam counted them and came up with a total of 12 cookies.

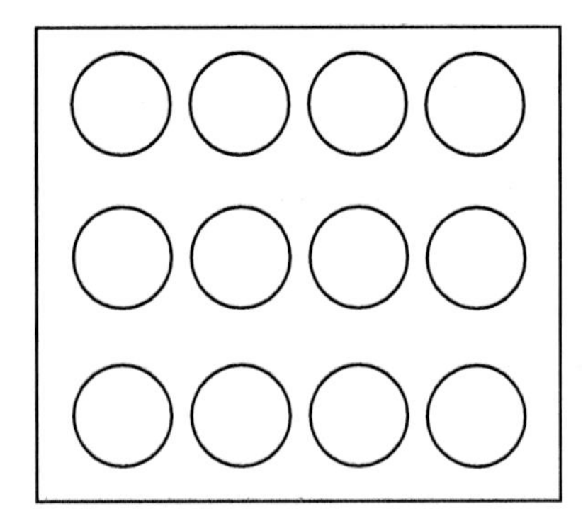

Maria said, "Let's divide the cookies evenly between the 3 of us." Sam took the cookies and placed an equal amount on each of 3 plates.

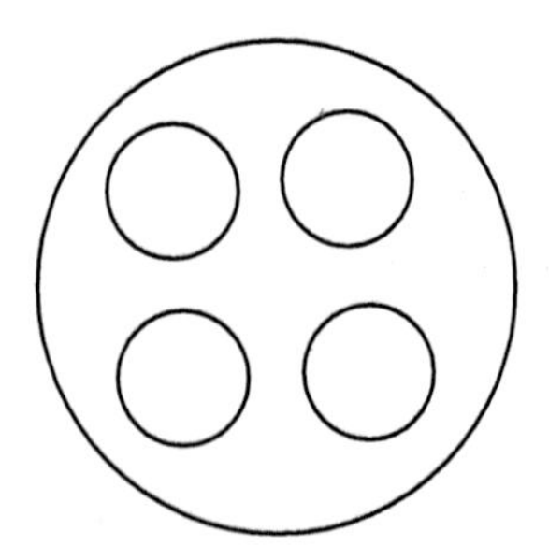
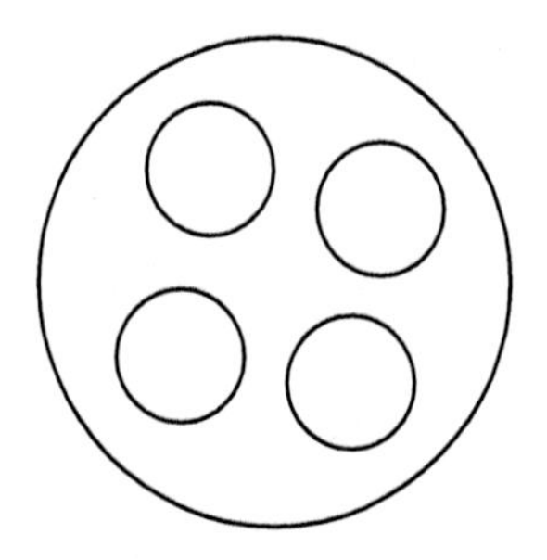
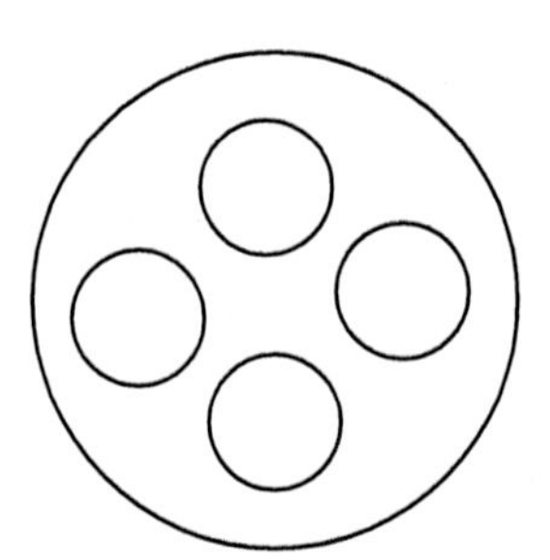

Joe noticed that there were 4 cookies on each plate. Maria said, "That's because 12 divided by 3 equals 4."

This **division** problem could be written in each of three different ways. Using the symbol $\overline{)\ }$, the symbol $\div$, or using a fraction bar.

$3\overline{)12}$ with quotient 4 $\qquad 12 \div 3 = 4 \qquad \dfrac{12}{3} = 4$

In each case, the 12 is called the **dividend**, the 3 is called the **divisor** and the 4 is called the **quotient**. Also, in each case the problem would be read, "twelve divided by three equals four."

The dividend is the number that is being divided, the divisor is the number that is doing the dividing and the quotient is the result or the answer.

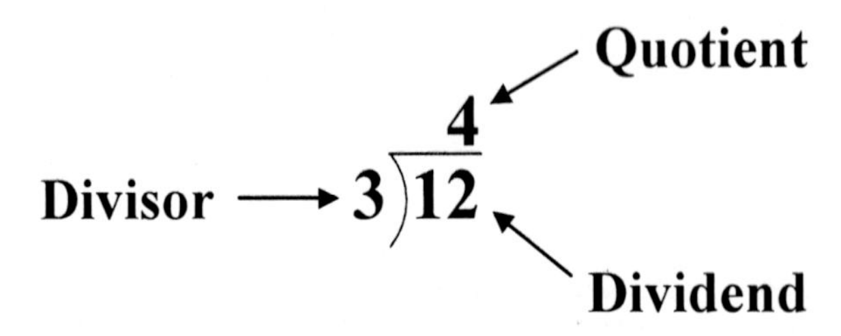

Note: Division is the inverse operation of multiplication. At the beginning of this section we determined that $4 \times 3 = 12$. By inverting this statement we get $12 \div 3 = 4$ and $12 \div 4 = 3$.

Since $9 \cdot 7 = 63$, then $63 \div 9 = 7$ and $63 \div 7 = 9$.

Since $6 \cdot 4 = 24$, then $24 \div 6 = 4$ and $24 \div 4 = 6$.

By inverting multiplication facts like these, we can establish division facts that we will use to divide large numbers.

Example 15: Divide 69 by 3.

Solution: The process used is referred to as **long division**. It starts by writing the problem using the $\overline{)\ \ }$ symbol.

$3\overline{)69}$

Start at the left end of the dividend, that is, the tens column of 69, and ask the following question. What whole number multiplied by 3 produces a product less than or equal to 6?

Since the answer is 2, put 2 above the 6 in the space for the quotient.

$$\begin{array}{r} 2 \\ 3\overline{)69} \end{array}$$

Next, since $2 \cdot 3 = 6$, put 6 below the 6 and subtract.

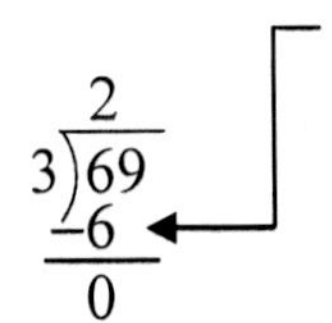

Proceed by bringing down the number in the next column to the right, which in this case, is the 9 in the ones column.

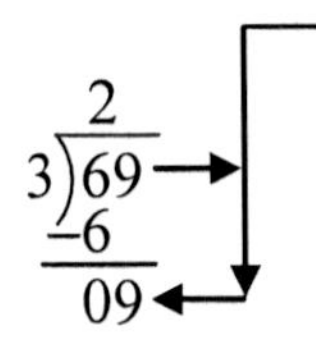

Now start the process over by asking the following question. What whole number multiplied by 3 produces a product less than or equal to 9?

Since the answer is 3, put 3 above the 9 in the space for the quotient.

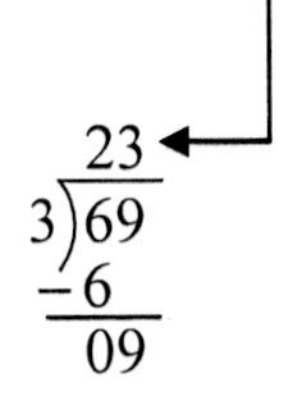

Then, since $3 \cdot 3 = 9$, put 9 below the 9 and subtract.

$$\begin{array}{r} 23 \\ 3\overline{)69} \\ \underline{-6} \\ 09 \\ \underline{-\ \ 9} \\ 0 \end{array}$$

Finally, since all that is left is 0, this means that 69 divided by 3 is exactly 23. Or, $69 \div 3 = 23$. This answer checks because $3 \cdot 23 = 69$.

Joe pulled a second batch of cookies out of the oven. Sam counted them and came up with a total of 10 cookies.

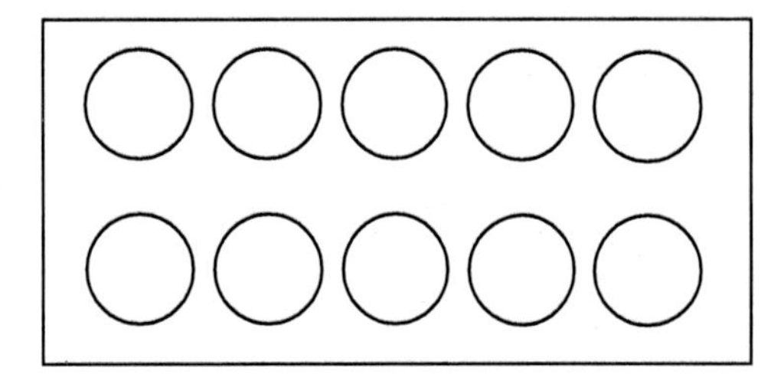

Maria said, "Let's divide the cookies evenly between the 3 of us." Sam took the cookies and placed an equal amount on each of 3 plates.

Joe noticed that there was 1 cookie left over. Maria said, "That's because 3 doesn't go into 10 evenly. It goes in 3 times with a **remainder** of 1." "What's a remainder?" asked Joe. It's the amount left over after a whole number of items has been divided by a whole number." Said Maria. "What if the remainder is 0?" asked Sam. "Then the divisor goes into the dividend evenly, like when $12 \div 3 = 4$," replied Maria.

$$\begin{array}{r} 3 \\ 3\overline{)10} \\ -\ 9 \\ \hline 1 \end{array}$$

Remainder (pointing to the 1)

When there is a remainder other than 0, the remainder is written to the right of the quotient after an "R."

Quotient (pointing to the 3) **Remainder** (pointing to the 1 after R)

$$\begin{array}{r} 3\ \text{R}\,1 \\ 3\overline{)10} \\ -\ 9 \\ \hline 1 \end{array}$$

Example 16: Divide 384 by 5.

Solution: Write the problem using the $\overline{)\ \ }$ symbol.

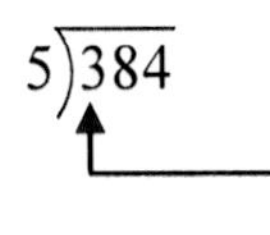

Start at the left end of the dividend, that is, the hundreds column of 384, and ask the following question. What whole number multiplied by 5 produces a product less than or equal to 3? Since there is none, then what whole number multiplied by 5 produces a product less than or equal to 38?

Since the answer is 7, put 7 above the 38 in the space for the quotient.

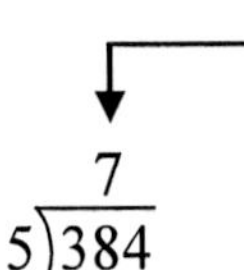

Next, since $7 \cdot 5 = 35$, put 35 below the 38 and subtract.

$$\begin{array}{r} 7 \\ 5\overline{)384} \\ -35 \\ \hline 3 \end{array}$$

Proceed by bringing down the number in the next column to the right, which in this case is the 4 in the ones column.

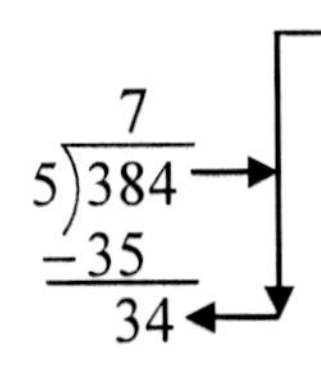

Now start the process over by asking the following question. What whole number multiplied by 5 produces a product less than or equal to 34?

Since the answer is 6, put 6 above the 34 in the space for the quotient.

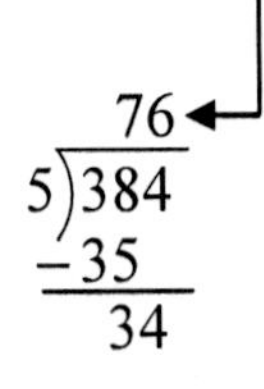

Then, since $6 \cdot 5 = 30$, put 30 below the 34 and subtract.

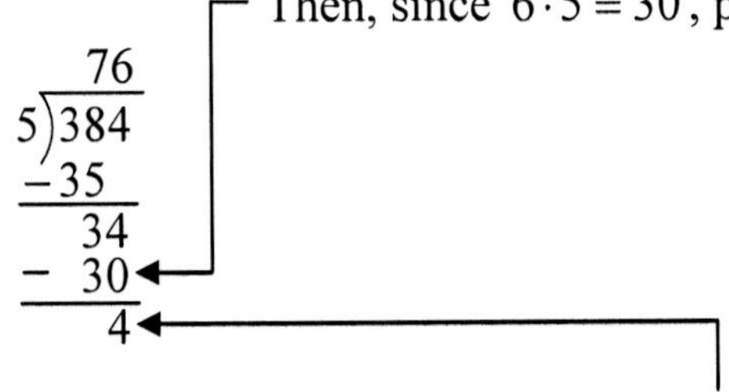

Since all that is left is 4, which is less than the divisor, 4 is the remainder. The final answer is as follows:

$$\begin{array}{r} 76\ \text{R}\,4 \\ 5\overline{)384} \\ -35 \\ \hline 34 \\ -\ 30 \\ \hline 4 \end{array}$$

This means that 384 divided by 5 has a quotient of 76 with a remainder of 4.

To check the answer, multiply the quotient by the divisor and add the remainder. That is, multiply 76 by 5 and then add 4. We'll leave the check to you.

Example 17: Divide 295 by 34.

Solution: Write the problem using the $\overline{)\ \ }$ symbol.

$$34\overline{)295}$$

Since 34 doesn't go into 2 and 34 doesn't go into 29 either, we must ask the following question. What whole number multiplied by 34 produces a product less than or equal to 295? Since 34 is approximately 30 and 295 is approximately 300, we could start with the fact that 30 multiplied by 10 is 300. However, we can easily see that 300 is greater than 295. Consequently 10 is too great a quotient. Since 300 is only slightly larger than 295, then 9 seems like a reasonable guess for the quotient.

$$\begin{array}{r} {}^{3} \\ 34 \\ \times\ \ 9 \\ \hline 306 \end{array}$$

Apparently 9 is still too large for the quotient. Let's try 8.

$$\begin{array}{r} {}^{3} \\ 34 \\ \times\ \ 8 \\ \hline 272 \end{array}$$

Finally! $8 \cdot 34$ is less than 295.

Since the answer is 8, put 8 above the 295 in the space for the quotient.

$$\begin{array}{r} 8 \\ 34\overline{)295} \end{array}$$

Next, since $8 \cdot 34 = 272$, put 272 below the 295 and subtract.

$$\begin{array}{r} 8 \\ 34\overline{)295} \\ -272 \\ \hline 23 \end{array}$$

Since all that is left is 23, which is less than the divisor, 23 is the remainder. The final answer is as follows:

$$\begin{array}{r} 8\text{ R }23 \\ 34\overline{)295}\phantom{\text{ R }23} \\ -272\phantom{\text{ R }23} \\ \hline 23\phantom{\text{ R }23} \end{array}$$

This means that 295 divided by 34 has a quotient of 8 with a remainder of 23. To check the answer, multiply the quotient by the divisor and add the remainder. That is, multiply 8 by 34 and then add 23.

$$\begin{array}{r} {}^{3} \\ 34 \\ \times\ \ 8 \\ \hline 272 \end{array} \qquad \begin{array}{r} 272 \\ +\ \ 23 \\ \hline 295 \end{array}$$

The answer checks.

Example 18: Find $11{,}592 \div 56$.

Solution: Write the problem using the $\overline{)}$ symbol.

$$56\overline{)11{,}592}$$

Since 56 doesn't go into 1 and 56 doesn't go into 11 either, we must ask the following question. What whole number multiplied by 56 produces a product less than or equal to 115?
Since the answer is 2, put 2 above the 115 in the space for the quotient.

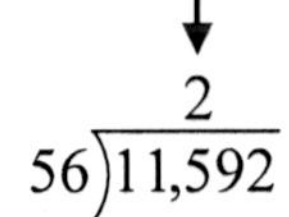

$$\begin{array}{r} 2 \\ 56\overline{)11{,}592} \end{array}$$

Next, since $2 \cdot 56 = 112$, put 112 below the 115 and subtract.

$$\begin{array}{r} 2 \\ 56\overline{)11{,}592} \\ \underline{-112} \\ 3 \end{array}$$

Proceed by bringing down the number in the next column to the right, which in this case is the 9 in the tens column.

$$\begin{array}{r} 2 \\ 56\overline{)11{,}592} \\ \underline{-112} \\ 39 \end{array}$$

Now start the process over by asking the following question. What whole number multiplied by 56 produces a product less than or equal to 39?
Since there is none, we must put a "0" placeholder in the quotient before continuing.

$$\begin{array}{r} 20 \\ 56\overline{)11{,}592} \\ \underline{-112} \\ 39 \end{array}$$

Since 56 doesn't go into 39, we must bring down the number in the next column to the right, which in this case is the 2 in the ones column.

$$\begin{array}{r} 20 \\ 56\overline{)11{,}592} \\ \underline{-112} \\ 392 \end{array}$$

What whole number multiplied by 56 produces a product less than or equal to 392? Since the answer is 7, put a 7 above the 2 in the space for the quotient.

$$\begin{array}{r} 207 \\ 56\overline{)11{,}592} \\ \underline{-112} \\ 392 \end{array}$$

Next, since $7 \cdot 56 = 392$, put 392 below the 392 and subtract.

$$\begin{array}{r} 207 \\ 56\overline{)11{,}592} \\ \underline{-112} \\ 392 \\ \underline{-\quad 392} \\ 0 \end{array}$$

Finally, since all that is left is 0, this means that 11,592 divided by 56 is exactly 207. Or, $11{,}592 \div 56 = 207$. We'll leave the check to you.

There are several different words or word phrases that can be used to express division. Here is a list of some of those phrases.

Word phrase	Used in an expression	Written as symbols
the quotient of	the quotient of ten and two	$10 \div 2$
divided by	eight divided by four	$8 \div 4$
divided into	three divided into fifteen	$15 \div 3$

Example 19: Translate the following expression into mathematical symbols: the quotient of sixteen and eight

Solution: Since "the quotient of" means to divide, the expression becomes $16 \div 8$.

Example 20: Translate the following expression into mathematical symbols: twelve divided by two

Solution: Since "divided by" means to divide, the expression becomes $12 \div 2$.

As with multiplication, there are several properties of division that hold true for real numbers.

THE DIVISION PROPERTIES OF ONE:

1) For any real number a,

$$a \div 1 = a.$$

If any real number a is divided by 1, the quotient is a.

2) For any real number a, when $a \neq 0$,

$$a \div a = 1$$

If any real number other than 0 is divided by itself, the quotient is 1.

Example 21: Use the number 4 to show examples of the division properties of one.

Solution: $4 \div 1 = 4$ and $4 \div 4 = 1$.

Conclusion: **Dividing a number by 1 does not change the number's original value and dividing a number by itself produces a quotient of 1.**

Note: Since 63 divided by 9 equals 7, then 9 times 7 equals 63. In the same manner, if 5 divided by 0 equals some real number, then you would think 0 times some real number should equal 5. However, 0 times some real number always equals 0. Therefore the division problem $5 \div 0$ can't be done. Consequently, mathematicians say that dividing by zero is undefined. Don't forget that $0 \div 5$ can be done. That is, $0 \div 5 = 0$.

THE DIVISION PROPERTIES OF ZERO:

1) For any real number a, when $a \neq 0$,

$$0 \div a = 0.$$

If 0 is divided by any real number other than 0, the quotient is 0.

2) For any real number a, when $a \neq 0$,

$$a \div 0 = \text{undefined}.$$

If any real number other than 0 is divided by 0, the quotient is undefined.

Example 22: Use the number 7 to show examples of the division properties of zero.

Solution: $0 \div 7 = 0$ and $7 \div 0 = \text{undefined}$.

Conclusion: **Dividing 0 by a number other than 0 produces a quotient of 0 and dividing a number other than 0 by 0 produces a quotient that is undefined.**

Earlier in this chapter, problems dealing with evaluating expressions involved addition or subtraction. Here are more examples, but this time the problems involve multiplication or division.

Example 23: Evaluate the expression for the given values of the variables: $4wy$, where $w = 7$ and $y = 3$

Solution:

$4wy$	Substitute 7 in the place of w and 3 in the place of y.
$4(7)(3)$	Multiply from left to right.
$4(7)(3) = 28(3) = 84$	When $w = 7$ and $y = 3$, the value of $4wy$ is 84.

Note: When replacing a variable with the number that it is equal to, it is a good idea to put parentheses around the number. This is especially important when multiplication or division is involved.

Example 24: Evaluate the expression for the given value of the variable: $15 \div x$, where $x = 5$

Solution:	
$15 \div x$	Substitute 5 in the place of x.
$15 \div (5)$	Divide.
$15 \div (5) = 3$	When $x = 5$, the value of $15 \div x$ is 3.

Example 25: Evaluate the expression for the given values of the variables: $\frac{a}{b}$, where $a = 35$ and $b = 7$

Solution:	
$\frac{a}{b}$	Substitute 35 in the place of a and 7 in the place of b.
$\frac{(35)}{(7)}$	Divide.
$\frac{(35)}{(7)} = 5$	When $a = 35$ and $b = 7$, the value of $\frac{a}{b}$ is 5.

Example 26: Evaluate the expression for the given value of the variable: y^3, where $y = 2$

Solution:	
y^3	Substitute 2 in the place of y.
$(2)^3$	Expand the exponent.
$2 \cdot 2 \cdot 2$	Then, multiply the factors.
8	When $y = 2$, the value of y^3 is 8.

Section 5 exercises. Multiply each of the following.

1. (3)(89) **2.** (0)(74) **3.** 861(14) **4.** 487(16)

5. (6,904)3 **6.** (4,870)6 **7.** $78 \cdot 0$ **8.** $91 \cdot 45$

9. $83{,}072 \cdot 84$ **10.** $67{,}409 \cdot 37$ **11.** $55 \cdot 798$ **12.** $44 \cdot 963$

13. 738×46 **14.** 629×37 **15.** 504×82 **16.** 802×27

17. 411×60 **18.** 344×70 **19.** 923×59 **20.** 287×95

21. $6{,}048 \times 32$ **22.** $7{,}094 \times 27$ **23.** $3{,}920 \times 68$ **24.** $5{,}640 \times 49$

25. $8{,}795 \times 621$ **26.** $4{,}638 \times 715$ **27.** $6{,}056 \times 703$ **28.** $7{,}037 \times 801$

Divide each of the following.

29. $723 \div 31$ **30.** $0 \div 496$ **31.** $19{,}754 \div 7$ **32.** $23{,}868 \div 6$

33. $58{,}034 \div 39$ **34.** $97{,}605 \div 48$ **35.** $6{,}932 \div 0$ **36.** $4{,}374 \div 71$

37. $\frac{756}{9}$ **38.** $\frac{632}{0}$ **39.** $\frac{0}{604}$ **40.** $\frac{3,647}{603}$

41. $\frac{955}{7}$ **42.** $\frac{688}{5}$ **43.** $\frac{1,240}{8}$ **44.** $\frac{1,755}{9}$

45. $3\overline{)4,376}$ **46.** $6\overline{)7,683}$ **47.** $73\overline{)683}$ **48.** $38\overline{)269}$

49. $17\overline{)47,683}$ **50.** $13\overline{)37,782}$ **51.** $436\overline{)8,764}$ **52.** $324\overline{)6,493}$

Translate each phrase into mathematical symbols. Then determine the result in each case.

53. What is seven times twelve?

54. What is sixteen multiplied by eight?

55. Find the product of twenty-seven and fourteen.

56. Find twice the number eighteen.

57. What is thirty-six divided by four?

58. What is the quotient of eighty-one and nine?

59. What is double the number nine?

60. What is triple the number five?

61. What is the quotient of seventy-two and nine?

62. What is seven divided into sixty-three?

63. Which property states that when three or more numbers are multiplied together, the numbers can be grouped in any order and the product will be the same?

64. Which property states that if two numbers are multiplied in any order, the product will be the same?

Use only the commutative property of multiplication to rewrite each expression. Then, simplify the expression.

65. $8 \cdot 5$ **66.** $2 \cdot 11$ **67.** $(9)(3)$ **68.** $(6)(7)$

69. $27 \cdot 0$ **70.** $79 \cdot 18$ **71.** $62(29)$ **72.** $34(0)$

73. $216 \cdot 77$ **74.** $319 \cdot 88$

Use only the associative property of multiplication to rewrite each expression. Then, simplify the expression.

75. $(13 \cdot 5) \cdot 2$ **76.** $(18 \cdot 4) \cdot 25$ **77.** $5 \cdot (20 \cdot 16)$

78. $20 \cdot (5 \cdot 9)$ **79.** $(7 \cdot 2) \cdot 50$ **80.** $5 \cdot (2 \cdot 16)$

81. Use the number 3 to show an example of the multiplication property of zero.

82. Use the number 3 to show an example of the multiplication property of one.

83. According to the division properties of one, if any real number other than 0 is divided by itself, the quotient is_____.

84. According to the division properties of one, if any real number a is divided by 1, the quotient is_____.

85. According to the division properties of zero, if 0 is divided by any real number other than 0, the quotient is_____.

86. According to the division properties of zero, if any real number other than 0 is divided by 0, the quotient is_____.

Write each of the following expressions in exponential form.

87. $4 \cdot 4 \cdot 4 \cdot 5 \cdot 5$

88. $2 \cdot 2 \cdot 7 \cdot 7 \cdot 7 \cdot 7 \cdot 7$

89. $x \cdot x \cdot x \cdot x \cdot y \cdot y$

90. $c \cdot c \cdot c \cdot m \cdot m \cdot m \cdot m$

91. $5 \cdot 6 \cdot 6 \cdot 10 \cdot 10 \cdot 10$

92. $2 \cdot 2 \cdot 3 \cdot 3 \cdot 3 \cdot 9$

93. $2 \cdot 2 \cdot 3 \cdot 3 \cdot 3 \cdot 3 \cdot y \cdot y$

94. $4 \cdot 4 \cdot 4 \cdot 5 \cdot w \cdot w \cdot w$

Evaluate each exponential expression.

95. 3^4

96. 5^3

97. 6^3

98. 4^4

99. 10^5

100. 10^6

101. 2^3

102. 10^4

103. 10^3

104. 3^3

105. 7^1

106. 2^1

Translate each phrase into mathematical symbols.

107. The sixth power of x

108. The square of 7

109. The cube of 4

110. The fourth power of w

111. The square of 3

112. The cube of 5

113. 4 squared

114. 5 to the eighth power

Evaluate each expression for the given values of the variables.

115. xy, where $x = 4$ and $y = 19$

116. mn, where $m = 17$ and $n = 8$

117. x^2, where $x = 7$

118. h^4, where $h = 2$

119. $x \div y$, where $x = 342$ and $y = 6$

120. $h \div k$, where $h = 434$ and $k = 7$

121. $4h$, where $h = 537$

122. $7k$, where $k = 621$

123. p^7, where $p = 10$

124. z^5, where $z = 10$

125. $\frac{a}{b}$, where $a = 3$ and $b = 0$

126. $\frac{w}{z}$, where $w = 0$ and $z = 6$

127. $6yz$, where $y = 794$, and $z = 0$

128. $8pq$, where $p = 47$, and $q = 19$

129. b^3, where $b = 4$

130. q^2, where $q = 5$

131. $p \div q$, where $p = 0$ and $q = 6$

132. $g \div m$, where $g = 3$ and $m = 0$

133. $7ab$, where $a = 62$, and $b = 14$

134. $9gh$, where $g = 0$, and $h = 154$

135. y^2, where $y = 6$

136. b^4, where $b = 3$

137. $\frac{c}{d}$, where $c = 3{,}480$ and $d = 15$

138. $\frac{e}{f}$, where $e = 5{,}166$ and $f = 18$

139. hkm, where $h = 5$, $k = 100$, and $m = 4$

140. wxy, where $w = 15$, $x = 1$, and $y = 40$

WHOLE NUMBERS

Section 6: More Multiplying and Dividing of Whole Numbers

In the equation $2 \cdot 6 = 12$, the 12 is called the product while the 2 and the 6 are called factors. Furthermore, 2 and 6 are called factors of 12 because they both divide or "go into" 12 evenly. That is, $12 \div 6 = 2$ with no remainder, and $12 \div 2 = 6$ with no remainder. 3 and 4 are also factors of 12 because $3 \cdot 4 = 12$. Finally, $1 \cdot 12 = 12$, meaning 1 and 12 are also factors of 12.

Let's look at this information organized in a slightly different way.

$$1 \cdot 12 = 12$$
$$2 \cdot 6 = 12$$
$$3 \cdot 4 = 12$$

1, 2, 3, 4, 6, and 12 are all factors of 12. To be more specific, these numbers are all of the **natural number factors** of 12.

Example 1: Find all the factors of 18.

Solution:

$1 \cdot 18 = 18$

$2 \cdot 9 = 18$

$3 \cdot 6 = 18$

4 doesn't go into 18 evenly.

5 doesn't go into 18 evenly.

$6 \cdot 3 = 18$

Since 6 and 3 have already been used, this means the factors are repeating. Therefore, we have found all the factors of 18.

The factors of 18 are 1, 2, 3, 6, 9, and 18.

Example 2: Find all the factors of 30.

Solution:

$1 \cdot 30 = 30$

$2 \cdot 15 = 30$

$3 \cdot 10 = 30$

4 doesn't go into 30 evenly.

$5 \cdot 6 = 30$

$6 \cdot 5 = 30$

Since 6 and 5 have already been used, this means the factors are repeating. Therefore, we have found all the factors of 30.

The factors of 30 are 1, 2, 3, 5, 6, 10, 15, and 30.

Example 3: Find all the factors of 7.

Solution:

$1 \cdot 7 = 7$

2 doesn't go into 7 evenly.

3 doesn't go into 7 evenly.

4 doesn't go into 7 evenly.

5 doesn't go into 7 evenly.

6 doesn't go into 7 evenly.

$7 \cdot 1 = 7$

Since 7 and 1 have already been used, this means the factors are repeating; therefore, we have found all the factors of 7.

The factors of 7 are 1 and 7.

Example 4: Find all the factors of 13.

Solution:

$1 \cdot 13 = 13$

2 doesn't go into 13 evenly.

3 doesn't go into 13 evenly.

4 doesn't go into 13 evenly.

5 doesn't go into 13 evenly.

6 doesn't go into 13 evenly.

7 doesn't go into 13 evenly.

8 doesn't go into 13 evenly.

9 doesn't go into 13 evenly.

10 doesn't go into 13 evenly.

11 doesn't go into 13 evenly.

12 doesn't go into 13 evenly.

$13 \cdot 1 = 13$

Since 13 and 1 have already been used, this means the factors are repeating; therefore, we have found all the factors of 13.

The factors of 13 are 1 and 13.

In the last two examples, the numbers 7 and 13 each had only two factors. For the number 7, the factors were 7 and 1. For the number 13, the factors were 13 and 1. The numbers 7 and 13 belong to a special group of numbers known as **prime numbers**. A prime number is a natural number that is larger than 1 and has only two factors, the number itself and the number 1. Another way of describing a prime number is to say that it can only be divided by itself and by the number 1 evenly, with no remainder. Prime numbers play an important role in many areas of mathematics. Because of this, we need to familiarize ourselves with the smaller prime numbers and be able to determine whether a larger number is prime or not.

We will start this process by looking at all of the natural numbers from 1 to 50. Since a prime number has to be larger than 1, we can immediately eliminate 1 from the list.

~~1~~, 2, 3, 4, 5, 6, 7, 8, 9, 10, 11, 12, 13, 14, 15, 16, 17, 18, 19, 20, 21, 22, 23, 24, 25, 26, 27,

28, 29, 30, 31, 32, 33, 34, 35, 36, 37, 38, 39, 40, 41, 42, 43, 44, 45, 46, 47, 48, 49, 50.

Note: 2 is a prime number since its only factors are itself and 1.

Any number larger than 2 that is an **even** number can be divided by 2, and therefore is not a prime number. So, we can eliminate all even numbers larger than 2 from the list of primes.

~~1~~, 2, 3, ~~4~~, 5, ~~6~~, 7, ~~8~~, 9, ~~10~~, 11, ~~12~~, 13, ~~14~~, 15, ~~16~~, 17, ~~18~~, 19, ~~20~~, 21, ~~22~~, 23, ~~24~~, 25, ~~26~~, 27,

~~28~~, 29, ~~30~~, 31, ~~32~~, 33, ~~34~~, 35, ~~36~~, 37, ~~38~~, 39, ~~40~~, 41, ~~42~~, 43, ~~44~~, 45, ~~46~~, 47, ~~48~~, 49, ~~50~~.

Note: 3 is a prime number since its only factors are itself and 1.

Any number larger than 3 that can be divided by 3, is not a prime number. It is fairly obvious that some numbers can be divided by 3, such as 6, 9, 12, and 15. But what about numbers that are much bigger, like 141? There is a special rule that works with 3's. Add up all the digits in a number. If the sum of the digits can be divided evenly by 3, then the original number can also be divided evenly by 3. For instance, the sum of the digits in the number 141 is $1 + 4 + 1 = 6$. Since 6 can be divided by 3, then 141 can be divided by 3. We will verify this using long division.

$$\begin{array}{r} 47 \\ 3\overline{)141} \\ -12 \\ \hline 21 \\ -21 \\ \hline 0 \end{array}$$

We can eliminate multiples of 3 that are larger than 3 from the list of primes. These include 9, 15, 21, 27, 33, 39, and 45.

~~1~~, 2, 3, ~~4~~, 5, ~~6~~, 7, ~~8~~, ~~9~~, ~~10~~, 11, ~~12~~, 13, ~~14~~, ~~15~~, ~~16~~, 17, ~~18~~, 19, ~~20~~, ~~21~~, ~~22~~, 23, ~~24~~, 25, ~~26~~, ~~27~~,

~~28~~, 29, ~~30~~, 31, ~~32~~, ~~33~~, ~~34~~, 35, ~~36~~, 37, ~~38~~, ~~39~~, ~~40~~, 41, ~~42~~, 43, ~~44~~, ~~45~~, ~~46~~, 47, ~~48~~, 49, ~~50~~.

Note: 5 is a prime number since its only factors are itself and 1.

Any number larger than 5 that ends in a 5 or 0 can be divided by 5 and therefore is not a prime number. This means we can eliminate 25 and 35 from the list of primes.

~~1~~, 2, 3, ~~4~~, 5, ~~6~~, 7, ~~8~~, ~~9~~, ~~10~~, 11, ~~12~~, 13, ~~14~~, ~~15~~, ~~16~~, 17, ~~18~~, 19, ~~20~~, ~~21~~, ~~22~~, 23, ~~24~~, ~~25~~, ~~26~~, ~~27~~,

~~28~~, 29, ~~30~~, 31, ~~32~~, ~~33~~, ~~34~~, ~~35~~, ~~36~~, 37, ~~38~~, ~~39~~, ~~40~~, 41, ~~42~~, 43, ~~44~~, ~~45~~, ~~46~~, 47, ~~48~~, 49, ~~50~~.

What about the rest of the numbers in the list? How can we be sure that a number is prime?

To see if a number is prime, check whether any primes that are smaller than that number can divide into that number evenly. We don't have to check all the primes smaller than the number on the list, however. We only have to check each prime below the number, starting with 2, and going up the list until we reach a prime whose square is larger the number we are checking. The process of finding prime numbers in this way is known as the Sieve of Eratosthenes.

We already have determined that 2, 3, 5, 7 and 13 are primes. Is 11 a prime number? 2 does not go into 11 because 11 is not an even number. 3 does not go into 11 because 11 is not a multiple of 3. 5 does not go into 11 because 11 does not end in a 5 or a 0. The square of 5 or 5^2, as it is written exponentially, is 25 and since $25 > 11$, we can conclude that 11 is a prime number.

Example 5: Determine if 37 is a prime number.

Solution:

Does 2 go into 37? No, because 37 is not an even number.

Does 3 go into 37? No, because $3 + 7 = 10$ and 3 doesn't go into 10. Therefore 3 doesn't go into 37.

Does 5 go into 37? No, because 37 doesn't end in a 5 or a 0.

Does 7 go into 37? Using long division $\begin{array}{r} 5\text{ R}2 \\ 7\overline{)37} \\ -35 \\ \hline 2 \end{array}$ we see that 7 doesn't go into 37 evenly.

However, since $7^2 = 49$ and $49 > 37$, we can conclude that 37 is a prime number.

Example 6: Determine if 49 is a prime number.

Solution:

Does 2 go into 49? No, because 49 is not an even number.

Does 3 go into 49? No, because $4 + 9 = 13$ and 3 doesn't go into 13. Therefore 3 doesn't go into 49.

Does 5 go into 49? No, because 49 doesn't end in a 5 or a 0.

Does 7 go into 49? Yes, because $7^2 = 49$. Since 49 has a factor other than itself and 1, then 49 is not a prime number.

By continuing the process used in examples 5 and 6, we can determine that the complete list of prime numbers less than 50 is as follows: 2, 3, 5, 7, 11, 13, 17, 19, 23, 29, 31, 37, 41, 43, and 47.

Example 7: Determine if 149 is a prime number.

Solution:

Does 2 go into 149? No, because 149 is not an even number.

Does 3 go into 149? No, because $1 + 4 + 9 = 14$ and 3 doesn't go into 14. Therefore 3 doesn't go into 149.

Does 5 go into 149? No, because 149 doesn't end in a 5 or a 0.

Does 7 go into 149? Using long division $\begin{array}{r} 21\text{ R}2 \\ 7\overline{)149} \\ -\underline{14} \\ 9 \\ -\underline{7} \\ 2 \end{array}$ we see that 7 doesn't go into 149 evenly.

Does 11 go into 149? Using long division $\begin{array}{r} 13\text{ R}6 \\ 11\overline{)149} \\ -\underline{11} \\ 39 \\ -\underline{33} \\ 6 \end{array}$ we see that 11 doesn't go into 149 evenly.

Does 13 go into 149? Using long division $\begin{array}{r} 11\text{ R}6 \\ 13\overline{)149} \\ -\underline{13} \\ 19 \\ -\underline{13} \\ 6 \end{array}$ we see that 13 doesn't go into 149 evenly.

However, since $13^2 = 169$ and $169 > 149$, we can conclude that 149 is a prime number.

We started with a list of 50 numbers and eventually eliminated all but 15 of the numbers because they were not prime. Except for the number 1, all the rest of the numbers that were eliminated have a special name. They are called **composite numbers**. A composite number is a natural number greater than 1 that is not prime. A composite number can be written as the product of two or more factors, each of which is a prime number. For example, the number 6 is a composite number. It can be written as the product of 2 and 3, both of which are prime numbers. Another example is the number 30. It can be written as the product of 2, 3 and 5, all of which are prime numbers.

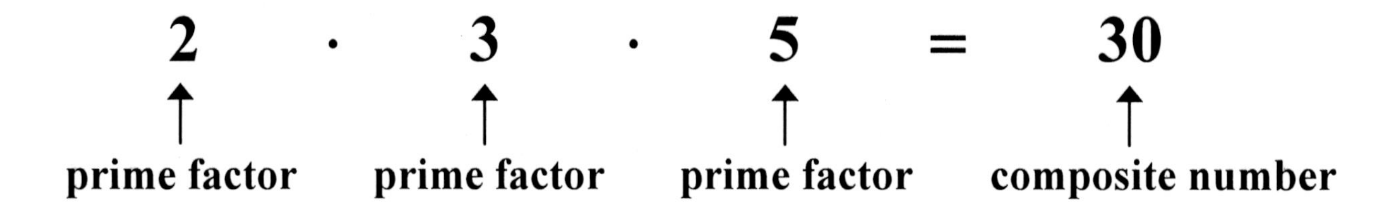

When a number is written as the product of prime factors, the result is called the **prime factorization** of the number. The prime factorization of 30 is $2 \cdot 3 \cdot 5$. The prime factorization of 34 is $2 \cdot 17$.

To write the prime factorization of a composite number, or **prime factored form** as it is also called, we break the number down as far as possible so that it is written as a product of 2 or more prime factors. A prime number can't be written as a product of 2 or more prime factors. Consequently, a prime number has no prime factorization.

Example 8: Find the prime factorization of 36.

Solution:

Since 36 is even, then 2 is one of its factors. Consequently, 36 can be written as $2 \cdot 18$. This is not the prime factorization of 36, because 18 is not a prime factor. Since 18 is even, then 2 is one of its factors. Consequently, 36 can be written as $2 \cdot 2 \cdot 9$. This is not the prime factorization of 36, because 9 is not a prime factor. Since 9 is a multiple of 3, then 3 is one of its factors. Consequently, 36 can be written as $2 \cdot 2 \cdot 3 \cdot 3$. Since 2 and 3 are both prime numbers, this is the prime factorization of 36. It can be written as $2 \cdot 2 \cdot 3 \cdot 3$, or in exponential form as $2^2 \cdot 3^2$. Either way, it is a good idea to write the prime factors in order from smallest to largest. In other words, $2^2 \cdot 3^2$ not $3^2 \cdot 2^2$.
Now let's look at a streamlined version of the above process.

36
$\wedge$
$2 \cdot 18$
$/ \ \wedge$
$2 \cdot 2 \cdot 9$
$/ \ / \ \wedge$
$2 \cdot 2 \cdot 3 \cdot 3$ or $2^2 \cdot 3^2$

Example 9 A:

Find the prime factorization of 630.

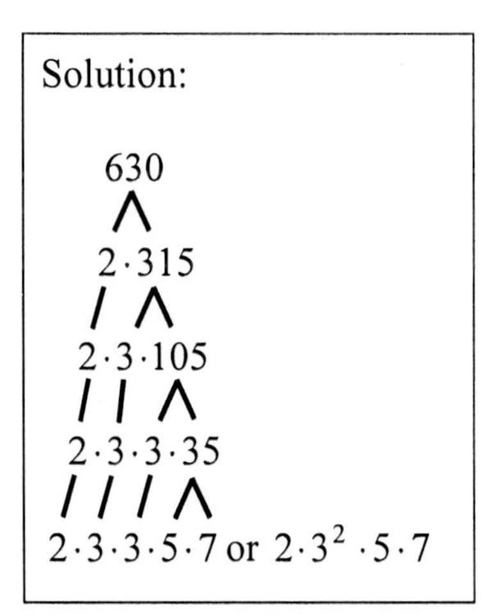

Example 9 B:

Find the prime factorization of 630.

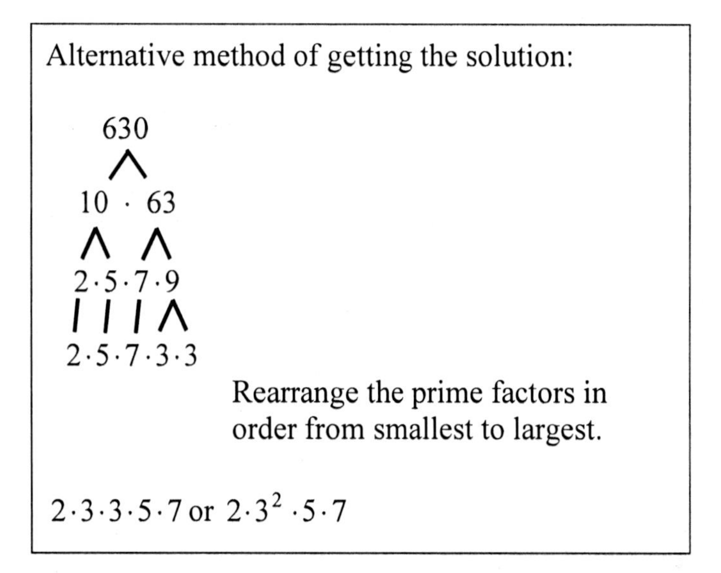

Note: It doesn't matter how you break the number apart into prime factors. If done correctly, the answer will always be the same. This leads to what is known as the <u>fundamental theorem of arithmetic</u>: Any composite number has exactly one set of prime factors.

Applications involving charts and graphs

Valuable information can be obtained from various charts or graphs by applying multiplication and/or division to quantities given.

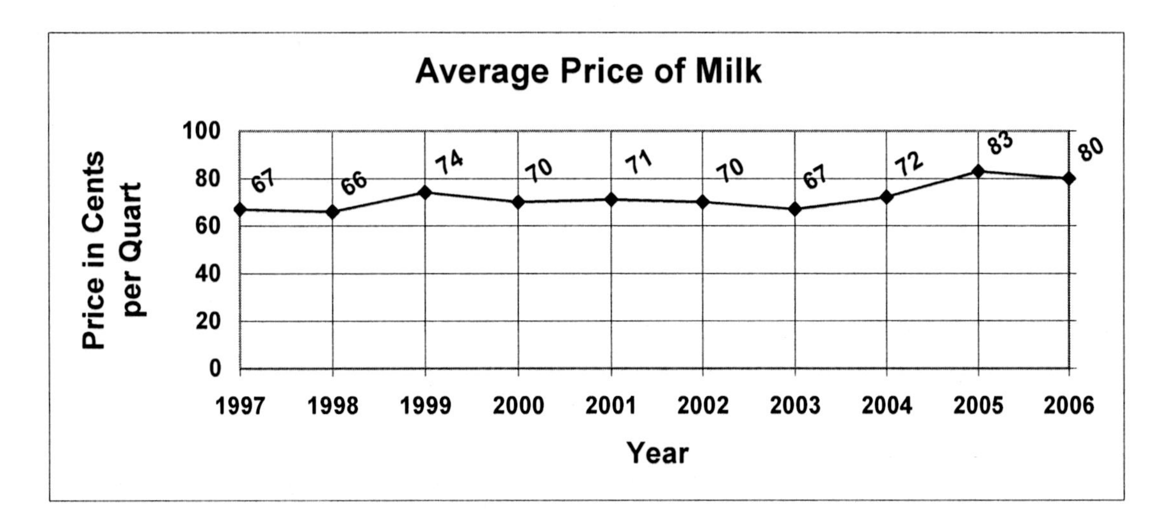

Example 10: Based on the broken-line graph above and the fact that 4 quarts = 1 gallon, what was the average price of a gallon of milk in 2001?

Solution: The average price of a quart of milk in 2001 was 71¢. There are 4 quarts in a gallon, so we multiply 71¢ by 4. Since $71 \cdot 4 = 284$, the answer is 284¢. This could also be written as $2.84.

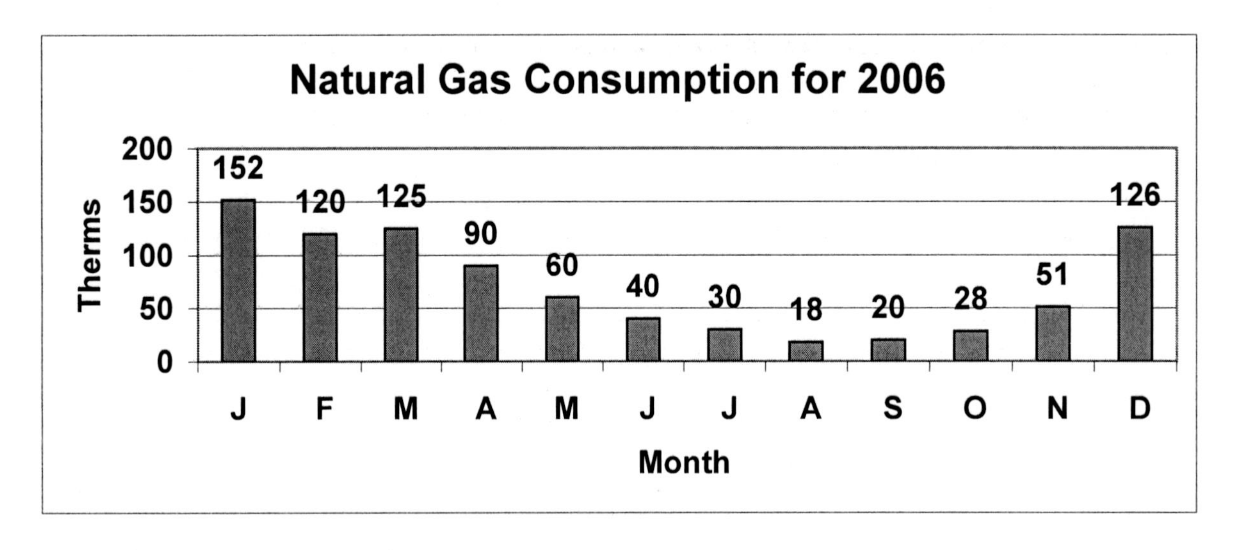

Example 11: Based on the bar graph above, the consumption of natural gas in February was how many times the consumption of natural gas in July?

Solution: Divide the amount of consumption in February by the amount of consumption in July. $120 \div 30 = 4$.
The consumption of natural gas in February was 4 times the consumption of natural gas in July.

In section 4, the formula for the perimeter of a rectangle was introduced as $P = L + W + L + W$. While this formula is correct, there is another version, which involves multiplication. Since the perimeter includes 2 lengths and 2 widths, the formula could also be written as follows.

FORMULA FOR THE PERIMETER (P) OF A RECTANGLE:

$$P = 2L + 2W$$

Example 12: Find the perimeter of the following rectangle.

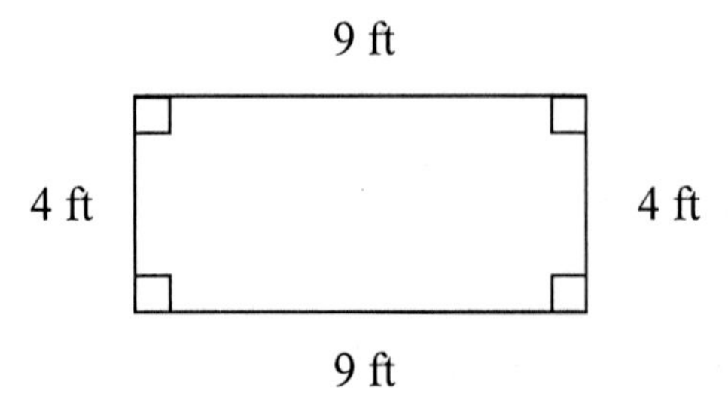

Solution: The length is 9 ft and the width is 4 ft. Using the formula for the perimeter of a rectangle, $P = 2L + 2W$ gives us

$P = 2(9\text{ ft}) + 2(4\text{ ft})$ which simplified further becomes

$P = 18\text{ ft} + 8\text{ ft}$ and finally

$P = 26\text{ ft}.$ Consequently, the perimeter of the rectangle is 26 feet.

Likewise, the formula for the perimeter of a square was introduced as $P = s + s + s + s$. While this formula is correct, there is another version which involves multiplication. Since the perimeter includes 4 equal sides, the formula could also be written as follows.

FORMULA FOR THE PERIMETER OF A SQUARE:

$$\boldsymbol{P = 4s}$$

Example 13: Find the perimeter of the following square.

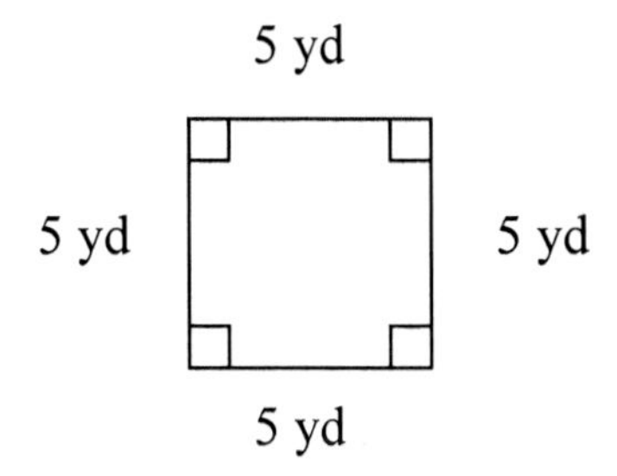

Solution: The length of each side is 5 yards. Using the formula for the perimeter of a square,

$P = 4s$	gives us
$P = 4(5 \text{ yd})$	which simplified becomes
$P = 20 \text{ yd}.$	Consequently, the perimeter of the square is 20 yards.

While perimeter is the measure of the distance around an object such as a rectangle, **area** is the measure of the surface enclosed by an object. Area is measured in square units such as square inches (written as in.^2) or square feet (written as ft^2).

A line that is an inch long is said to be 1 inch in length.

A square that has sides 1 inch long is said to have an area of 1 square inch.

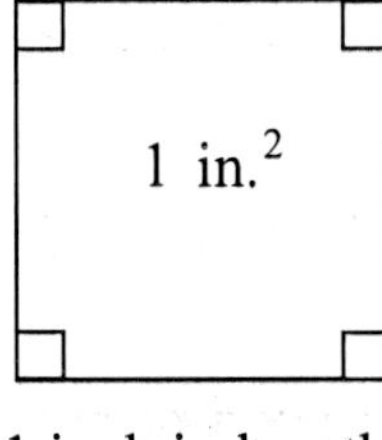

1 inch in length

A rectangle that is 3 inches long and 2 inches wide contains 6 square inches, or 6 in.^2.

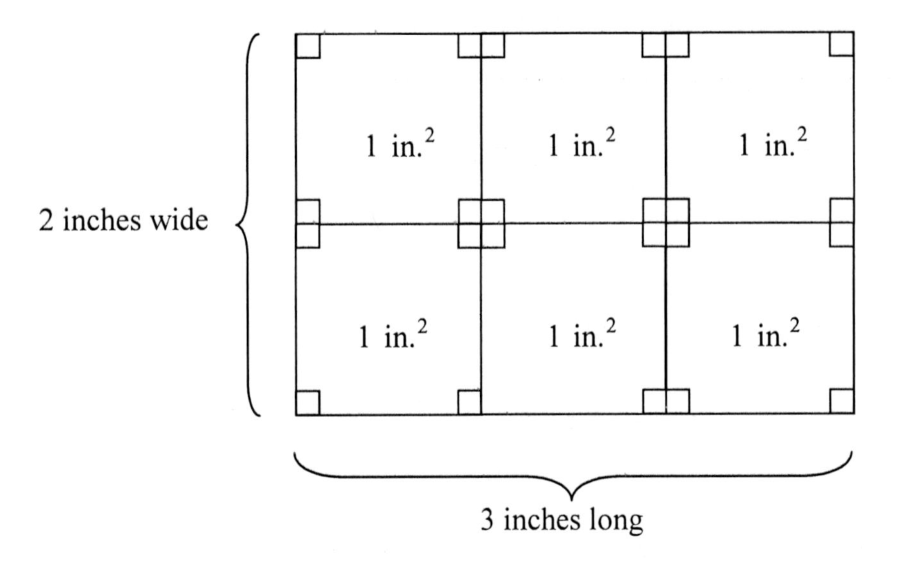

Note: The area of a rectangle is the product of the rectangle's length and it's width. This leads to the formula for finding the area of a rectangle. In this formula, "*A*" stands for area and as before, "*L*" stands for length while "*W*" stands for width.

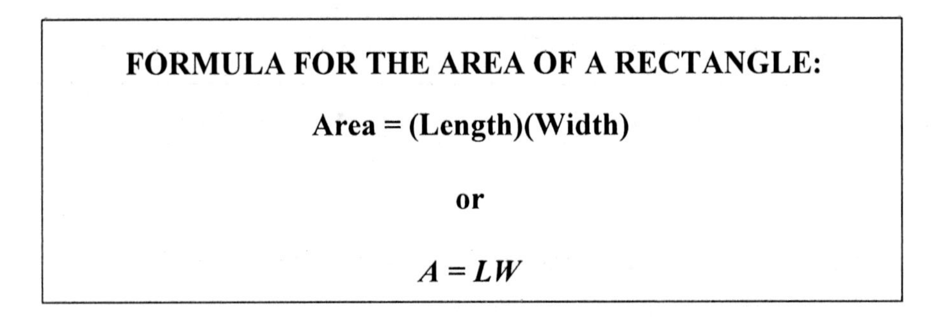

FORMULA FOR THE AREA OF A RECTANGLE:

Area = (Length)(Width)

or

$$A = LW$$

Example 14: Find the area of the following rectangle.

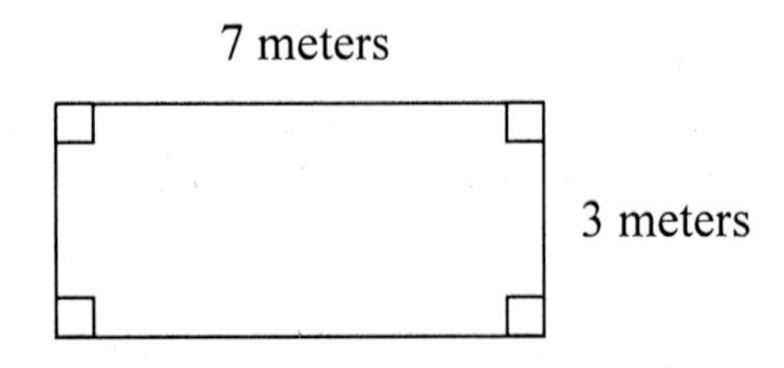

Solution: The length is 7 m and the width is 3 m. Using the formula for the area of a rectangle,

$A = LW$ gives us

$A = (7\text{ m})(3\text{ m})$ which simplified further becomes

$A = 21\text{ m}^2$.

Consequently, the area of the rectangle is 21 square meters or 21 m^2.

Since the length of a square is equal to the width of the same square, we can use a single variable to express both the length and the width. In this formula "A" stands for area, and "s" stands for the length of each side of a square. (Remember that it doesn't matter which side is used because with a square all four sides are the same length).

FORMULA FOR THE AREA OF A SQUARE:

Area = (Length of side)(Length of side)

or

$$A = s \cdot s \text{ or } A = s^2$$

Example 15: Find the area of the following square.

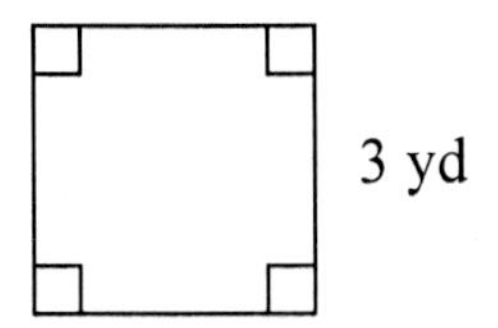

Solution: The length is each side is 3 yd. Using the formula for the area of a square,

$A = s^2$ gives us

$A = (3\text{ yd})^2$ which simplified becomes

$A = 9\text{ yd}^2$.

Consequently, the area of the square is 9 square yards or 9 yd^2.

There are many other formulas besides those used for finding the area of geometric figures such as a square or a rectangle. The formula $d = rt$ (where d is distance, r is rate of speed, and t is the time spent traveling), can be used to calculate how far an object can travel given its rate of speed and how long it is traveling.

Example 16: Find the distance a car travels if it is going 50 miles per hour for 6 hours.

Solution: Since the rate of speed is 50 miles per hour, replace r with 50.

Since the time traveled is 6 hours, replace t with 6.

$d = rt$ becomes

$d =$ (50 miles per hour)(6 hours) and since (50 miles per hour)(6 hours) = 300 miles, the distance traveled is 300 miles.

Example 17: Use the formula $R = \frac{p}{h}$, (where R is the rate of pay, p is the total amount of pay, and h is the number of hours worked), to find the rate of pay for a person that earns $84 in 7 hours.

Solution: Since the total amount of pay is $84, replace p with 84.

Since the number of hours worked is 7 hours, replace h with 7.

$R = \frac{p}{h}$ becomes

$R = \frac{\$84}{7 \text{ hours}}$ and since $\frac{\$84}{7 \text{ hours}} = \$12 \text{ per hour}$, the rate of pay is $12 per hour.

Here is a review of word phrases that indicate multiplication:

Times, the product of, multiplied by, twice, double, triple

Other expressions that may imply multiplication include:

How many times? What is the total…? Per, as in "so much per month."

Here is a review of word phrases that indicate division:

The quotient of, divided by, divided into

Other expressions that may imply division include:

Find the rate. Per, as in "so much per month."

Note: The word "per" can be used to imply multiplication or division depending on the context.

Section 6 exercises. Find all of the factors of each of the following numbers.

1. 12	**2.** 18	**3.** 35	**4.** 25
5. 48	**6.** 36	**7.** 54	**8.** 56
9. 98	**10.** 99	**11.** 19	**12.** 23
13. 80	**14.** 100	**15.** 85	**16.** 45
17. 64	**18.** 32	**19.** 33	**20.** 55

Determine whether each of the following numbers is prime or composite.

21. 89	**22.** 91	**23.** 57	**24.** 59
25. 83	**26.** 73	**27.** 97	**28.** 51

Classify each of the following numbers as prime or composite. If the number is composite, write its prime factorization.

29. 36	**30.** 54	**31.** 24	**32.** 75
33. 125	**34.** 81	**35.** 98	**36.** 70
37. 39	**38.** 65	**39.** 31	**40.** 71
41. 140	**42.** 145	**43.** 87	**44.** 148
45. 34	**46.** 38	**47.** 93	**48.** 86

49. List all the prime numbers between 150 and 160.

50. List all the prime numbers between 160 and 170.

51. Only one of the following numbers is prime. Determine which one it is by eliminating all the other numbers from the list. Explain how you eliminated the other numbers.

934, 935, 937, 939

52. Only one of the following numbers is prime. Determine which one it is by eliminating all the other numbers from the list. Explain how you eliminated the other numbers.

616, 619, 621, 625

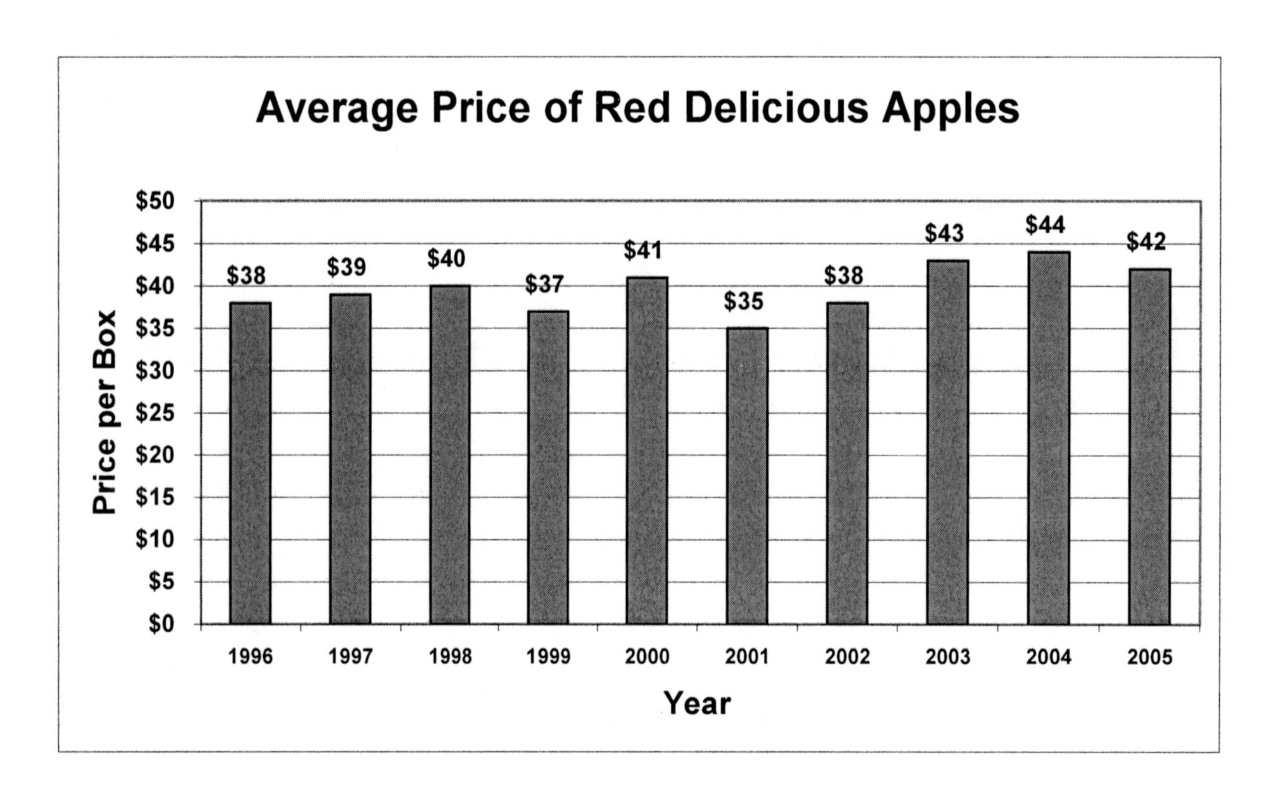

Use the bar graph above to answer the following questions.

53. If there are 25 boxes in a bin of apples, what was the average price of a bin of red delicious apples in 2003?

54. If there are 25 boxes in a bin of apples, what was the average price of a bin of red delicious apples in 1999?

55. If there are 25 boxes in a bin of apples, and a box of apples weighs 35 pounds, then what is the total weight of a bin of apples?

56. If there are 25 boxes in a bin of apples, and a box of apples weighs 35 pounds, then what is the total weight of 2 bins of apples?

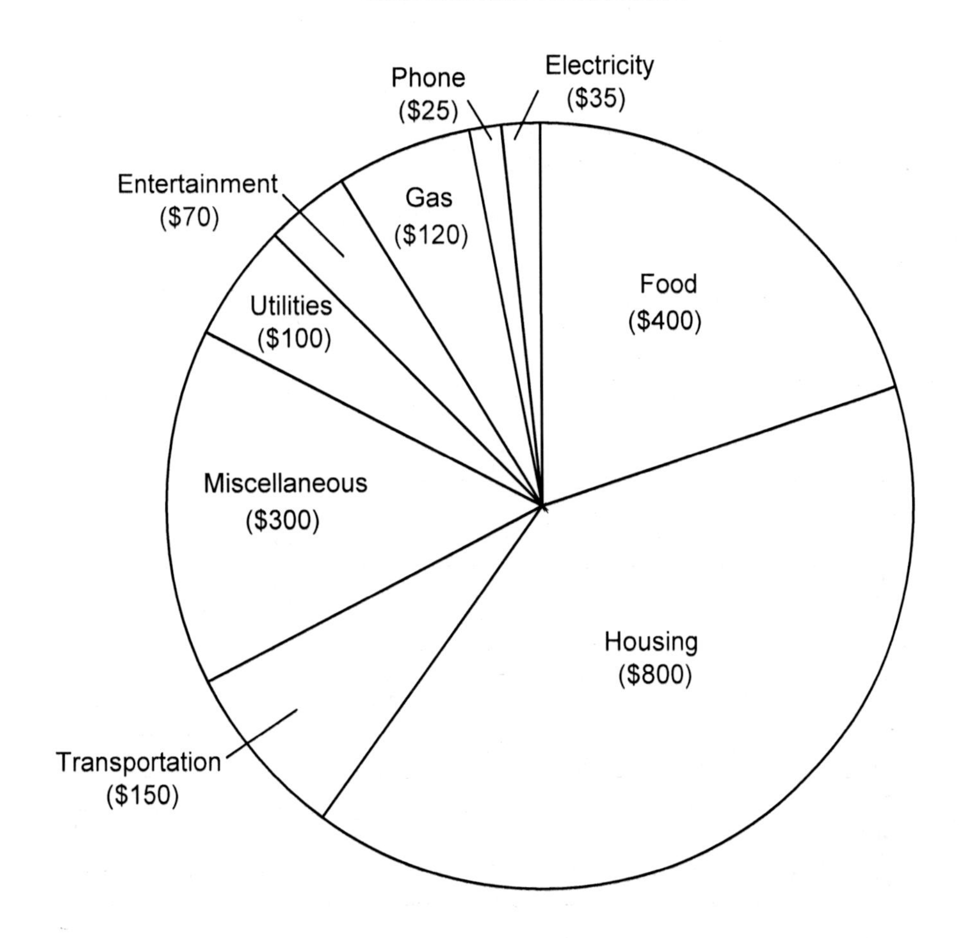

Use the pie chart above to answer the following questions.

57. What is Janet's transportation budget per year?

58. What is Janet's electricity budget per year?

59. Assuming that there are 4 weeks in a month, what is Janet's budget for food, per week?

60. Assuming that there are 4 weeks in a month, what is Janet's budget for housing, per week?

The "Nutrition Facts" on the label of a 64 fluid ounce container of apple juice state that a serving size of 8 fluid ounces contains 120 calories and 280 milligrams of potassium.

Nutrition Facts Serving Size 8 fl. oz. (240mL) Servings Per Container: 8	
Amount Per Serving	
Calories 120	
	% Daily Value*
Total Fat 0g	0 %
Sodium 25mg	1 %
Potassium 280mg	8 %
Total Carbohydrate 29g	10 %
Sugars 26g	
Protein 0g	

61. How many calories would 1 fluid ounce of apple juice contain?

62. How many milligrams of potassium would 1 fluid ounce of apple juice contain?

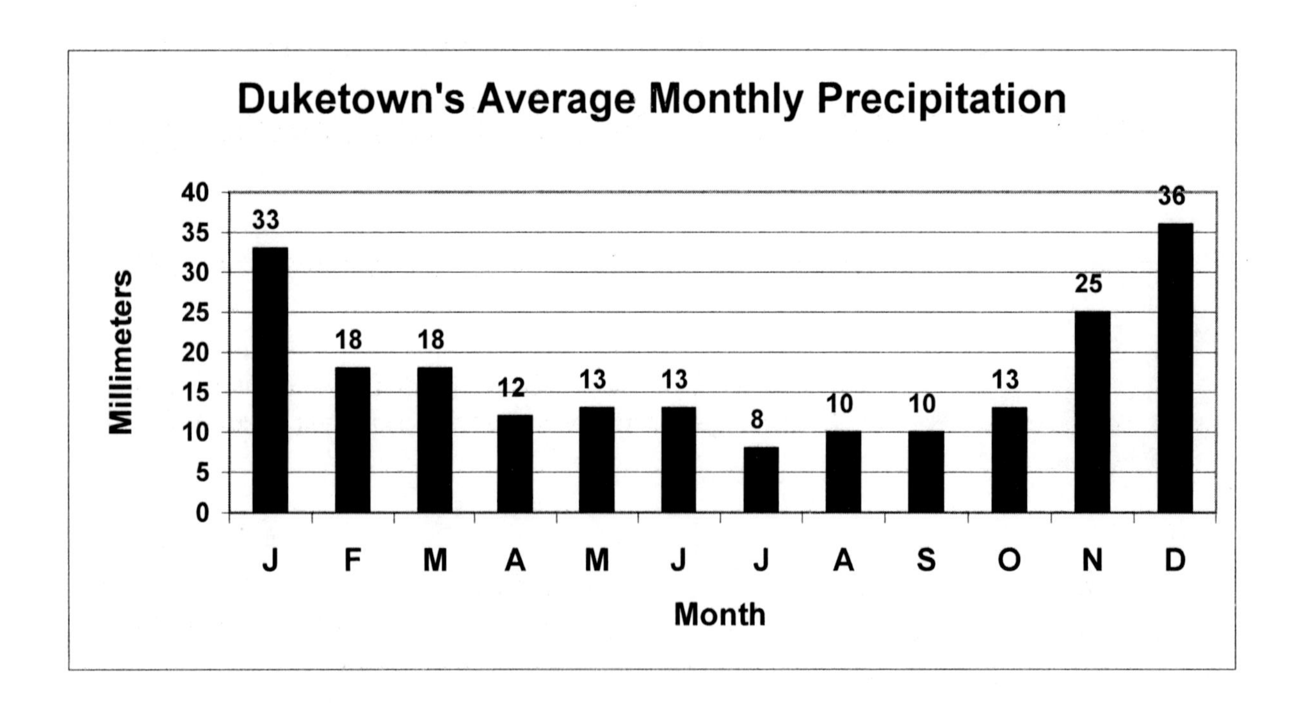

Use the bar graph above to answer the following questions.

63. The average monthly precipitation in December is how many times the average monthly precipitation in April?

64. The average monthly precipitation in December is how many times the average monthly precipitation in March?

Find the perimeter and area of each figure.

65.

8 in.

4 in.

66.

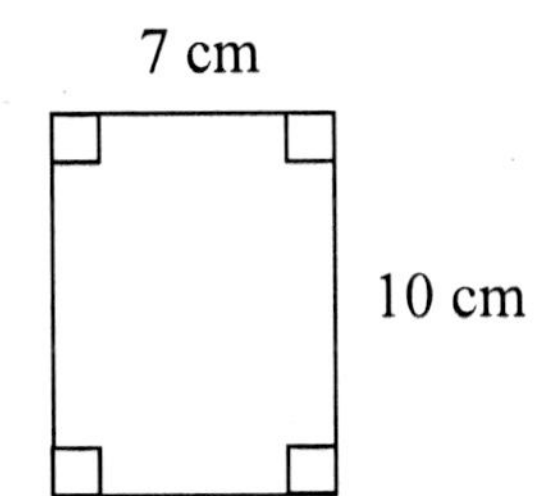

67.

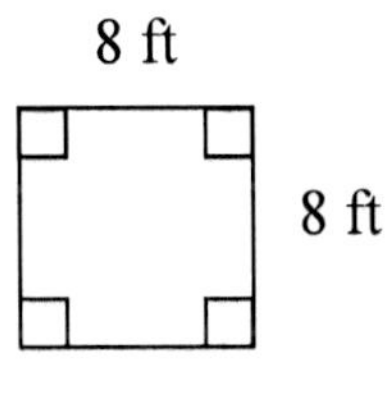

68.

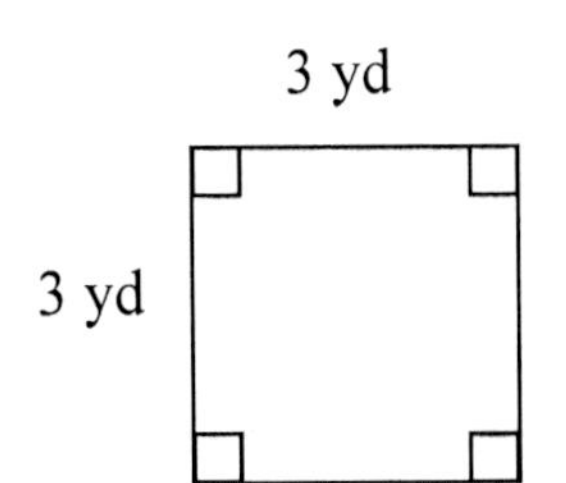

69.

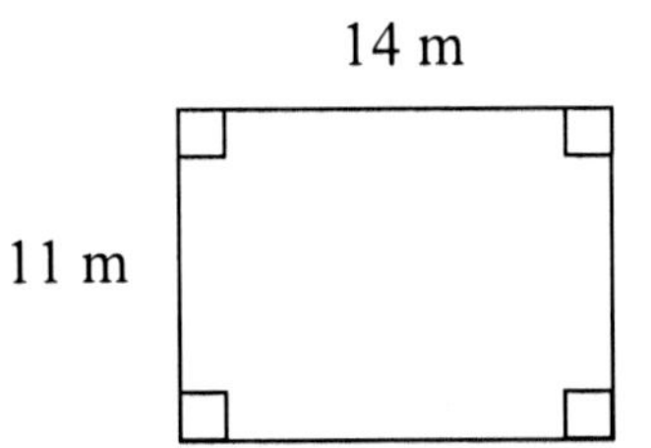

70.

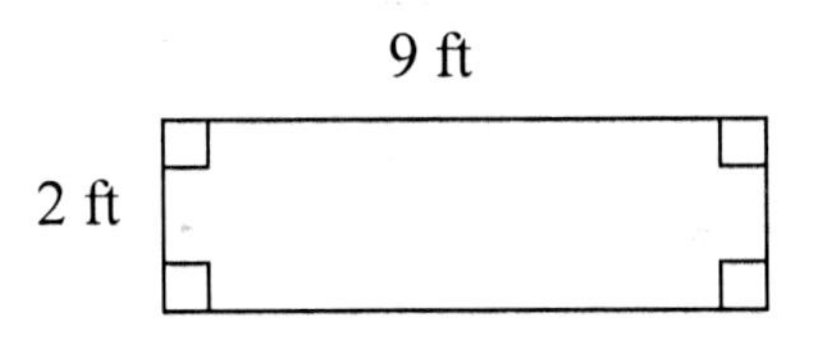

71. If a square has a perimeter of 24 feet, then what is the length of each side of the square?

72. If a square has a perimeter of 52 feet, then what is the length of each side of the square?

73. A farmer wants to put a fence around a rectangular shaped garden to keep out his cows. If the dimensions of the garden are 15 feet long by 8 feet wide, how many feet of fence will he need to enclose the entire garden?

74. A rancher wants to put a fence around a rectangular shaped garden to keep out her horses. If the dimensions of the garden are 18 feet long by 7 feet wide, how many feet of fence will she need to enclose the entire garden?

75. How many square feet of tile are needed to cover a bathroom floor if the dimensions are 8 feet long by 6 feet wide?

76. How many square yards of carpet are needed to cover a living room floor if the dimensions are 7 yards long by 4 yards wide?

77. Use the formula $d = rt$ (where d is distance, r is rate of speed, and t is the time spent traveling), to determine how far a truck can travel if it is going 55 miles per hour for 4 hours.

78. Use the formula $d = rt$ (where d is distance, r is rate of speed, and t is the time spent traveling), to determine how far a motorcycle can travel if it is going 60 miles per hour for 3 hours.

79. Use the formula $R = \frac{p}{h}$ (where R is the rate of pay, p is the total amount of pay, and h is the number of hours worked), to find the rate of pay for a person that earns $48 in 6 hours.

80. Use the formula $R = \frac{p}{h}$ (where R is the rate of pay, p is the total amount of pay, and h is the number of hours worked), to find the rate of pay for a person that earns $56 in 8 hours.

81. How much greater is the surface area of a floor if the dimensions are 15 feet long by 12 feet wide, than the surface area of a floor where the dimensions are 18 feet long by 9 feet wide?

82. How much greater is the surface area of a roof if the dimensions are 20 feet long by 14 feet wide, than the surface area of a roof where the dimensions are 22 feet long by 12 feet wide?

83. The surface area of a roof with dimensions of 28 feet long by 14 feet wide is how many times the surface area of a floor where the dimensions are 8 feet long by 7 feet wide?

84. The surface area of a roof with dimensions of 24 feet long by 8 feet wide is how many times the surface area of a floor where the dimensions are 16 feet long by 4 feet wide?

WHOLE NUMBERS

Section 7: Order of Operations

Mathematical expressions often contain more than one operation. For instance, the expression $3 \cdot 7 + 4$ contains both multiplication and addition. It is important to do the operations in the correct order because we get a different answer depending upon the order in which we perform them. If we do the multiplication first, $3 \cdot 7 + 4$ becomes 21 + 4, which equals 25. If, however, we do the addition first, $3 \cdot 7 + 4$ becomes $3 \cdot 11$ which equals 33. Below is the universally agreed upon order in which operations are to be performed.

Order of Operations: When simplifying a mathematical expression, do the following operations in the order that they are listed.

1. Perform all calculations within grouping symbols.

2. Evaluate all exponential expressions.

3. Do all multiplication and division in order from left to right.

4. Do all addition and subtraction in order from left to right.

Note: Grouping symbols include parentheses and fraction bars. The fraction bar "groups together" the numerator (the part above the fraction bar) separately from the denominator (the part below the fraction bar). So, when simplifying a fraction, first simplify the numerator completely and then simplify the denominator completely.

Example 1: Simplify the expression: $4(7+5)-3^2$

Solution:

$4(7+5)-3^2$	First perform all calculations within parentheses.
$4(12)-3^2$	Then evaluate the exponential expression.
$4(12)-9$	Now multiply.
$48-9$	Finally, subtract.
39	The answer is **39**.

Note: If one of the operations is not included in a particular problem, we will just skip that step in the order of operations and continue on to the next one.

Example 2: Simplify the expression: $15-9+2^4$

Solution:	
$15-9+2^4$	First evaluate the exponential expression.
$15-9+16$	Then add and subtract in order from left to right.
$6+16$	
22	The answer is **22**.

Example 3: Simplify the expression: $\dfrac{5^2-2^2}{12\div4\cdot2+1}$

Solution:	
$\dfrac{5^2-2^2}{12\div4\cdot2+1}$	First simplify the numerator above the fraction bar.
	Evaluate the exponential expressions.
$\dfrac{25-4}{12\div4\cdot2+1}$	Subtract.
$\dfrac{21}{12\div4\cdot2+1}$	Then simplify the denominator below the fraction bar. Do all multiplication and division in order from left to right.
$\dfrac{21}{3\cdot2+1}$	
$\dfrac{21}{6+1}$	Add.
$\dfrac{21}{7}$	Now divide the numerator by the denominator of the fraction.
3	The answer is **3**.

Following the "order of operations" is necessary when evaluating algebraic expressions, since the process involves simplifying a mathematical expression.

Example 4: Evaluate the expression for the given values of the variables: $3x^2 + 2y$, where $x = 2$ and $y = 4$

Solution:	
$3x^2 + 2y$	Substitute 2 in the place of x and 4 in the place of y.
$3(2)^2 + 2(4)$	Evaluate the expression using order of operations.
	First evaluate the exponential expression.
$3(4) + 2(4)$	Then multiply.
$12 + 8$	Finally, add.
20	When $x = 2$ and $y = 4$, the value of $3x^2 + 2y$ is **20**.

Note: When replacing a variable with the number that it is equal to, put parentheses around the number. This is especially important when exponents, multiplication, or division are involved.

Following the "order of operations" is also necessary when solving problems involving formulas. The formula for finding the area of a triangle is $A = \frac{bh}{2}$ (where A is area, b is the base and h is the height of the triangle). When two sides of a triangle form a right angle, the triangle is called a **right triangle**. The base and the height of a right triangle are always the two sides that meet to form this right angle.

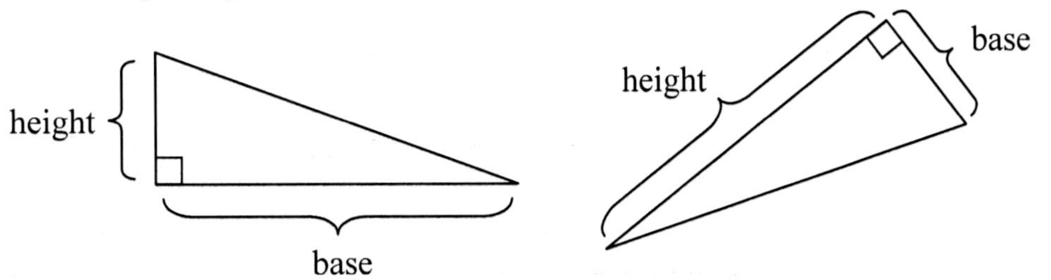

Example 5: Using the formula $A = \frac{bh}{2}$, find the area of the following triangle.

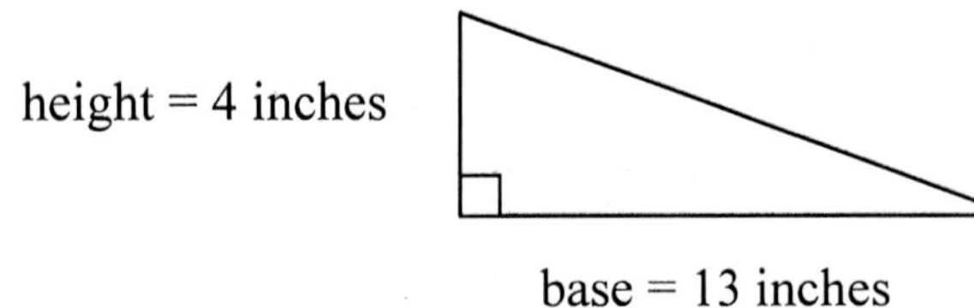

base = 13 inches

Solution: Use the formula for the area of a triangle.

$A = \frac{bh}{2}$ Substitute 13 inches in the place of b, and 4 inches in the place of h.

$A = \frac{(13\,\text{in.})(4\,\text{in.})}{2}$ Evaluate the expression using order of operations.

First simplify the numerator above the fraction bar by multiplying.

$A = \frac{(52\,\text{in.}^2)}{2}$ Now divide the numerator by the denominator of the fraction.

$A = 26\,\text{in.}^2$ Consequently, **the area of the triangle is 26 square inches, or $26\,\textbf{in.}^2$**.

Countries that use the metric system of measurement calculate temperature in degrees Celsius. Countries that use the system of measurements that we use in the United States calculate temperature in degrees Fahrenheit. The formula used to convert degrees Fahrenheit (°F) to degrees Celsius (°C) is as follows. $\mathbf{C = \frac{5(F - 32)}{9}}$ (Where C is degrees Celsius and F is degrees Fahrenheit).

Example 6: Using the formula $C = \frac{5(F-32)}{9}$, convert 77°F into degrees Celsius.

Solution: Use the formula to convert from degrees Fahrenheit to degrees Celsius.

$C = \frac{5(F-32)}{9}$ Substitute 77° in the place of F.

$C = \frac{5(77-32)}{9}$ Evaluate the expression using order of operations.

First simplify the numerator above the fraction bar.
Perform all calculations within parentheses.

$C = \frac{5(45)}{9}$ Multiply.

$C = \frac{225}{9}$ Now divide the numerator by the denominator of the fraction.

$C = 25$ Consequently, **77 degrees Fahrenheit is equivalent to 25 degrees Celsius, or 77°F = 25°C.**

Section 7 exercises. Simplify each expression.

1. $12-2\cdot4$

2. $16-3\cdot5$

3. $(12-2)\cdot4$

4. $(16-3)\cdot5$

5. $(18+0)\cdot7$

6. $(16+9)\cdot3$

7. $18+0\cdot7$

8. $16+9\cdot3$

9. $15\div5-2$

10. $18\div6-3$

11. $15\div(5-2)$

12. $18\div(6-3)$

13. $60\div(10+5)$

14. $45\div(3+0)$

15. $60\div10+5$

16. $45\div3+0$

17. $8\div2\cdot4$

18. $18\div2\cdot3$

19. $8\div(2\cdot4)$

20. $18\div(2\cdot3)$

21. $4\cdot(12\div6)$

22. $3\cdot(15\div5)$

23. $4\cdot12\div6$

24. $3\cdot15\div5$

25. $7+5^2$

26. $8+3^2$

27. $(7+5)^2$

28. $(8+3)^2$

29. $(8\div2)^3$

30. $(12\div2)^2$

31. $8\div2^3$

32. $12\div2^2$

33. $\dfrac{3^2-3}{6+0}$

34. $\dfrac{4^2-4}{4+0}$

35. $\dfrac{6^2+5}{(5-4)^2}$

36. $\dfrac{5^2+6}{(7-6)^3}$

37. $7\cdot(8-2)+5$

38. $9\cdot(10-3)+6$

39. $7\cdot 8-2+5$

40. $9\cdot 10-3+6$

41. $7\cdot 8-(2+5)$

42. $9\cdot 10-(3+6)$

43. $4^2+3\cdot 5-4$

44. $2^3+7\cdot 6-5$

45. $4^2+3\cdot(5-4)$

46. $2^3+7\cdot(6-5)$

47. $\dfrac{12-6}{4^2-2\cdot 5}$

48. $\dfrac{15-7}{3^2-1\cdot 1}$

49. $\dfrac{18-6^2\div 2}{4^2-9\div 3}$

50. $\dfrac{15\div 5+8}{12-6^2\div 3}$

51. $\dfrac{(5-2)^2+(11-7)^2}{3^2-2^2}$

52. $\dfrac{(1+5)^2-(2+2)^2}{5^2-7\cdot 3}$

53. $10^2-(6+9)\div 3$

54. $12^2-(12+18)\div 6$

55. $10^2-6+9\div 3$

56. $12^2-12+18\div 6$

57. $10^2-(6+9\div 3)$

58. $12^2-(12+18\div 6)$

59. $2\cdot(18+9)\div 3^2$

60. $3\cdot(32+16)\div 4^2$

61. $2\cdot 18+9\div 3^2$

62. $3\cdot 32+16\div 4^2$

63. $2^3-6\div 2+15\cdot 0$

64. $4^3-20\div 4+15\cdot 0$

65. $4^2+3^2\cdot 2^3$

66. $5^2+4^2\cdot 3^3$

67. $6^2-8^2\div 4^2$

68. $9^2-6^2\div 3^2$

Put the correct inequality symbol $<$, $>$, or $=$ in the box between each pair of expressions.

69. $60+12-5\cdot 8 \;\square\; 60+(12-5)\cdot 8$

70. $50+10-2\cdot 6 \;\square\; 50+(10-2)\cdot 6$

71. $18+(12-4)^2 \div 2 \;\square\; 18+12-4^2 \div 2$

72. $21+(18-6)^2 \div 3 \;\square\; 21+18-6^2 \div 3$

73. $(3^2+6)\cdot 2-15\div 3 \;\square\; 3^2+6\cdot 2-15\div 3$

74. $(3^4+20)\cdot 4-15\div 5 \;\square\; 3^4+20\cdot 4-15\div 5$

Put the number in the box that makes each statement true.

75. $36-4(7-5)^2+\square=(8-3)^2+3(5)$

76. $18+4(2+1)^2+\square=3(3+2)^2-5(3)$

77. $115-\left(34+(9-6)^3-2^5\right)-\square=6^2-5^2+\left(66-(3+7)-9\right)$

78. $72-\left(84-(7-3)^3+2^4\right)-\square=3^4-2^6+\left(6-(4-3)+8\right)$

79. $2(6\div 3\cdot 4)^2-7(3\cdot 2^2)=\square+16\div 2\cdot 3^2-5(5^2\cdot 2\div 5)$

80. $52\div 2^2+3^2\cdot 2\div 3\cdot 2^3=\square\cdot 4\cdot 9+6\left(8\div 2^2\right)+5^2-3\cdot 2^2$

Evaluate each expression for the given values of the variables.

81. $7x+3y$, where $x=0$ and $y=9$

82. $6x+8y$, where $x=12$ and $y=0$

83. $(2x-z)^2+3y$, where $x=6$, $y=7$, and $z=2$

84. $(x-2z)^2+5y$, where $x=15$, $y=8$, and $z=3$

85. $a^2+b^2\div c$, where $a=13$, $b=6$, and $c=4$

86. $a^2+b^2\div c$, where $a=9$, $b=4$, and $c=2$

87. $\dfrac{b^2-4ac}{2a}$, where $a=3$, $b=12$, and $c=2$

88. $\dfrac{b^2-4ac}{2a}$, where $a=4$, $b=16$, and $c=5$

89. Using the formula $A=\dfrac{bh}{2}$ (where A is area, b is the base and h is the height of the triangle), find the area of the following triangle.

height = 6 inches

base = 15 inches

90. Using the formula $A=\dfrac{bh}{2}$ (where A is area, b is the base and h is the height of the triangle), find the area of the following triangle.

height = 7 inches

base = 18 inches

91. Using the formula $C = \dfrac{5(F-32)}{9}$, convert 59°F into degrees Celsius.

92. Using the formula $C = \dfrac{5(F-32)}{9}$, convert 104°F into degrees Celsius.

93. Using the formula $F = \dfrac{9C}{5} + 32$, convert 20°C into degrees Fahrenheit.

94. Using the formula $F = \dfrac{9C}{5} + 32$, convert 35°C into degrees Fahrenheit.

A trapezoid is a 4-sided polygon that has 2 parallel sides. These 2 sides are called the bases of the trapezoid. The height of a trapezoid is the shortest distance between its 2 bases. The formula used to find the area of a trapezoid is $A = \dfrac{h(b_1 + b_2)}{2}$ (Where A is the area, h is the height, b_1 is one of the bases, and b_2 is the other base of the trapezoid.

Note: The subscripts on the b_1 and the b_2 are to distinguish between the two bases.

95. Using the formula $A = \dfrac{h(b_1 + b_2)}{2}$, find the area of the following trapezoid.

base 2 (b_2) = 16 inches

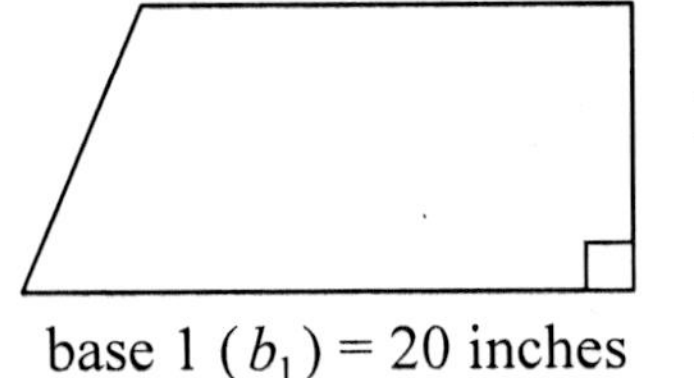

height = 8 inches

base 1 (b_1) = 20 inches

96. Using the formula $A = \dfrac{h(b_1 + b_2)}{2}$, find the area of the following trapezoid.

base 2 (b_2) = 13 inches

height = 7 inches

base 1 (b_1) = 21 inches

WHOLE NUMBERS

Section 8: Solving Equations

An **equation** is a mathematical statement that contains two quantities separated by an equal sign. If these quantities are equal to each other then the equation is a true statement. If these quantities are not equal to each other then the equation is a false statement. For example, the mathematical statement $3 + 4 = 7$ is an equation. Since $3 + 4$ equals 7, this is a true statement. The mathematical statement $5 + 6 = 15$ is also an equation. However, since $5 + 6$ doesn't equal 15, this is a false statement. **Beware of false statements!**

Sometimes an equation contains a variable. For example, the equation $x + 3 = 10$ contains the variable x. When x is 7, the equation becomes $7 + 3 = 10$. The number 7 that replaces the x is called a **solution** because it makes the equation a true statement. If x is 9, the equation becomes $9 + 3 = 10$. Since $9 + 3 = 12$ and $12 \neq 10$, then this is a false statement, and 9 is not a solution.

Note: the symbol $\neq$ means "is not equal to."

Example 1: Is 5 a solution of the equation $x + 2 = 8$?

Solution:

$x+2=8$	Substitute 5 in the place of x.
$\underbrace{5+2}\overset{?}{=}8$	Simplify the left side of the equation.
$7 \overset{?}{=} 8$	However,
$7 \neq 8$.	This is a false statement. Consequently, 5 is not a solution.

Example 2: Is 11 a solution of the equation $x - 4 = 7$?

Solution:

$x-4=7$	Substitute 11 in the place of x.
$\underbrace{11-4}\overset{?}{=}7$	Simplify the left side of the equation.
$7 \overset{\checkmark}{=} 7$	This is a true statement. Consequently, 11 is a solution.

Example 3: Is 7 a solution of the equation $12 = y + 5$?

Solution:	
$12 = y + 5$	Substitute 7 in the place of y.
$12 \stackrel{?}{=} \underbrace{7 + 5}$	Simplify the right side of the equation.
$12 \stackrel{\checkmark}{=} 12$.	This is a true statement. Consequently, 7 is a solution.

Example 4: Is 4 a solution of the equation $3x = 12$?

Solution:	
$3x = 12$	Substitute 4 in the place of x.
$\underbrace{3(4)} \stackrel{?}{=} 12$	Simplify the left side of the equation.
$12 \stackrel{\checkmark}{=} 12$	This is a true statement. Consequently, 4 is a solution.

Example 5: Is 6 a solution of the equation $\frac{18}{x} = 4$?

Solution:	
$\frac{18}{x} = 4$	Substitute 6 in the place of x.
$\underbrace{\frac{18}{6}} \stackrel{?}{=} 4$	Simplify the left side of the equation.
$3 \stackrel{?}{=} 4$	However,
$3 \neq 4$.	This is a false statement. Consequently, 6 is not a solution.

So far, problems involving formulas in this chapter were set up in such a way that all of the information on the right side of the formula was provided. By simplifying this information we determined the value of the variable on the left side of the formula. For instance, if asked to find the area of a rectangle, the length and the width would be provided such as in the example below.

Example 6: Find the area of a rectangle if the dimensions are 10 feet long by 3 feet wide.

Solution: Using the formula for the area of a rectangle,

$A = LW$ gives us

$A = (10 \text{ ft})(3 \text{ ft})$ which simplified further becomes

$A = 30 \text{ ft}^2$. The area of this rectangle is 30 square feet or 30 ft^2.

Again, notice that all of the information on the right side of the formula is provided. This allows us to determine the value of the variable on the left side of the formula. Suppose however that different information was provided. What if we were asked to find the width of a rectangle by being given the area and the length?

Example 7: Find the width of a rectangle if the area is 40 square feet and the length is 8 feet.

Solution: Using the formula for the area of a rectangle,

$A = LW$ gives us

$40 \text{ ft}^2 = (8 \text{ ft})W$.

The problem here is that the variable W isn't all by itself. To determine its value we need to isolate W by removing the 8. This process of isolating a variable (in this case the W), and determining its value is called **solving an equation**. The answer to an equation is called a **solution**. In this section we will look at several methods of solving equations. The method we use will depend on the situation, or structure, of the equation needing to be solved. These methods are called properties of equalities.

If a number is being subtracted from a variable on one side of an equation, we can add that same number to both sides of the equation in order to remove the number. This process will isolate the variable, and is called **The Addition Property of Equality**.

THE ADDITION PROPERTY OF EQUALITY:

When a, b, and c are real numbers, the following is true:

If $a = b$ then $a + c = b + c$.

If the same quantity is added to both sides of an equation, the new equation is equivalent to the old equation. That is, both equations have the same solution.

Note: Equations having the same solution are said to be equivalent equations.

Example 8: Solve the equation: $x - 4 = 12$

Solution:

$x - 4 = 12$	Use the addition property of equality by adding 4 to both sides of the equation.
$x - 4 + 4 = 12 + 4$	Simplify the left side of the equation.
$x + 0 = 12 + 4$	Use the identity property of zero to simplify further.
$x = 12 + 4$	Simplify the right side of the equation.
$x = 16$	The solution is 16. To check the solution, substitute it back into the original equation in place of the variable.
$x - 4 = 12$	becomes
$16 - 4 \stackrel{?}{=} 12$	which further simplifies to
$12 \stackrel{\checkmark}{=} 12.$	The statement is true, therefore the solution is correct.

Note: In the example above, each equation is equivalent to the one before it. In the equation $x = 16$, however, the variable has been isolated and the solution becomes obvious.

If a number is being added to a variable on one side of an equation, we can subtract that same number from both sides of the equation in order to remove the number. This process will isolate the variable. To do this, we use what is called **The Subtraction Property of Equality**.

THE SUBTRACTION PROPERTY OF EQUALITY:

When a, b, and c are real numbers, the following is true:

If $a = b$ then $a - c = b - c$.

If the same quantity is subtracted from both sides of an equation, the new equation is equivalent to the old equation. That is, both equations have the same solution.

Example 9: Solve: $23 = y + 9$

Solution:

$23 = y + 9$	Use the subtraction property of equality by subtracting 9 from both sides of the equation.
$23 - 9 = y + 9 - 9$	Simplify the left side of the equation.
$14 = y + 9 - 9$	Simplify the right side of the equation.
$14 = y + 0$	Use the identity property of zero to simplify further.
$14 = y$	The solution is 14. Though this answer is correct, it is considered more appropriate to write the answer with the variable first.
$14 = y$	becomes
$y = 14$.	To check the solution, substitute it back into the original equation in place of the variable.
$23 = y + 9$	becomes
$23 \stackrel{?}{=} 14 + 9$	which further simplifies to
$23 \stackrel{\checkmark}{=} 23$.	The statement is true, therefore the solution is correct.

If a number is being multiplied by a variable on one side of an equation, we can divide by that same number on both sides of the equation in order to remove the number. This process will isolate the variable. To do this, we use what is called **The Division Property of Equality**.

THE DIVISION PROPERTY OF EQUALITY:

When a, b, and c are real numbers with $c \neq 0$, the following is true:

If $a = b$ then $\frac{a}{c} = \frac{b}{c}$.

If both sides of the equation are divided by the same non-zero quantity, the new equation is equivalent to the old equation. That is, both equations have the same solution.

Example 10: Solve: $3x = 12$

Solution:

$3x = 12$	Use the division property of equality by dividing both sides of the equation by 3.
$\frac{3x}{3} = \frac{12}{3}$	Simplify the left side of the equation.
$1x = \frac{12}{3}$	Use the identity property of one to simplify further.
$x = \frac{12}{3}$	Simplify the right side of the equation.
$x = 4$	The solution is 4. To check the solution, substitute it back into the original equation in place of the variable.
$3x = 12$	becomes
$3(4) \stackrel{?}{=} 12$	which further simplifies to
$12 \stackrel{\checkmark}{=} 12.$	The statement is true, therefore the solution is correct.

Note: When a number is multiplied by a variable, as in the case of $3x$ above, the number has a special name. It is called the coefficient of the variable. To solve the equation $3x = 12$ we divide both sides of the equation by the coefficient of the variable.

Look again at example 9. Now we know that we can use the division property of equality to finish solving the formula.

Example 9 revisited: Find the width of a rectangle if the area is 40 square feet and the length is 8 feet. Use the formula $A = LW$ (where A is the area, L is the length, and W is the width of a rectangle).

Solution: Using the formula for the area of a rectangle, $A = LW$ gives us

$40\text{ ft}^2 = (8\text{ ft})W.$ Use the division property of equality by dividing both sides of the equation by 8 feet.

$\frac{40\text{ ft}^2}{8\text{ ft}} = \frac{(8\text{ ft})W}{8\text{ ft}}$ Simplify the left side of the equation.

$5\ ft = \frac{(8\text{ ft})W}{8\text{ ft}}$ Simplify the right side of the equation.

$5\text{ ft} = W$ The width is 5 feet. To check the solution, substitute it back into the original equation in place of the variable.

$40\text{ ft}^2 = (8\text{ ft})W$ becomes

$40\text{ ft}^2 \stackrel{?}{=} (8\text{ ft})(5\text{ ft})$ which further simplifies to

$40\text{ ft}^2 \stackrel{\checkmark}{=} 40\text{ ft}^2.$ The statement is true, therefore the solution is correct.

The addition, subtraction, and division properties of equality can be used to solve a variety of formulas.

Example 11: Find the amount of interest earned on a savings account if the principal is \$400 and the total amount in the account is \$453. Use the formula $A = P + I$ (where A is the total amount in a savings account, P is the principal or amount put into the account, and I is the amount of interest earned on the account).

Solution: Using the formula $A = P + I$ gives us

$\$453 = \$400 + I.$ Use the subtraction property of equality by subtracting \$400 from both sides of the equation.

$\$453 - \$400 = \$400 - \$400 + I$ Simplify the left side of the equation.

$\$53 = \$400 - \$400 + I$ Simplify the right side of the equation.

$\$53 = I$, or $I = \$53.$ The amount of interest is \$53. To check the solution, substitute it back into the original equation in place of the variable.

$\$453 = \$400 + I.$ becomes

$\$453 \stackrel{?}{=} \$400 + \$53$ which further simplifies to

$\$453 \stackrel{\checkmark}{=} \$453.$ The statement is true, therefore the solution is correct.

Example 12: Find the number of payments to be made on a car loan if the total amount of the loan is $7,800 and the monthly payments are $325. Use the formula $A = MN$ (where A is the total amount of the loan, M is the monthly payment, and N is the number of payments).

Solution: Using the formula	$A = MN$ gives us
$\$7{,}800 = (\$325)(N)$.	Use the division property of equality by dividing both sides of the equation by $325.
$\frac{\$7{,}800}{\$325} = \frac{\$325(N)}{\$325}$	Simplify the left side of the equation.
$24 = \frac{\$325(N)}{\$325}$	Simplify the right side of the equation.
$24 = N$, or $N = 24$.	The solution is 24 payments. To check the solution, substitute it back into the original equation in place of the variable.
$\$7{,}800 = (\$325)(N)$	becomes
$\$7{,}800 \stackrel{?}{=} (\$325)(24)$	which simplifies further to
$\$7{,}800 \stackrel{\checkmark}{=} \$7{,}800$.	The statement is true, therefore the solution is correct.

Example 13: Find the amount of revenue generated by a coffee shop in one month if the monthly cost to run the shop is $3,600 and the monthly profit is $1,200. Use the formula $P = R - C$ (where P is the profit, R is the revenue, and C is the cost).

Solution: Using the formula	$P = R - C$ gives us
$\$1{,}200 = R - \$3{,}600$.	Use the addition property of equality by adding $3,600 to both sides of the equation.
$\$1{,}200 + \$3{,}600 = R - \$3{,}600 + \$3{,}600$	Simplify the left side of the equation.
$\$4{,}800 = R - \$3{,}600 + \$3{,}600$	Simplify the right side of the equation.
$\$4{,}800 = R$ or $R = \$4{,}800$.	The solution is $4,800 in monthly revenue. To check the solution, substitute it back into the original equation in place of the variable.
$\$1{,}200 = R - \$3{,}600$	becomes
$\$1{,}200 \stackrel{?}{=} \$4{,}800 - \$3{,}600$	which simplifies further to
$\$1{,}200 \stackrel{\checkmark}{=} \$1{,}200$.	The statement is true, therefore the solution is correct.

Monday is June 27th. In this sentence, both Monday and June 27th describe the same day. They are connected by the word "is." We could write the same statement as an equation. Monday = June 27th. When two mathematical statements are equal they form an equation. $7+3=10$ is a true equation since the information on the left side of the equal sign has the same value as the information on the right side of the equal sign. In mathematics it is often necessary to translate words or sentences into mathematical equations. For instance "the sum of three and ten is thirteen" becomes $3+10=13$. "The product of seven and two equals fourteen" becomes $7\cdot 2=14$.

There are several different words or word phrases that can be used to indicate equality. Here is a list of some of those phrases.

Word phrase	Used in an expression	Written as symbols
is	three plus four is seven	$3+4=7$
equals	the product of three and two equals six	$3\cdot 2=6$
is equal to	the difference of five and two is equal to three	$5-2=3$

Sometimes a sentence or paragraph is asking a question about an unknown quantity. By **translating words into an equation** we can use techniques discussed in this section to solve the equation and determine the unknown quantity.

Example 14: Translate the following expression into an equation using mathematical symbols. Then, solve the equation and answer the question.
The sum of a number and seven is twelve. What is the number?

Solution: First we need to choose a variable to represent the unknown quantity. Since the unknown quantity is "a number" let's use the letter N. The statement

"The sum of	a number	and	seven	is	twelve"	translates into
add	the unknown "N"		7	equals	12	

which becomes the equation: N + 7 = 12

Now we can solve the equation.

$N+7=12$	Use the subtraction property of equality by subtracting 7 from both sides of the equation.
$N+7-7=12-7$	Simplify the left side of the equation.
$N=12-7$	Simplify the right side of the equation.
$N=5$	The solution is the number 5. To check the solution, substitute it back into the original equation in place of the variable.
$N+7=12$	becomes
$5+7\overset{?}{=}12$	which simplifies further to
$12\overset{\checkmark}{=}12$.	The statement is true, therefore the solution is correct.

Example 15: Translate the following expression into an equation using mathematical symbols. Then, solve the equation and answer the question.
The product of nine and a number is equal to fifty-four. What is the number?

Solution: First we need to choose a variable to represent the unknown quantity. Since the unknown quantity is "a number" let's use the letter N. The statement

"The product of	nine	and	a number	is equal to	fifty-four"	translates into
multiply	9		the unknown "N"	equals	54	
which becomes the equation:			9N	=	54	

Now we can solve the equation.

$9N = 54$ Use the division property of equality by dividing both sides of the equation by 9.

$\frac{9N}{9} = \frac{54}{9}$ Simplify the left side of the equation.

$N = \frac{54}{9}$ Simplify the right side of the equation.

$N = 6$ The solution is the number 6. To check the solution, substitute it back into the original equation in place of the variable.

$9N = 54$ becomes

$9(6) \stackrel{?}{=} 54$ which simplifies further to

$54 \stackrel{\checkmark}{=} 54$. The statement is true, therefore the solution is correct.

Example 16: Translate the following situation into an equation using mathematical symbols. Then, solve the equation and answer the question.
John is three years older than Mary. If John is eleven years old, how old is Mary?

Solution: First we need to choose a variable to represent the unknown quantity. Since the unknown quantity is "how old is Mary" let's use the letter M. The statement "John is three years older than Mary" becomes John = M + 3. The statement "John is eleven years old" becomes John = 11. Since John = M + 3 and John = 11, by putting these two statements together we get M + 3 =11.

Now we can solve the equation.

$M + 3 = 11$ Use the subtraction property of equality by subtracting 3 from both sides of the equation.

$M + 3 - 3 = 11 - 3$ Simplify the left side of the equation.

$M = 11 - 3$ Simplify the right side of the equation.

$M = 8$ The solution is 8. Therefore, Mary is 8 years old. We'll leave verifying the solution up to you.

Example 17: Translate the following situation into an equation using mathematical symbols. Then, solve the equation and answer the question.
The width of a rectangle is 6 feet less than the length. If the width is 9 feet, what is the length?

Solution: First we need to choose a variable to represent the unknown quantity. Since the part of the question that refers to the unknown quantity is "what is the length," let's use the letter L. The statement "The width of a rectangle is 6 feet less than the length" becomes $\text{width} = L - 6$. The statement "The width is 9 feet" becomes $\text{width} = 9$. Since $\text{width} = L - 6$ and $\text{width} = 9$, by putting these two statements together, we get $L - 6 = 9$.

Now we can solve the equation.

$L - 6 = 9$	Use the addition property of equality by adding 6 to both sides of the equation.
$L - 6 + 6 = 9 + 6$	Simplify the left side of the equation.
$L = 9 + 6$	Simplify the right side of the equation.
$L = 15$	The solution is 15. Therefore, the length is 15 feet. To check the solution, substitute it back into the original equation in place of the variable.
$L - 6 = 9$	becomes
$15 - 6 \stackrel{?}{=} 9$	which simplifies further to
$9 \stackrel{\checkmark}{=} 9$.	The statement is true, therefore the solution is correct.

Example 18: Translate the following situation into an equation using mathematical symbols. Then, solve the equation and answer the question. Tomorrow I will be twice the age of my cousin. If I will be 48 years of age, then what age will my cousin be?

Solution: First we need to choose a variable to represent the unknown quantity. Since the unknown quantity is "what age will my cousin be" let's use the letter C. The statement "Tomorrow I will be twice the age of my cousin" becomes my age = 2C. The statement "I will be 48 years of age" becomes my age = 48. Since my age = 2C and my age = 48, by putting these two statements together, we get 2C = 48.

Now we can solve the equation.

$2C = 48$	Use the division property of equality by dividing both sides of the equation by 2.
$\frac{2C}{2} = \frac{48}{2}$	Simplify the left side of the equation.
$C = \frac{48}{2}$	Simplify the right side of the equation.
$C = 24$	The solution is 24. Therefore, my cousin will be 24 years of age. Once again, we'll leave verifying the solution up to you.

Note: "Will be" is the future tense of "is" and therefore translates into "equals."

Section 8 exercises. Check the solutions.

1. Is 28 a solution of the equation $w+6=35$?

2. Is 17 a solution of the equation $a+8=25$?

3. Is 38 a solution of the equation $k-7=31$?

4. Is 32 a solution of the equation $m-26=4$?

5. Is 9 a solution of the equation $37=q+28$?

6. Is 14 a solution of the equation $46=h+34$?

7. Is 25 a solution of the equation $37=g-12$?

8. Is 61 a solution of the equation $46=y-15$?

9. Is 8 a solution of the equation $7y=49$?

10. Is 5 a solution of the equation $6x=32$?

11. Is 11 a solution of the equation $\frac{55}{x}=5$?

12. Is 48 a solution of the equation $\frac{y}{6}=8$?

13. Is 12 a solution of the equation $60=5w$?

14. Is 7 a solution of the equation $56=8a$?

Solve each of the following equations.

15. $x-7=15$

16. $w-9=25$

17. $H+7=74$

18. $R+9=92$

19. $7y=35$

20. $9k=72$

21. $34+n=81$

22. $52+p=67$

23. $43=z-8$

24. $19=b-0$

25. $96=6w$

26. $96=4x$

27. $12m=72$

28. $11y=132$

29. $28=W+17$

30. $75=y+26$

31. $x-0=14$

32. $h-47=2$

33. $w=14-6$

34. $m=21-5$

35. $0=7k$

36. $0=14d$

37. $117=53+k$

38. $142=37+p$

39. $16x=16$

40. $14y=14$

41. $n+41=41$

42. $b+67=67$

43. $97=y-17$

44. $91=x-31$

Answer each question by using the given formula.

45. How many hours will it take for a truck traveling at a rate of 52 miles per hour to go 260 miles? Use the formula $d=rt$ (where d is distance, r is rate of speed, and t is the time spent traveling).

46. How many hours will it take for a car traveling at a rate of 68 miles per hour to go 476 miles? Use the formula $d=rt$ (where d is distance, r is rate of speed, and t is the time spent traveling).

47. What is the wholesale cost of an item, if the retail cost is \$36 and the amount of markup is \$14? Use the formula $R = W + M$ (where R is the retail cost, W is the wholesale cost, and M is the amount of mark up).

48. What is the wholesale cost of an item, if the retail cost is \$84 and the amount of markup is \$37? Use the formula $R = W + M$ (where R is the retail cost, W is the wholesale cost, and M is the amount of mark up).

49. How many miles per hour must a car travel in order to go 148 miles in 4 hours? Use the formula $d = rt$ (where d is distance, r is rate of speed, and t is the time spent traveling).

50. How many miles per hour must a car travel in order to go 294 miles in 6 hours? Use the formula $d = rt$ (where d is distance, r is rate of speed, and t is the time spent traveling).

51. Find the amount of revenue generated by a hotdog stand in one week if the weekly cost to run the stand is \$2,450 and the weekly profit is \$850. Use the formula $P = R - C$ (where P is the profit, R is the revenue, and C is the cost).

52. Find the amount of revenue generated by a magazine stand in one week if the weekly cost to run the stand is \$1,725 and the weekly profit is \$1,345. Use the formula $P = R - C$ (where P is the profit, R is the revenue, and C is the cost).

53. Find the length of a rectangle if the area is 450 square feet and the width is 15 feet. Use the formula $A = LW$ (where A is the area, L is the length, and W is the width of a rectangle).

54. Find the width of a rectangle if the area is 368 square feet and the length is 23 feet. Use the formula $A = LW$ (where A is the area, L is the length, and W is the width of a rectangle).

55. Find the amount of interest earned on a savings account if the principal is \$580 and the total amount in the account is \$642. Use the formula $A = P + I$ (where A is the total amount in a savings account, P is the principal or amount put into the account, and I is the amount of interest earned on the account).

56. Find the amount of interest earned on a savings account if the principal is \$868 and the total amount in the account is \$879. Use the formula $A = P + I$ (where A is the total amount in a savings account, P is the principal or amount put into the account, and I is the amount of interest earned on the account).

Translate each expression into an equation using mathematical symbols. Then, solve the equation and answer the question.

57. The sum of a number and eight is thirty-nine. What is the number?

58. The difference of a number and sixteen is equal to seventy-three. What is the number?

59. The product of a number and nine equals forty-five. What is the number?

60. Six added to a number is equal to twenty-one. What is the number?

61. Nineteen subtracted from a number is ninety-eight. What is the number?

62. Twice a number equals sixty-four. What is the number?

63. Three more than a number is equal to eighty-eight. What is the number?

64. Forty increased by a number is seventy-one. What is the number?

65. Seven multiplied by a number is eighty-four. What is the number?

66. The total of a number and five is equal to one hundred seventeen. What is the number?

67. A number minus fifteen is twelve. What is the number?

68. A number decreased by seven equals seven. What is the number?

69. A number plus eight equals fourteen. What is the number?

70. A number less five equals seventy-eight. What is the number?

71. Sixty less than a number is forty-two. What is the number?

72. Nine times a number is equal to eighty-one. What is the number?

Translate each expression into an equation using mathematical symbols. Then, solve the equation and answer the question.

73. Maria is five years younger than Joe. If Maria is eighteen years old, how old is Joe?

74. Marlene is twice as old as Sam. If Marlene is ten years old, how old is Sam?

75. The length of a rectangle is three times the width. If the length is twenty-four inches, what is the width?

76. The width of a rectangle is five feet less than the length. If the width is sixty-two feet, what is the length?

77. Ralph weighs fifteen pounds more than Steve does. If Ralph weighs one hundred eighty-five pounds, then how much does Steve weigh?

78. The white horse is six inches taller than the black horse. If the white horse is forty-three inches tall, then how tall is the black horse?

79. Teresa is three inches shorter than Stephanie. If Teresa is fifty-eight inches tall, then how tall is Stephanie?

80. Mark is six years older than Paul. If Mark is thirty-two years old, then how old is Paul?

81. The length of a rectangle is eight inches more than the width. If the length is forty-two inches, what is the width?

82. Stacy is fourteen pounds lighter than her brother Doug. If Stacy weighs one hundred twelve pounds, then how much does her brother Doug weigh?

83. The number of hamburgers sold yesterday was six times the number of corn dogs sold. If thirty hamburgers were sold, then how many corn dogs were sold?

84. The perimeter of a rectangle is five times the width. If the perimeter is 20 yards, then what is the width of the rectangle?

WHOLE NUMBERS

Section 9: Estimating

A number can be estimated, or approximated, by rounding it to a certain place value. Sometimes, estimating involves rounding several different numbers in the same problem. Suppose we want to **estimate** the sum of 2,485 and 5,723. One way we can accomplish this process is by using a method called **front end rounding**. This is done by rounding each number to its highest place value and then adding together the results.

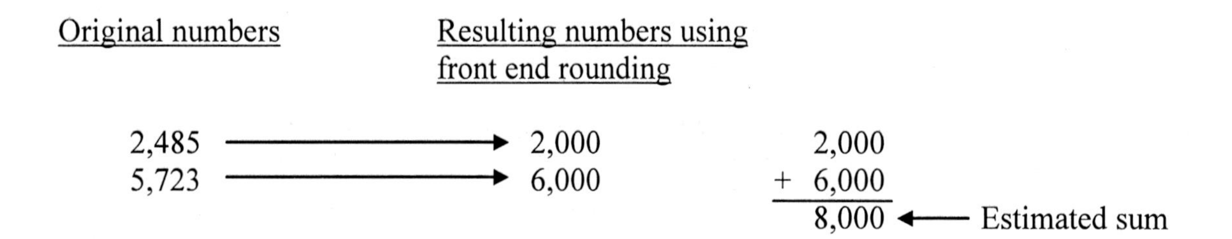

This method can also be used when estimating a difference. Suppose we want to estimate the difference of 416 and 273. The process would be as follows:

Original numbers	Resulting numbers using front end rounding
416 →	400
273 →	300

$$\begin{array}{r} 400 \\ -300 \\ \hline 100 \end{array} \leftarrow \text{Estimated difference}$$

Note: Keep in mind that there are several different methods that can be used in the estimation process. However, in this chapter we will limit the process to the front end rounding method.

Example 1: Estimate the sum of 3,425, 6,643 and 234.

Solution:

Original numbers	Resulting numbers using front end rounding
3,425 →	3,000
6,643 →	7,000
234 →	200

$$\begin{array}{r} 3{,}000 \\ 7{,}000 \\ +\ \ 200 \\ \hline 10{,}200 \end{array} \leftarrow \text{Estimated sum}$$

Example 2: Estimate the difference of 7,439 and 2,852.

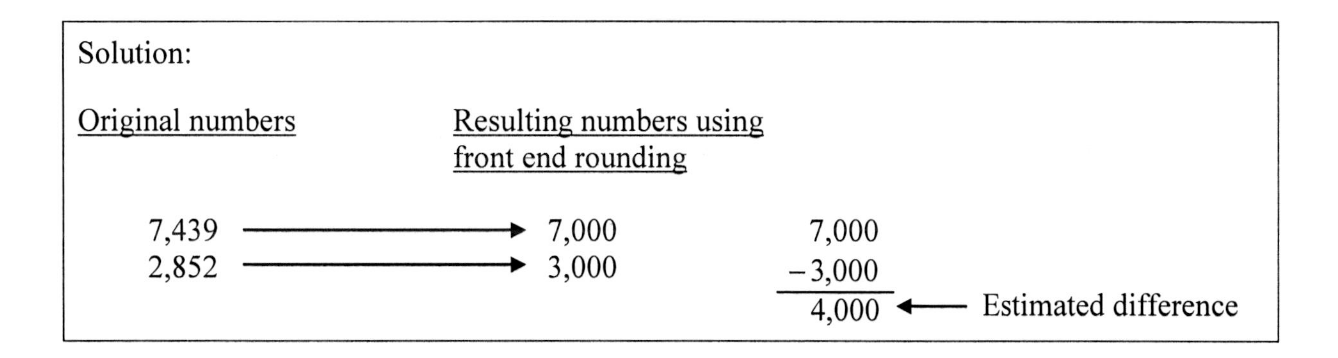

As with sums and differences, products can also be **estimated**, or approximated. This is accomplished by rounding each factor in the product to a certain place value before multiplying them together. We can accomplish this process by using a method mentioned previously called **front end rounding**. Round each number to its highest place value and then multiply the results.

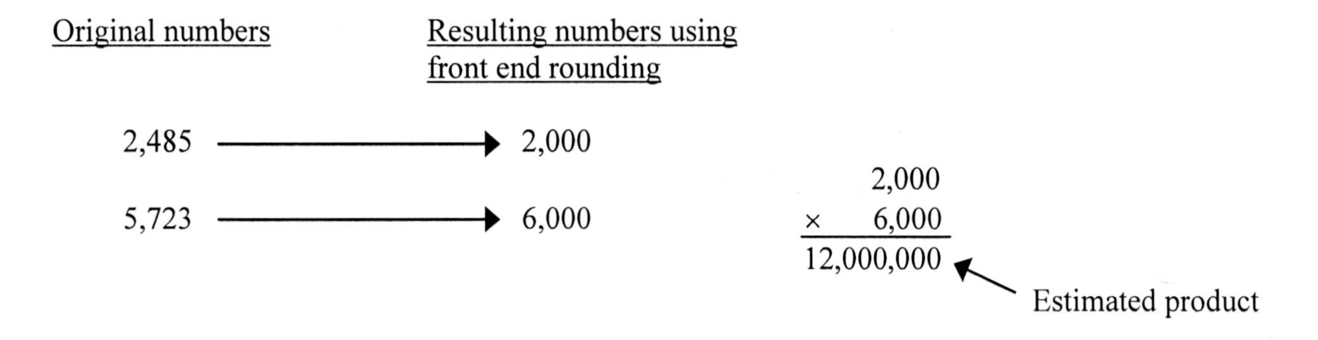

Example 3: Estimate the product of 765 and 64.

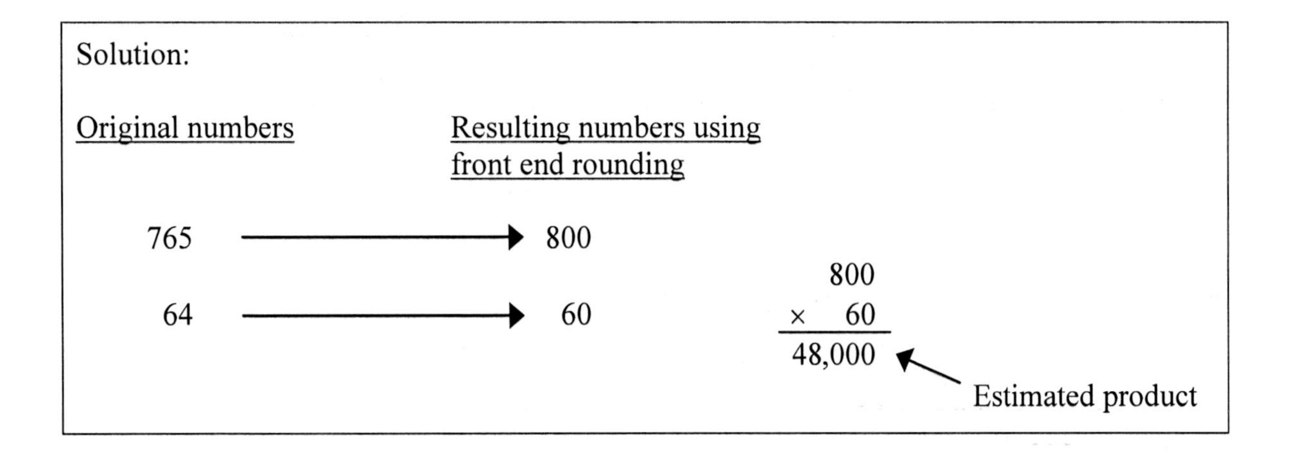

Example 4: Estimate the product of 439 and 235.

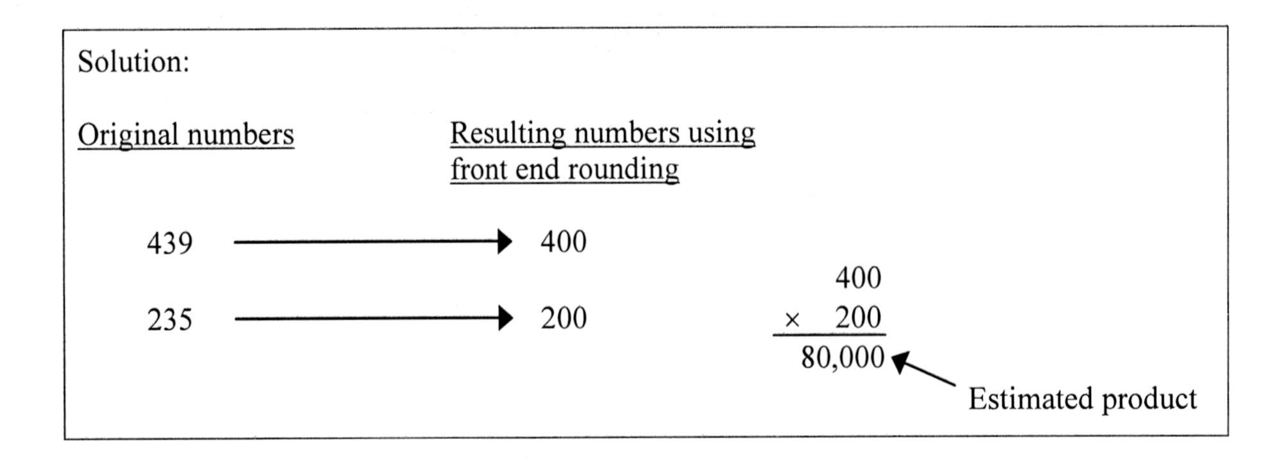

Quotients can also be estimated, or approximated, by rounding both the dividend and the divisor to a certain place value before dividing them to get a quotient. Again, we can accomplish this process by using front end rounding.

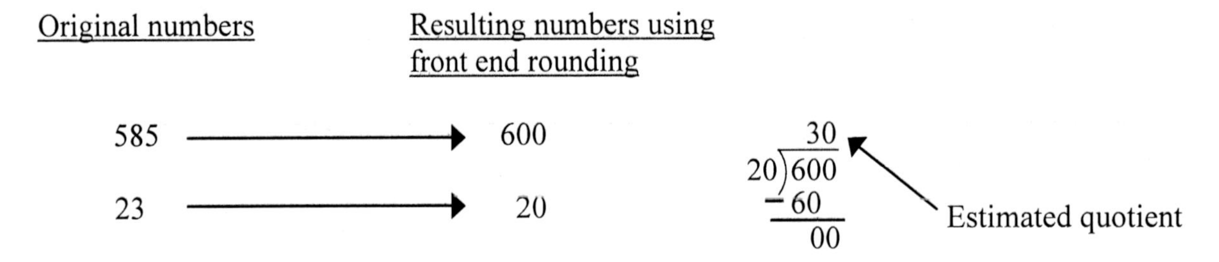

Example 5: Estimate the quotient of 7,657 and 37.

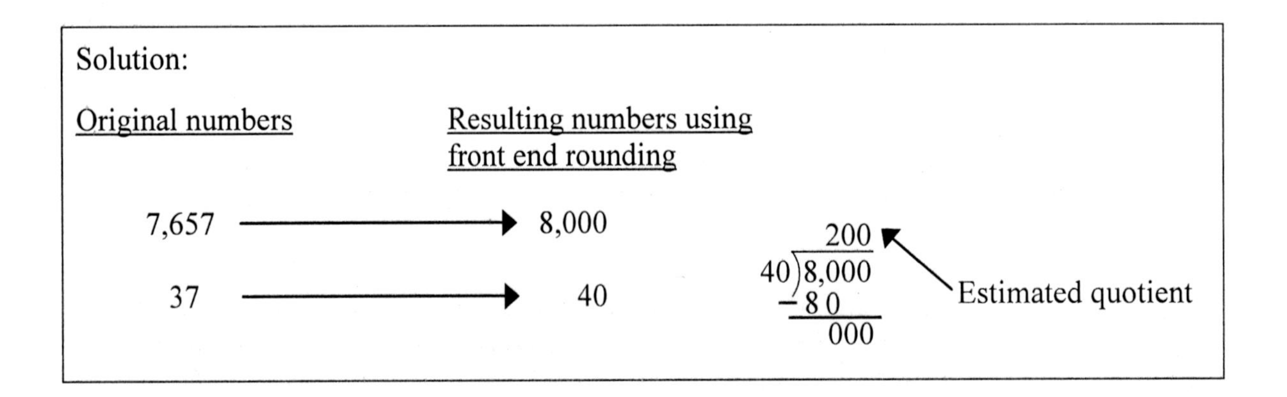

Section 9 exercises. Estimate each sum or difference by using front end rounding.

1. $3{,}497 + 6{,}872$

2. $5{,}280 + 2{,}698$

3. $44{,}599 - 28{,}654$

4. $42{,}764 - 18{,}673$

5. $314{,}500 + 449{,}999$

6. $675{,}999 + 145{,}743$

7. $4{,}500 - 5{,}497$

8. $6{,}699 - 7{,}486$

9. $73{,}573 + 24{,}955$

10. $81{,}786 + 15{,}499$

11. $123{,}699 - 24{,}792$

12. $205{,}352 - 33{,}654$

13.
$$\begin{array}{r} 486 \\ 324 \\ 849 \\ +\ 470 \\ \hline \end{array}$$

14.
$$\begin{array}{r} 762 \\ 420 \\ 642 \\ +\ 278 \\ \hline \end{array}$$

15.
$$\begin{array}{r} 6{,}420 \\ -\ 327 \\ \hline \end{array}$$

16.
$$\begin{array}{r} 7{,}846 \\ -\ 942 \\ \hline \end{array}$$

17.
$$\begin{array}{r} 6{,}230 \\ -\ 4{,}807 \\ \hline \end{array}$$

18.
$$\begin{array}{r} 2{,}904 \\ -\ 1{,}372 \\ \hline \end{array}$$

19.
$$\begin{array}{r} 27{,}986 \\ 4{,}099 \\ +\ 18{,}490 \\ \hline \end{array}$$

20.
$$\begin{array}{r} 16{,}087 \\ 8{,}796 \\ +\ 26{,}408 \\ \hline \end{array}$$

Estimate each product or quotient by using front end rounding.

21. $728 \cdot 39$

22. $643 \cdot 27$

23. $624 \div 26$

24. $756 \div 43$

25. $123\overline{)35{,}876}$

26. $143\overline{)47{,}093}$

27. $9{,}253(48)$

28. $8{,}554(24)$

29. $55{,}809 \div 29$

30. $26{,}756 \div 47$

31. $2{,}099 \cdot 511$

32. $5{,}353 \cdot 421$

33. $247\overline{)645{,}876}$

34. $445\overline{)847{,}474}$

35. $37{,}550(19)$

36. $88{,}250(45)$

37. $222{,}888 \div 82$

38. $777{,}333 \div 37$

39. $640 \cdot 460$

40. $530 \cdot 350$

WHOLE NUMBERS

Chapter Review

Section 1: An Introduction to Whole Numbers

Review Exercises: In each of the following problems, graph the given numbers.

1. Graph the natural numbers that are 7 or less.

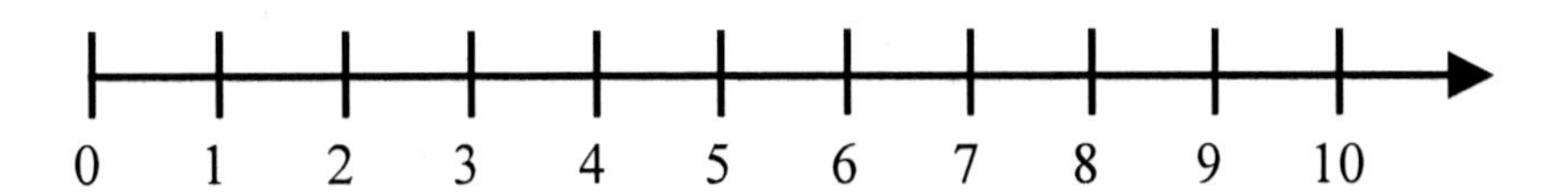

2. Graph the whole numbers that are larger than 3 and less than 8.

Place the correct inequality symbol $<$ or $>$ between the pair of numbers.

3. 5,670 56,700

4. The elevation of Mt. Rainier is 14,409 feet, while the elevation of Mt. Hood is 11,245 feet. Using an inequality symbol, tell which elevation is higher.

5. For the number 43,871, what digit is in the thousands column?

Write the following number in words.

6. 906,522

Write the following number in standard form.

7. five million, twenty-seven thousand, thirty-two

Write the following number in expanded form.

8. 309,205

Section 2: Rounding, Charts, Graphs and an Introduction to Geometry

Review Exercises: Round the number to the place value given.

9. 3,899,827 ten-thousands

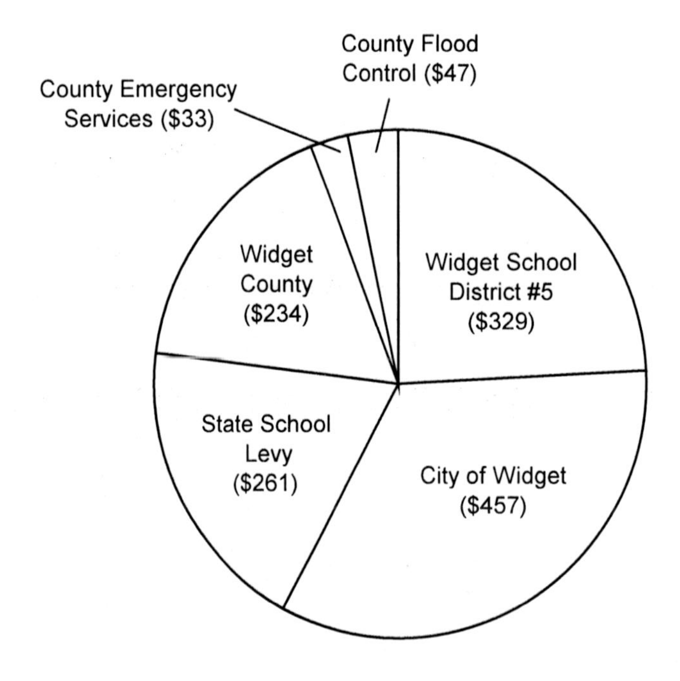

Use the pie chart above to answer the following questions.

10. Which category on the chart gets the most amount of money?

11. Which is greater, the amount paid to the Widget School District #5 or the amount paid to the State School Levy?

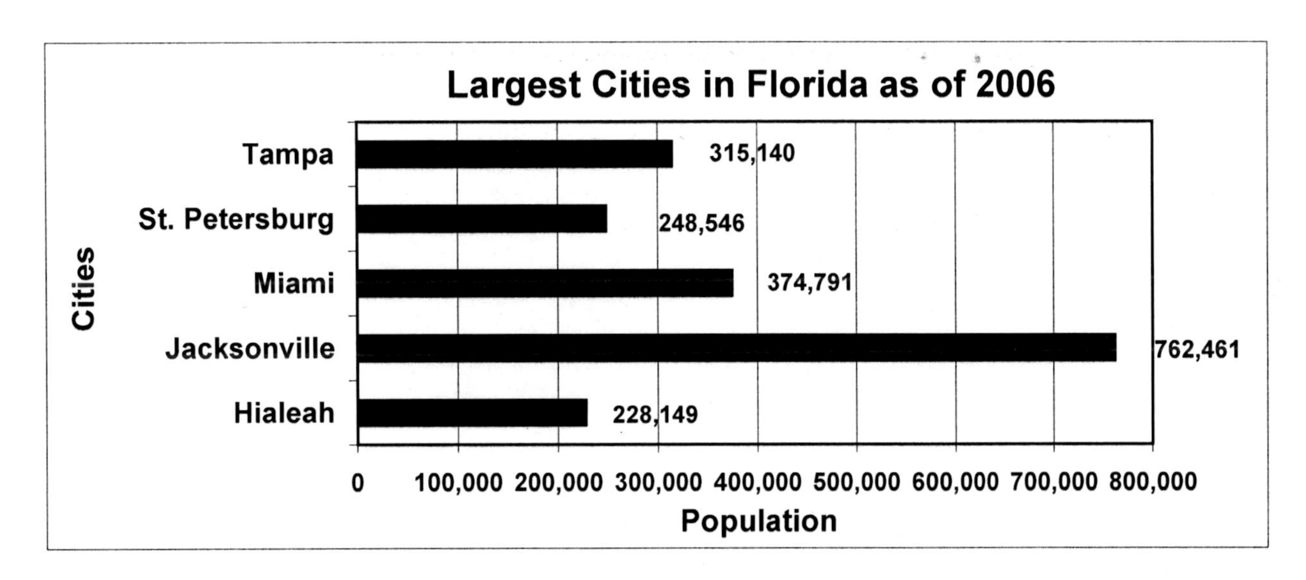

12. Using the bar graph above, rank the five cities from smallest to largest, based on their population.

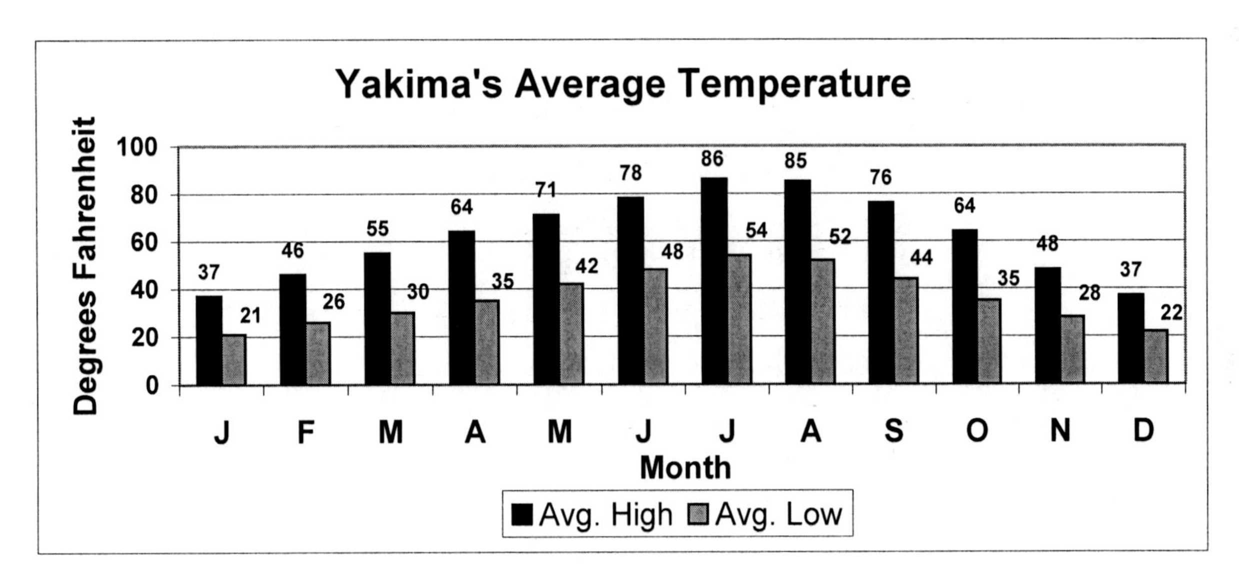

Use the double bar graph above to answer the following questions.

13. During which month(s) is Yakima's average temperature the highest?

14. During which month(s) is Yakima's average temperature the lowest?

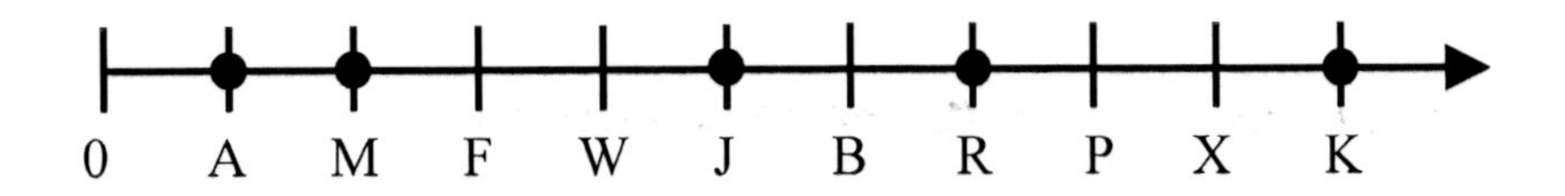

Use the number line above to place the correct inequality symbol < or > between the pair of letters.

15. R M

Section 3: Adding and Subtracting Whole Numbers

Review Exercises:

16. Add.

$$\begin{array}{r} 21{,}754 \\ 396 \\ 4{,}738 \\ 7 \\ +\quad 39 \\ \hline \end{array}$$

17. Subtract.

$$\begin{array}{r} 8{,}123 \\ -\,7{,}208 \\ \hline \end{array}$$

Translate each phrase into mathematical symbols. Then determine the result in each case.

18. What is twelve more than four?

19. Find ninety-three decreased by ten.

Evaluate the expression $x - y$ for the given values of x and y.

20. $x = 8{,}427;\ y = 579$

Evaluate the expression $x + y + z$ for the given values of x, y, and z.

21. $x = 977;\ y = 53;\ z = 6{,}860$

Use only the commutative property of addition to rewrite the expression. Then simplify the expression.

22. $416 + 99$

Use only the associative property of addition to rewrite the expression. Then simplify the expression.

23. $718 + (82 + 641)$

Section 4: More Adding and Subtracting of Whole Numbers

Review Exercises:

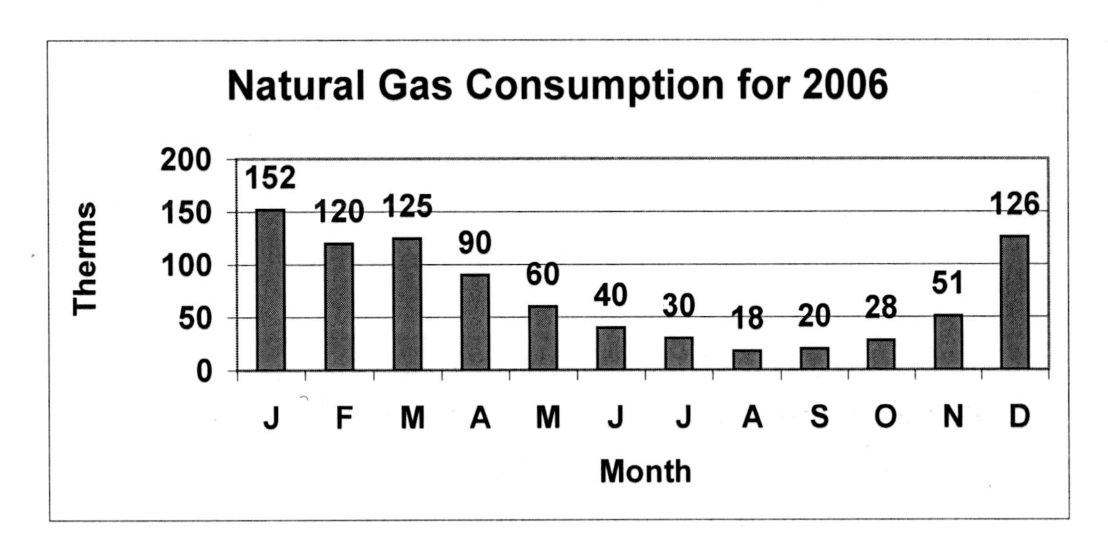

Use the bar graph above to answer the following question.

24. How many therms of natural gas were consumed altogether in June, July and August?

Find the perimeter of the polygon. Note: 12 in. = 1 ft.

25.

10 in.

2 ft 2 in.

2 ft

26. Ben wants to take 12 lb of peanut butter on a trip. If he already has jars of peanut butter weighing 3 lb 9 oz and 6 lb 8 oz, how much more peanut butter does he need to take? Note: 16 oz = 1 lb.

27. Given that $\angle C = 132°$, find $\angle D$ such that $\angle C$ and $\angle D$ are supplementary angles.

28. Given that $\angle P = 6°$, find $\angle R$ such that $\angle P$ and $\angle R$ are complementary angles.

29. A given triangle contains interior angles $\angle R$, $\angle K$ and $\angle W$. If $\angle R = 86°$ and $\angle K = 43°$, then find $\angle W$.

Section 5: Multiplying and Dividing Whole Numbers

Review Exercises:

Multiply.

30. $\begin{array}{r} 4{,}780 \\ \times \quad 39 \\ \hline \end{array}$

Divide.

31. $7{,}106 \div 0$

Divide.

32. $74\overline{)684}$

Translate each phrase into mathematical symbols. Then determine the result in each case.

33. Find the product of seventy-two and eighteen.

34. What is the quotient of sixty-nine and three?

Use only the commutative property of multiplication to rewrite the expression. Then simplify the expression.

35. $92(26)$

Use only the associative property of multiplication to rewrite the expression. Then simplify the expression.

36. $25 \cdot (4 \cdot 7)$

Write the following expression in exponential form.

37. $3 \cdot 3 \cdot 7 \cdot 7 \cdot 7 \cdot 7 \cdot x \cdot x$

Evaluate the exponential expression.

38. 7^3

Translate the phrase into mathematical symbols.

39. The cube of 12

Evaluate each expression for the given values of the variables.

40. z^4, where $z = 10$

41. $\frac{e}{f}$, where $e = 6{,}785$ and $f = 23$

Section 6: More Multiplying and Dividing of Whole Numbers

Review Exercises:

42. Find all of the factors of 70.

Classify the following numbers as prime or composite. If the number is composite, write its prime factorization.

43. 101

44. 143

The "Nutrition Facts" on the label of a 64 fluid ounce container of grape juice state that a serving size of 8 fluid ounces contains 160 calories.

45. How many calories would 1 fluid ounce of grape juice contain?

Nutrition Facts	
Serving Size: 8 FL. OZ. (240mL) Servings Per Container: 8	
Amount Per Serving	
Calories 160	
	% Daily Value*
Total Fat 0g	**0 %**
Sodium 20mg	**1 %**
Total Carb. 42g	**14 %**
Sugars 40g	
Protein 0g	

Find the perimeter and area of the figure.

46.

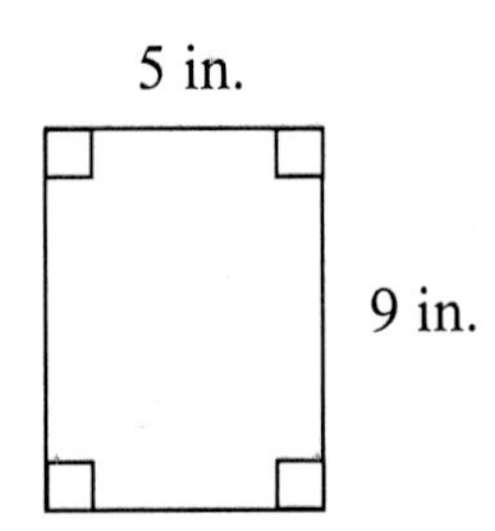

47. How many square yards of carpet are needed to cover a living room floor if the dimensions are 8 yards long by 6 yards wide?

48. Use the formula $R = \frac{p}{h}$ (where R is the rate of pay, p is the total amount of pay, and h is the number of hours worked), to find the rate of pay for a person that earns $96 in 8 hours.

49. How much greater is the surface area of a floor if the dimensions are 16 feet long by 11 feet wide, than the surface area of a floor where the dimensions are 19 feet long by 9 feet wide?

50. The surface area of a roof with dimensions of 25 feet long by 8 feet wide is how many times the surface area of a floor where the dimensions are 10 feet long by 4 feet wide?

Section 7: Order of Operations

Review Exercises:

Put the correct inequality symbol <, >, or = in the box between the pair of expressions.

51. $3^2 + 5 \cdot 2 - 18 \div 3$ $\square$ $(3^2 + 5) \cdot 2 - 18 \div 3$

Evaluate the expression for the given values of the variables.

52. $(x+2z)^2+5y$, where $x=11$, $y=7$, and $z=1$

Convert.

53. Using the formula $\mathrm{C}=\dfrac{5(\mathrm{F}-32)}{9}$, convert 86°F into degrees Celsius.

Section 8: Solving Equations

Review Exercises: Check the solution.

54. Is 38 a solution of the equation $64=h+28$?

55. Is 8 a solution of the equation $56=7a$?

56. Is 4 a solution of the equation $40=\dfrac{10}{y}$?

Solve the following equations.

57. $w-11=26$

58. $12y=156$

59. $133=47+p$

Answer the question by using the given formula.

60. How many miles per hour must a car travel in order to go 336 miles in 7 hours? Use the formula $d = rt$ (where d is distance, r is rate of speed, and t is the time spent traveling).

Translate each expression into an equation using mathematical symbols. Then, solve the equation and answer the question.

61. A number decreased by twelve equals thirteen. What is the number?

62. The length of a rectangle is seven inches more than the width. If the length is fifty-three inches, what is the width?

63. The number of hamburgers sold yesterday was eight times the number of chilidogs sold. If ninety-six hamburgers were sold, then how many chilidogs were sold?

Section 9: Estimating

Estimate each sum or difference by using front end rounding.

64. $34{,}987 + 26{,}009$

65. $\begin{array}{r} 7{,}400 \\ -\ 2{,}195 \\ \hline \end{array}$

Estimate each product or quotient by using front end rounding.

66. $463 \cdot 72$

67. $449\overline{)849{,}000}$

WHOLE NUMBERS

Chapter Test

1. Graph the whole numbers that are less than 7.

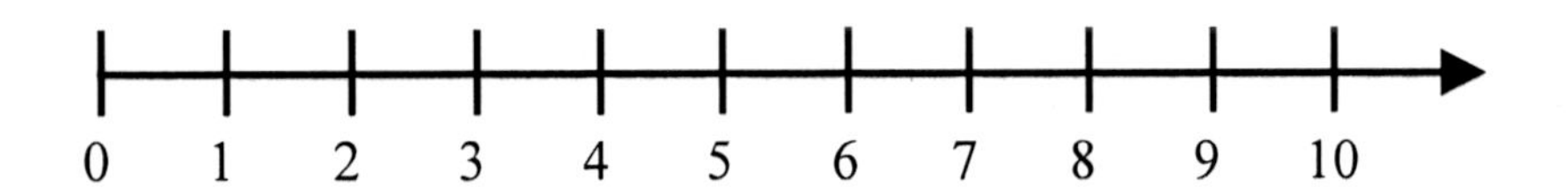

2. In 2006, the population of Pomona, California was 153,555, while the population of Chattanooga, Tennessee was 155,404. Using an inequality symbol, tell which population was larger.

1, 2, 5, 13, 15, 16, 20, 32, 34, 35, 36 Not on Test

Write the following number in words.

3. 306,823

Write the following number in standard form.

4. sixty-nine thousand, three hundred seventy-five

Round the number to the place value given.

5. 649,987 thousands

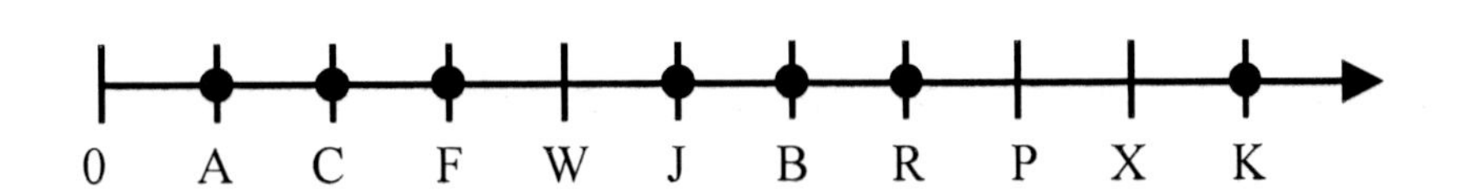

Use the number line above to place the correct inequality symbol < or > between the pair of letters.

6. B C

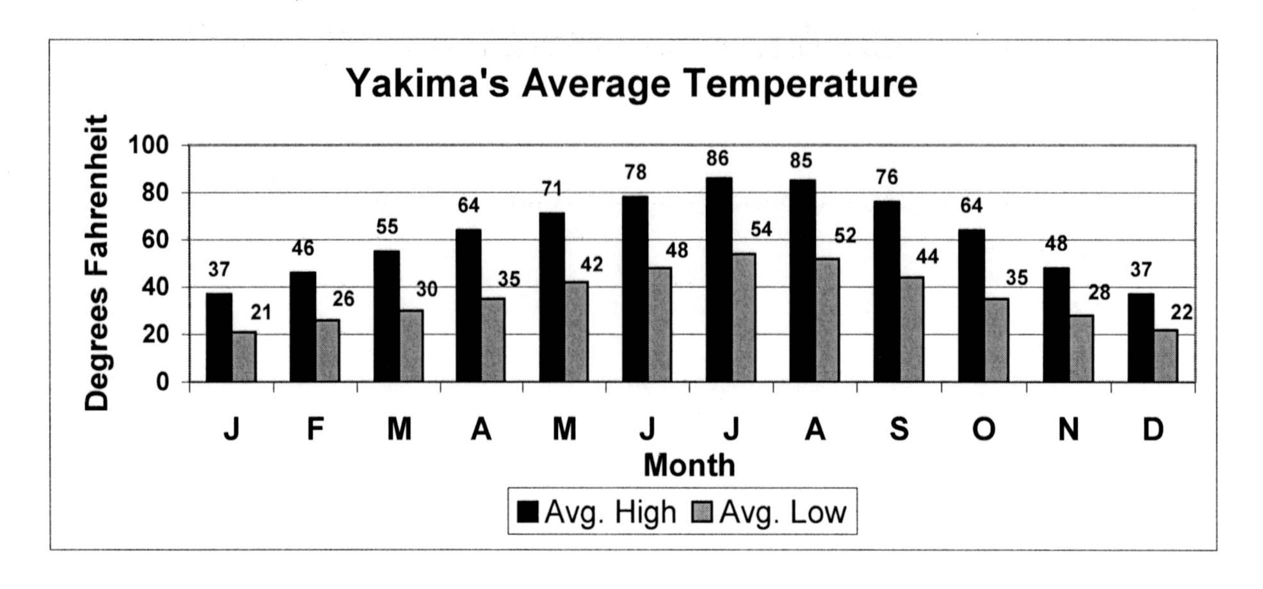

Use the double bar graph above to answer the following questions.

7. Which month has the greatest difference between its highest temperature and its lowest temperature?

8. Which month has the least amount of difference between its highest temperature and its lowest temperature?

9. Add.

$7{,}801 + 392 + 60{,}356$

10. Subtract.

$31{,}642 - 3{,}717$

Translate the phrase into mathematical symbols. Then determine the result.

11. Find the difference of sixty-five and twenty-nine.

Evaluate the expression $x + y - z$ for the given values of x, y, and z.

12. $x = 6{,}451;\ y = 575;\ z = 479$

Use only the associative property of addition to rewrite the expression. Then simplify the expression.

13. $83 + (117 + 312)$

Find the perimeter of the polygon. Note: 12 in. = 1 ft.

14.

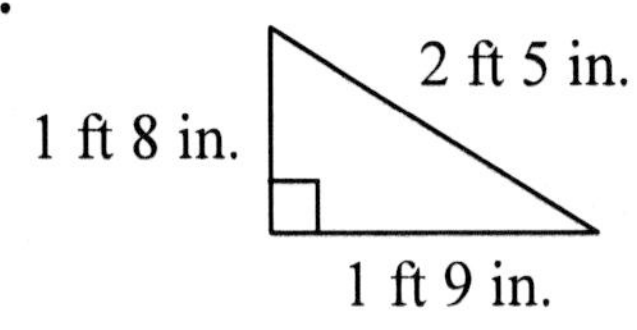

15. Sue wants to take 15 lb of potatoes on a camping trip. If she already has bags of potatoes weighing 7 lb 3 oz and 5 lb 15 oz, how many more pounds of potatoes does she need to take? Note: 16 oz = 1 lb.

16. Given that $\angle P = 59°$, find $\angle R$ such that $\angle P$ and $\angle R$ are complementary angles.

Divide.

17. $0 \div 631$

Divide.

18. $427\overline{)9{,}634}$

Translate the phrase into mathematical symbols. Then determine the result.

19. What is the quotient of seventy-six and four?

Use only the commutative property of multiplication to rewrite the expression. Then simplify the expression.

20. 47(3,860)

Write the following expression in exponential form.

21. $5 \cdot 5 \cdot 5 \cdot 6 \cdot y \cdot y$

Evaluate the expression for the given values of the variables.

22. x^3, where $x = 11$

23. Find all of the factors of 90.

Classify the following numbers as prime or composite. If the number is composite, write its prime factorization.

24. 107

25. 90

26. How many square yards of carpet are needed to cover a living room floor if the dimensions are 9 yards long by 5 yards wide?

27. Use the formula $R = \frac{p}{h}$ (where R is the rate of pay, p is the total amount of pay, and h is the number of hours worked), to find the rate of pay for a person that earns \$84 in 6 hours.

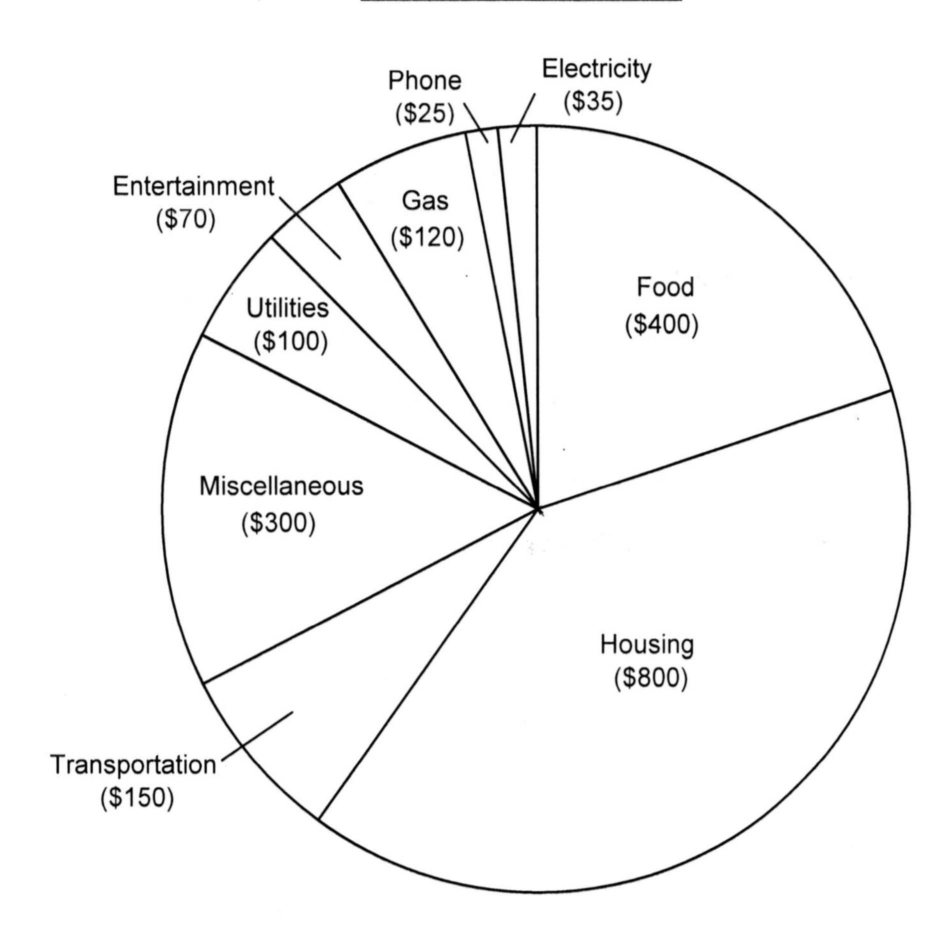

Use the pie chart above to answer the following question.

28. Janet's monthly housing cost is how many times her monthly phone bill?

Put the correct inequality symbol <, >, or = in the box between the pair of expressions.

29. $(4^2-7)^2 \div 3+2$ $\square$ $(7^2-4)\div 3\cdot 2$

Evaluate the expression for the given values of the variables.

30. $(2x-y)^2-3z$, where $x=10$, $y=3$, and $z=4$

31. Using the formula $F = \frac{9C}{5} + 32$, convert 15°C into degrees Fahrenheit.

Solve the following equation.

32. $x + 84 = 113$

Answer the question by using the given formula.

33. How many hours will it take for a motorcycle traveling at a rate of 69 miles per hour to go 414 miles? Use the formula $d = rt$ (where d is distance, r is rate of speed, and t is the time spent traveling).

Translate the expression into an equation using mathematical symbols. Then, solve the equation and answer the question.

34. A number decreased by eighty-two equals nineteen. What is the number?

Estimate the difference by using front end rounding.

35. $249{,}873 - 19{,}461$

Estimate the product by using front end rounding.

36. $64 \cdot 278$

CHAPTER 2

INTEGERS

Section 1: An Introduction to Integers

Integers
Signed Numbers
Absolute Value
Opposites
Evaluating Expressions
Applications with Bar Graphs

Section 2: Addition of Integers

Rules for the Addition of Integers
Properties of Addition
Evaluating Variable Expressions

Section 3: Subtraction of Integers

Rule for the Subtraction of Integers
Vocabulary of Addition and Subtraction
Evaluating Variable Expressions
Applications with Bar Graphs
Other Applications

Section 4: Multiplication and Division of Integers

Rules for the Multiplication of Integers
Properties of Multiplication
Rules for the Division of Integers
Vocabulary of Multiplication and Division
Properties of Division
Evaluating Variable Expressions
Applications with Bar Graphs

Section 5: Order of Operations with Integers

Rules of Order of Operations
Evaluating Variable Expressions using Order of Operations
Formulas Involving Order of Operations

Section 6: Solving Equations with Integers

The Addition Property of Equality
The Subtraction Property of Equality
The Division Property of Equality
Translating Words into Equations

INTEGERS

Section 1: An Introduction to Integers

If you have ever had a balance of $-\$43$ in your checking account or been outside when the temperature was $-10°$ Fahrenheit, then you know that numbers can be negative, not just positive or zero. -43 and -10 are examples of numbers that we call **integers**. Integers are the set of all positive whole numbers, the negatives of the whole numbers and zero.

The set of integers: $\ldots -5, -4, -3, -2, -1, 0, 1, 2, 3, 4, 5, \ldots$

The three dots before the -5 and after the 5 are to imply that the list of integers continues on forever in both a positive and a negative direction.

In Chapter 1 we used a number line that started with zero and continued to the right, that is, in a positive direction. Now, with the introduction of negative numbers we can expand our number line to continue to the left as well, that is, in a negative direction.

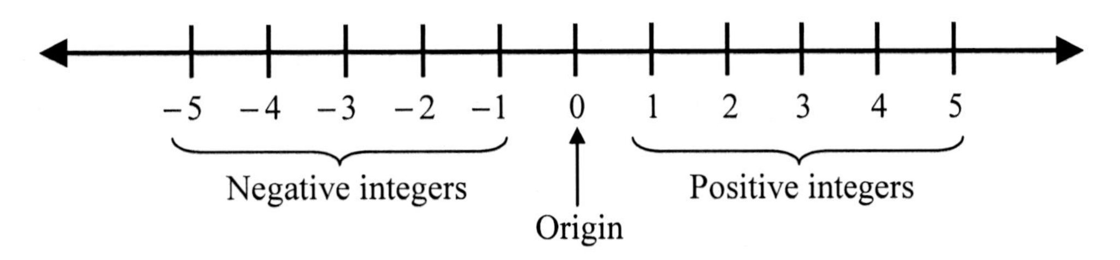

Note: Zero is an integer but it is neither positive nor negative.

Positive and negative numbers are referred to as **signed numbers**. A negative number is always written with a negative sign (–) in front of it. For example, negative seven is written -7. A positive number can be written with or without a positive sign (+) in front of it. For example, positive four can be written as $+4$ or just 4.

As with whole numbers, integers can be compared by their locations on a number line.

Example 1: Place the correct inequality symbol < or > between the two numbers: $-3 \quad 2$

Solution: Since -3 is to the left of 2 on the number line,

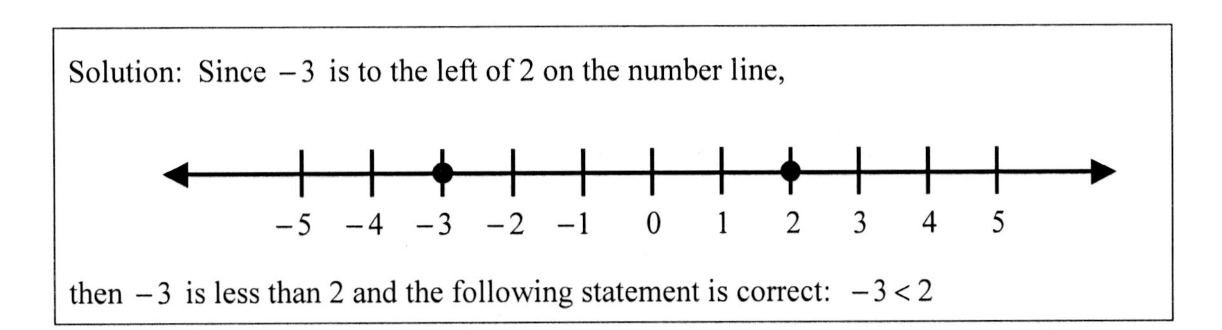

then -3 is less than 2 and the following statement is correct: $-3 < 2$

Example 2: Place the correct inequality symbol < or > between the two numbers: $1 \quad -5$

Solution: Since 1 is to the right of -5 on the number line,

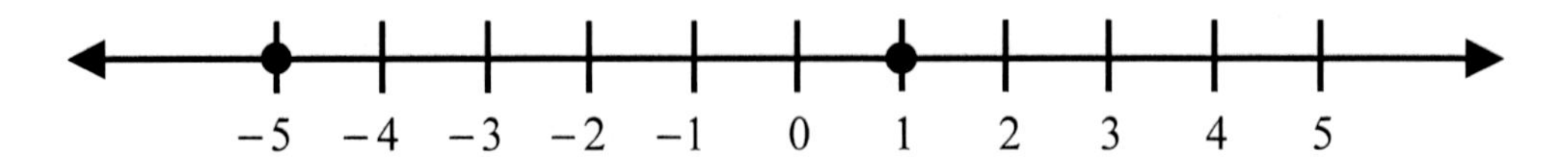

then 1 is greater than -5 and the following statement is correct: $1 > -5$

Example 3: Place the correct inequality symbol < or > between the two numbers: $-2 \quad -4$

Solution: Since -2 is to the right of -4 on the number line,

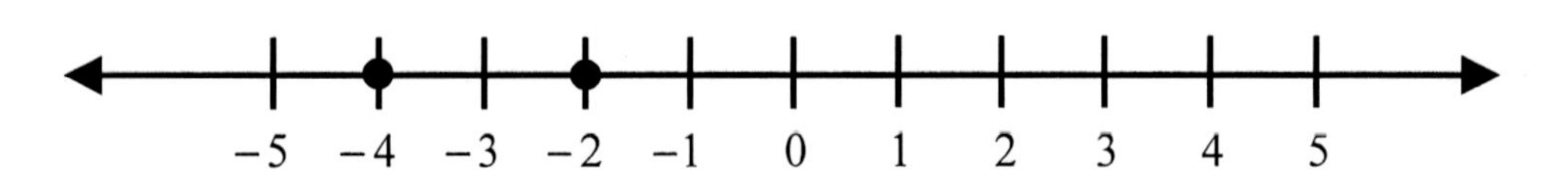

then -2 is greater than -4 and the following statement is correct: $-2 > -4$

The distance from Yakima to Seattle is about 145 miles. The distance from Seattle to Yakima is also about 145 miles. The point here is that distance is a positive amount and never a negative amount, regardless of which direction you are going. The only exception to this is if you didn't move at all. Then the distance would be zero. Distance is always either positive or zero.

You can move in a positive direction or a negative direction on a number line. The actual distance you move however, is considered to be a positive amount. In the case of no movement, it is considered to be zero amount. This leads to a concept involving distance called **absolute value**.

<u>Absolute Value:</u> The absolute value of a number is the distance from zero to that number on the number line. An absolute value is never a negative amount. Two vertical bars, one on each side of a number, are used to indicate that we wish to find the absolute value of a number. For example, $|-3|$ expresses that we wish to find the absolute value of -3.

<u>Example 4:</u> Find the following absolute value: $|-4|$

Solution: The distance from 0 to -4 is 4 units, so $|-4| = \mathbf{4}$.

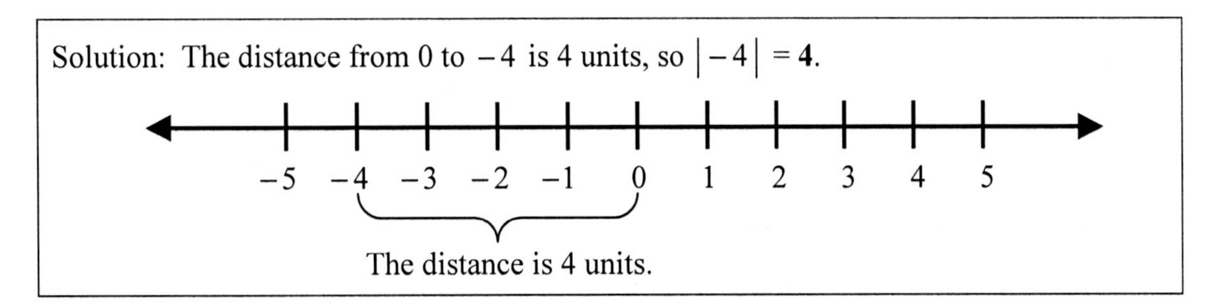

<u>Example 5:</u> Find the following absolute value: $|5|$

Solution: The distance from 0 to 5 is 5 units, so $|5| = \mathbf{5}$.

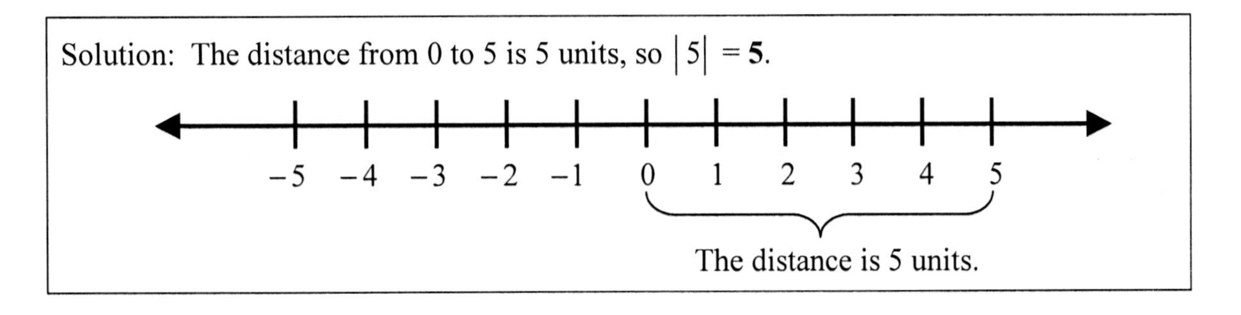

<u>Example 6:</u> Find the absolute value of each of the following numbers: $6, -2, 0$

Solution: Find the distance from zero to the given number on the number line.

Number	Absolute value
6	$|6| = \mathbf{6}$
-2	$|-2| = \mathbf{2}$
0	$|0| = \mathbf{0}$

The number 3 is 3 units to the right of zero on the number line. The number -3 is 3 units to the left of zero on the number line. Consequently, 3 and -3 have the same absolute value, that is, $|3| = 3$ and $|-3| = 3$. However, since 3 and -3 are on opposite sides of zero on the number line, they are called **opposites**.

Opposites: Two numbers that are the same distance from zero on a number line, but on opposite sides of zero, are called opposites.

Example 7: Find the opposite of 2.

Solution: The distance from 0 to 2 is 2 units.

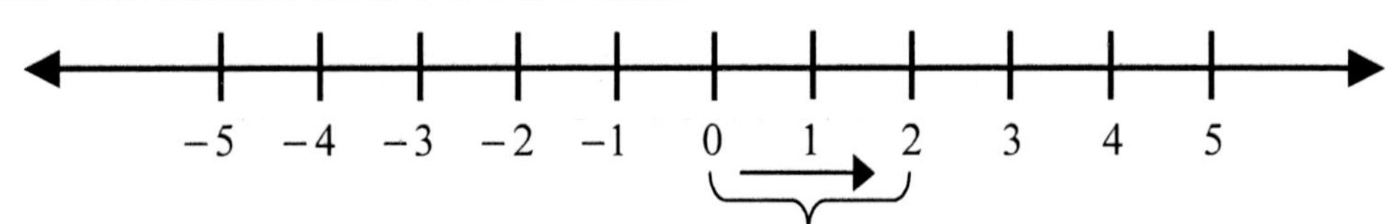

The distance is 2 units.

If we travel 2 units from 0 in the opposite direction, we will reach the opposite of 2.

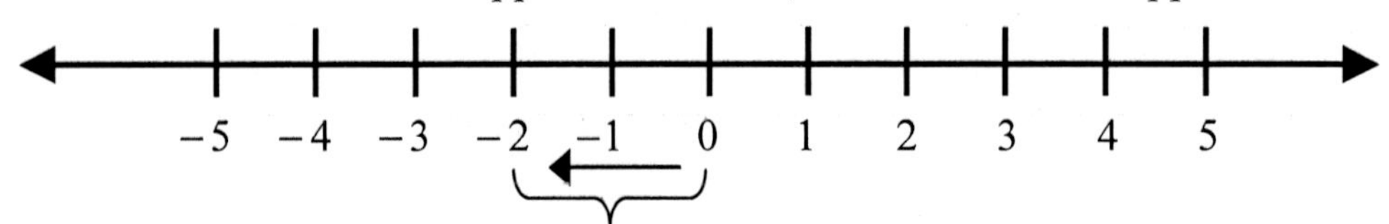

Traveling 2 units in the opposite direction we arrive at -2.

So, **the opposite of 2 is -2**.

Example 8: Find the opposite of -4.

Solution: The distance from 0 to -4 is 4 units.

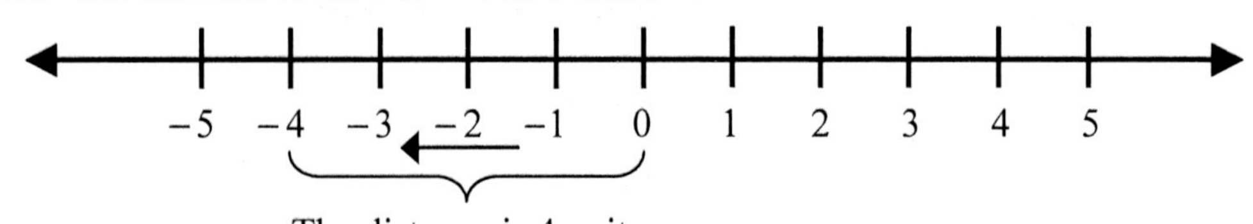

The distance is 4 units.

If we travel 4 units from 0 in the opposite direction we will reach the opposite of -4.

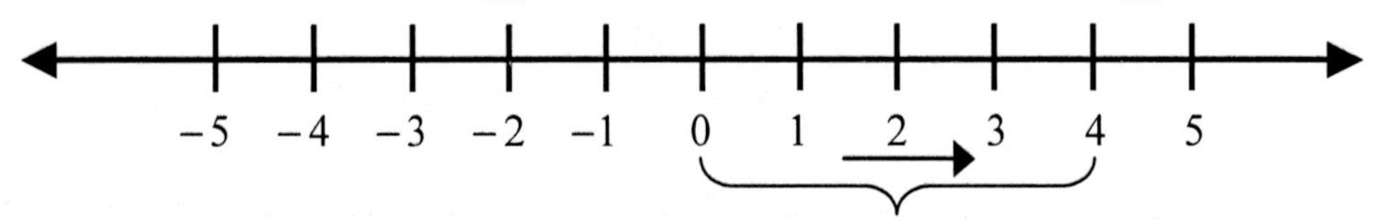

The distance is still 4 units.

So, **the opposite of -4 is 4.**

Another way of determining the opposite of a number is by applying a negative sign to the number. The opposite of 6 is -6 and the opposite of 12 is -12. Following this same pattern, the opposite of -4 is $-(-4)$. However, as we see from example 8, the opposite of -4 is 4. Our conclusion is that since the opposite of -4 is $-(-4)$, and the opposite of -4 is also 4, then $-(-4)=4$. Or, in general,

The opposite of a negative number is a positive number.

Example 9: Find the opposite of each of the following numbers: 6, -5, 0

Solution: Apply a negative sign to each number and then simplify.

Number	Apply a negative sign	Opposite
6	$-(6)$	**-6**
-5	$-(-5)$	**5**
0	$-(0)$	**0**

0, -0, and $+0$ are all equal to just 0. This is because zero is neither positive nor negative. It is considered to be neutral.

Note: The $-$ symbol can be used to indicate a negative number, the opposite of a number, or the operation of subtraction.

Here is a list of examples using the $-$ symbol.

Expression written as symbols	Expression written in words
$9-5$	nine minus five
-6	negative six
$-x$	the opposite of x
$-(-3)$	the opposite of negative three
$-(-a)$	the opposite of the opposite of a

Note: Earlier in this section we defined integers as the set of all positive whole numbers, the negatives of the whole numbers and zero. Integers could also be defined as the set of whole numbers and their opposites.

As with whole numbers, integers can be used to evaluate expressions. Here are some examples.

Example 10: Evaluate: $-|7|$

Solution:	
$-\|7\|$	The absolute value of 7 is 7.
$-(7)$	Apply the negative sign to the results.
-7	The final answer is -7.

Example 11: Evaluate: $-|-9|$

Solution:	
$-\|-9\|$	The absolute value of -9 is 9.
$-(9)$	Apply the negative sign to the results.
-9	The final answer is -9.

Example 12: Evaluate: $|x|$, where $x=-12$

Solution:	
$\|x\|$	Substitute -12 in place of x.
$\|-12\|$	The absolute value of -12 is 12.
12	The final answer is 12.

Note: Just like a set of parentheses, a set of absolute value bars creates what is known as a grouping symbol. Following the order of operations, perform all calculations within grouping symbols first.

Example 13: Evaluate: $|-y|$, where $y=-15$

Solution:	
$\lvert -y \rvert$	Substitute -15 in place of y.
$\lvert -(-15) \rvert$	The opposite of -15 is 15.
$\lvert 15 \rvert$	The absolute value of 15 is 15.
15	The final answer is 15.

As with whole numbers, integers can be used to display information on bar graphs. Below is a double bar graph providing information about the high and low temperatures of a 5-day forecast in degrees Celsius.

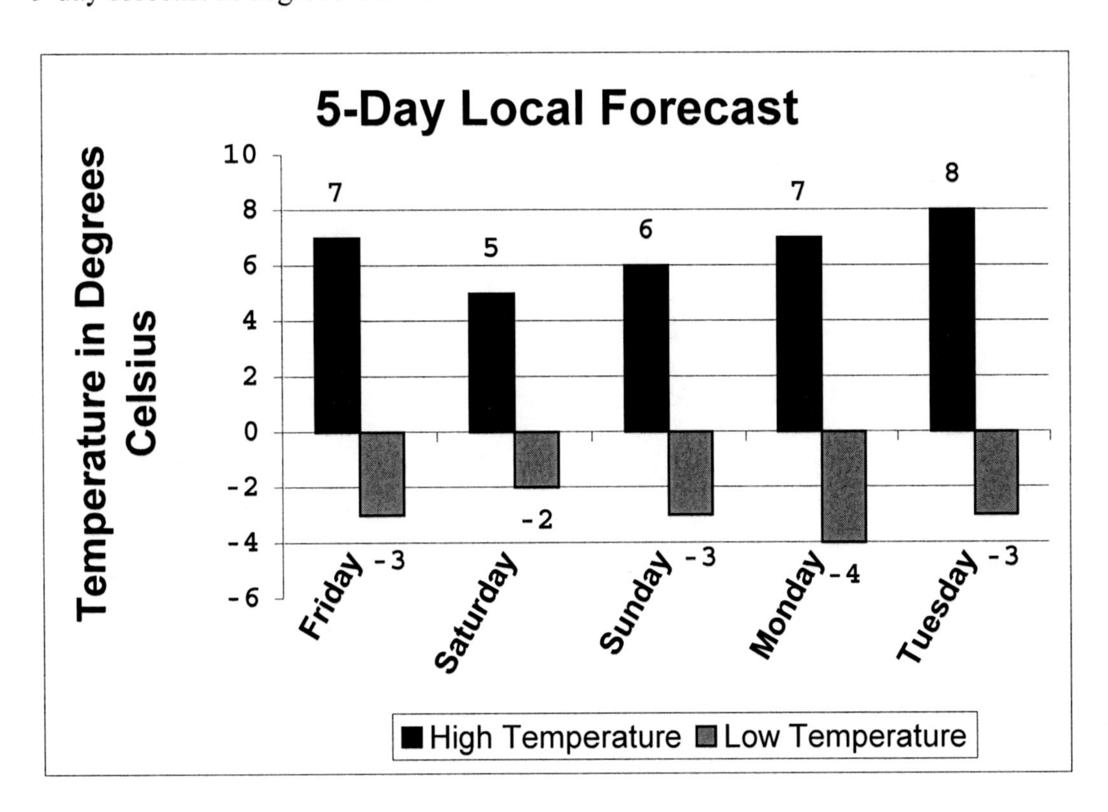

Example 14: Based on the double bar graph, what day had the lowest temperature? What was the lowest temperature? What day had the highest temperature? What was the highest temperature? On what day(s) did both the high temperature increase and the low temperature decrease?

Solution: The lowest temperature occurred on Monday. The low temperature was -4° C. The highest temperature occurred on Tuesday. The high temperature was 8° C. On Sunday and Monday the high temperature increased and the low temperature decreased.

Section 1 exercises.

1. Are all integers also whole numbers? Explain your answer.

2. Are all whole numbers also integers? Explain your answer.

In each of the following problems, graph the given numbers.

3. $-4, 2$

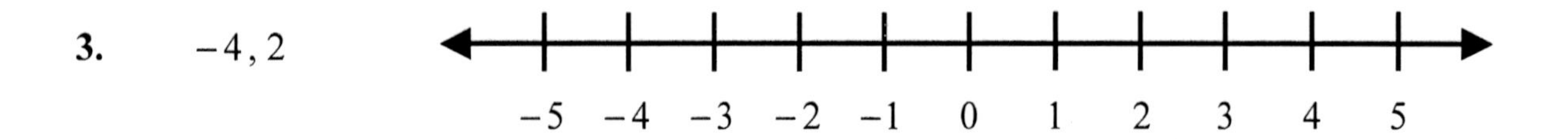

4. $-2, 4$

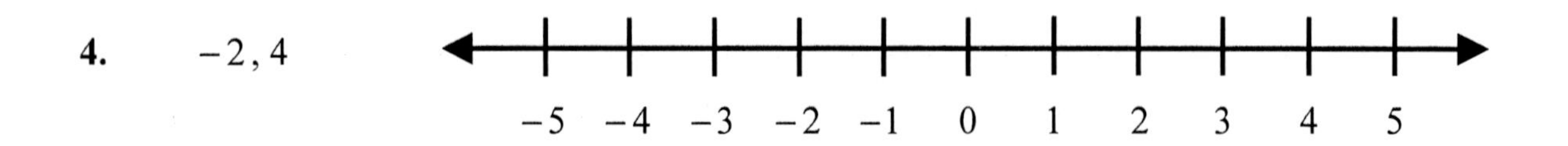

5. $-5, 0, -3$

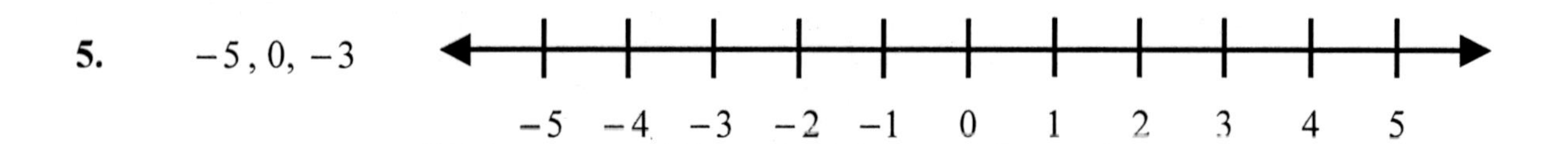

6. $5, -1, 0$

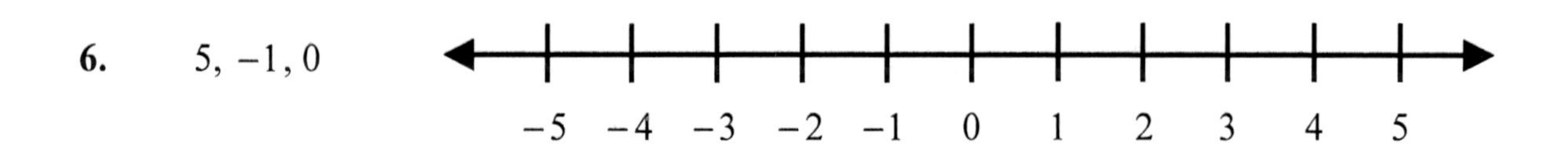

7. Graph the integers that are between -3 and 2.

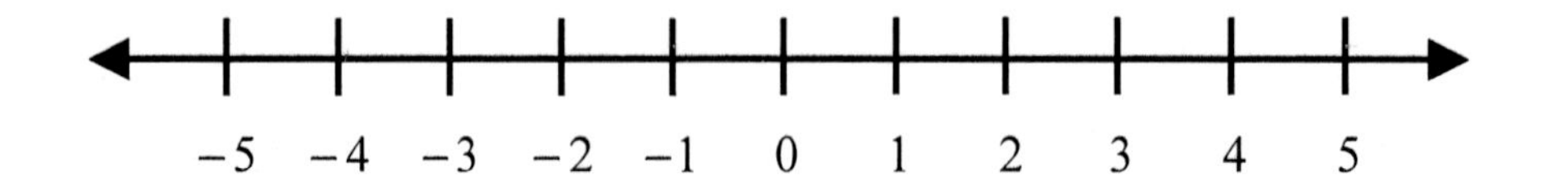

8. Graph the integers that are between -4 and 5.

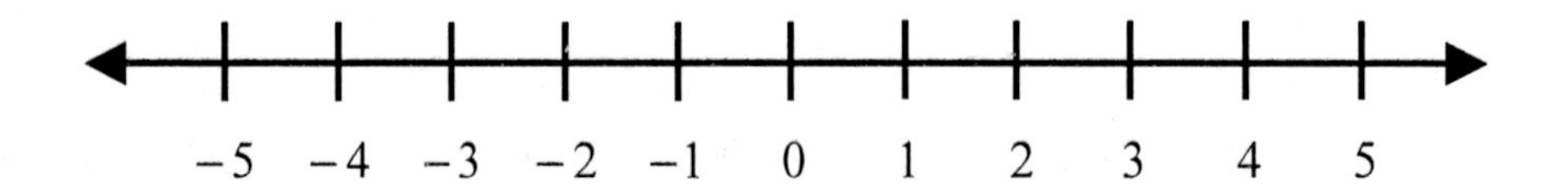

9. Graph the integers that are greater than -5 and less than 1.

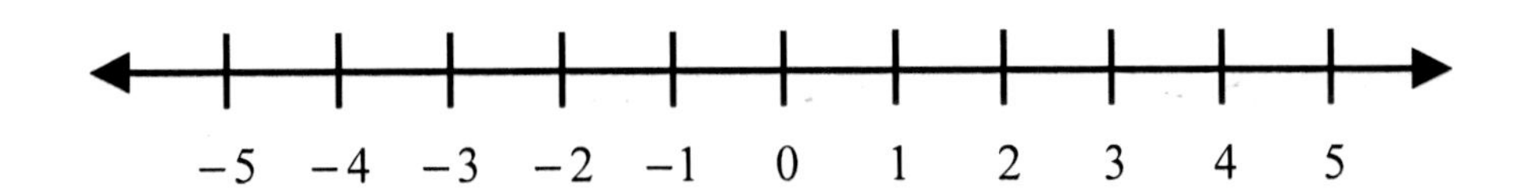

10. Graph the integers that are greater than -2 and less than 4.

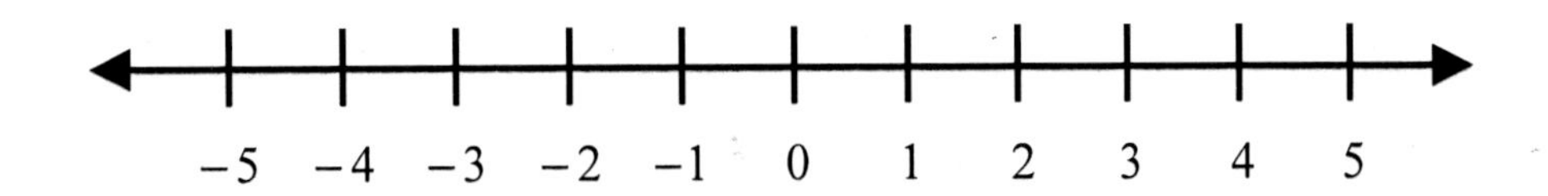

Place the correct inequality symbol $<$ or $>$ between each pair of numbers. (Hint: Use a number line to visualize the correct answer.)

11. $-4 \quad -7$ **12.** $-2 \quad -8$ **13.** $-16 \quad -9$

14. $-14 \quad -3$ **15.** $-8 \quad 0$ **16.** $-5 \quad 4$

17. $-6 \quad 5$ **18.** $0 \quad -5$ **19.** $126 \quad -127$

20. $-143 \quad 142$ **21.** $-10 \quad -11$ **22.** $-15 \quad -16$

Find the absolute value of each number.

23. -3 **24.** 8 **25.** 9 **26.** -7

27. 0 **28.** -34 **29.** 14 **30.** 16

31. -26 **32.** -1 **33.** -86 **34.** -105

Find the opposite of each number.

35. 6 **36.** 14 **37.** -12 **38.** -8

39. k **40.** m **41.** $-n$ **42.** $-p$

43. 7 **44.** -3 **45.** 0 **46.** 9

Evaluate each expression.

47. $-(-3)$ **48.** $-(-6)$ **49.** $|9|$

50. $|4|$ **51.** $-(9)$ **52.** $-(12)$

53. $|-7|$ **54.** $|-62|$ **55.** $-|42|$

56. $-|57|$ **57.** $-|-14|$ **58.** $-|-23|$

59. $-(w)$ **60.** $-(x)$ **61.** $-(-y)$

62. $-(-z)$ **63.** $|a|$, where $a=-53$ **64.** $|-(-5)|$

65. $|-m|$, where $m=69$ **66.** $|h|$, where $h=-74$ **67.** $|-(-12)|$

68. $|-n|$, where $n=63$ **69.** $|-p|$, where $p=-13$ **70.** $-|-(-9)|$

71. $-|-(-3)|$ **72.** $|-k|$, where $k=-83$

Place the correct symbol <, >, or = between each pair of numbers.

73. $|-4| \quad -|4|$

74. $-|7| \quad |-7|$

75. $|-1| \quad |14|$

76. $|61| \quad |-3|$

77. $|16| \quad |-16|$

78. $|-37| \quad |37|$

79. $-|-2| \quad -(-2)$

80. $-(-8) \quad -|-8|$

81. $|-a| \quad |a|$

82. $|p| \quad |-p|$

83. $|-9| \quad |-7|$

84. $|-13| \quad |-17|$

Football teams gain or lose yardage by attempting to move the football up and down the football field. This is accomplished by either passing the football or carrying the football, which is called rushing. A positive amount indicates a gain while a negative amount indicates a loss.

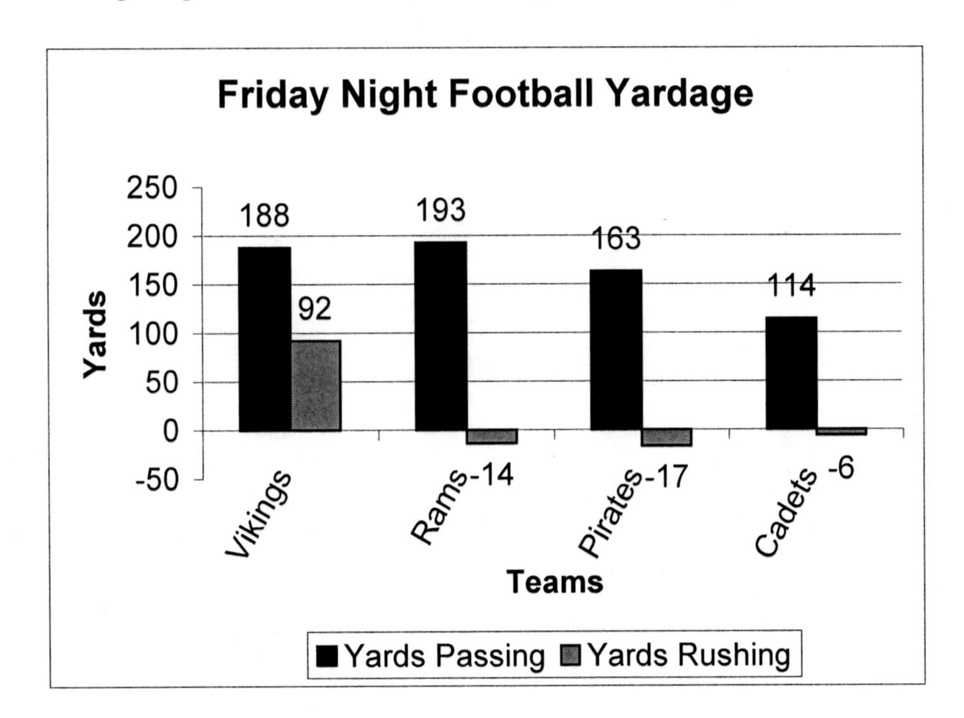

Use the bar graph above to answer the following questions.

85. Which team gained the greatest amount of yards by rushing? How many yards was it?

86. Which team gained the least amount of yards by rushing? How many yards was it?

87. Which team gained the least amount of yards by passing?

88. Which team gained the greatest amount of yards by passing?

The elevation of a location is given in terms of sea level. If a location is above sea level it has a positive elevation. If a location is below sea level it has a negative elevation.

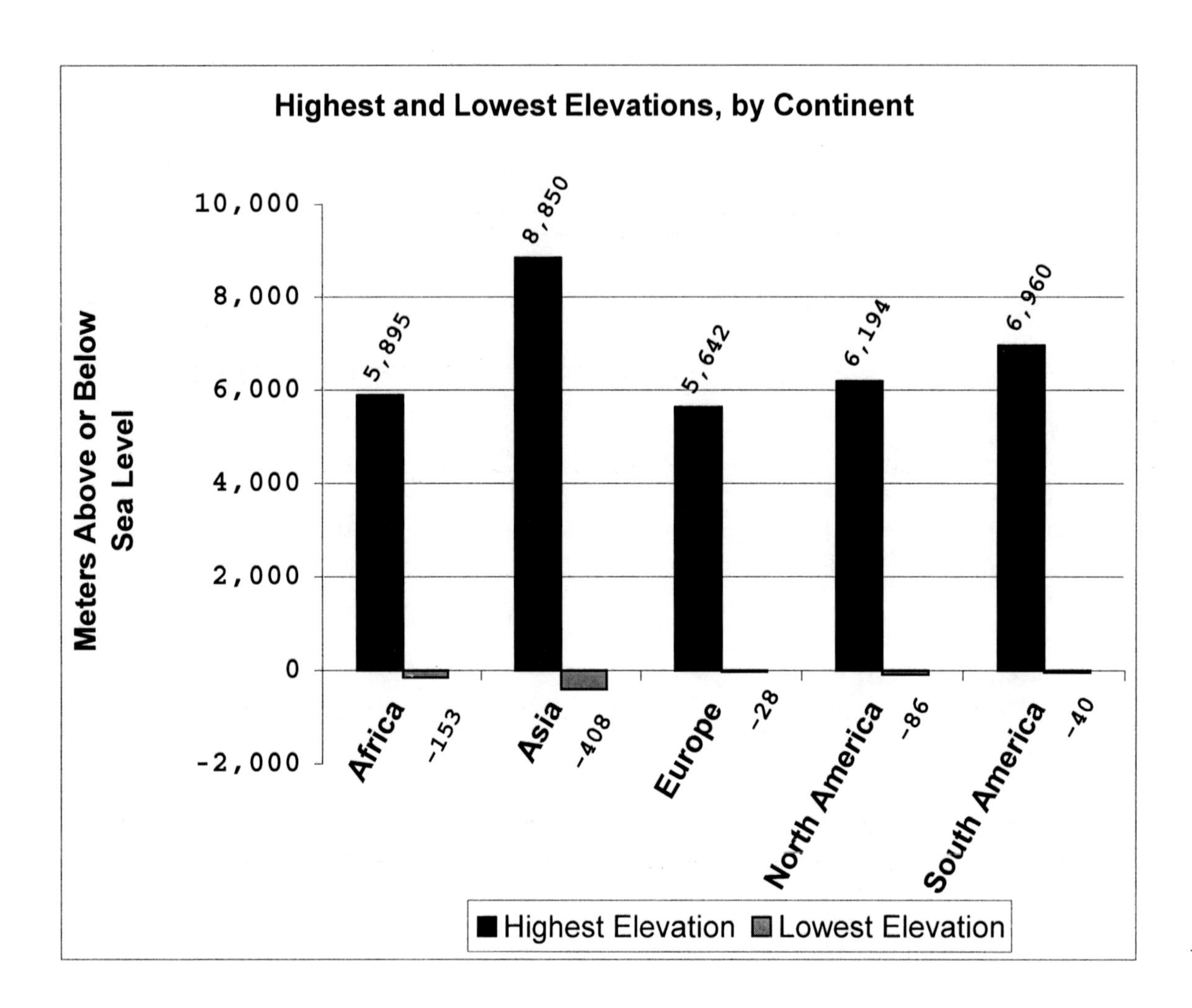

Use the bar graph above to answer the following questions.

89. Which continent has the lowest elevation? What is that elevation?

90. Which continent has the highest elevation? What is that elevation?

91. Which continent has the greatest distance between its highest elevation and its lowest elevation?

92. Which continent has the least distance between its highest elevation and its lowest elevation?

Companies can display their yearly earnings in bar graph form. A company's profit is shown as a positive amount and a company's loss is shown as a negative amount.

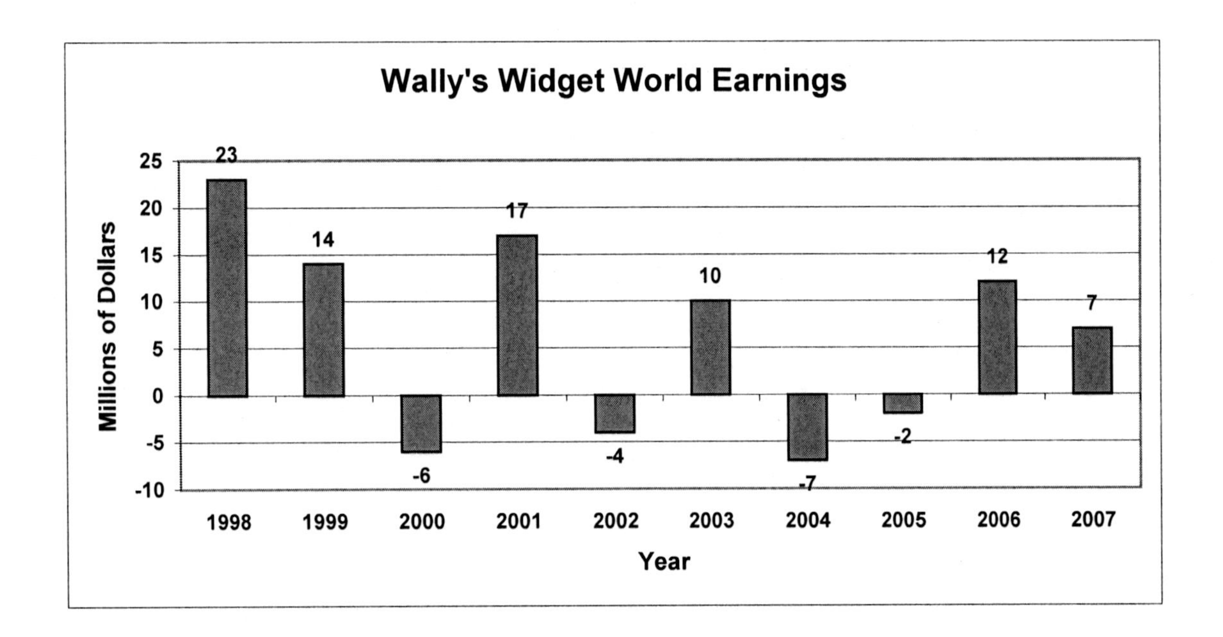

Use the bar graph above to answer the following questions.

93. During what year(s) did Wally's Widget World suffer a loss?

94. During what year(s) did Wally's Widget World show a profit?

95. Which year had the greater profit, 2003 or 2006?

96. Which year had a greater loss, 2000 or 2002?

97. During which year did Wally's Widget World show the greatest loss?

98. During which year did Wally's Widget World show the greatest profit?

99. What was the greatest loss experienced in a single year?

100. What was the greatest profit experienced in a single year?

INTEGERS

Section 2: Addition of Integers

Adding integers is a bit more complicated than adding whole numbers. With negative numbers involved, it becomes necessary to break the process down into two different cases. The first one involves adding two integers with the same sign. The second one involves adding two integers with opposite signs.

Addition of Integers: To add two integers, apply the following rules:

1. **To add two integers with the same sign, add their absolute values and attach their common sign to the resulting sum. If both numbers are positive, then the final answer is positive. If both numbers are negative, then the final answer is negative.**

2. **To add two integers with opposite signs, subtract the smaller absolute value from the larger absolute value. Then attach the sign of the number with the larger absolute value to the resulting difference in order to get the final answer.**

Example 1: Find the sum: $6+9$

Solution: When adding two integers with the same sign, (in this case both numbers are positive) add their absolute values.

$|6|+|9|=$

$6 + 9 =$

15 Now attach their common sign (positive) to the resulting sum.

$+15$ $6+9=$ **+15** or just **15**.

Example 2: Find the sum: $-3+(-14)$

Solution: When adding two integers with the same sign, (in this case both numbers are negative) add their absolute values.

$|-3|+|-14|=$

$3 + 14 =$

17 Now attach their common sign (negative) to the resulting sum.

-17 $-3+(-14)=$ $\mathbf{-17}$.

Note: When a negative number, such as -14, comes after an operation sign such as a plus sign (+), the negative number is enclosed in parentheses to separate it from the operation sign. (See example 2 above).

Example 3: Find the sum: $-9+4$

Solution: When adding two integers with opposite signs, subtract the smaller absolute value from the larger absolute value.

$|-9|=9$ and $|4|=4$. Since 4 is smaller than 9, we subtract it from 9.

$9-4=5$ Finally, attach the sign of the number with the larger absolute value to the resulting difference. Since -9 has the larger absolute value, attach a negative sign to the 5 and the final answer becomes

-5. $-9+4=\mathbf{-5}$.

Example 4: Find the sum: $14+(-11)$

Solution: When adding two integers with opposite signs, subtract the smaller absolute value from the larger absolute value.

$|14|=14$ and $|-11|=11$. Since 11 is smaller than 14, we subtract it from 14.

$14-11=3$ Finally, attach the sign of the number with the larger absolute value to the resulting difference. Since 14 has the larger absolute value, attach a positive sign to the 3 and the final answer becomes

+3 or just 3. $14+(-11)=\mathbf{3}$.

Example 5: Find the sum: $9+(-9)$

Solution: When adding two integers with opposite signs, subtract the smaller absolute value from the larger absolute value.

$|9|=9$ and $|-9|=9$.

Since both numbers have the same absolute value, we can't subtract the smaller absolute value from the larger absolute value. The result is the same no matter which way we subtract the two absolute values. That is, $9-9=0$. This is because 9 and -9 are opposites and **whenever you add two opposite numbers together the result is always zero**. $9+(-9)=\mathbf{0}$.

Note: The opposite of a number is called its additive inverse. The sum of a number and its additive inverse is always zero.

Note: Here is a saying to help you remember what to do when adding signed numbers.

SAME SIGN SUM **DIFFERENT SIGN DIFFERENCE**

There are alternate approaches to adding signed numbers that don't require the use of absolute value. One such method is to think in terms of matter and anti-matter. In this method, matter takes on a positive value while anti-matter takes on a negative value.

A white circle represents one unit of matter, 

and a black circle represents one unit of anti-matter.

One unit of matter and one unit of anti-matter cancel each other out. That is,  = 0.

Suppose we have the problem $-7+3$. We could represent this in the following way:

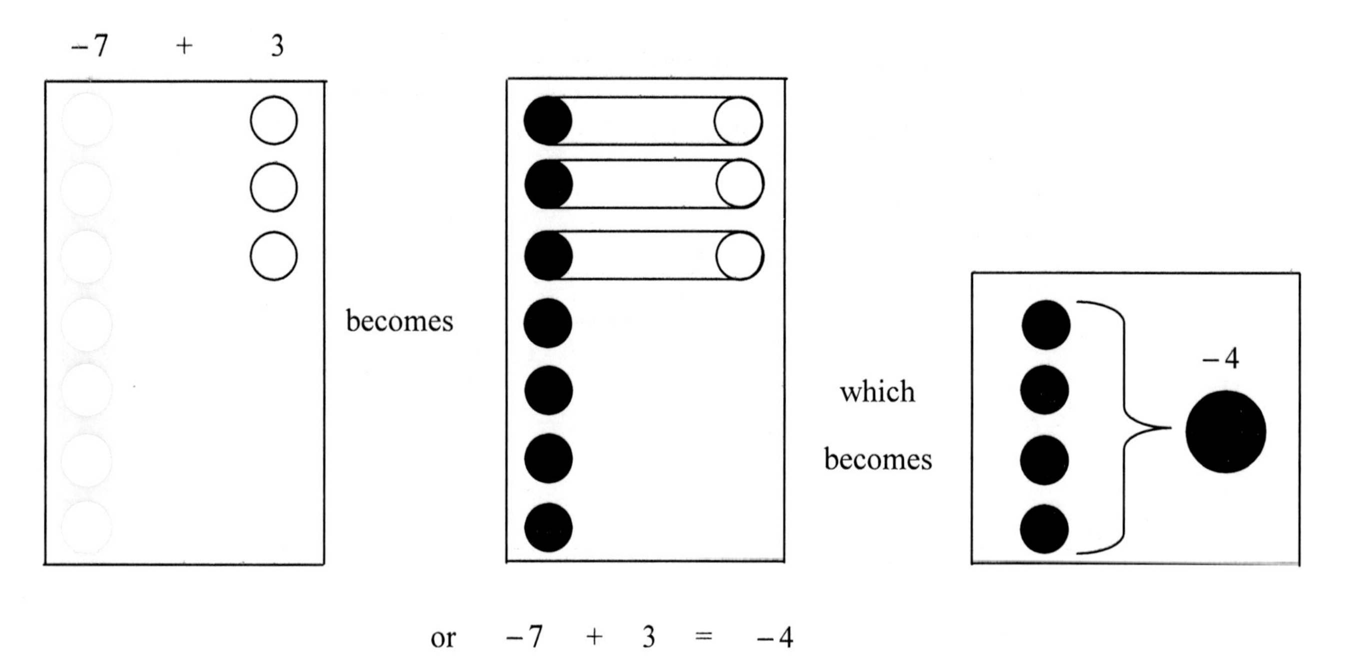

or $-7 + 3 = -4$

Suppose we have the problem $5+(-2)$. We could represent this in the following way:

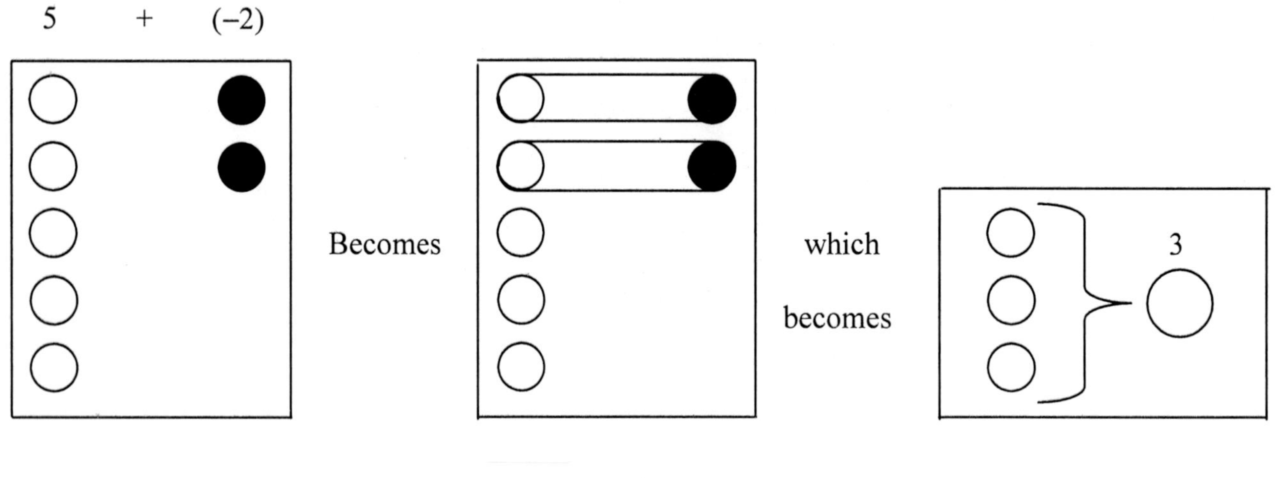

or $5 + (-2) = 3$

Suppose we have the problem $-5+(-4)$. We could represent this in the following way:

$-5 \quad + \quad (-4)$

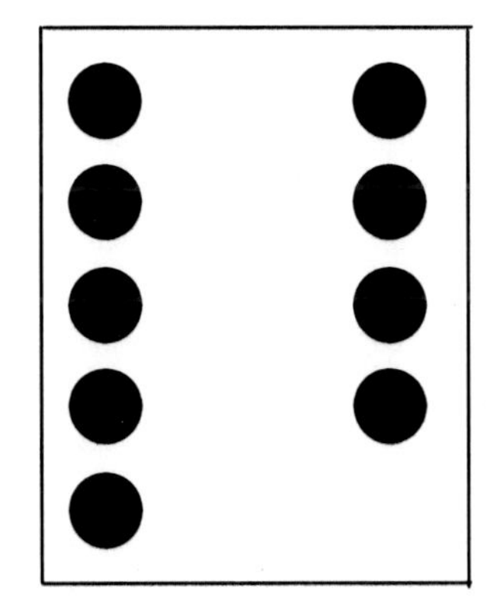

becomes

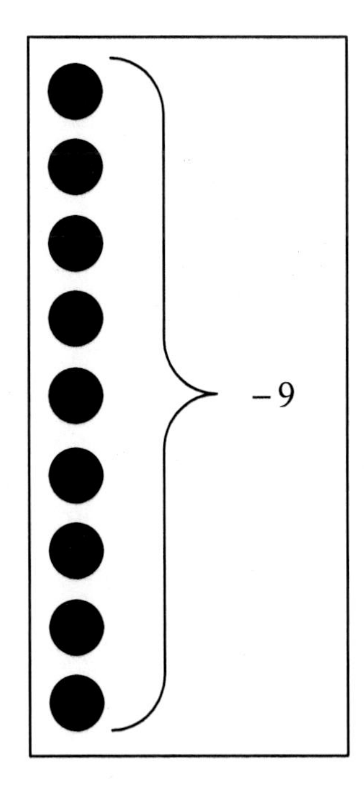

or $\quad -5 \quad + \quad (-4) \quad = \quad -9$

Suppose we have the problem $3+(-3)$. We could represent this in the following way:

$3 \quad + \quad (-3)$

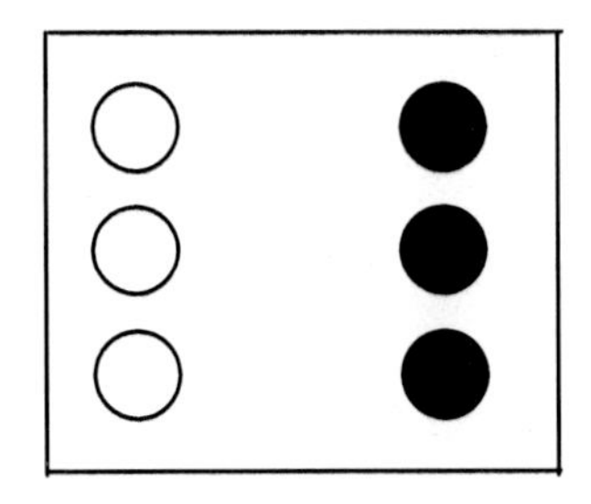

becomes

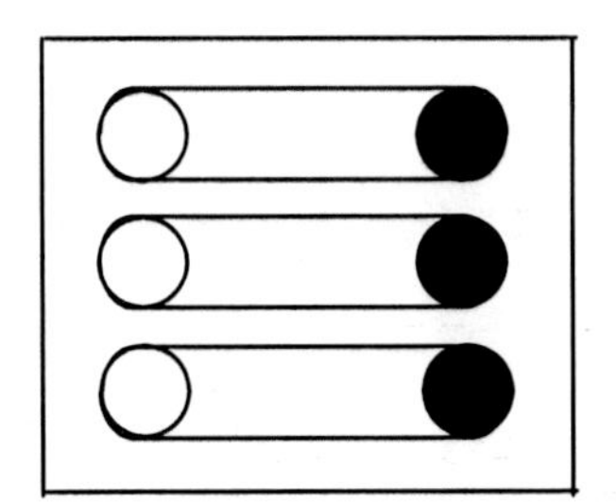

which becomes

0

or $\quad 3 \quad + \quad (-3) \quad = \quad 0$

In Chapter 1 we looked at the commutative property of addition, the associative property of addition and the identity property of zero. Each of these properties includes the expression "for any real number." Real numbers include not only whole numbers, but also integers. This means that all of these properties apply to integers. With that in mind, let's revisit these properties and look at examples involving integers.

THE COMMUTATIVE PROPERTY OF ADDITION:

For any real numbers a and b,

$$a + b = b + a.$$

Two numbers can be added in any order and the sum will be the same.

Example 6: Use the fact that $-7+3=-4$ to show that addition is commutative.

Solution: $-7+3=-4$ and $3+(-7)=-4$. Therefore, $-7+3=3+(-7)$.

Conclusion: The order in which numbers are added does not change the resulting sum. This is an example showing that **addition is commutative**.

THE ASSOCIATIVE PROPERTY OF ADDITION:

For any real numbers a, b, and c,

$$(a+b)+c=a+(b+c).$$

When three or more numbers are added together, the way in which they are grouped does not change the resulting sum.

Example 7: Use the fact that $(8+(-5))+(-6)=3+(-6)=-3$ to show that addition is associative.

Solution: Following order of operations,

$$(8+(-5))+(-6)=3+(-6)=-3 \text{ and } 8+(-5+(-6))=8+(-11)=-3.$$

Therefore, $(8+(-5))+(-6)=8+(-5+(-6))$.

Conclusion: When three or more numbers are added together, the way in which they are grouped does not change the resulting sum. This is an example showing that **addition is associative**.

Note: Remember that the numbers inside the grouping symbol (in this case, parentheses) are to be added first. The result is added to the remaining addend.

THE IDENTITY PROPERTY OF ZERO:

For any real number a,

$a + 0 = a$ and $0 + a = a$

If 0 is added to any real number a, the sum is a.

Note: Remember that the number 0 is called the additive identity.

Example 8: Use the number -9 to show an example of the identity property of zero.

Solution: $-9 + 0 = -9$ and $0 + (-9) = -9$.

Conclusion: **Adding 0 to a number does not change the number's original value.**

We've already mentioned opposites, or additive inverses, as they are also called. We've also mentioned that the sum of opposites is zero and that the sum of additive inverses is zero. This leads to another property called the additive inverse property.

THE ADDITIVE INVERSE PROPERTY:

For any real number a,

$a + (-a) = 0$ and $-a + a = 0$.

The sum of a number and its additive inverse (opposite) equals the additive identity 0.

Example 9: Show an example of the additive inverse property.

Solution: $7 + (-7) = 0$ and $-7 + 7 = 0$.

Conclusion: **7 and -7 are additive inverses.**

It is generally considered easier to add two numbers with the same sign than it is to add two numbers with opposite signs. We will use this information, along with the fact that addition is commutative and associative, to do an addition problem involving a large amount of addends.

Example 10: Add. $4+(-6)+9+(-3)+(-5)+7+4+(-1)$

Solution: We could just follow the order of operations and add the integers from left to right. However, since addition is commutative and associative, we could rearrange the addends so that all the positive addends are together and all the negative addends are together.

$4+(-6)+9+(-3)+(-5)+7+4+(-1)$	becomes
$\underbrace{4+9+7+4}+\underbrace{(-6)+(-3)+(-5)+(-1)}$.	Now add the positive addends together by adding their absolute values and attaching the common positive sign, then add the negative addends together by adding their absolute values and attaching the common negative sign. This becomes
$24 + (-15)$.	
	When adding two integers with opposite signs, subtract the smaller absolute value from the larger absolute value.
$\lvert 24\rvert = 24$ and $\lvert -15\rvert = 15$.	Since 15 is smaller than 24, we subtract it from 24.
$24-15=9$	Finally, attach the sign of the number with the larger absolute value to the result. Since 24 has the larger absolute value, attach a positive sign to the 9 and the final answer becomes
$+9$ or just 9.	$4+(-6)+9+(-3)+(-5)+7+4+(-1)=\mathbf{9}$.

Example 11: In a football game a gain of yardage is a positive amount and a loss of yardage is a negative amount. On four consecutive downs (plays) a team did the following. On the first down they gained 3 yards. On the second down they lost 7 yards. On the third down they lost 6 yards and on the fourth down they gained 5 yards. What was the final net yardage?

Solution:

3 yards + $(-7$ yards$)$ + $(-6$ yards$)$ + 5 yards	Commute the addends.
3 yards + 5 yards +$(-7$ yards$)$ + $(-6$ yards$)$	Simplify.
8 yards + $(-13$ yards$)$	Simplify further.
-5 yards	

At the end of four downs the team had a net of **-5 yards**, or an overall **loss of 5 yards**.

In Chapter 1 we evaluated variable expressions using whole numbers. Now we will evaluate expressions, using integers in the process.

Example 12: Evaluate the expression for the given values of the variables:
$-m+n$, where $m=-17$ and $n=-5$

Solution:

$-m+n$	Substitute -17 in the place of m and -5 in the place of n.
$-(-17)+(-5)$	Simplify $-(-17)$.
$17+(-5)$	When adding two integers with opposite signs, subtract the smaller absolute value from the larger absolute value.
$\|17\|=17$ and $\|-5\|=5$.	Since 5 is smaller than 17, we subtract it from 17.
$17-5=12$	Finally, attach the sign of the number with the larger absolute value to the resulting difference. Since 17 has the larger absolute value, attach a positive sign to the 12 and the final answer becomes
+12 or just 12.	When $m=-17$ and $n=-5$, the value of $-m+n$ is **12**.

Section 2 exercises. Add each of the following.

1. $-9+(-7)$
2. $-4+(-12)$
3. $6+(-8)$
4. $9+(-14)$
5. $-17+5$
6. $-21+15$
7. $-18+(-18)$
8. $8+(-62)$
9. $14+(-87)$
10. $-13+(-13)$
11. $42+(-18)$
12. $63+(-24)$
13. $-10+24$
14. $-12+37$
15. $-12+(-12)$
16. $0+(-8)$
17. $-18+(-24)$
18. $-42+(-6)$
19. $17+(-18)$
20. $15+(-14)$
21. $-3+0$
22. $61+(-61)$
23. $-3+4+(-9)$
24. $-7+12+(-4)$
25. $7+(-12)+8$
26. $6+(-14)+9$
27. $-5+(-3)+(-10)$
28. $-6+(-9)+(-8)$
29. $6+0+(-6)$
30. $-14+0+14$
31. $6+(-16)+4$
32. $7+(-19)+3$
33. $7+(-3)+3+(-7)$

34. $-6+12+6+(-12)$

35. $-14+(-6)+8+(-10)$

36. $-16+(-1)+(-8)+(-9)$

37. $-12+(-7)+(-9)+(-4)$

38. $-7+5+10+(-6)$

39. $-8+3+(-13)+7$

40. $-10+7+(-3)+14$

Use only the commutative property of addition to rewrite each expression. Then, simplify the expression.

41. $3+(-14)$

42. $5+(-19)$

43. $-7+(-12)$

44. $-9+(-11)$

45. $-23+17$

46. $-18+37$

47. $-92+(-42)$

48. $-56+(-23)$

49. $-9+0$

50. $-83+74$

51. $47+(-41)$

52. $0+(-16)$

Use only the associative property of addition to rewrite each expression. Then, simplify the expression.

53. $(4+(-3))+(-2)$

54. $(7+(-1))+(-9)$

55. $-8+(-4+16)$

56. $-21+(-6+53)$

57. $65+(54+(-73))$

58. $46+(39+(-47))$

59. $(-45+7)+63$

60. $(-27+84)+92$

Find the additive inverse of each number.

61. -10 **62.** -18 **63.** 7 **64.** 15

65. -43 **66.** 0 **67.** $-w$ **68.** $-x$

69. n **70.** c **71.** 0 **72.** 73

Use addition of signed numbers to help answer each question.

73. Fred's fridge was on the fritz. On Sunday the temperature inside his fridge was 34°F. On Monday the temperature dropped 3°F. On Tuesday the temperature rose 5°F. On Wednesday the temperature dropped 7°F. On Thursday the temperature dropped 1°F. On Friday the temperature didn't change. On Saturday the temperature rose 4°F. What was the temperature inside Fred's fridge after it rose on Saturday?

74. Sarah's stock price started suffering. On Monday her stock sold for $67 per share. On Tuesday the price dropped $4 per share. On Wednesday the price dropped $5 per share. On Thursday the price rose $3 per share. Finally, on Friday the price dropped $2 per share. After the price dropped on Friday, what was the value of Sarah's stock per share?

75. Gary's gambling is getting gross. His wife Gail wants him to give it up. In a recent poker game, Gary started with $100. He lost $26 during the first hand. He won $17 during the second hand. He lost $62 during the third hand. He won $12 during the fourth hand. Finally, he won $32 during the last hand. After he quit, how much money did he have?

76. In the game of golf a score that is "under par" is represented using a negative number while a score that is "over par" is represented using a positive number. In a recent golf game, Greg shot the first round at 2 under par, the second round at 5 over par, the third round at 3 under par and the fourth round at 1 over par. What was his score after the four rounds, in terms of par?

In the game of football, if a team gains at least 10 yards after four consecutive plays (downs), then that team gets to keep the football and will continue to try to move it towards the other team's goal.

77. During a Friday night football game, the Franklin Fighters took on the Grangeville Gophers. On the first down the Fighters gained 3 yards passing the ball. On the second down they lost 5 yards trying to run the ball. On the third down they lost 4 yards when the quarterback got sacked. Finally they gained 15 yards on a pass over the middle. What was the net gain of the four downs? Did the Fighters get to keep the ball?

78. During a Friday night football game, the Franklin Fighters took on the Grangeville Gophers. On the first down the Gophers lost 7 yards trying to run the ball. On the second down they gained 15 yards on a passing play. On the third down they lost 6 yards when the quarterback got sacked. Finally they gained 9 yards on a running play. What was the net gain of the four downs? Did the Gophers get to keep the ball?

Evaluate each expression for the given values of the variables.

79. $m+n$, where $m=-3$ and $n=-8$

80. $h+k$, where $h=-9$ and $k=-4$

81. $-a+b$, where $a=-17$ and $b=-6$

82. $-w+p$, where $w=-23$ and $p=-7$

83. $|x|+y$, where $x=-5$ and $y=-11$

84. $c+|d|$, where $c=-19$ and $d=-14$

85. $h+k+w$, where $h=-43$, $k=-72$, and $w=-81$

86. $a+b+c$, where $a=-64$, $b=-38$, and $c=-97$

87. $m+|n|+(-p)$, where $m=-34$, $n=-18$, and $p=29$

88. $x+|y|+(-z)$, where $x=-53$, $y=-37$, and $z=41$

INTEGERS

Section 3: Subtraction of Integers

The process of subtracting integers occurs in everyday situations. Let's review the idea of a $-\$43$ balance in a checking account, which was mentioned at the beginning of Section 1 of this chapter. Suppose you have $57 in a checking account and you write a check for $100. The ledger in your checkbook would look something like this: $\begin{array}{r} \$57 \\ -\$100 \\ \hline \end{array}$

You know that you will have a negative balance, because you can't take $100 away from $57 without being overdrawn. The question is, "How much of a negative balance will you have?"

Let's also look again at the idea of an outdoor temperature being $-10°\text{F}$. This was mentioned at the beginning of Section 1 of this chapter, as well. Suppose the temperature outside is $-7°\text{F}$ and then the temperature drops another 3°F. As a math problem it would look like this: $-7°\text{F} - 3°\text{F}$. You know the temperature will be lower than it was because it's going down. The question is, "How much of a negative temperature will it be?"

Both of these situations, the money and the temperature, lead to questions that involve subtraction of integers. In order to answer these questions, let's look at the rule of subtraction of signed numbers.

<u>Subtraction of Integers</u>: To subtract two integers, apply the following rule.

To subtract two integers, add the first integer and the opposite of the second integer.

Or, in symbolic form: $a - b = a + (-b)$.

Another way of describing the situation is to say, subtracting a number is like adding its opposite.

<u>Example 1:</u> What is $\$57 - \$100$?

Solution: Change subtraction to addition of the opposite.

$\$57 - \$100.$ becomes $\$57 + (-\$100).$

Apply the rule for adding two numbers with opposite signs and subtract the smaller absolute value from the larger absolute value.

$|\$57| = \$57$ and $|-\$100| = \$100.$

Since $57 is smaller than $100, we subtract it from $100. $\$100 - \$57 = \$43$

Finally, attach the sign of the number with the larger absolute value to the resulting difference. Since $-\$100$ has the larger absolute value, attach a negative sign to the $43 and the final answer becomes $-\$43$. $\$57 - \$100 = \mathbf{-\$43}$.

Example 2: What is $-7°F-3°F$?

Solution: Change subtraction to addition of the opposite.	
$-7°F-3°F$	becomes
$-7°F+(-3°F)$.	Now, apply the rule for adding two numbers with the same sign and add their absolute values.
$\lvert -7°F\rvert + \lvert -3°F\rvert =$	
$7°F + 3°F =$	
$10°F$	Finally, attach their common sign (negative) to the resulting sum.
$-10°F$	$-7°F-3°F = \mathbf{-10°F}$.

The idea of "subtracting a number is like adding its opposite" can be applied in any subtraction situation. However, just because something can be done doesn't mean that it should be done. For instance, the subtraction problem $7-3$ could be rewritten as $7+(-3)$. In both cases the answer is 4, so there is no point in changing the form of the original problem. In many cases however, changing subtraction to addition of the opposite does make the situation easier to understand and consequently easier to do. Let's look at several subtraction situations and see how changing them into addition of the opposite would look.

Original problem	Revised problem (Subtraction changed to addition of the opposite)	Final answer
$12-7$	There is no reason to change this problem	5
$-12-7$	$-12+(-7)$	-19
$12-(-7)$	$12+(+7)$	19
$-12-(-7)$	$-12+(+7)$	-5
$7-12$	$7+(-12)$	-5
$-7-12$	$-7+(-12)$	-19
$7-(-12)$	$7+(+12)$	19
$-7-(-12)$	$-7+(+12)$	5

Let's look at more examples of changing subtraction to addition of the opposite.

Example 3: Find the difference: $9-23$

Solution: Change subtraction to addition of the opposite.

$9-23$	becomes
$9+(-23)$.	Now, applying the rule for adding two numbers with opposite signs, subtract the smaller absolute value from the larger absolute value.
$\lvert 9\rvert=9$ and $\lvert -23\rvert=23$.	Since 9 is smaller than 23, we subtract it from 23.
$23-9=14$	Finally, attach the sign of the number with the larger absolute value to the resulting difference. Since -23 has the larger absolute value, attach a negative sign to the 14 and the final answer becomes
-14.	$9-23=\mathbf{-14}$.

Example 4: Subtract: $-14-(-18)$

Solution: Change subtraction to addition of the opposite.

$-14-(-18)$	becomes
$-14+(+18)$.	Now, applying the rule for adding two numbers with opposite signs, subtract the smaller absolute value from the larger absolute value.
$\lvert -14\rvert=14$ and $\lvert 18\rvert=18$.	Since 14 is smaller than 18, we subtract it from 18.
$18-14=4$	Finally, attach the sign of the number with the larger absolute value to the resulting difference. Since 18 has the larger absolute value, attach a positive sign to the 4 and the final answer becomes
$+4$ or just 4.	$-14-(-18)=\mathbf{4}$.

The same words or word phrases that are used to express addition or subtraction of whole numbers can also be used with integers. Here is a review of several of those phrases, but now they are applied to integers.

Word phrase	Used in an expression	Written as symbols
plus	four plus the absolute value of negative nine	$4+\lvert -9\rvert$
increased by	negative three increased by two	$-3+2$
added to	negative ten added to negative seven	$-10+(-7)$
the sum of	the sum of five and negative five	$5+(-5)$
more than	twelve more than negative six	$-6+12$
total	the total of negative fifteen and twenty	$-15+20$
minus	negative seven minus negative four	$-7-(-4)$
decreased by	six decreased by negative thirty	$6-(-30)$
subtracted from	negative five subtracted from nine	$9-(-5)$
the difference between	the difference between negative eight and one	$-8-1$
the difference of	the difference of eleven and negative five	$11-(-5)$
less than	negative six less than negative nine	$-9-(-6)$
less	the absolute value of forty, less negative five	$\lvert 40\rvert-(-5)$

Example 5: Translate the following expression into words: $-(-14)$

Solution: The opposite of negative fourteen

Example 6: Translate the following expression into words: $-7-(-6)$

Solution: Negative seven minus negative six

Example 7: Translate the following expression into mathematical symbols:
The absolute value of negative three, subtracted from negative five.

Solution: Since the absolute value of negative three is written as $\lvert -3\rvert$, the expression becomes $-5-\lvert -3\rvert$.

Let's look at some examples that involve both addition and subtraction in the original problems.

Example 8: Simplify: $-18-(-4)+8$

Solution: Following the order of operations, add and subtract from left to right.

$-18-(-4)+8$	Change subtraction to addition of the opposite.
$-18+(+4)+8$	Since addition is associative, we can group together the two positive addends. We will add the positive numbers first since it is easier to add numbers with the same sign than to add numbers with opposite signs.
$-18+12$.	Now, applying the rule for adding two numbers with opposite signs, subtract the smaller absolute value from the larger absolute value.
$\lvert -18\rvert=18$ and $\lvert 12\rvert=12$.	Since 12 is smaller than 18, we subtract it from 18.
$18-12=6$	Finally, attach the sign of the number with the larger absolute value to the resulting difference. Since -18 has the larger absolute value, attach a negative sign to the 6 and the final answer becomes
-6.	$-18-(-4)+8$ = $\mathbf{-6}$.

Example 9: Simplify: $-17-(-23)+5-8$

Solution: First change subtraction to addition of the opposite.

$-17-(-23)+5-8$	becomes
$-17+(+23)+5+(-8)$.	Use the commutative and associative properties of addition to group together addends with the same signs.
$\underbrace{23+5}+\underbrace{(-8)+(-17)}$	Add the integers with like signs.
$28 \quad + \quad (-25)$	Now, applying the rule for adding two numbers with opposite signs, subtract the smaller absolute value from the larger absolute value.
$\lvert 28\rvert=28$ and $\lvert -25\rvert=25$.	Since 25 is smaller than 28, we subtract it from 28.
$28-25=3$	Finally, attach the sign of the number with the larger absolute value to the resulting difference. Since 28 has the larger absolute value, attach a positive sign to the 3 and the final answer becomes
$+3$ or just 3.	$-17-(-23)+5-8$ $=\mathbf{3}$.

In the previous section we evaluated variable expressions using addition of integers. Now we will evaluate expressions involving addition and/or subtraction of integers.

Example 10: Evaluate the expression for the given values of the variables: $a-b-c$, where $a=12$, $b=-15$, and $c=45$

Solution:	
$a-b-c$	Substitute 12 in the place of a, -15 in the place of b, and 45 in the place of c.
$12-(-15)-45$	Change subtraction to addition of the opposite.
$\underbrace{12+(+15)}+(-45)$	Add the integers with like signs.
$27+(-45)$	When adding two integers with opposite signs, subtract the smaller absolute value from the larger absolute value.
$\lvert 27\rvert=27$ and $\lvert -45\rvert=45$.	Since 27 is smaller than 45, we subtract it from 45.
$45-27=18$	Finally, attach the sign of the number with the larger absolute value to the resulting difference. Since -45 has the larger absolute value, attach a negative sign to the 18 and the final answer becomes
-18.	When $a=12$, $b=-15$, and $c=45$, the value of $a-b-c$ is $\mathbf{-18}$.

As we continue to expand our knowledge of numbers, the possibilities for the use of bar graphs expands as well. Below is an example of how subtraction of integers can be used to gather useful information from bar graphs.

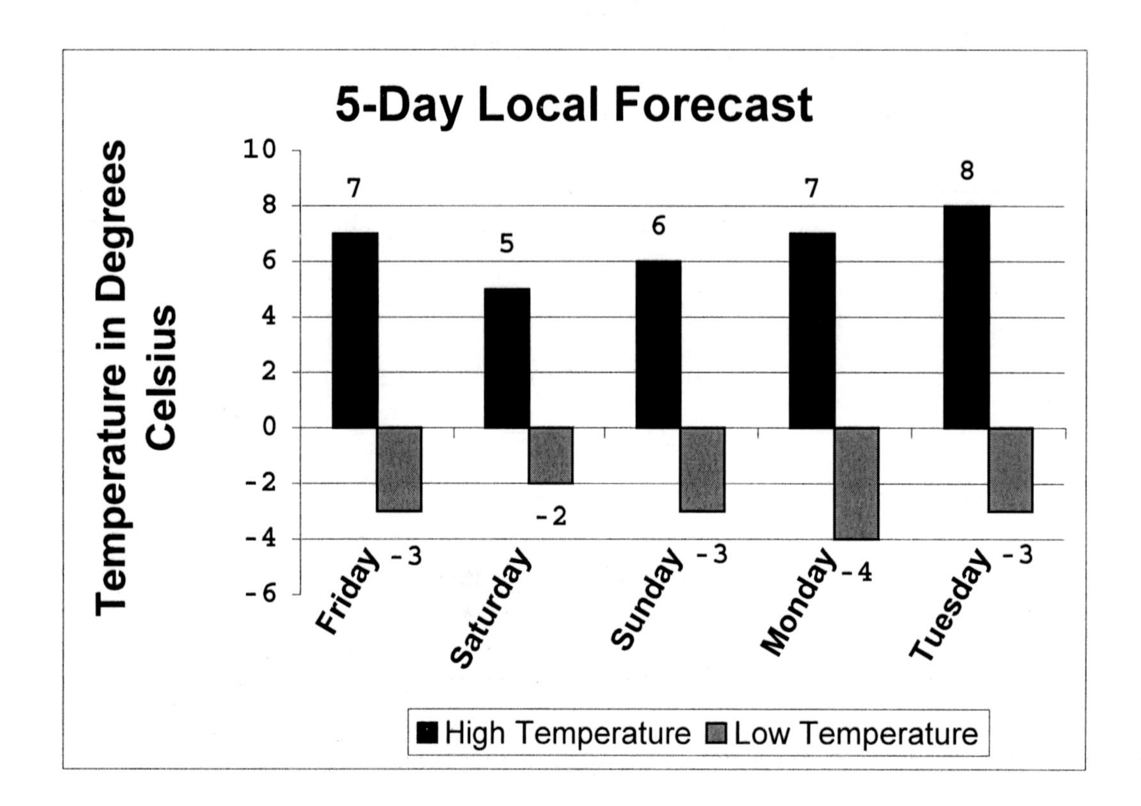

Example 11: Based on the double bar graph above, find the difference between the high temperature on Monday and the low temperature on Monday.

Solution: The high temperature on Monday is $7°\,C$ while the low temperature on Monday is $-4°\,C$. In this case, subtract the smaller amount from the larger amount to find the difference. The problem becomes $7°\,C-(-4°\,C)$.

$7°\,C-(-4°\,C)$	becomes
$7°\,C+(+4°\,C)$	which in turn becomes
$11°\,C$.	The difference between the high temperature and the low temperature on Monday is $11°\,C$.

Example 12: At 10:00A.M. a hiker starts at the bottom of a ravine that has an elevation of -76 feet, that is, 76 feet below sea level. During the next 2 hours the hiker climbs up (ascends) 320 feet in elevation. After a 1-hour lunch break, the hiker climbs down (descends) 165 feet in elevation arriving at his destination about 2:30 P.M. What is the elevation of his destination?

Solution: Climbing up or ascending would represent a positive amount of elevation. Climbing down or descending would represent a negative amount of elevation. Consequently, the problem would look like this:

$-76 \text{ feet} + 320 \text{ feet} + (-165 \text{ feet})$	Use the commutative property of addition to put addends with the same sign next to each other.
$\underbrace{-76 \text{ feet} + (-165 \text{ feet})} + 320 \text{ feet}$	Add the quantities with like signs.
$-241 \text{ feet} \quad + \quad 320 \text{ feet}$	When adding two quantities with opposite signs, subtract the smaller absolute value from the larger absolute value.
$\lvert -241 \text{ feet} \rvert = 241 \text{ feet}$ and $\lvert 320 \text{ feet} \rvert = 320 \text{ feet}$.	Since 241 feet is smaller than 320 feet, we subtract it from 320 feet.
$320 \text{ feet} - 241 \text{ feet} = 79 \text{ feet}$	Finally, attach the sign of the number with the larger absolute value to the resulting difference. Since 320 feet has the larger absolute value, attach a positive sign to the 79 feet and the final answer becomes
$+79$ feet or just 79 feet.	$-76 \text{ feet} + 320 \text{ feet} - 165 \text{ feet} = 79 \text{ feet}$.

The elevation of his destination is 79 feet above sea level.

Example 13: At 7 A.M. the temperature is $-12°\text{F}$. Two hours later the temperature increases $19°\text{F}$. At 9 A.M., what is the temperature?

Solution: To find the new temperature, add $19°\text{F}$ to the original $-12°\text{F}$. The problem becomes

$-12°\text{F} + 19°\text{F}$.	Now, applying the rule for adding two numbers with opposite signs, subtract the smaller absolute value from the larger absolute value.
$\lvert -12°\text{F} \rvert = 12°\text{F}$ and $\lvert 19°\text{F} \rvert = 19°\text{F}$.	Since $12°\text{F}$ is smaller than $19°\text{F}$, we subtract it from $19°\text{F}$.
$19°\text{F} - 12°\text{F} = 7°\text{F}$	Finally, attach the sign of the number with the larger absolute value to the resulting difference. Since $19°\text{F}$ has the larger absolute value, attach a positive sign to the $7°\text{F}$ and the final answer becomes
$+7°\text{F}$ or just $7°\text{F}$.	At 9 A.M. the temperature is $7°\text{F}$.

Section 3 exercises. Subtract each of the following.

1.	$8-12$	**2.**	$7-13$	**3.**	$-5-17$	**4.**	$-9-14$
5.	$6-(-32)$	**6.**	$12-(-26)$	**7.**	$32-15$	**8.**	$41-17$
9.	$-26-(-27)$	**10.**	$-31-(-30)$	**11.**	$-23-8$	**12.**	$-52-9$
13.	$61-(-37)$	**14.**	$74-(-43)$	**15.**	$0-12$	**16.**	$0-42$
17.	$-19-(-17)$	**18.**	$-5-(-27)$	**19.**	$26-18$	**20.**	$38-17$

Write each mathematical expression in words.

21.	$-(-63)$	**22.**	$-(-49)$	**23.**	$6-(-10)$
24.	$3-(-54)$	**25.**	$7-\lvert-4\rvert$	**26.**	$8-\lvert-9\rvert$
27.	$-4+(-34)$	**28.**	$-17+(-43)$	**29.**	$\lvert-6\rvert+(-4)$
30.	$\lvert-5\rvert+(-3)$	**31.**	$-9-(-36)$	**32.**	$-12-(-2)$
33.	$4+(-28)$	**34.**	$3+(-14)$	**35.**	$-4-\lvert 6\rvert$
36.	$-9-\lvert 12\rvert$	**37.**	$-5-6$	**38.**	$-8-3$
39.	$-\lvert-3\rvert-14$	**40.**	$-\lvert-9\rvert-12$		

Translate each phrase into mathematical symbols. Then determine the result in each case.

41. What is negative seven increased by nine?

42. What is negative three more than five?

43. Find seven less than two.

44. Find negative thirteen decreased by the absolute value of negative eight.

45. What is the absolute value of negative four, less sixteen?

46. What is the difference between twelve and negative twenty?

47. Find the sum of eighty and negative seventy-three.

48. Find the total of negative sixty-nine and negative fifty.

49. What is eighteen minus the absolute value of negative forty-seven?

50. What is negative three subtracted from negative one?

51. What is negative six plus negative thirty-nine?

52. What is seventeen added to the absolute value of negative seventeen?

Simplify.

53. $7-19+8$

54. $16-25+4$

55. $-7-17-24$

56. $-18-3-72$

57. $13-(-19)-7$

58. $25-(-36)-4$

59. $-28+36-(-43)$

60. $-39+23-(-37)$

61. $-4-(-6)+8$

62. $9-4-(-3)+9$

63. $2-(-7)+5-6$

64. $-3-6-2-8$

65. $7-9-(-6)+7$

66. $-3+11+(-24)-5$

67. $-2-5-7-1$

68. $3-(-8)+4-0$

69. $-8+5+(-16)-6$

70. $-9-(-3)+5$

Evaluate each expression for the given values of the variables.

71. $h-w$, where $h=-7$ and $w=-4$

72. $k-m$, where $k=-12$ and $m=-9$

73. $-n-p$, where $n=-53$ and $p=76$

74. $-d-u$, where $d=-48$ and $u=97$

75. $b-a-c$, where $a=-8$, $b=-26$, and $c=13$

76. $y-x-z$, where $x=-11$, $y=-37$, and $z=29$

77. $-x+y-(-z)$, where $x=5$, $y=-14$, and $z=-4$

78. $-a-(-b)+c$, where $a=23$, $b=-53$, and $c=-7$

79. $-|-h|-|-k|$, where $h=-14$ and $k=-3$

80. $-|-m|+|-w|$, where $m=9$ and $w=-17$

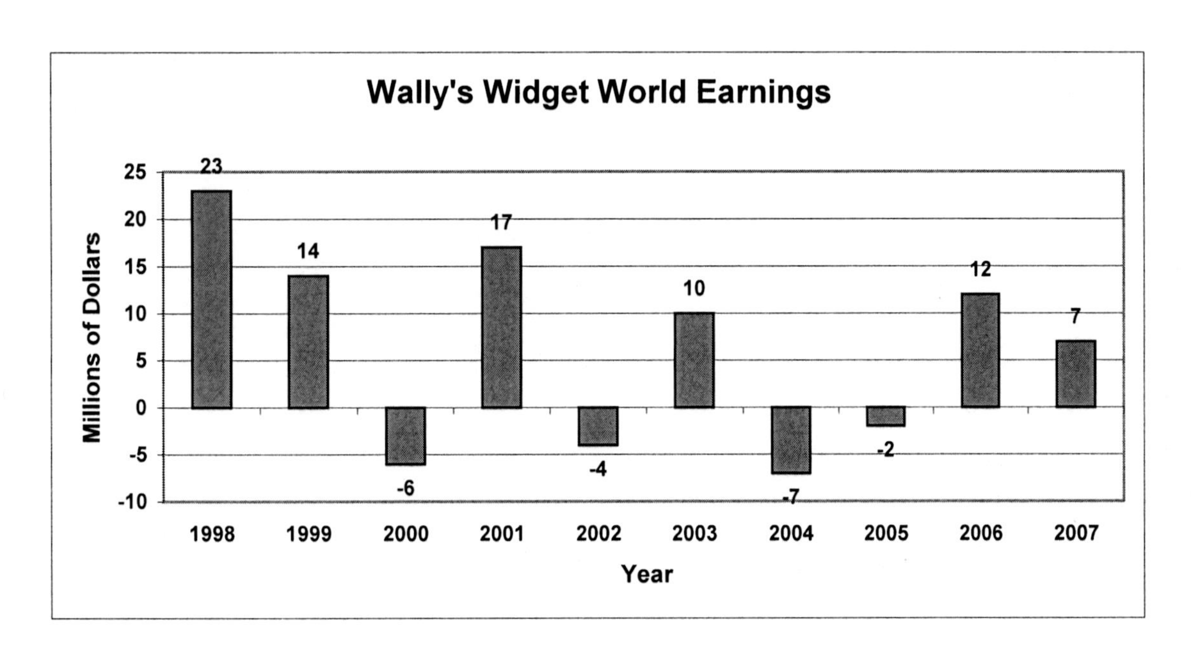

Use the bar graph above to answer the following questions.

81. What is the difference in earnings between the year that had the most profit and the year that had the worst loss?

82. What is the difference in earnings between 1999 and 2005?

The elevation of a location is given in terms of sea level. If a location is above sea level it has a positive elevation. If a location is below sea level it has a negative elevation.

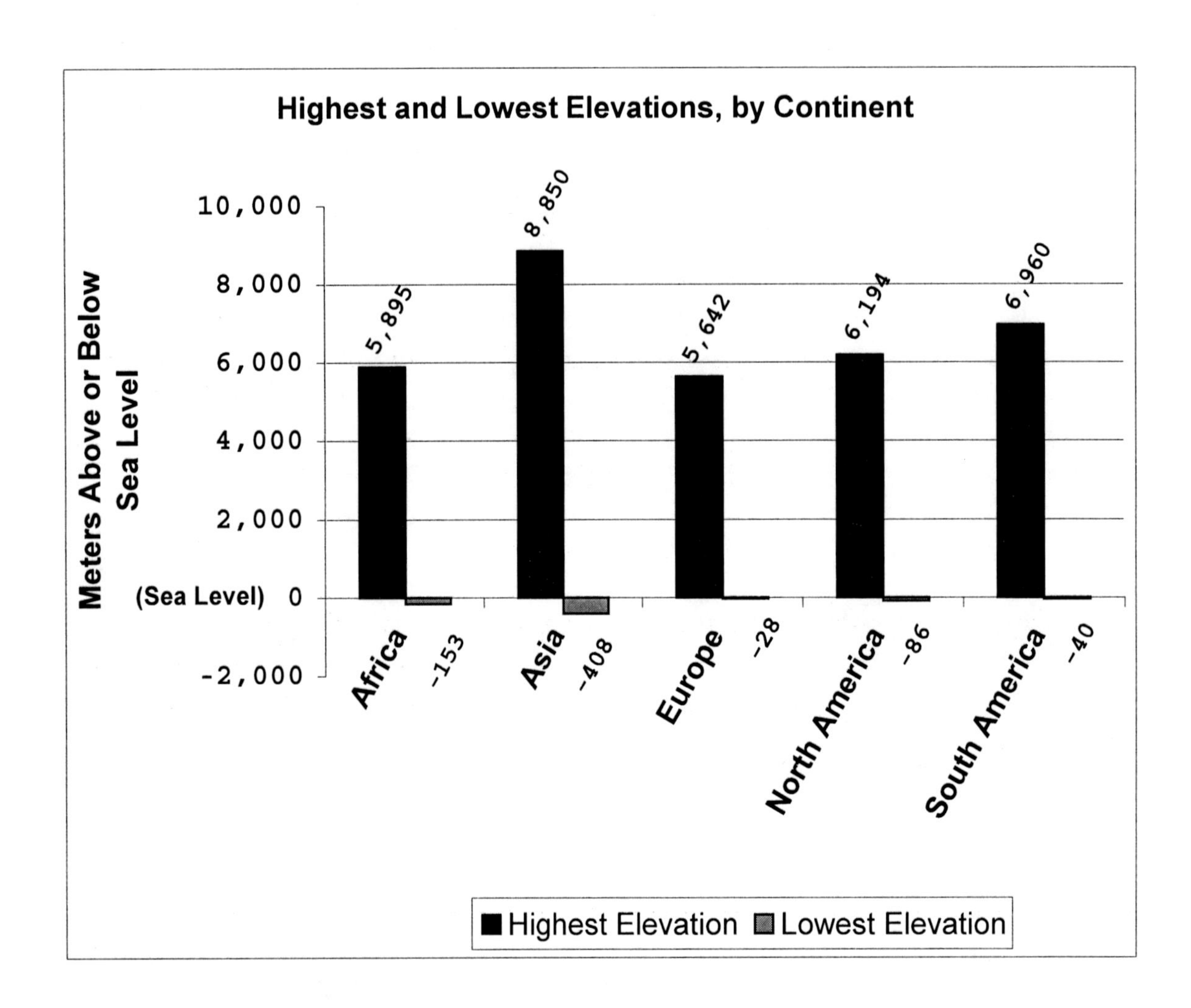

Use the bar graph above to answer the following questions.

83. What is the difference between the highest elevation in Asia and the lowest elevation in North America?

84. What is the difference between the highest elevation in Europe and the lowest elevation in Asia?

85. What is the difference in elevation between the lowest place in South America and the lowest place in Africa?

86. What is the difference in elevation between the lowest place in Europe and the lowest place in North America?

87. In the game of golf, a score that is "under par" is represented using a negative number, while a score that is "over par" is represented using a positive number. In a recent miniature golf tournament, Jessica had a final score of 5 strokes under par, while Ben had a final score of 4 strokes over par. What was the difference between Ben's and Jessica's final scores?

88. In the game of golf, a score that is "under par" is represented using a negative number, while a score that is "over par" is represented using a positive number. In a recent miniature golf tournament, Sean had a final score of 3 strokes over par, while Sue had a final score of 2 strokes under par. What was the difference between Sean's and Sue's final scores?

89. On Monday, Mary had $40 in her checking account. On Tuesday she deposited $57 in her account. On Wednesday she wrote a check for $85. On Thursday she deposited $52 in her account. On Friday she wrote checks for $46 and $27. At the end of Friday what was the balance in her checking account?

90. At 3 P.M. the temperature is -7°F. By 4 P.M. the temperature had dropped 2°F. By 6 P.M. the temperature had dropped an additional 5°F. What was the temperature at 6 P.M.?

91. A climber started out at 845 feet below base camp where the temperature was 14°F. She climbed up 1,532 feet in elevation. At her new elevation the temperature was -12°F. What was her new elevation in terms of base camp? What was the temperature change from her starting point?

92. A climber started out at 965 feet below base camp where the temperature was 18°F. He climbed up 1,734 feet in elevation. At his new elevation the temperature was -9°F. What was his new elevation in terms of base camp? What was the temperature change from his starting point?

INTEGERS

Section 4: Multiplication and Division of Integers

In Chapter 1 we said multiplication is repeated addition of the same number or, $3 \cdot 4 = 4 + 4 + 4 = 12$. We conclude from this example that positive three times positive four equals positive twelve. A positive number times a positive number equals a positive number, that is, $\mathbf{(+)(+) = (+)}$.

Using the idea that multiplication is repeated addition of the same number, $3 \cdot (-4) = (-4) + (-4) + (-4) = -12$. We conclude from this example that positive three times negative four equals negative twelve. A positive number times a negative number equals a negative number, that is, $\mathbf{(+)(-) = (-)}$.

Since multiplication is commutative, $3 \cdot (-4) = -4 \cdot 3 = -12$. No matter which order it is written, a negative number times a positive number equals a negative number. That is, $\mathbf{(-)(+) = (-)}$.

So far we've looked at three cases. They are as follows: $(+)(+) = (+)$, $(+)(-) = (-)$, and $(-)(+) = (-)$. All that's left is to determine what a negative number times a negative number equals. To establish this we will look at a pattern that develops.

Notice that in each case

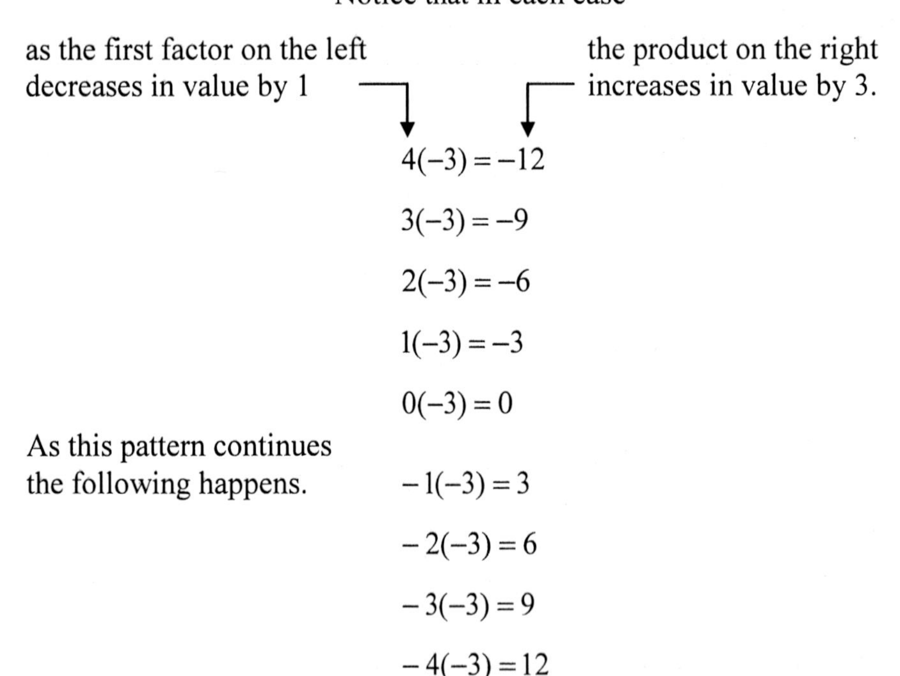

What do you notice about a negative number times a negative number? The product is positive. A negative number times a negative number equals a positive number, that is, $\mathbf{(-)(-) = (+)}$.

The four cases, $(+)(+) = (+)$, $(+)(-) = (-)$, $(-)(+) = (-)$ and $(-)(-) = (+)$ are summarized on the next page.

<u>Multiplication of Integers:</u> When multiplying two integers, apply the following rules:

1. **If the signs of the integers are the same, both positive or both negative, then their product is a positive number.**

2. **If the signs of the integers are opposites, one positive and one negative, then their product is a negative number.**

Example 1: Multiply: $7(-5)$

Solution: The signs are opposites, therefore the product is negative.

$$7(-5) = \mathbf{-35}$$

Example 2: Multiply: $-9(-6)$

Solution: The signs are the same, therefore the product is positive.

$$-9(-6) = \mathbf{54}$$

Example 3: Multiply: $(-x)(5)$

Solution: The signs are opposites, therefore the product is negative.

$$(-x)(5) = \mathbf{-5x}$$

Note: We write the final answer with the coefficient in front of the variable.

Example 4: Multiply: $(-y)(-2)$

Solution: The signs are the same, therefore the product is positive.

$$(-y)(-2) = \mathbf{2y}$$

Note: We write the final answer with the coefficient in front of the variable.

Note: When multiplying several integers together, it's possible to determine the sign of the final product by counting the number of negative factors in the problem. If the number of negative factors is odd, then the final product will be negative. If the number of negative factors is even, then the final product will be positive.

Example 5: Find the product by first determining the sign of the answer: $-6 \cdot 5 \cdot (-4) \cdot 2 \cdot (-3)$

Solution: $-6 \cdot 5 \cdot (-4) \cdot 2 \cdot (-3)$. The number of negative factors is 3, which is an odd number. Therefore, the final answer will be negative. Now we can multiply from left to right but we don't have to keep track of the signs of the factors.

$6 \cdot 5 \cdot 4 \cdot 2 \cdot 3$

$30 \cdot 4 \cdot 2 \cdot 3$

$120 \cdot 2 \cdot 3$

$240 \cdot 3$

720 Attach a negative sign to the final product.

-720

In Chapter 1 we looked at the commutative property of multiplication, the associative property of multiplication, the identity property of one, and the multiplication property of zero. Each of these properties included the expression "for any real number." Real numbers include not only whole numbers, but also integers. Therefore these properties apply to integers. With that in mind, let's look again at these properties and examples involving integers.

THE COMMUTATIVE PROPERTY OF MULTIPLICATION:

For any real numbers a and b,

$$a \cdot b = b \cdot a.$$

Two numbers can be multiplied in any order and the product will be the same.

Example 6: Use the fact that $-3 \cdot 7 = -21$ to show an example of the commutative property of multiplication.

Solution: $-3 \cdot 7 = -21$ and $7 \cdot (-3) = -21$. Therefore, $-3 \cdot 7 = 7 \cdot (-3)$.

Conclusion: The order in which numbers are multiplied does not change the resulting product. This is an example showing that **multiplication is commutative**.

THE ASSOCIATIVE PROPERTY OF MULTIPLICATION:

For any real numbers a, b, and c, $(a \cdot b) \cdot c = a \cdot (b \cdot c)$.

When three or more numbers are multiplied together, the way in which they are grouped does not change the resulting product.

Example 7: Use the fact that $(3 \cdot 4) \cdot (-5) = 12 \cdot (-5) = -60$ to show an example of the associative property of multiplication.

Solution: Following order of operations,

$(3 \cdot 4) \cdot (-5) = 12 \cdot (-5) = -60$ and $3 \cdot (4 \cdot (-5)) = 3 \cdot (-20) = -60$.

Therefore, $(3 \cdot 4) \cdot (-5) = 3 \cdot (4 \cdot (-5))$.

Conclusion: When three or more numbers are multiplied together, the way in which they are grouped does not change the resulting product. This is an example showing that **multiplication is associative**.

Note: Remember "order of operations" means that the numbers inside the grouping symbol (in this case, parentheses) are to be multiplied first. The result is multiplied by the remaining factor.

THE IDENTITY PROPERTY OF ONE:

For any real number a, $a \cdot 1 = a$ and $1 \cdot a = a$.

If 1 is multiplied by any real number a, the product is a.

Note: Remember that the number 1 is called the multiplicative identity.

Example 8: Use the number -5 to show an example of the identity property of one.

Solution: $-5 \cdot 1 = -5$ and $1 \cdot (-5) = -5$.

Conclusion: **Multiplying 1 by a number does not change the number's original value.**

THE MULTIPLICATION PROPERTY OF ZERO:

For any real number a, $a \cdot 0 = 0$ and $0 \cdot a = 0$.

If 0 is multiplied by any real number a, the product is 0.

Example 9: Use the number -7 to show an example of the multiplication property of zero.

Solution: $-7 \cdot 0 = 0$ and $0 \cdot (-7) = 0$.

Conclusion: **Multiplying 0 by a number or multiplying a number by 0 produces a product that is 0.**

Every division problem has a related multiplication problem. For instance, look at the problem $\frac{12}{4}=3$. We can use $3\cdot 4=12$ to check that the quotient is 3. Consequently, $\frac{12}{4}=3$ because $3\cdot 4=12$. We use this relationship between division and multiplication to establish rules involving division of integers. For example, we can conclude that positive twelve divided by positive four equals positive three, because positive three times positive four equals positive twelve. **A positive number divided by a positive number equals a positive number, that is, $\frac{(+)}{(+)}=+$.**

Using this relationship between division and multiplication, we see that $\frac{12}{-4}=-3$ because $-3\cdot(-4)=12$. **A positive number divided by a negative number equals a negative number, that is, $\frac{(+)}{(-)}=-$.**

So then, we know that $\frac{-12}{4}=-3$ because $-3\cdot 4=-12$. **A negative number divided by a positive number equals a negative number, that is, $\frac{(-)}{(+)}=-$.**

Finally, we see that $\frac{-12}{-4}=3$ because $3\cdot(-4)=-12$. **A negative number divided by a negative number equals a positive number, that is, $\frac{(-)}{(-)}=+$.**

The four cases, $\frac{(+)}{(+)}=+$, $\frac{(+)}{(-)}=-$, $\frac{(-)}{(+)}=-$ and $\frac{(-)}{(-)}=+$ are summarized as follows:

Division of Integers: When dividing two integers, apply the following rules.

1. **If the signs of the integers are the same, both positive or both negative, then their quotient is a positive number.**

2. **If the signs of the integers are opposites, one positive and one negative, then their quotient is a negative number.**

Example 10: Divide: $18\div(-3)$

Solution: The signs are opposites, therefore the quotient is negative.

$18\div(-3)=\mathbf{-6}$

Example 11: Divide: $\frac{-28}{-4}$

Solution: The signs are the same, therefore the quotient is positive.

$$\frac{-28}{-4} = \mathbf{7}$$

Example 12: Find the quotient: $-48 \div 6$

Solution: The signs are opposites, therefore the quotient is negative.

$$-48 \div 6 = \mathbf{-8}$$

The same words or word phrases used to express multiplication or division of whole numbers can also be used with integers. Here is a review of several of those phrases but now they're applied to integers.

Word phrase	Used in an expression	Written as symbols
times	negative two times five	$-2 \cdot 5$
the product of	the product of ten and negative two	$10 \cdot (-2)$
multiplied by	negative seven multiplied by negative three	$-7 \cdot (-3)$
twice	twice the number negative one	$-1 \cdot 2$
double	double the number negative eighteen	$-18 \cdot 2$
triple	triple the number negative twelve	$-12 \cdot 3$
the quotient of	the quotient of negative ten and two	$-10 \div 2$
divided by	negative eight divided by negative four	$-8 \div (-4)$
divided into	negative three divided into fifteen	$\frac{15}{-3}$

Example 13: Translate the following expression into mathematical symbols:
the product of sixteen and negative three

Solution: Since "the product of" means to multiply, the expression becomes $16 \cdot (-3)$.

Example 14: Translate the following expression into mathematical symbols:
double the absolute value of negative three

Solution: Since the absolute value of negative three is written as $|-3|$, and "double" means to multiply by two, the expression becomes $2|-3|$.

Example 15: Translate the following expression into mathematical symbols:
the quotient of sixteen and negative eight

Solution: Since "the quotient of" means to divide, the expression becomes $16 \div (-8)$ or $\frac{16}{-8}$.

Example 16: Translate the following expression into mathematical symbols:
negative fifteen divided by negative three

Solution: Since "divided by" means to divide, the expression becomes $-15 \div (-3)$.

In Chapter 1 we looked at the division properties of one and the division properties of zero. Each of these properties included the expression "for any real number." Real numbers include not only whole numbers, but also integers. Therefore these properties apply to integers. With that in mind, let's look again at these properties and examples involving integers.

THE DIVISION PROPERTIES OF ONE:

1) For any real number a,

$$a \div 1 = a.$$

If any real number a is divided by 1, the quotient is a.

2) For any real number a, when $a \neq 0$,

$$a \div a = 1$$

If any real number other than 0 is divided by itself, the quotient is 1.

Example 17: Use the number -4 to show examples of the division properties of one.

Solution: $-4 \div 1 = -4$ and $-4 \div (-4) = 1$.

Conclusion: **Dividing a number by 1 does not change the number's original value and dividing a number by itself produces a quotient of 1.**

THE DIVISION PROPERTIES OF ZERO:

1) For any real number a, when $a \neq 0$,

$0 \div a = 0$.

If 0 is divided by any real number other than 0, the quotient is 0.

2) For any real number a, when $a \neq 0$,

$a \div 0 = \text{undefined}$.

If any real number other than 0 is divided by 0, the quotient is undefined.

Example 18: Use the number -7 to show examples of the division properties of zero.

Solution: $0 \div (-7) = 0$ and $-7 \div 0 = \text{undefined}$.

Conclusion: **Dividing 0 by a number other than 0 produces a quotient of 0 and dividing a number other than 0 by 0 produces a quotient that is undefined.**

In the previous section we evaluated variable expressions using addition and/or subtraction of integers. Now we'll evaluate expressions involving multiplication or division of integers.

Example 19: Evaluate the expression for the given values of the variables. $-3wy$, where $w = -6$ and $y = -5$

Solution:

$-3wy$	Substitute -6 in the place of w and -5 in the place of y.
$-3(-6)(-5)$	Multiply from left to right.
$18(-5)$	
-90	When $w = -6$ and $y = -5$, the value of $-3wy$ is $\mathbf{-90}$.

Example 20: Evaluate the expression for the given value of the variable. $a \div 4$, where $a = -36$

Solution:	
$a \div 4$	Substitute -36 in the place of a.
$(-36) \div 4$	Divide.
-9	When $a = -36$, the value of $a \div 4$ is $\mathbf{-9}$.

Example 21: Evaluate the expression for the given values of the variables: $\frac{|a|}{b}$, where $a = -35$ and $b = -7$

Solution:	
$\frac{\lvert a \rvert}{b}$	Substitute -35 in the place of a and -7 in the place of b.
$\frac{\lvert(-35)\rvert}{(-7)}$	Following the order of operations, find the absolute value of -35, which is 35.
$\frac{35}{-7}$	Divide.
-5	When $a = -35$ and $b = -7$, the value of $\frac{\lvert a \rvert}{b}$ is **5**.

Note: To find the "average" for a set of numbers, add the numbers together and then divide the total by how many numbers there are in the set.

Example 22: The daily low temperatures for a 5 day period were as follows: $-6°F$, $5°F$, $-8°F$, $3°F$, and $-4°F$. What was the average daily low temperature for the 5-day period?

Solution:
To find the average daily low temperature, add the 5 temperatures and divide the total by 5.
$-6°F + 5°F + (-8°F) + 3°F + (-4°F) = -10°F$
$-10°F \div 5 = -2°F$ The average daily low temperature for the 5-day period was $\mathbf{-2°F}$.

Applications involving graphs

Valuable information can be obtained from various charts or graphs by applying multiplication, and/or division, to quantities given.

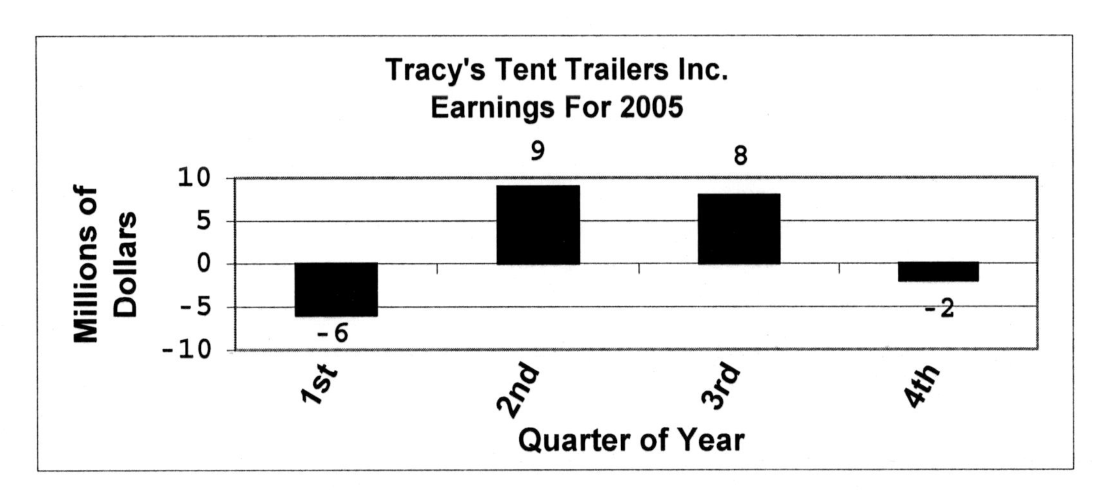

Example 23: Based on the bar graph above, what were the average earnings per month during the 1st quarter of 2005?

Solution: Since there are 3 months in 1 quarter of a year, obtain the monthly average by dividing the earnings for the 1st quarter of 2005 by 3.

$-6 \div 3 = -2$ The average monthly earnings for the 1st quarter of 2005 was **– $2 million**.

Example 24: Based on the bar graph above, if each of the four quarters of projected earnings for 2006 matched the last quarter of 2005, what would the net earnings be for the entire year of 2006?

Solution: Since there are 4 quarters in a year, obtain the net earnings for the entire year of 2006 by multiplying the earnings of the last quarter of 2005 by 4.

$-2 \cdot 4 = -8$ Based on the last quarter of 2005, the projected net earnings for the entire year of 2006 would be **– $8 million**.

Section 4 exercises. Multiply each of the following.

1. $4(-12)$ **2.** $5(-11)$ **3.** $-7(-17)$ **4.** $-8(-16)$

5. $-9(6)$ **6.** $-3(18)$ **7.** $21(14)$ **8.** $34(10)$

9. $9|-43|$ **10.** $19|-37|$ **11.** $-1\cdot 27$ **12.** $-36\cdot 0$

13. $24\cdot 60$ **14.** $40\cdot 72$ **15.** $0(-97)$ **16.** $38(-1)$

17. $3(-x)$ **18.** $7(-w)$ **19.** $(-y)(-6)$ **20.** $(-k)(-9)$

21. $-a\cdot 4$ **22.** $-h\cdot 2$ **23.** $-6(-6)$ **24.** $-8(-8)$

For the following problems, first determine the sign of the answer, and then find the answer.

25. $-2(-7)(-3)$ **26.** $4(-8)(-3)$ **27.** $-6(5)(-2)$

28. $-4(-1)(-7)$ **29.** $-3(-5)(5)(-7)$ **30.** $-2(3)(6)(-4)$

31. $-5(-3)(-8)(-1)$ **32.** $5(-6)(-4)(-1)$

33. $4(-5)(7)(-2)(-3)$ **34.** $-5(2)(-3)(-6)(-1)$

Use only the commutative property of multiplication to rewrite each expression. Then, simplify the expression.

35. $3(-14)$ **36.** $5(-19)$ **37.** $-7(-12)$

38. $-9(-11)$ **39.** $-23\cdot 17$ **40.** $-18\cdot 37$

41. $-9\cdot 0$ **42.** $0(-16)$

Use only the associative property of multiplication to rewrite each expression. Then, simplify the expression.

43. $(4 \cdot (-5)) \cdot (-2)$

44. $(7 \cdot (-2)) \cdot (-50)$

45. $-4 \cdot (25 \cdot (-27))$

46. $-50 \cdot (2 \cdot (-6))$

47. $(15 \cdot 50) \cdot (-2)$

48. $(16 \cdot 25) \cdot (-4)$

49. $25 \cdot (4 \cdot (-45))$

50. $5 \cdot (2 \cdot (-27))$

Divide each of the following.

51. $8 \div (-2)$

52. $12 \div (-4)$

53. $|-22| \div (-11)$

54. $|-36| \div (-9)$

55. $-5 \div 0$

56. $-42 \div 7$

57. $-37 \div 1$

58. $-94 \div 1$

59. $-39 \div 3$

60. $-64 \div 0$

61. $-119 \div (-119)$

62. $-83 \div (-83)$

63. $0 \div (-19)$

64. $0 \div (-21)$

65. $\frac{72}{-3}$

66. $\frac{56}{|-4|}$

67. $\frac{|-45|}{-9}$

68. $\frac{-132}{-12}$

69. $\frac{-91}{7}$

70. $\frac{-70}{14}$

71. $\frac{-16}{0}$

72. $\frac{-84}{0}$

73. $-65 \div (-5)$

74. $-85 \div (-5)$

Translate each phrase into mathematical symbols. Then determine the result in each case.

75. What is negative six multiplied by eighteen?

76. Find the product of fifty-one and negative four.

77. Find twice the number negative two.

78. What is eighty-four divided by negative two?

79. What is triple the number negative fifty-five?

80. What is the quotient of seventy-two and negative nine?

81. What is negative seven divided into negative sixty-three?

82. What is negative seventeen times negative four?

83. What is the quotient of negative eighty-one and nine?

84. What is double the number negative fifteen?

Evaluate each expression for the given values of the variables.

85. ab, where $a=-5$ and $b=7$

86. km, where $k=-4$ and $m=8$

87. $-a \div |b|$, where $a=28$ and $b=-7$

88. $-m \div |p|$, where $m=-39$ and $p=13$

89. $-xy$, where $x=-10$ and $y=-8$

90. $-wz$, where $w=-17$ and $z=-10$

91. $\dfrac{x}{-y}$, where $x=-63$ and $y=-9$

92. $\dfrac{h}{-k}$, where $h=-98$ and $k=-14$

93. $-3dh$, where $d = 4$ and $h = -9$

94. $-8fg$, where $f = 2$ and $g = -14$

95. $\frac{-a}{b}$, where $a = 42$ and $b = -6$

96. $\frac{-m}{x}$, where $m = -57$ and $x = -3$

97. $w \div (-z)$, where $w = -91$ and $z = -13$

98. $g \div (-n)$, where $g = 0$ and $n = 52$

99. $km|p|$, where $k = -7$, $m = 12$, and $p = -6$

100. $hw|y|$, where $h = 14$, $w = -3$, and $y = -1$

101. $5w(-k)$, where $w = -13$ and $k = -20$

102. $12(-m)n$, where $m = -7$ and $n = 36$

103. Joe was not a very good gambler. During the last 6 days his daily net winnings were as follows: $-\$6$, $\$14$, $-\$20$, $-\$10$, $\$5$, and $-\$7$. What was the amount of his average daily net winnings?

104. A group of 5 golfers had the following scores after a round of golf: 3 under par, 2 over par, 5 under par, 1 over par, and par. What was their average score in terms of par?

105. During a recent football game Tom carried the football 7 times. He gained 2 yards on each of 3 plays, he lost 7 yards on 1 play, he lost 8 yards on 1 play, he gained 5 yards on 1 play and he lost 10 yards on his last play. What was his average net yardage per carry?

106. During a week of cold weather the daily low temperatures were as follows: $-12°F$, $6°F$, $-15°F$, $-9°F$, $3°F$, $-2°F$, and $1°F$. What was the average daily low temperature for the week?

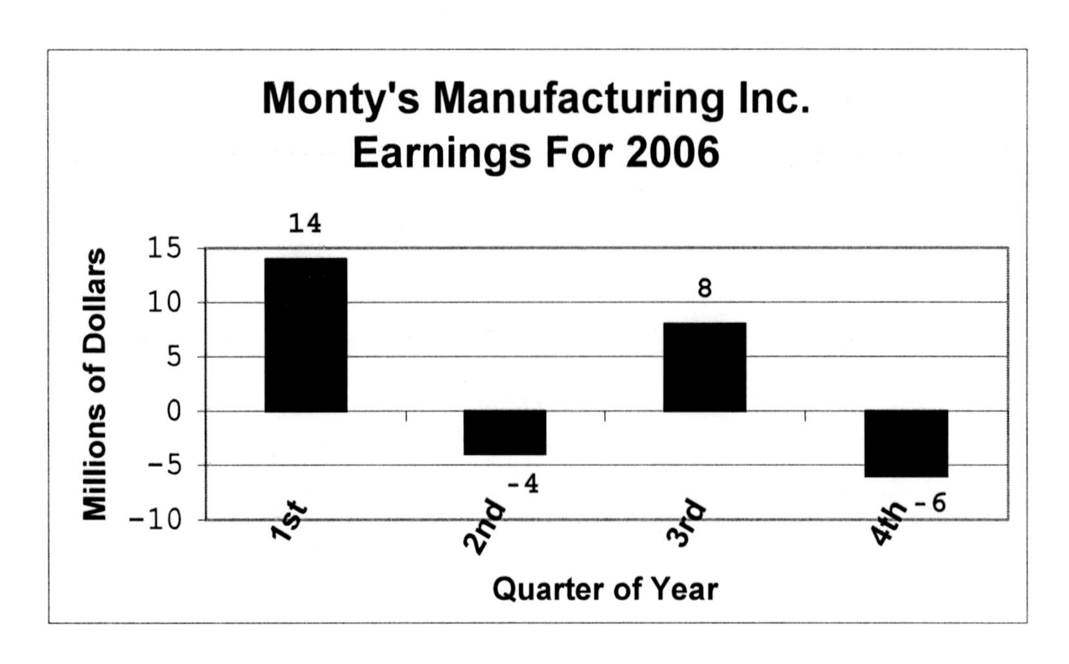

Use the bar graph above to answer the following questions.

107. What were the average earnings per month during the last quarter of 2006?

108. What were the average monthly earnings for the entire year?

109. Which quarter had the greatest amount of earnings?

110. Which quarter had the least amount of earnings?

111. If each of the four quarters of projected earnings for 2007 matched the last quarter of 2006, what would the net earnings be for the entire year of 2007?

112. What were the total net earnings for Monty's Manufacturing in 2006?

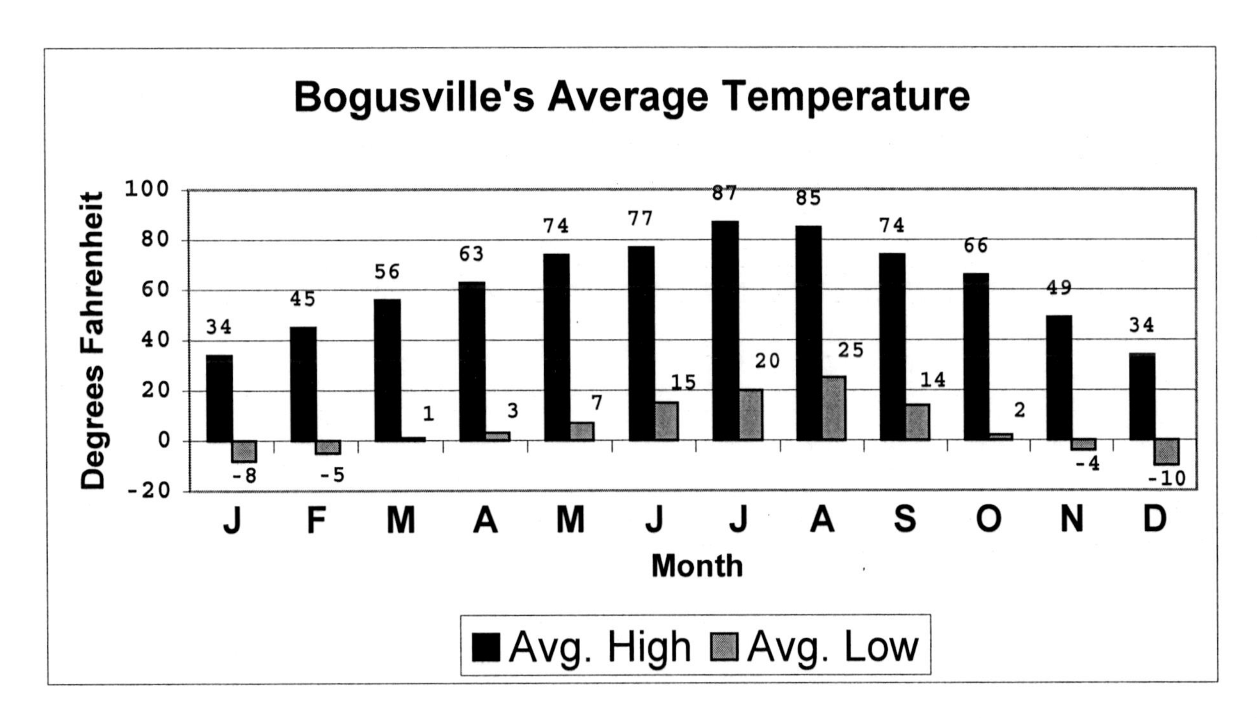

Use the bar graph above to answer the following questions.

113. What is the average monthly low temperature for Bogusville?

114. What is the average monthly high temperature for Bogusville?

115. What is the average monthly high temperature for Bogusville during the first quarter of the year?

116. What is the average monthly high temperature for Bogusville during the third quarter of the year?

117. What is the average monthly low temperature for Bogusville during the first quarter of the year?

118. What is the average monthly low temperature for Bogusville during the fourth quarter of the year?

INTEGERS

Section 5: Order of Operations with Integers

In Chapter 1, we established the order of operations for whole numbers, which consisted of four main steps. In Chapter 2, the order of operations for integers contains the same four steps. However, the first step needs to be expanded. Instead of just using parentheses and fraction bars, we also need to include absolute value bars as grouping symbols. There are several other grouping symbols, but for now we will look at only these three. The order of operations is as follows:

Order of Operations: When simplifying a mathematical expression, do the following operations in the order that they are listed.

1. **Perform all calculations within grouping symbols.**
2. **Evaluate all exponential expressions.**
3. **Do all multiplication and division in order from left to right.**
4. **Do all addition and subtraction in order from left to right.**

The introduction of integers brings up several situations involving exponents. Let's clarify the difference between two sets of notation. For example, $(-3)^2$ and -3^2. In the first instance, $(-3)^2$, the base is -3. The entire base is being squared, so $(-3)^2=(-3)(-3)=9$. In the second instance, -3^2, the base is just the 3 and the negative sign is attached to the 3^2. So, $-3^2=-(3\cdot 3)=-(9)=-9$. Let's look at another set of examples, but this time without all the explanation.

$(-4)^2=(-4)(-4)=16$ while $-4^2=-(4\cdot 4)=-(16)=-16$

Another way to help clarify the situation is to think of -5^2 as $-(5)^2$. Following the order of operations, evaluate the exponential expression before attaching the negative sign.
$-(5)^2=-(5\cdot 5)=-(25)=-25$

Example 1: Simplify the expression: $-4+8(-5)$

Solution:

$-4+8(-5)$	First multiply.
$-4+(-40)$	Finally, add.
-44	The answer is $\mathbf{-44}$.

Example 2: Simplify the expression: $(15-9)^2 - 3^3$

Solution:	
$(15-9)^2 - 3^3$	Perform all calculations within grouping symbols.
$6^2 - 3^3$	Evaluate the exponential expressions.
$6 \cdot 6 - 3 \cdot 3 \cdot 3$	This simplifies further to become
$36 - 27$.	Finally, subtract.
9	The answer is **9**.

Example 3: Simplify the expression: $6^2 - (-3)^3$

Solution:	
$6^2 - (-3)^3$	Evaluate the exponential expressions.
$6 \cdot 6 - (-3)(-3)(-3)$	This simplifies further to become
$36 - (-27)$.	Change subtraction into addition of the opposite.
$36 + (+27)$	Finally, add.
63	The answer is **63**.

Example 4: Simplify the expression: $|6 - 2^3|$

Solution:	
$\|6 - 2^3\|$	Perform all calculations within grouping symbols. Following the order of operations inside the absolute value bars, evaluate the exponential expression first.
$\|6 - 8\|$	Change subtraction into addition of the opposite.
$\|6 + (-8)\|$	Add the two numbers inside the absolute value bars.
$\|-2\|$	Finally, take the absolute value of -2.
2	The answer is **2**.

Remember that following "order of operations" is necessary when evaluating algebraic expressions, since the process involves simplifying a mathematical expression.

Example 5: Evaluate the expression for the given values of the variables: $\frac{a^2 - b^2}{c^4}$, where $a = 5$, $b = -3$, and $c = -2$

Solution:

$\frac{a^2 - b^2}{c^4}$	Substitute 5 in the place of *a*, -3 in the place of *b*, and -2 in the place of *c*.
$\frac{(5)^2 - (-3)^2}{(-2)^4}$	Evaluate the expression using order of operations. Simplify the numerator of the fraction. Do the exponents first.
$\frac{(5)(5) - (-3)(-3)}{(-2)^4}$	Multiply.
$\frac{25 - 9}{(-2)^4}$	Subtract.
$\frac{16}{(-2)^4}$	Simplify the denominator.
$\frac{16}{(-2)(-2)(-2)(-2)}$	Multiply.
$\frac{16}{16}$	Divide the fraction.
1	When $a = 5$, $b = -3$, and $c = -2$, the value of $\frac{a^2 - b^2}{c^4}$ is **1**.

Note: When replacing a variable with the number that it is equal to, remember to put parentheses around the number. This is especially important when exponents, multiplication, or division are involved.

Here is a problem that models the idea of subtracting exponential expressions.

Example 6: Find the shaded area of the figure by subtracting the area of the smaller square from the area of the larger square. Start by writing a subtraction problem involving exponential expressions. Be sure to attach the correct units to the answer.

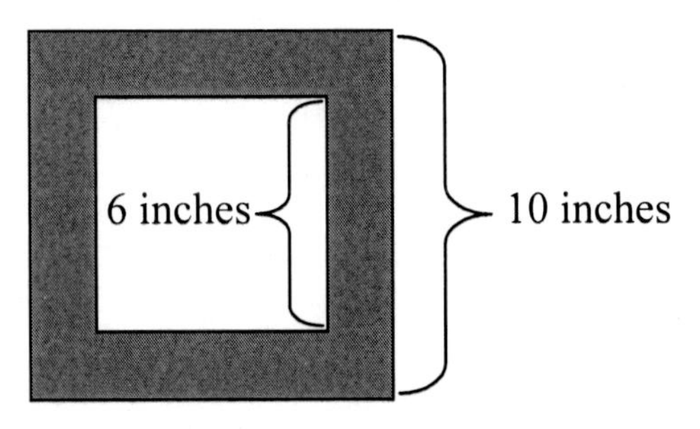

Solution: The area of the larger square can be represented by the quantity 10^2, while the area of the smaller square can be represented by the quantity 6^2. The problem becomes $10^2 - 6^2$.

$10^2 - 6^2$	Evaluate the expression using order of operations, that is, exponents before subtraction.
$(10)(10) - (6)(6)$	Now multiply.
$100 - 36$	Finally, subtract.
64	Attaching the correct units, the final answer is **64 square inches**.

In Chapter 1 we looked at formulas for converting back and forth between degrees Celsius and degrees Fahrenheit. Here is an example of using these formulas when negative temperatures are involved.

Example 7: Using the formula $F = \frac{9C}{5} + 32$, convert $-25°C$ into degrees Fahrenheit.

Solution: Use the formula to convert from degrees Celsius to degrees Fahrenheit.

$F = \frac{9C}{5} + 32$	Substitute $-25°$ in the place of C.
$F = \frac{9(-25)}{5} + 32$	Evaluate the expression using order of operations. Simplify the numerator of the fraction.
$F = \frac{-225}{5} + 32$	Divide the fraction.
$F = -45 + 32$	Add.
$F = -13$	Consequently, **-25 degrees Celsius is equivalent to -13 degrees Fahrenheit, or $-25°C = -13°F$**.

Section 5 exercises. Simplify each expression.

1. $-27-28\div 4$

2. $-28-27\div 3$

3. $-38+3\cdot(-7)$

4. $-47+4\cdot(-9)$

5. -3^2-4^2

6. -2^3-5^2

7. $(-3)^2-5^2$

8. $(-4)^2-6^2$

9. $7|3|$

10. $8|5|$

11. $\dfrac{(3-7)(7-3)}{2^3}$

12. $\dfrac{(2-8)(8-2)}{3^2}$

13. $(8-5)^2-(2-9)^2$

14. $(7-2)^2-(3-11)^2$

15. $|-3+7-11|$

16. $|-5+6-9|$

17. $\dfrac{-14\div 7(-2)}{4^2\div 2-2^3}$

18. $\dfrac{-15\div 5(-3)}{5^2-(3^2+4^2)}$

19. $-14\div(-2)7$

20. $-15\div(-3)5$

21. $-5|-7|$

22. $-4|-9|$

23. $\dfrac{|-5(-7)|}{2^4-3^2}$

24. $\dfrac{|-4(-9)|}{2\cdot 3^2}$

25. -7^2+7^2

26. -8^2+8^2

27. $|5-9|\cdot|9-5|$

28. $|4-10|\cdot|10-4|$

29. $-20-4(-3)^2$

30. $-15-5(-2)^3$

31. $|(-4)^2-7\cdot 3|$

32. $|(-7)^2-9\cdot 6|$

33. $4^2-(-4-7)$

34. $6^2-(-6-3)$

35. $-|4-(7-19)|$

36. $-|8-(5-23)|$

37. $\dfrac{-3(12 \div 3)^2}{12 \div 3(-2)}$ **38.** $\dfrac{-9(15 \div 3)^2}{(4^2 - 1^3)^2}$ **39.** $\left(4^2 - |3-9|^2\right)^2$

40. $\left(5^2 - |6-13|^2\right)^2$ **41.** $-7 + \left(-3 + (-12) \div 4\right)^2$ **42.** $-6 + \left(-5 + (-8) \div 4\right)^2$

Put the correct symbol <, >, or = in the box between each pair of expressions.

43. $-4 - 9 \div 3 \cdot 5 + (4-8)^2 \; \square \; \left|9 - 7^2\right| - (-5)(-8) - 3$

44. $-7 - 18 \div 3 \cdot 8 + (5-12)^2 \; \square \; \left|8 - 9^2\right| - (-6)(-12) - 7$

45. $(-1)^5(-12)(-2)^3 \; \square \; (8 \div 2 \cdot 5 + 7 - 11)(11-5)$

46. $(-1)^6(-4)(-3)^3 \; \square \; (14 \div 2 \cdot 4 + 9 - 10)(12-16)$

47. $-10 - 6^2 - (8-9)^3 \; \square \; -11^2 - 3 - (-8)^2$

48. $-4 - 5^2 - (6-7)^3 \; \square \; -7^2 - 6 - (-4)^2$

Evaluate each expression for the given values of the variables.

49. w^2, where $w = -4$ **50.** k^2, where $k = -6$ **51.** x^3, where $x = -3$

52. m^3, where $m = -5$ **53.** n^4, where $n = -2$ **54.** y^4, where $y = -1$

55. $-3g^2$, where $g = -5$ **56.** $-5b^2$, where $b = -3$

57. $3x-7y$, where $x=-5$ and $y=-6$

58. $8d-6f$, where $d=-3$ and $f=-9$

59. $\frac{a^2}{b^2}+c^3$, where $a=-9$, $b=-3$, and $c=-4$

60. $\frac{m^2}{p^3}-z^2$, where $m=-4$, $p=-2$, and $z=-7$

61. $w^2(h-k^2)$, where $h=9$, $k=-6$, and $w=-3$

62. $n^3(g^2+j)$, where $g=5$, $j=-18$, and $n=-1$

63. $-|7x-y|+|-3z|$, where $x=-6$, $y=-39$, and $z=-5$

64. $-|3a+2b|-|-5c|$, where $a=-4$, $b=-8$, and $c=-6$

65. **a)** Evaluate $|x|$, where $x=3$

b) Evaluate $|x|$, where $x=-3$

c) What do you notice about the answers to part a and part b? Explain what is happening.

66. **a)** Evaluate $|y|$, where $y=-7$

b) Evaluate $|y|$, where $y=7$

c) What do you notice about the answers to part a and part b? Explain what is happening.

67. Find the shaded area of the figure by subtracting the area of the smaller square from the area of the larger square. Start by writing a subtraction problem involving exponential expressions. Be sure to attach the correct units to the answer.

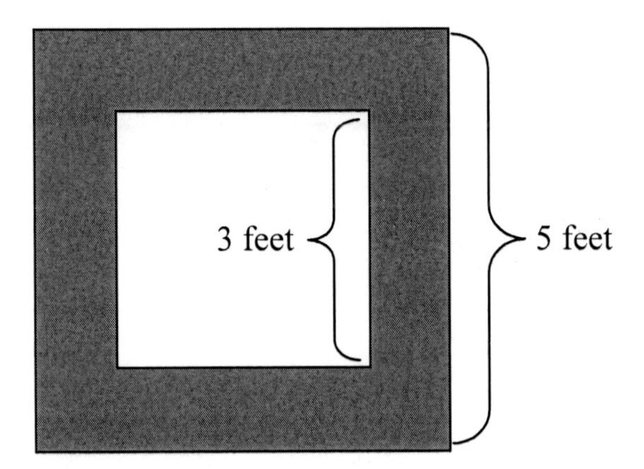

68. Find the shaded area of the figure by subtracting the area of the smaller square from the area of the larger square. Start by writing a subtraction problem involving exponential expressions. Be sure to attach the correct units to the answer.

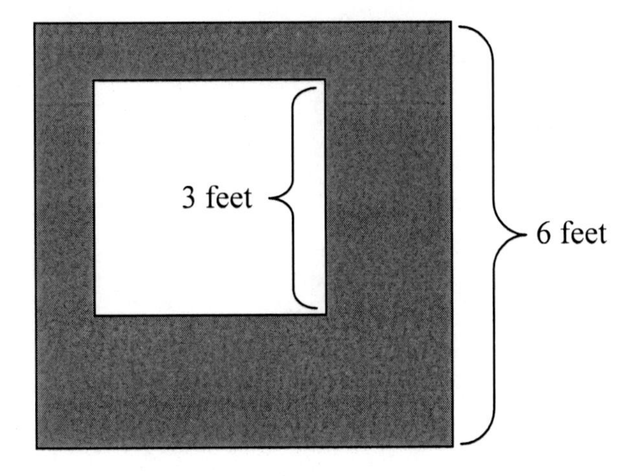

Convert.

69. Using the formula $C = \dfrac{5(F-32)}{9}$, convert 23°F into degrees Celsius.

70. Using the formula $C = \dfrac{5(F-32)}{9}$, convert 5°F into degrees Celsius.

71. Using the formula $F = \frac{9C}{5} + 32$, convert $-15°C$ into degrees Fahrenheit.

72. Using the formula $F = \frac{9C}{5} + 32$, convert $-30°C$ into degrees Fahrenheit.

73. Using the formula $C = \frac{5(F-32)}{9}$, convert $-4°F$ into degrees Celsius.

74. Using the formula $C = \frac{5(F-32)}{9}$, convert $-40°F$ into degrees Celsius.

75. Using the formula $F = \frac{9C}{5} + 32$, convert $-40°C$ into degrees Fahrenheit.

76. Using the formula $F = \frac{9C}{5} + 32$, convert $-35°C$ into degrees Fahrenheit.

INTEGERS

Section 6: Solving Equations with Integers

In Chapter 1 we considered possible solutions of equations using whole numbers. Now we will consider possible solutions of equations, using integers in the process.

Example 1: Is 9 a solution of the equation $-4-x=-13$?

Solution:

$-4-x=-13$	Substitute 9 in the place of x.
$\underbrace{-4-9}\stackrel{?}{=}-13$	Simplify the left side of the equation.
$-13\stackrel{\checkmark}{=}-13$	This is a true statement. Consequently, 9 is a solution.

Example 2: Is -4 a solution of the equation $3x=-12$?

Solution:

$3x=-12$	Substitute -4 in the place of x.
$\underbrace{3(-4)}\stackrel{?}{=}-12$	Simplify the left side of the equation.
$-12\stackrel{\checkmark}{=}-12$	This is a true statement. Consequently, -4 is a solution.

Example 3: Is -6 a solution of the equation $\dfrac{18}{x}=-4$?

Solution:

$\dfrac{18}{x}=-4$	Substitute -6 in the place of x.
$\underbrace{\dfrac{18}{-6}}\stackrel{?}{=}-4$	Simplify the left side of the equation.
$-3\stackrel{?}{=}-4$	However,
$-3\neq-4$.	This is a false statement. Consequently, -6 is not a solution.

In Chapter 1 we established properties that are used to solve equations. In this chapter we will use these same properties to solve equations that involve integers. Let's review these properties along with an example of how each property is used with integers.

THE ADDITION PROPERTY OF EQUALITY:

When a, b, and c are real numbers, the following is true:

If $a = b$ then $a + c = b + c$.

If the same quantity is added to both sides of an equation, the new equation is equivalent to the old equation. That is, both equations have the same solution.

Example 4: Solve the equation: $x - 9 = -14$

Solution:

$x - 9 = -14$	Use the addition property of equality by adding 9 to both sides of the equation.
$x - 9 + 9 = -14 + 9$	Simplify the left side of the equation.
$x = -14 + 9$	Simplify the right side of the equation.
$x = -5$	The solution is -5. To check the solution, substitute it back into the original equation in place of the variable.
$x - 9 = -14$	becomes
$-5 - 9 \stackrel{?}{=} -14$	which simplifies to
$-14 \stackrel{\checkmark}{=} -14$.	The statement is true, therefore the solution is correct.

THE SUBTRACTION PROPERTY OF EQUALITY:

When a, b, and c are real numbers, the following is true:

If $a = b$ then $a - c = b - c$.

If the same quantity is subtracted from both sides of an equation, the new equation is equivalent to the old equation. That is, both equations have the same solution.

Example 5: Solve: $7 = y + 19$

Solution:

$7 = y + 19$	Use the subtraction property of equality by subtracting 19 from both sides of the equation.
$7 - 19 = y + 19 - 19$	Simplify the left side of the equation.
$-12 = y + 19 - 19$	Simplify the right side of the equation.
$-12 = y$	The solution is -12. Though this answer is correct, it is considered more appropriate to write the answer with the variable first.
$-12 = y$	becomes
$y = -12$.	To check the solution, substitute it back into the original equation in place of the variable.
$7 = y + 19$	becomes
$7 \stackrel{?}{=} -12 + 19$	which simplifies to
$7 \stackrel{\checkmark}{=} 7$.	The statement is true, therefore the solution is correct.

THE DIVISION PROPERTY OF EQUALITY:

When a, b, and c are real numbers with $c \neq 0$, the following is true:

$$\text{If} \quad a = b \quad \text{then} \quad \frac{a}{c} = \frac{b}{c}.$$

If both sides of the equation are divided by the same non-zero quantity, the new equation is equivalent to the old equation. That is, both equations have the same solution.

Example 6: Solve: $-6x = 48$

Solution:

$-6x = 48$	Use the division property of equality by dividing both sides of the equation by -6.
$\dfrac{-6x}{-6} = \dfrac{48}{-6}$	Simplify the left side of the equation.
$x = \dfrac{48}{-6}$	Simplify the right side of the equation.
$x = -8$	The solution is -8. To check the solution, substitute it back into the original equation in place of the variable.
$-6x = 48$	becomes
$-6(-8) \stackrel{?}{=} 48$	which further simplifies to
$48 \stackrel{\checkmark}{=} 48.$	The statement is true, therefore the solution is correct.

Note: Remember that when a number is multiplied by a variable, as in the case of $-6x$ above, the number has a special name. It is called the <u>coefficient of the variable</u>. To solve the equation $-6x = 48$ divide both sides of the equation by the coefficient of the variable.

Example 7: Translate the following expression into an equation using mathematical symbols. Then, solve the equation and answer the question.
The sum of a number and five is negative thirteen. What is the number?

Solution: First we need to choose a variable to represent the unknown quantity. Since the unknown quantity is "a number" let's use the letter N. The statement

"The sum of	a number	and	five	is	negative thirteen"	translates into
add	the unknown "N"		5	equals	-13	

which becomes the equation: $N + 5 = -13$

Now we can solve the equation.

$N+5=-13$ Use the subtraction property of equality by subtracting 5 from both sides of the equation.

$N+5-5=-13-5$ Simplify both sides of the equation.

$N=-18$ The solution is the number -18. To check the solution, substitute it back into the original equation in place of the variable.

$N+5=-13$ becomes

$-18+5\stackrel{?}{=}-13$ which simplifies further to

$-13\stackrel{\checkmark}{=}-13.$ The statement is true, therefore the solution is correct.

Example 8: Translate the following expression into an equation using mathematical symbols. Then, solve the equation and answer the question.
The product of negative five and a number is equal to thirty-five. What is the number?

Solution: First we need to choose a variable to represent the unknown quantity. Since the unknown quantity is "a number" let's use the letter N. The statement

"The product of	negative five	and	a number	is equal to	thirty-five"	translates into
multiply	-5		the unknown "N"	equals	35	

which becomes the equation: $-5N = 35$

Now we can solve the equation.

$-5N=35$ Use the division property of equality by dividing both sides of the equation by -5.

$\frac{-5N}{-5}=\frac{35}{-5}$ Simplify both sides of the equation.

$N=-7$ The solution is the number -7. To check the solution, substitute it back into the original equation in place of the variable.

$-5N=35$ becomes

$-5(-7)\stackrel{?}{=}35$ which simplifies further to

$35\stackrel{\checkmark}{=}35.$ The statement is true, therefore the solution is correct.

Example 9: Translate the following situation into an equation using mathematical symbols. Then, solve the equation and answer the question.
The low temperature today was 6° less than the low temperature yesterday. If the low temperature today was $-7°$, then what was the low temperature yesterday?

Solution: The letter Y is used to represent the unknown quantity, which is "what was the low temperature yesterday." The statement "The low temperature today was 6° less than the low temperature yesterday" becomes: $\text{today} = Y - 6$. The statement "the low temperature today was $-7°$" becomes: $\text{today} = -7$. Since $\text{today} = Y - 6$ and $\text{today} = -7$, by putting these two statements together, we get the equation $Y - 6 = -7$.

Now we can solve the equation.

$Y - 6 = -7$	Use the addition property of equality by adding 6 to both sides of the equation.
$Y - 6 + 6 = -7 + 6$	Simplify both sides of the equation.
$Y = -1$	The solution is -1. Therefore, the low temperature yesterday morning was $-1°$. We'll leave verifying the solution up to you.

Example 10: Translate the following situation into an equation using mathematical symbols. Then, solve the equation and answer the question.
A gambler's net winnings for today's poker game consisted of three times the net winnings he made during last week's poker game. If the net winnings he made during today's poker game were $-\$48$, then what were his net winnings during last week's poker game?

Solution: The letter L is used to represent the unknown quantity, which was "his net winnings during last week's poker game." The statement "The net winnings of a gambler for today's poker game consisted of three times the net winnings that he made during last week's poker game" becomes: today's game = 3L. The statement "the net winnings he made for today's poker game were $-\$48$" becomes: today's game = -48. Since today's game = 3L and today's game = -48, by putting these two statements together, we get the equation $3L = -48$.

Now we can solve the equation.

$3L = -48$	Use the division property of equality by dividing both sides of the equation by 3.
$\frac{3L}{3} = \frac{-48}{3}$	Simplify both sides of the equation.
$L = -16$	The solution is -16. Therefore, his net winnings during last week's poker game was $-\$16$. Once again, we'll leave verifying the solution up to you.

Section 6 exercises. Check the solutions.

1. Is -26 a solution of the equation $7=-33+w$?

2. Is -31 a solution of the equation $-4=27+z$?

3. Is -6 a solution of the equation $7-a=-13$?

4. Is -9 a solution of the equation $12-b=-21$?

5. Is -14 a solution of the equation $-x-10=4$?

6. Is -18 a solution of the equation $-y-7=11$?

7. Is -7 a solution of the equation $-7y=-49$?

8. Is -5 a solution of the equation $6x=30$?

9. Is -12 a solution of the equation $-72=6w$?

10. Is -8 a solution of the equation $-56=7a$?

11. Is 3 a solution of the equation $-45=\dfrac{15}{-y}$?

12. Is 108 a solution of the equation $-12=\dfrac{-g}{9}$?

Solve each of the following equations.

13. $x - 6 = -22$ **14.** $w - 8 = -37$ **15.** $H + 47 = 36$

16. $R + 75 = 43$ **17.** $-7y = 63$ **18.** $-8k = 72$

19. $28 + n = -99$ **20.** $53 + p = -76$ **21.** $-65 = z - 7$

22. $-17 = b - 0$ **23.** $-96 = -12w$ **24.** $-39 = -3x$

25. $9m = -99$ **26.** $13y = -143$ **27.** $-29 = W + 16$

28. $-57 = y + 23$ **29.** $x - 0 = -66$ **30.** $h - 27 = -42$

31. $-w = 8$ **32.** $-m = 25$ **33.** $0 = -8k$

34. $0 = -15d$ **35.** $-119 = -53 + k$ **36.** $-124 = -38 + p$

37. $-17x = -17$ **38.** $-19y = -19$ **39.** $n - 43 = -43$

40. $b - 76 = -76$ **41.** $-97 = -y$ **42.** $-91 = -x$

Translate each expression into an equation using mathematical symbols. Then, solve the equation and answer the question.

43. The difference of a number and fourteen is equal to three. What is the number?

44. The product of a number and eight equals negative thirty-two. What is the number?

45. Nine added to a number is equal to negative seventeen. What is the number?

46. Nine subtracted from a number is negative twenty-eight. What is the number?

47. Twice a number equals negative sixty-eight. What is the number?

48. Thirteen more than a number is equal to seven. What is the number?

49. Sixty increased by a number is thirty-nine. What is the number?

50. Negative six multiplied by a number is eighty-four. What is the number?

51. The total of a number and ninety-five is equal to seventeen. What is the number?

52. A number minus twelve is negative fifteen. What is the number?

53. A number decreased by five equals negative five. What is the number?

54. A number plus eighteen equals fourteen. What is the number?

55. A number less forty-five equals negative eight. What is the number?

56. Sixty-three less than a number is negative forty-seven. What is the number?

57. Negative nine times a number is equal to eighty-one. What is the number?

58. The sum of a number and fifty-nine is twelve. What is the number?

Translate each expression into an equation using mathematical symbols. Then, solve the equation and answer the question.

59. The lowest temperature for the month of December was $3°$ less than the lowest temperature for the month of November. If the lowest temperature in December was $-9°$, then what was the lowest temperature in November?

60. The lowest temperature for the month of February was $5°$ more than the lowest temperature for the month of January. If the lowest temperature in February was $-4°$, then what was the lowest temperature in January?

61. A company's earnings for 2006 were four times its earnings for 2005. If the company's earnings for 2006 were $-\$12$ million, then how much were its earnings for 2005?

62. A company's earnings for 2004 were five times its earnings for 2003. If the company's earnings for 2004 were $-\$10$ million, then how much were its earnings for 2003?

63. The lowest elevation in Africa is 125 meters less than the lowest elevation in Europe. If the lowest elevation in Africa is -153 meters, then what is the lowest elevation in Europe?

64. The lowest elevation in North America is 46 meters less than the lowest elevation in South America. If the lowest elevation in North America is -86 meters, then what is the lowest elevation in South America?

65. During the second play of the game, John lost twice as much yardage as he had during the first play of the game. If during the second play of the game he lost 8 yards, then how many yards did he lose during the first play of the game?

66. During the third play of the game, Jim lost twice as much yardage as he had during the second play of the game. If during the third play of the game he lost 12 yards, then how many yards did he lose during the second play of the game?

INTEGERS

Chapter Review

Section 1: An Introduction to Integers

Review Exercises.

1. Graph the integers that are greater than -4 and less than 3.

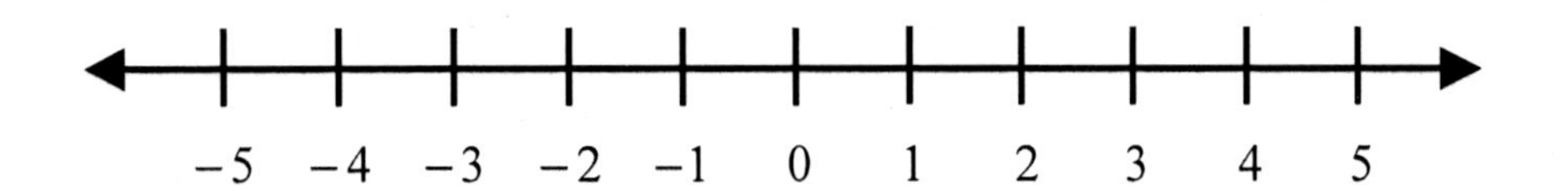

Place the correct inequality symbol < or > between the pair of numbers.

2. $-12 \quad -13$

Find the absolute value of the number.

3. -37

Find the opposite of the number.

4. $-y$

Evaluate the expression.

5. $-|-78|$

Place the correct symbol <, >, or = between the pair of numbers.

6. $-(-11) \qquad -|-11|$

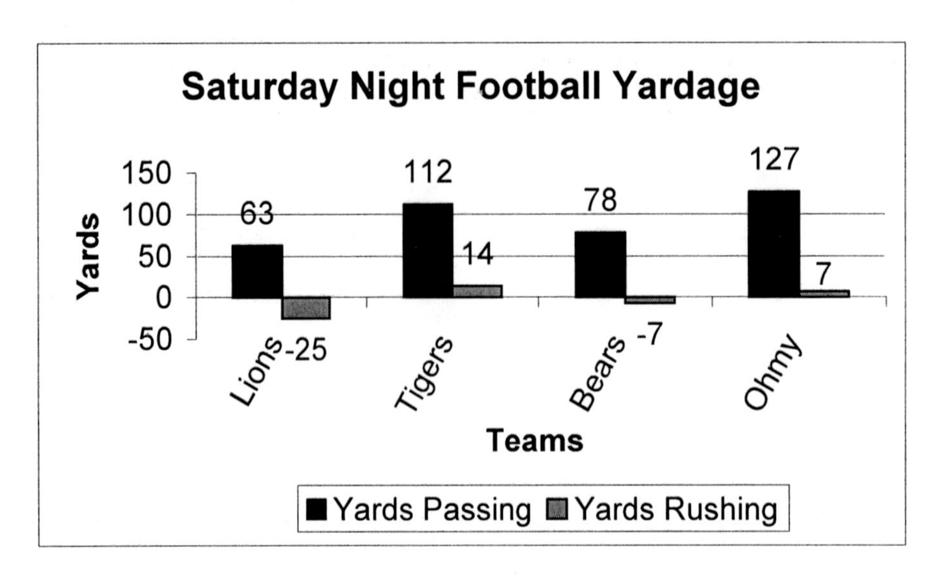

Use the bar graph above to answer questions 7 and 8.

7. Which team gained the greatest amount of yards by rushing? How many yards was it?

8. Which team gained the least amount of yards by rushing? How many yards was it?

Section 2: Addition of Integers

Review Exercises: Add each of the following.

9. $34 + 0 + (-34)$

10. $-15 + (-4) + 13 + (-29)$

Use only the commutative property of addition to rewrite the expression. Then, simplify the expression.

11. $-92 + 77$

Use only the associative property of addition to rewrite the expression. Then, simplify the expression.

12. $-12 + (-8 + 35)$

Find the additive inverse of the number.

13. -84

Use addition of signed numbers to help answer the question.

14. Frank's freezer was on the fritz. On Tuesday the temperature inside his freezer was 26° degrees Fahrenheit. On Wednesday the temperature dropped 4°F. On Thursday the temperature rose 2°F. On Friday the temperature dropped 9°F. On Saturday the temperature dropped 3°F. On Sunday the temperature didn't change. On Monday the temperature rose 5°F. What was the temperature inside Frank's freezer after it rose on Monday?

Evaluate the expression for the given values of the variables.

15. $x+|y|+(-z)$, where $x=-41$, $y=-27$, and $z=33$

Section 3: Subtraction of Integers

Review Exercises: Subtract the following.

16. $-52-(-51)$

Translate the phrase into mathematical symbols. Then determine the result.

17. What is the difference between eight and negative sixty?

Simplify.

18. $-4+12+(-23)-7$

Evaluate the expression for the given values of the variables.

19. $-a-(-b)+c$, where $a=26$, $b=-47$, and $c=-9$

The elevation of a location is given in terms of sea level. If a location is above sea level it has a positive elevation. If a location is below sea level it has a negative elevation.

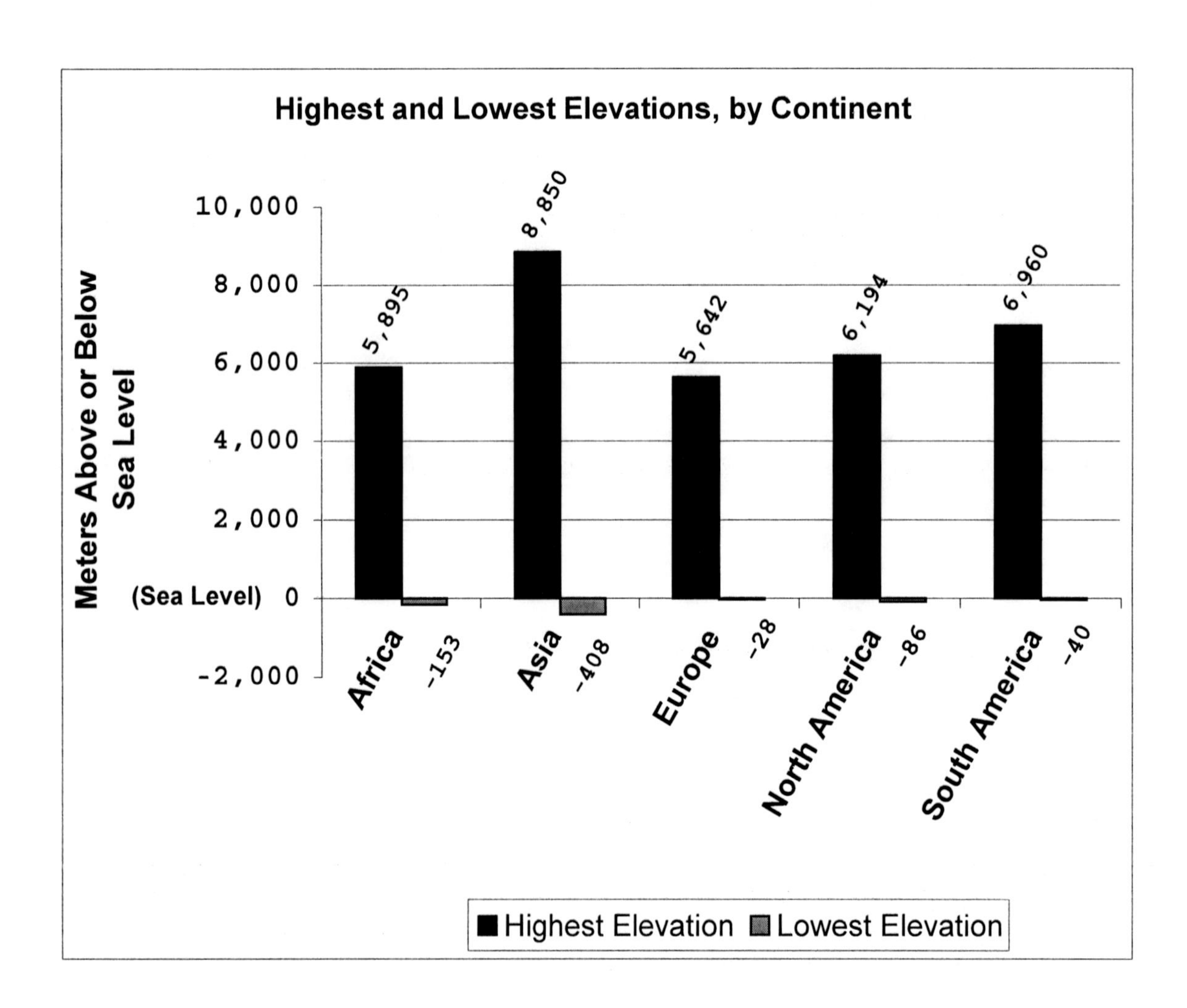

Use the bar graph above to answer questions 20 and 21.

20. What is the difference between the highest elevation in Africa and the lowest elevation in North America?

21. What is the difference between the highest elevation in South America and the lowest elevation in Asia?

22. A climber started out at 672 feet below base camp where the temperature was 12° F. She climbed up 1,486 feet in elevation. At her new elevation the temperature was -10° F. What was her new elevation in terms of base camp? How much did the temperature change from her starting point?

Section 4: Multiplication and Division of Integers

Review Exercises: Multiply the following.

23. $-h(-4)$

Use only the commutative property of multiplication to rewrite the expression. Then, simplify the expression.

24. $-81 \cdot 16$

Use only the associative property of multiplication to rewrite the expression. Then, simplify the expression.

25. $-2 \cdot (50 \cdot (-7))$

Divide the following.

26. $\dfrac{|-42|}{-7}$

Translate the phrase into mathematical symbols. Then determine the result.

27. What is the quotient of ninety-one and negative seven?

Evaluate each expression for the given values of the variables.

28. $\dfrac{-n}{x}$, where $n = -54$ and $x = -3$

29. $bm|w|$, where $b = 17$, $m = -2$, and $w = -1$

30. A group of 4 golfers had the following scores after a round of golf: 3 under par, 2 over par, par, and 3 under par. What was their average score in terms of par?

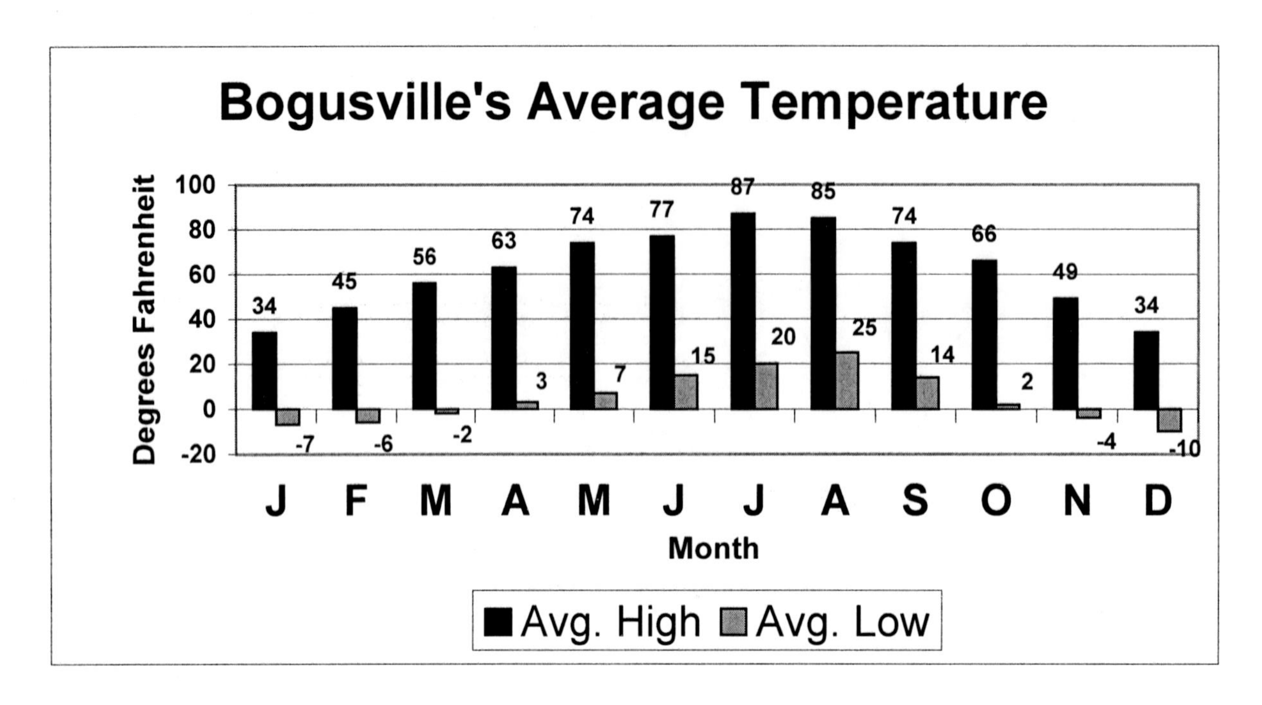

Use the bar graph above to answer question 31.

31. What is the average monthly low temperature for Bogusville during the first quarter of the year?

Section 5: Order of Operations with Integers

Review Exercises: Simplify each expression.

32. $(9-3)^2-(4-8)^2$

33. $\dfrac{-18\div(-2)9}{(5-2)^3}$

34. $\left|(-9)^2-10\cdot 9\right|$

35. $-\left|7-(4-29)\right|$

Put the correct symbol <, >, or = in the box between the pair of expressions.

36. $(-1)^7(-5)(-2)^3\ \square\ (15\div 3\cdot 7-5^2)(13-17)$

Evaluate the expression for the given values of the variables.

37. $n^5(g^2+j)$, where $g=7$, $j=-26$, and $n=-1$

Convert.

38. Using the formula $F = \frac{9C}{5} + 32$, convert $-20°C$ into degrees Fahrenheit.

39. Using the formula $C = \frac{5(F-32)}{9}$, convert $-31°F$ into degrees Celsius.

Section 6: Solving Equations with Integers

Review Exercises: Check the solution.

40. Is -15 a solution of the equation $a + (-7) = -22$?

41. Is -14 a solution of the equation $-y - 5 = 9$?

42. Is 108 a solution of the equation $-27 = \frac{-g}{-4}$?

Solve each of the following equations.

43. $R + 74 = 63$

44. $14x = -154$

45. $-y = 38$

46. $-142 = -83 + p$

Translate each expression into an equation using mathematical symbols. Then, solve the equation and answer the question.

47. The product of five and a number equals negative thirty-five. What is the number?

48. Twenty-nine less than a number is negative seventy-seven. What is the number?

49. A company's earnings for 2005 were four times its earnings for 2004. If the company's earnings for 2005 were $-\$28$ million, then how much were its earnings for 2004?

50. The lowest elevation in North America is 58 meters less than the lowest elevation in Europe. If the lowest elevation in North America is -86 meters, then what is the lowest elevation in Europe?

INTEGERS

Chapter Test

1. Graph the integers that are greater than -3 and less than 4.

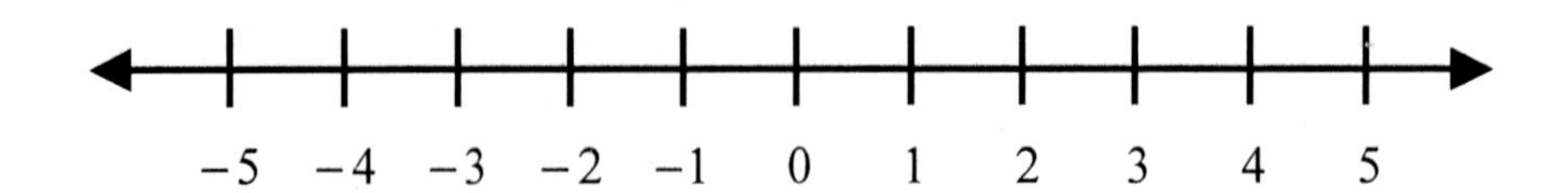

Find the opposite of the number.

2. w

Place the correct symbol <, >, or = between the pair of numbers.

3. $-|-25|$ $\qquad -(25)$

Use only the commutative property of addition to rewrite the expression. Then, simplify the expression.

4. $-47+39$

Find the additive inverse of the number.

5. $-a$

Use addition of signed numbers to help answer the question.

6. Sally's stock price slid severely. On Monday her stock sold for $86 per share. On Tuesday the price dropped $12 per share. On Wednesday the price rose $8 per share. On Thursday the price dropped $17 per share. Finally, on Friday the price dropped $6 per share. After the price dropped on Friday, what was the value of Sally's stock per share?

Translate the phrase into mathematical symbols. Then determine the result.

7. What is the difference between negative eighty-five and negative forty-six?

Simplify.

8. $-7+15-(-13)-24$

Evaluate the expression for the given values of the variables.

9. $-x+y-(-z)$, where $x=-42$, $y=-7$, and $z=-10$

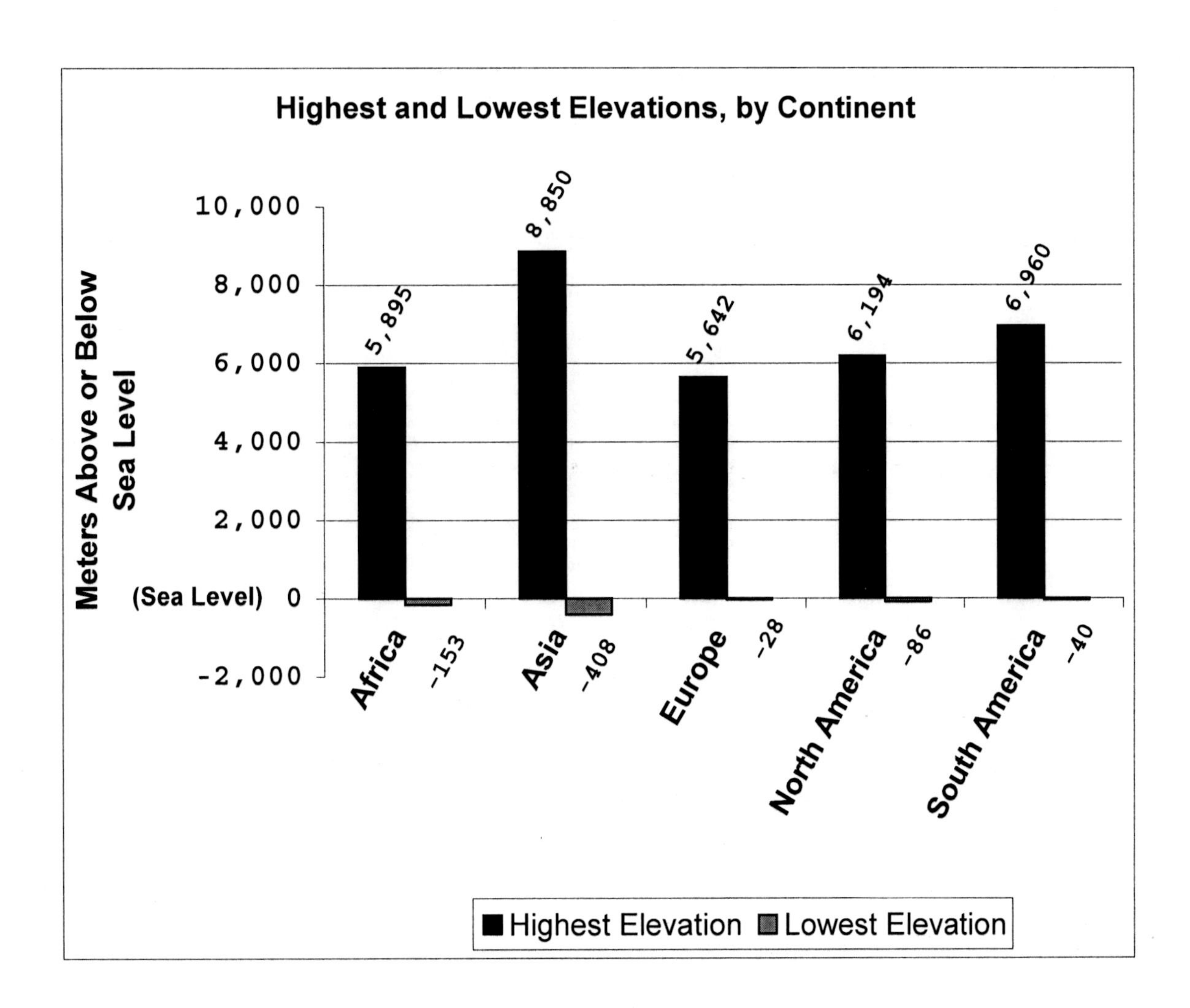

Use the bar graph above to answer question 10.

10. What is the difference between the lowest elevation in Europe and the lowest elevation in Africa?

Multiply the following.

11. $-y(3)$

Use only the associative property of multiplication to rewrite the expression. Then, simplify the expression.

12. $(53 \cdot (-4))(25)$

Translate the phrase into mathematical symbols. Then determine the result.

13. What is the quotient of negative seventy-four and negative thirty-seven?

Evaluate the expression for the given values of the variables.

14. $\frac{p}{-w}$, where $p = -51$ and $w = 17$

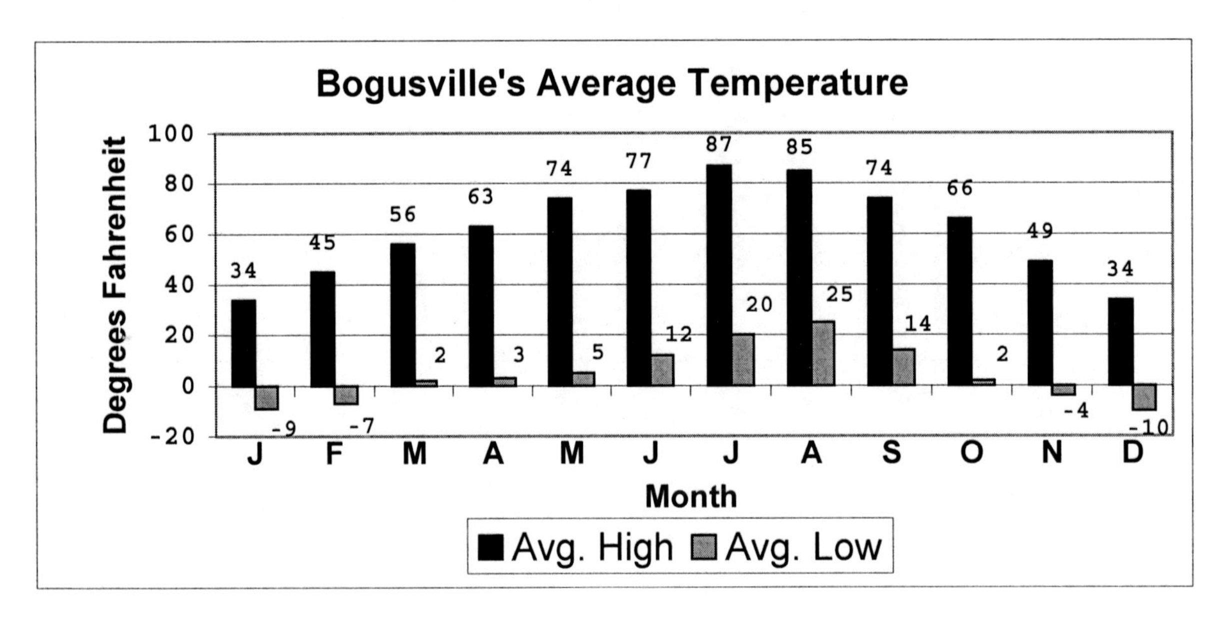

Use the bar graph above to answer question 15.

15. What is the average monthly low temperature for Bogusville during the first six months of the year?

Simplify the expression.

16. $(3-13)^2 - (12-7)^2$

Put the correct symbol <, >, or = in the box between the pair of expressions.

17. $-\left|(-7)^2 + 6^2\right| \ \square \ (27 \div 3 \cdot 9 - 8^2)(11-16)$

Evaluate the expression for the given values of the variables.

18. $w^3(h - m^2)$, where $h = 7$, $m = -3$, and $w = -2$

Convert.

19. Using the formula $C = \dfrac{5(F - 32)}{9}$, convert $14°F$ into degrees Celsius.

Check the solution.

20. Is -17 a solution of the equation $-k - 12 = 5$?

21. Is 145 a solution of the equation $-29 = \dfrac{-h}{-5}$?

Solve each of the following equations.

22. $M + 85 = 26$

23. $71 = -k$

Translate the expression into an equation using mathematical symbols. Then, solve the equation and answer the question.

24. The product of negative seven and a number equals thirty-five. What is the number?

25. The lowest elevation in Asia is 380 meters less than the lowest elevation in Europe. If the lowest elevation in Asia is -408 meters, then what is the lowest elevation in Europe?

CHAPTER 3

FRACTIONS

Section 1: The Least Common Multiple and The Greatest Common Factor

Least Common Multiple
Greatest Common Factor
Applications

Section 2: An Introduction to Fractions

Numerator, Denominator, and Fraction Bar
Proper Fractions
Improper Fractions
Mixed Numbers
Equivalent Fractions
Reducing a Fraction to Lowest Terms

Section 3: Comparing Fractions

Number Line Graphing
Least Common Denominator
Applications

Section 4: Adding Fractions and Mixed Numbers

Adding Fractions with a Common Denominator
Adding Fractions with Different Denominators
Adding Mixed Numbers
Evaluating Variable Expressions
Applications

Section 5: Subtracting Fractions and Mixed Numbers

Subtracting Fractions with a Common Denominator
Subtracting Fractions with Different Denominators
Subtracting Mixed Numbers
Evaluating Variable Expressions
Applications
Applications Involving Angles

Section 6: Multiplying Fractions and Mixed Numbers

Multiplying Fractions
Reciprocals
Multiplicative Inverse Property
Evaluating Variable Expressions
Applications

Section 7: Dividing Fractions and Mixed Numbers

Dividing Fractions
Evaluating Variable Expressions
Applications

Section 8: Order of Operations with Fractions

Rules of Order of Operations
Complex Fractions
Evaluating Variable Expressions

Section 9: Solving Equations with Fractions

Addition Property of Equality
Subtraction Property of Equality
Division Property of Equality
Multiplication Property of Equality
Translating Expressions into Equations

FRACTIONS

Section 1: The Least Common Multiple and The Greatest Common Factor

In order to add or subtract fractions there are certain procedures to follow. This section will introduce material used in some of those procedures. In Chapter 1 we said that the product of any whole number and 10 was called a **multiple** of 10. For example, $10 = 1 \times 10$; $20 = 2 \times 10$; and $30 = 3 \times 10$. So, 10, 20, and 30 are all multiples of 10. We could also produce numbers that are multiples of 15. For example, $15 = 1 \times 15$; $30 = 2 \times 15$; and $45 = 3 \times 15$. So, 15, 30, and 45 are all multiples of 15. Note that 30 is both a multiple of 10 and a multiple of 15. Based on this information we can make the following statement. 30 is a **common multiple** of 10 and 15.

Let's look at a larger list of multiples of 10 and multiples of 15.

Multiples of 10	Multiples of 15
10	15
20	**30**
30	45
40	**60**
50	75
60	**90**
70	
80	
90	

From these lists we can see that 30, 60, and 90 are **common multiples** of 10 and 15. The smallest common multiple, in this case 30, is called the **least common multiple**. Said another way, 30 is the smallest number that both 10 and 15 can be divided into evenly.

Let's look at another example of finding the least common multiple, this time using the numbers 9 and 12.

Multiples of 9	Multiples of 12
9	12
18	24
27	**36**
36	48
45	60
54	**72**
63	
72	

From these lists we can see that 36 and 72 are common multiples of 9 and 12. Since 36 is the smallest common multiple, or the smallest number that both 9 and 12 can be divided into evenly, then 36 is the **least common multiple** of 9 and 12.

The previous method of finding the least common multiple for these numbers is not a very effective process in advanced algebra courses. Therefore, we will look at another method that involves the use of prime factoring. Chapter 1 showed us that prime factoring is the process where a number is written as a product of all prime factors. For example, the prime factorization of 60 is $2 \cdot 2 \cdot 3 \cdot 5$ or $2^2 \cdot 3 \cdot 5$ when written using exponents.

Let's look at a different way of finding the least common multiple of 9 and 12. This process has 4 steps:

Step 1: Find the prime factorization of each number.

```
 9              12
 /\             /\
3·3 or         2·6
               | /\
3^2           2·2·3 or
              2^2·3
```

The prime factorization of 9 is 3^2, and the prime factorization of 12 is $2^2 \cdot 3$.

Step 2: Create a list of all the different prime factors in each of the original numbers. In this case, that would be 2 and 3.

Step 3: Raise each different prime factor to its highest power within any of the prime factorizations. In this case, it would be 2^2 and 3^2.

Step 4: Write these powers as a product: $2^2 \cdot 3^2$. Since $2^2 \cdot 3^2 = 36$, the least common multiple of 9 and 12 is 36.

Let's look again at finding the least common multiple of 10 and 15.

Step 1: Find the prime factorization of each number. The prime factorization of 10 is $2 \cdot 5$ and the prime factorization of 15 is $3 \cdot 5$.

Step 2: Create a list of all the different prime factors in each of the original numbers. In this case, that would be 2, 3 and 5.

Step 3: Raise each different prime factor to its highest power within any of the prime factorizations. In this case, it would be 2^1 or just 2, 3^1 or just 3 and 5^1 or just 5.

Step 4: Write these powers as a product: $2 \cdot 3 \cdot 5$. Since $2 \cdot 3 \cdot 5 = 30$, the least common multiple of 10 and 15 is 30.

We can summarize this 4-step process as follows: **The least common multiple of two or more numbers is the product of the highest power of each different prime factor.**

Let's look at some other examples of **LCM**'s (least common multiples).

Example 1: Find the least common multiple of 42 and 98.

Solution:

Step 1: Find the prime factorization of each number. The prime factorization of 42 is $2 \cdot 3 \cdot 7$ and the prime factorization of 98 is $2 \cdot 7^2$.

Step 2: Create a list of all the different prime factors in each of the original numbers. In this case, that would be 2, 3 and 7.

Step 3: Raise each different prime factor to its highest power within any of the prime factorizations. In this case, it would be 2, 3 and 7^2.

Step 4: Write these powers as a product: $2 \cdot 3 \cdot 7^2$. Since $2 \cdot 3 \cdot 7^2 = 294$, the least common multiple of 42 and 98 is 294.

Example 2: Find the least common multiple of 20, 75 and 90.

Solution:

Step 1: Find the prime factorization of each number. The prime factorization of 20 is $2^2 \cdot 5$, the prime factorization of 75 is $3 \cdot 5^2$ and the prime factorization of 90 is $2 \cdot 3^2 \cdot 5$.

Step 2: Create a list of all the different prime factors in each of the original numbers. In this case, that would be 2, 3 and 5.

Step 3: Raise each different prime factor to its highest power within any of the prime factorizations. In this case, it would be 2^2, 3^2 and 5^2.

Step 4: Write these powers as a product: $2^2 \cdot 3^2 \cdot 5^2$. Since $2^2 \cdot 3^2 \cdot 5^2 = 900$, the least common multiple of 20, 75 and 90 is 900.

Note: If one of the original numbers is a prime number, then in place of finding the prime factorization, just list the prime number by itself.

Example 3: Find the least common multiple of 7 and 12.

Solution:

Step 1: Find the prime factorization of each number. Since 7 is a prime number, list it by itself. The prime factorization of 12 is $2 \cdot 2 \cdot 3$.

Step 2: Create a list of all the different prime factors in each of the original numbers. In this case, that would be 2, 3 and 7.

Step 3: Raise each different prime factor to its highest power within any of the prime factorizations. In this case, it would be 2^2, 3 and 7.

Step 4: Write these powers as a product: $2^2 \cdot 3 \cdot 7$. Since $2^2 \cdot 3 \cdot 7 = 84$, the least common multiple of 7 and 12 is 84.

Example 4: Find the least common multiple of 6 and 18.

Solution:

Step 1: Find the prime factorization of each number. The prime factorization of 6 is $2 \cdot 3$ and the prime factorization of 18 is $2 \cdot 3^2$.

Step 2: Create a list of all the different prime factors in each of the original numbers. In this case, that would be 2 and 3.

Step 3: Raise each different prime factor to its highest power within any of the prime factorizations. In this case, it would be 2 and 3^2.

Step 4: Write these powers as a product: $2 \cdot 3^2$. Since $2 \cdot 3^2 = 18$, the least common multiple of 6 and 18 is 18.

Another procedure that involves prime factorization is called finding the **greatest common factor**. This process can be used in multiplying and dividing fractions. The greatest common factor of two numbers is the largest number that is a factor of both numbers.

Look at the numbers 12 and 18. To find the number that is the greatest common factor of both numbers, we follow a 3-step process.

Step 1: Find the prime factorization of each number. The prime factorization of 12 is $2 \cdot 2 \cdot 3$ and the prime factorization of 18 is $2 \cdot 3 \cdot 3$.

Step 2: Determine what factors are common to each prime factorization. In this case they each have common factors of 2 and 3.

Step 3: Form the product of these common factors. The result is the greatest common factor. In this case that would be the product of 2 and 3, which is 6. The greatest common factor of 12 and 18 is the number 6.

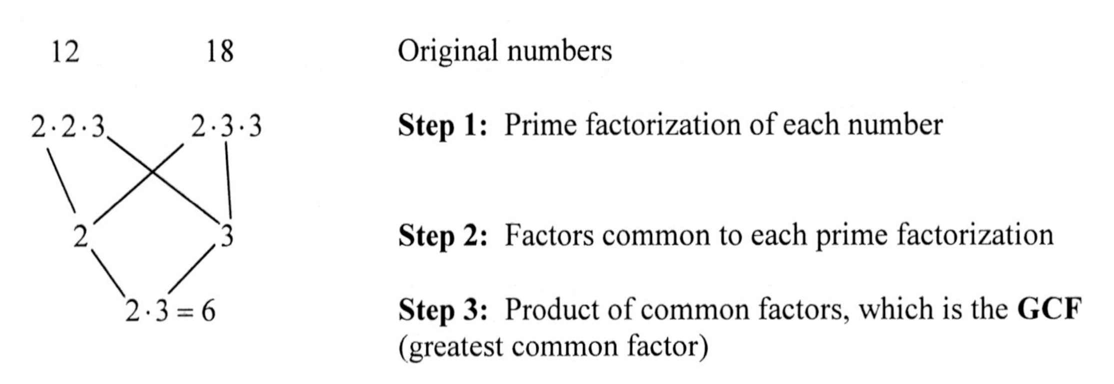

Using the numbers 45 and 60, find the greatest common factor of both numbers following the 3-step process.

Step 1: Find the prime factorization of each number. The prime factorization of 45 is $3 \cdot 3 \cdot 5$ and the prime factorization of 60 is $2 \cdot 2 \cdot 3 \cdot 5$.

Step 2: Determine what factors are common to each prime factorization. In this case, they each have common factors of 3 and 5.

Step 3: Form the product of these common factors. The result is the greatest common factor. In this case, that would be the product of 3 and 5, which is 15. The greatest common factor of 45 and 60 is the number 15.

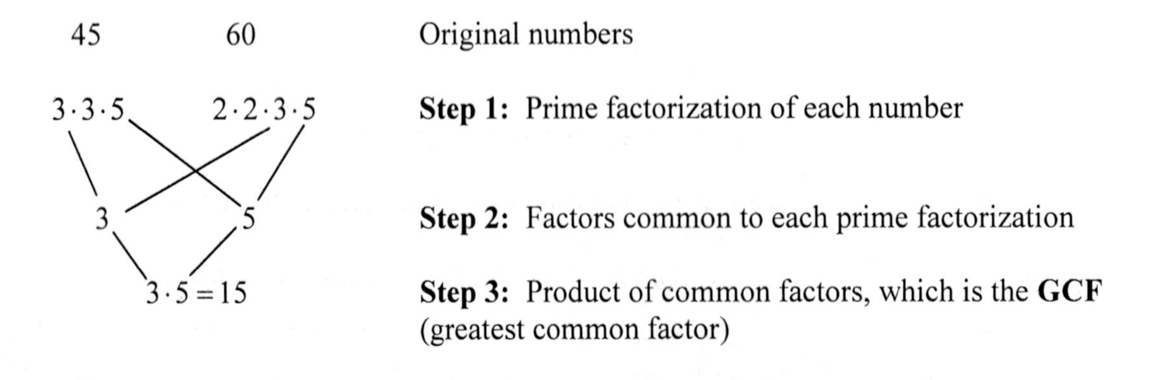

We can summarize this 3-step process as follows: **The greatest common factor of two or more numbers is the product of the prime factors that are common to all of these numbers.**

Note: There is an exception to this rule. If two or more numbers have no prime factors in common, then we say that their greatest common factor is 1.

Example 5: Find the greatest common factor of 42 and 98.

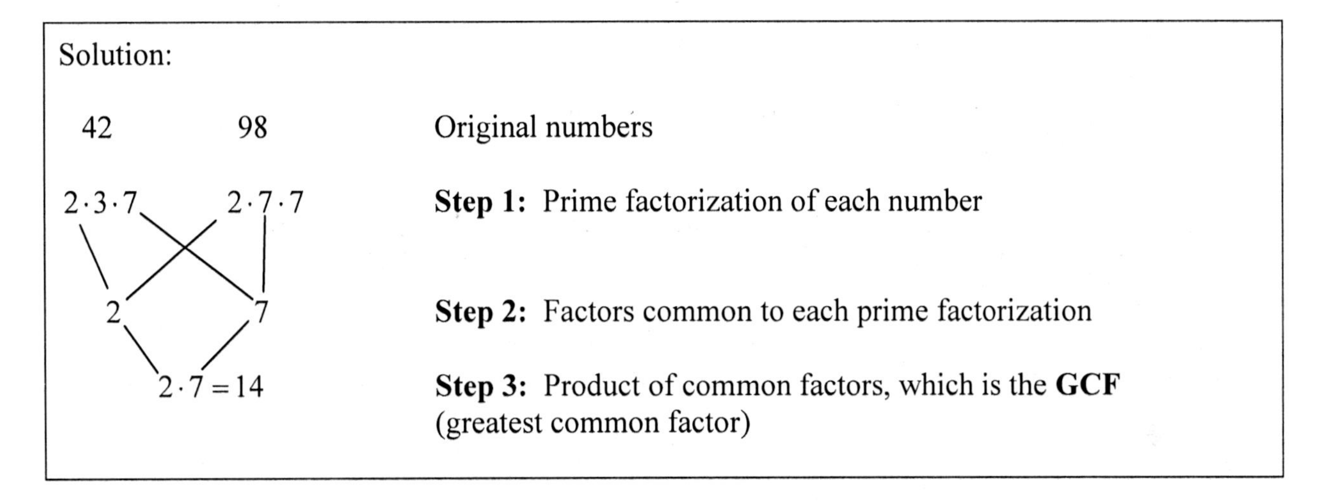

Example 6: Find the greatest common factor of 20, 75 and 90.

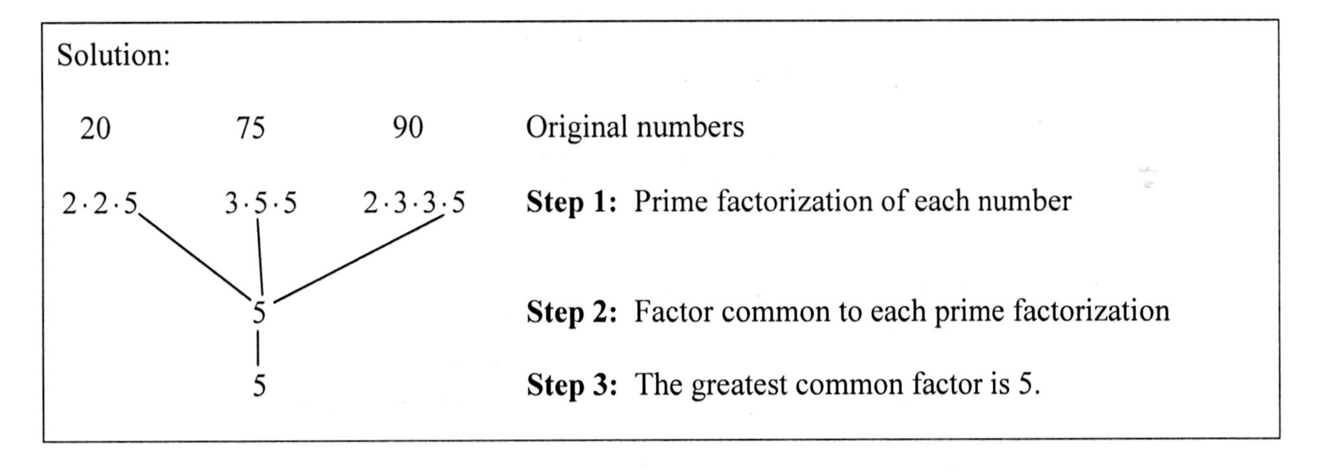

Example 7: Find the greatest common factor of 14 and 25.

Solution:

14	25	Original numbers
$2 \cdot 7$	$5 \cdot 5$	**Step 1:** Prime factorization of each number
No common prime factors		**Step 2:** Factors common to each prime factorization
		Step 3: The greatest common factor is the number 1.

Here are some situations where we can use the idea of the least common multiple or the greatest common factor to solve application problems.

Example 8: Ben and Doug are jogging around an oval shaped track. It takes Ben 6 minutes to complete each lap of the track while it takes Doug 4 minutes to complete the same lap. If they start at the same place and at the same time, how often will they be together at the same place they started? How many laps will Doug jog in between each time he joins Ben at the starting place?

Solution: Since it takes Ben 6 minutes to complete a lap and it takes Doug 4 minutes to complete the same lap, in order to find out how often they will be together at the same place they started, we need to find the LCM of 6 and 4.

Step 1: Find the prime factorization of each number. The prime factorization of 6 is $2 \cdot 3$ and the prime factorization of 4 is 2^2.

Step 2: Create a list of all the different prime factors in each of the original numbers. In this case, that would be 2 and 3.

Step 3: Raise each different prime factor to its highest power within any of the prime factorizations. In this case, it would be 2^2 and 3.

Step 4: Write these powers as a product: $2^2 \cdot 3$. Since $2^2 \cdot 3 = 12$, the least common multiple of 6 and 4 is 12.

Ben and Doug will be together at the starting place every 12 minutes. Since Doug completes a lap every 4 minutes, and 12 minutes divided by 4 minutes equals 3, Doug will jog 3 laps between each time he joins Ben at the starting place.

Example 9: Jim delivers bundles of newspapers to the paperboys on 3 different paper routes. The amount of newspapers required for the routes is 50, 75, and 125. What's the largest amount of newspapers that could be bundled together so that Jim can make his deliveries without opening any bundles?

Solution: We are looking for the largest number that goes into 50, 75, and 125 at the same time. In other words, we are looking for the GCF of 50, 75, and 125.

Step 1: Find the prime factorization of each number. The prime factorization of 50 is $2 \cdot 5 \cdot 5$, the prime factorization of 75 is $3 \cdot 5 \cdot 5$ and the prime factorization of 125 is $5 \cdot 5 \cdot 5$.

Step 2: Determine what factors are common to each prime factorization. In this case, they each have common factors of 5 and 5.

Step 3: Form the product of these common factors. The result is the greatest common factor. In this case, that would be the product of 5 and 5, which is 25. The greatest common factor of 50, 75 and 125 is the number 25.

The largest number of newspapers that could be put in each bundle is 25.

Section 1 exercises. Find the Least Common Multiple (LCM) of each group of numbers.

1. 5 and 10

2. 3 and 6

3. 3 and 10

4. 5 and 7

5. 4 and 6

6. 9 and 12

7. 15 and 25

8. 10 and 15

9. 18 and 27

10. 24 and 40

11. 8 and 12

12. 6 and 14

13. 17 and 51

14. 13 and 39

15. 32 and 48

16. 24 and 36

17. 30 and 40

18. 20 and 30

19. 25 and 40

20. 35 and 60

21. 3, 5, and 7

22. 2, 3, and 5

23. 4, 6, and 15

24. 9, 10 and 15

25. 15, 27, and 30

26. 6, 8, and 12

27. 30, 40, and 50

28. 15, 20, and 25

29. 14, 20, and 24

30. 21, 30, and 54

31. 6, 10, and 15

32. 15, 21, and 35

Find the Greatest Common Factor (GCF) of each group of numbers.

33. 4 and 18

34. 9 and 12

35. 21 and 28

36. 20 and 45

37. 24 and 56

38. 24 and 60

39. 10 and 21

40. 15 and 28

41. 36 and 63

42. 45 and 54

43. 12 and 21

44. 39 and 93

45. 20 and 50

46. 30 and 70

47. 44 and 52

48. 66 and 78

49. 60 and 105

50. 48 and 80

51. 38 and 95

52. 65 and 91

53. 2, 3, and 5

54. 3, 5, and 7

55. 4, 6, and 15

56. 15, 20 and 30

57. 18, 30, and 42

58. 28, 70, and 98

59. 36, 72, and 96

60. 90, 108, and 126

61. 39, 51, and 69

62. 52, 68, and 76

63. 21, 49, and 84

64. 42, 54, and 66

Solve the following application problems.

65. **a)** If hotdog buns come in a package of 8 and all beef franks come in a package of 10, then what's the fewest number of people you could serve a hotdog to and not have any partial packages left over? (Serving no people is not considered an option).

b) Now, suppose that everyone wants relish on their hotdog. If relish comes in a 12 serving package, what's the fewest number of people you could serve a hotdog with relish to without having any partial packages left over?

c) How many packages of relish would be used?

66. **a)** If hamburger buns come in a package of 12 and hamburger patties come in a package of 9, then what's the fewest number of people you could serve a hamburger to and not have any partial packages left over? (Serving no people is not considered an option).

b) Now, suppose that everyone wants cheese on their hamburger. If cheese comes 15 slices per package, what's the fewest number of people you could serve a hamburger with cheese to without having any partial packages left over?

c) How many packages of cheese would be used?

67. Chocolate chip cookies come in boxes of 36 and boxes of 60. If the cookies are sealed in several plastic bags inside of the boxes, what's the largest amount of cookies that the manufacturer can put in each bag so that they can be used in either box?

68. Peanut butter cookies come in boxes of 45 and boxes of 60. If the cookies are sealed in several plastic bags inside of the boxes, what's the largest amount of cookies that the manufacturer can put in each bag so that they can be used in either box?

69. Based on the drawing above, how many times would the middle gear have to rotate in order for all of the gears to return to the same places that they are now?

70. Based on the drawing above, how many times would the middle gear have to rotate in order for all of the gears to return to the same places that they are now?

71. A restaurant serves three different dishes that use bacon. One requires 8 strips of bacon, another requires 12 strips of bacon and a third requires 20 strips of bacon. Each time any one of the dishes is made, all the packages of bacon that are opened must be used up. If the bacon comes in sealed packages that are all the same size, what's the largest number of strips of bacon that could be in each package?

72. An espresso bar serves three different sizes of lattés. The small size uses 12 ounces of milk, the medium size uses 18 ounces of milk and the large size uses 30 ounces of milk. Each time any one of the lattés is made, all the cartons of milk that are opened must be used up. If the milk comes in sealed cartons that are all the same size, what's the largest number of ounces of milk that could be in each carton?

FRACTIONS

Section 2: An Introduction to Fractions

Statements like, "All fabric is $\frac{1}{3}$ off the regular price" or "The distance is $\frac{1}{4}$ of a mile" are common everyday expressions. Each statement includes a number known as a **fraction**. A fraction consists of two integers separated by a line that is called a **fraction bar**. Typically, the integers are stacked vertically. The top number is called the **numerator** and the bottom number is called the **denominator**.

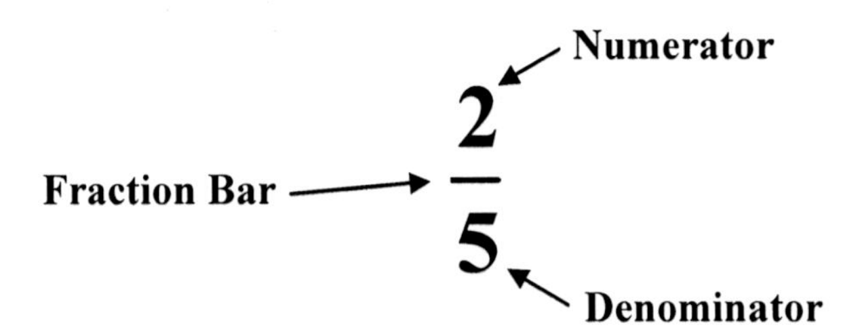

The denominator of a fraction tells into how many equal parts a quantity has been divided. The numerator of a fraction tells how many of those parts are present or being considered. For instance, suppose that a pie is cut into 6 equal pieces. Now, suppose that you eat 5 of those pieces. What fraction of the pie have you eaten? Since the pie was cut into 6 equal pieces, the denominator of the fraction would be a 6. Since you ate 5 pieces of the pie, the numerator would be 5. Consequently the fraction would be $\frac{5}{6}$. That is to say, you ate $\frac{5}{6}$ of the pie.

There are two types of fractions, proper and improper.

In a **proper fraction,** the numerator is smaller than the denominator. For example, $\frac{3}{7}$, $\frac{5}{8}$, or $\frac{1}{2}$.

A partially shaded object can be used to represent a proper fraction. For instance, in the following drawing the rectangle is divided into 8 equal parts. 5 of these parts are shaded, so the fraction of the rectangle that is shaded is $\frac{5}{8}$.

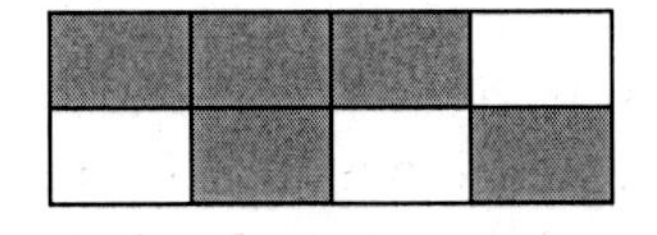

In an **improper fraction,** the numerator is greater than or equal to the denominator. For example, $\frac{21}{16}$, $\frac{9}{4}$, or $\frac{5}{5}$.

The following drawings can be used to represent an improper fraction. Each circle is divided into 6 equal parts. 13 of these parts are shaded, so the fraction of a circle that is shaded is $\frac{13}{6}$.

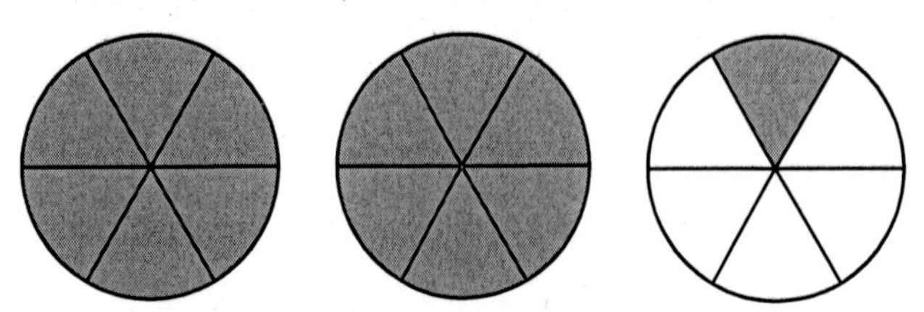

In Chapter 1, we stated that a division problem could be written in three different ways. Using the symbol $\overline{)\ }$, the symbol $\div$, or using a fraction bar.

$$3\overline{)12}^{\,4} \qquad 12 \div 3 = 4 \qquad \frac{12}{3} = 4$$

In other words, **a fraction bar is a division symbol**. Therefore, the fraction $\frac{13}{6}$ could be read as "$13 \div 6$" or "13 divided by 6."

In Chapter 1, we also stated that if any real number "a" is divided by 1, the quotient is "a."

In other words, $\frac{a}{1} = a$ and $a = \frac{a}{1}$. This means that any integer can be written as an improper fraction just but putting the integer over a denominator of 1. For example, 7 can be written as an improper fraction by writing it as $\frac{7}{1}$.

In Chapter 1, we learned about the division properties of zero. Let's look at what this means in terms of fractions.

For any real number a when $a \neq 0$, $0 \div a = 0$.

This means that 0 can be written as a fraction with 0 in the numerator and any number other than 0 in the denominator. For example, $\frac{0}{4}$.

For any real number a when $a \neq 0$, $a \div 0 =$ undefined.

This means that 0 can't be in the denominator of a fraction because then that fraction would be undefined. For example, $\frac{4}{0}$ is undefined.

Let's look again at these circles.

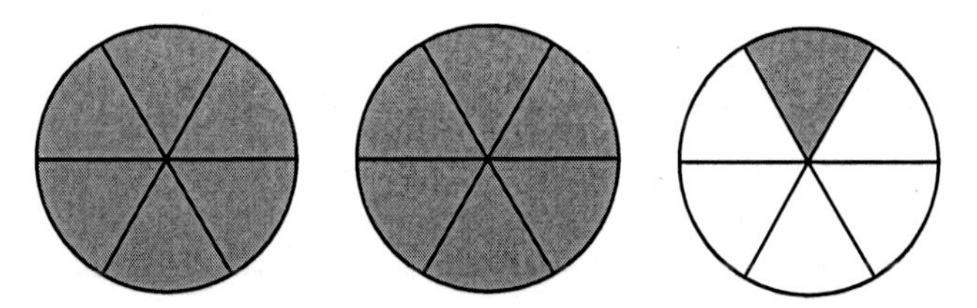

We established earlier that the shaded parts represented $\frac{13}{6}$, which is an improper fraction. We could also look at the drawings as 2 whole circles and $\frac{1}{6}$ of a circle being shaded, or $2\frac{1}{6}$ circles are shaded. So we see that $\frac{13}{6}$ and $2\frac{1}{6}$ are equal. The number $2\frac{1}{6}$ is called a **mixed number**. It consists of a whole-number part and a fraction part.

Whole-Number Part ⟶ $\mathbf{2\frac{1}{6}}$ ⟵ **Fraction Part**

Changing an improper fraction into a mixed number is a three-step process.
To change $\frac{13}{6}$ into $2\frac{1}{6}$, do the following:

Step 1: Divide the numerator by the denominator. The quotient becomes the whole-number part of the mixed number answer.

$$\begin{array}{r} 2 \\ 6\overline{)13} \\ -\,12 \\ \hline 1 \end{array}$$

Divisor ⟶ 6; 2 ⟵ **Quotient**; 1 ⟵ **Remainder**

Step 2: The remainder becomes the numerator and the divisor becomes the denominator of the fraction part of the mixed number answer.

$\frac{1}{6}$ — 1 ⟵ **Remainder**; **Divisor** ⟶ 6

Step 3: The mixed number is the sum of the whole-number part and the fraction part.

$$\begin{array}{r} 2\frac{1}{6} \leftarrow \\ 6\overline{)13} \\ -\,12 \\ \hline 1 \end{array}$$

Note: Instead of writing the remainder as R 1 like we did back in Chapter 1, the remainder becomes $\frac{1}{6}$, which is the fraction part of the mixed number answer. In this way, $\frac{13}{6}$ becomes $2\frac{1}{6}$.

Example 1: Change the improper fraction $\frac{17}{4}$ into a mixed number.

Solution: Step 1: Divide the numerator by the denominator. The quotient becomes the whole-number part of the mixed number answer.

$$\begin{array}{r} 4 \\ 4\overline{)17} \\ -16 \\ \hline 1 \end{array}$$

Divisor → 4; Quotient ← 4; Remainder ← 1

Step 2: The remainder becomes the numerator and the divisor becomes the denominator of the fraction part of the mixed number answer.

$\frac{1}{4}$ (1 ← Remainder; Divisor → 4)

Step 3: The mixed number is the sum of the whole-number part and the fraction part.

$$\begin{array}{r} 4\frac{1}{4} \\ 4\overline{)17} \\ -16 \\ \hline 1 \end{array}$$

← Final Answer

Example 2: Change the improper fraction $\frac{14}{5}$ into a mixed number.

Solution: Step 1: Divide the numerator by the denominator. The quotient becomes the whole-number part of the mixed number answer.

$$\begin{array}{r} 2 \\ 5\overline{)14} \\ -10 \\ \hline 4 \end{array}$$

Divisor → 5; Quotient ← 2; Remainder ← 4

Step 2: The remainder becomes the numerator and the divisor becomes the denominator of the fraction part of the mixed number answer.

$\frac{4}{5}$ (4 ← Remainder; Divisor → 5)

Step 3: The mixed number is the sum of the whole-number part and the fraction part.

$$\begin{array}{r} 2\frac{4}{5} \\ 5\overline{)14} \\ -10 \\ \hline 4 \end{array}$$

← Final Answer

Note: An improper fraction with a denominator of 1 changes into a whole number rather than a mixed number. For example $\frac{8}{1}$ becomes 8.

Just as an improper fraction can be written as a mixed number, a mixed number can be written as an improper fraction. Changing a mixed number into an improper fraction is a 3-step process.

Earlier we looked at how to change $\frac{13}{6}$ into $2\frac{1}{6}$. Now let's look at how to change $2\frac{1}{6}$ into $\frac{13}{6}$.

Step 1: Multiply together the whole number and the denominator of the fraction.

Whole Number → $2\frac{1}{6}$ ← **Denominator of the Fraction**

$$2 \cdot 6 = 12$$

Step 2: Add this product to the numerator of the fraction.

$2\frac{1}{6}$ ← **Numerator of the Fraction**

$$1 + 12 = 13$$

Step 3: The result of step 2 becomes the numerator of the improper fraction. The denominator of the improper fraction remains the same as the denominator of the fraction part of the original mixed number.

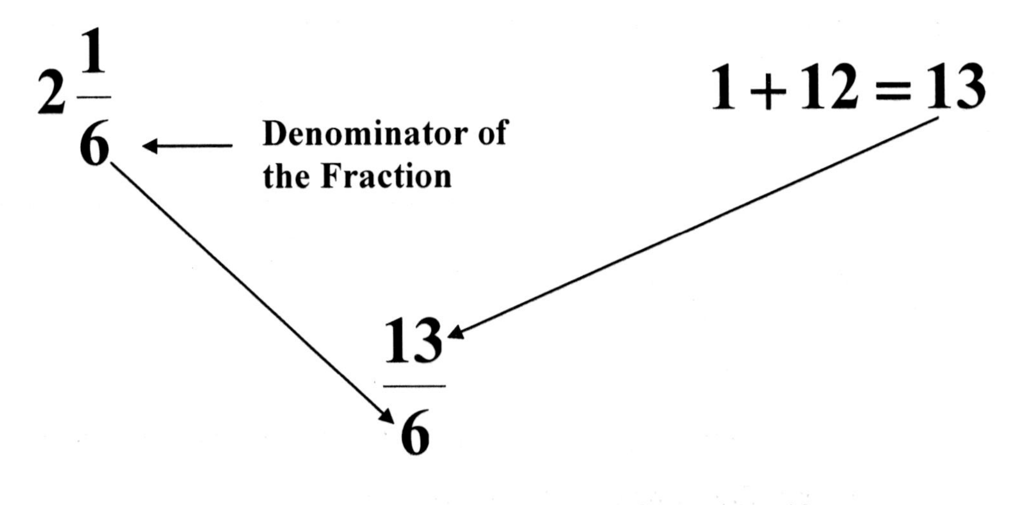

So, $2\frac{1}{6} = \frac{13}{6}$.

Example 3: Change the mixed number $3\frac{7}{8}$ into an improper fraction.

Solution: Step1: Multiply together the whole number and the denominator of the fraction.

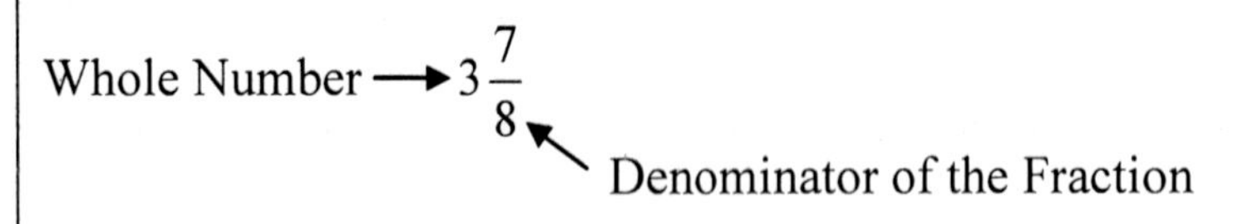

$3 \cdot 8 = 24$

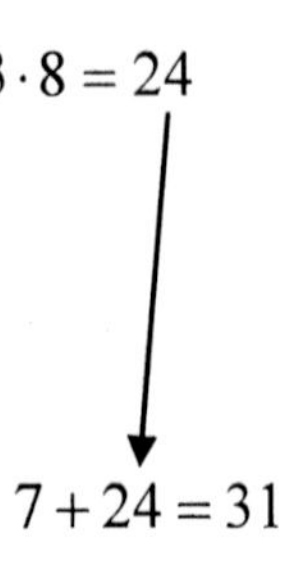

Step 2: Add this product to the numerator of the fraction.

$3\frac{7}{8}$ ← Numerator of the Fraction

$7 + 24 = 31$

Step 3: The result of step 2 becomes the numerator of the improper fraction. The denominator of the improper fraction remains the same as the denominator of the fraction part of the original mixed number.

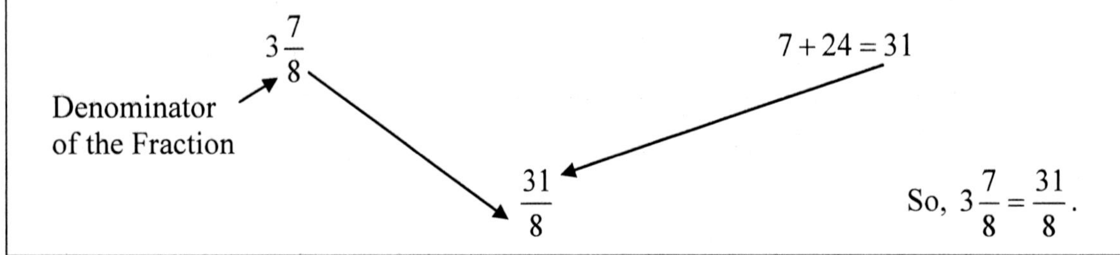

So, $3\frac{7}{8} = \frac{31}{8}$.

Example 4: Change the mixed number $5\frac{3}{7}$ into an improper fraction.

Solution: Step1: Multiply together the whole number and the denominator of the fraction.

Whole Number → $5\frac{3}{7}$ ← Denominator of the Fraction

$5 \cdot 7 = 35$

Step 2: Add this product to the numerator of the fraction.

$5\frac{3}{7}$ ← Numerator of the Fraction

$3 + 35 = 38$

Step 3: The result of step 2 becomes the numerator of the improper fraction. The denominator of the improper fraction remains the same as the denominator of the fraction part of the original mixed number.

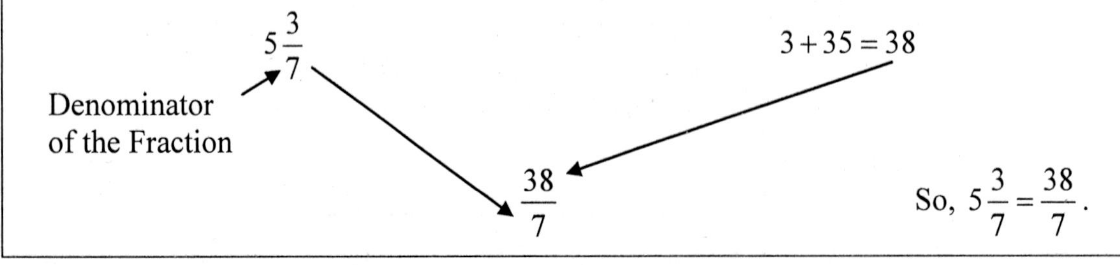

So, $5\frac{3}{7} = \frac{38}{7}$.

At the beginning of Chapter 1 when we looked at how to write numbers using words, we were careful to avoid the use of the word **"and"**. This was because **"and"** is used to separate the whole-number part from the fraction part when writing a mixed number. In Chapter 4 we will use the word **"and"** to indicate the location of the decimal point in a decimal number.

Example 5: Write the mixed number $7\frac{1}{2}$ in words.

Solution: Seven and one half

When writing a fraction in words, the number in the denominator tells what each part is worth. The number in the numerator tells how many of these parts there are.

Example 6: Write the fraction $\frac{2}{3}$ in words.

Solution: The three in the denominator indicates dividing into three equal parts called thirds. The two in the numerator indicates how many thirds there are. Therefore, the answer is two thirds.

Example 7: Write the fraction $\frac{19}{4}$ in words.

Solution: The four in the denominator indicates dividing into four equal parts called fourths. The nineteen in the numerator indicates how many fourths there are. Therefore, the answer is nineteen fourths.

Example 8: Write thirteen halves using digits.

Solution: The word used to describe the denominator is halves. This indicates dividing into two equal parts, so a two is in the denominator. Since there are thirteen of these halves, the number in the numerator is a thirteen. Therefore, the answer is $\frac{13}{2}$.

Example 9: Write five and seven eighteenths using digits.

Solution: The word "and" separates the whole-number part from the fraction part of a mixed number. Five is the whole-number part while seven eighteenths is the fraction part of the mixed number. The word used to describe the denominator of the fraction is eighteenths. This indicates dividing into eighteen equal parts, so an eighteen is in the denominator. Since there are seven of these eighteenths, the number in the numerator is a seven. Therefore, the answer is $5\frac{7}{18}$.

Different fractions can be used to represent the same quantity. For instance, the same size of rectangle can be divided into a different amount of equal parts.

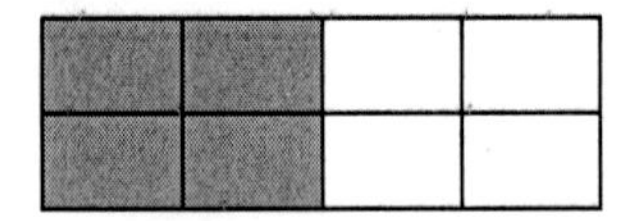

The fraction that represents the shaded area of this rectangle is $\frac{4}{8}$.

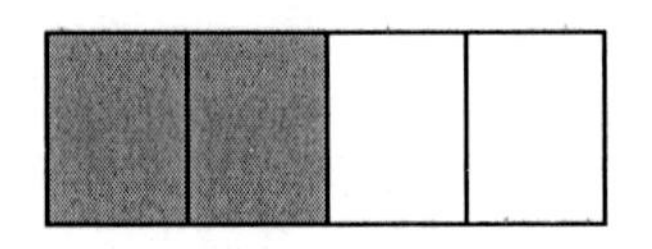

The fraction that represents the shaded area of this rectangle is $\frac{2}{4}$.

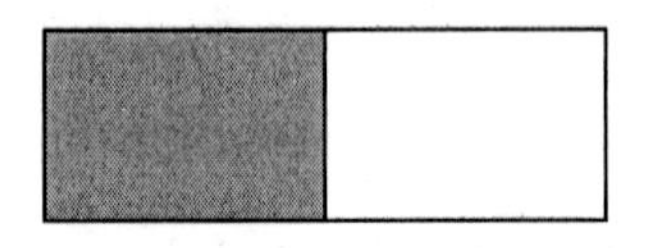

The fraction that represents the shaded area of this rectangle is $\frac{1}{2}$.

Since all three rectangles are the same size and the shaded areas of all three rectangles are the same size, we can conclude that $\frac{4}{8}=\frac{2}{4}=\frac{1}{2}$.

$\frac{4}{8}$, $\frac{2}{4}$ and $\frac{1}{2}$ are what are known as **equivalent fractions**. Equivalent fractions are fractions that represent the same numerical value. There are two ways to create a fraction equivalent to an existing fraction. One way is to multiply both the numerator and the denominator of the existing fraction by the same non-zero number. The other way is to divide both the numerator and the denominator of the existing fraction by the same non-zero number.

For example, if we start with the fraction $\frac{2}{4}$ and multiply both the numerator and the denominator by 2 we get $\frac{2\cdot 2}{4\cdot 2}$, which equals $\frac{4}{8}$. So $\frac{2}{4}=\frac{4}{8}$, or $\frac{2}{4}$ and $\frac{4}{8}$ are equivalent fractions.

On the other hand, if we start with the fraction $\frac{2}{4}$ and divide both the numerator and the denominator by 2 we get $\frac{2\div 2}{4\div 2}$, which equals $\frac{1}{2}$. So $\frac{2}{4}=\frac{1}{2}$, or $\frac{2}{4}$ and $\frac{1}{2}$ are equivalent fractions.

A more generalized way of describing this process is as follows:

If $\frac{a}{b}$ is a fraction, then $\frac{a \cdot c}{b \cdot c}$ is an equivalent fraction, provided that $b \neq 0$ and $c \neq 0$.

Multiplying the numerator and the denominator of a fraction by the same non-zero number creates a new equivalent fraction.

If $\frac{a}{b}$ is a fraction, then $\frac{a \div c}{b \div c}$ is an equivalent fraction, provided that $b \neq 0$ and $c \neq 0$.

Dividing the numerator and the denominator of a fraction by the same non-zero number creates a new equivalent fraction.

(Remember that dividing by zero is undefined.)

Suppose we want to rewrite the fraction $\frac{3}{8}$ as an equivalent fraction with a denominator of 40. In other words, $\frac{3}{8} = \frac{?}{40}$. Now the question is, what number do we multiply both the numerator and the denominator of $\frac{3}{8}$ by, in order to create the new equivalent fraction? To find this number, divide the new denominator by the old denominator. This is $40 \div 8 = 5$. Since $40 \div 8 = 5$, then $8 \cdot 5 = 40$. Now multiply both the numerator and the denominator of $\frac{3}{8}$ by the number 5 and we get $\frac{3 \cdot 5}{8 \cdot 5} = \frac{15}{40}$.

Example 10: Rewrite the fraction $\frac{4}{7}$ as an equivalent fraction that has a denominator of 42.

Solution: $\frac{4}{7} = \frac{?}{42}$

Divide the new denominator by the old denominator. $42 \div 7 = 6$.

Multiply both the numerator and the denominator of $\frac{4}{7}$ by the number 6.

$\frac{4 \cdot 6}{7 \cdot 6} = \frac{24}{42}$ So, $\frac{24}{42}$ is equivalent to $\frac{4}{7}$.

Sometimes we need to write a fraction in what is called **reduced form** or **lowest terms**. Writing a fraction in this form involves two steps.

Step 1: Find the prime factorization of both the numerator and the denominator of the fraction.

Step 2: Divide the numerator and the denominator by any common prime factors in order to reduce the fraction to lowest terms. (Reduce out common factors.)

Example 11: Rewrite the fraction $\frac{35}{55}$ in lowest terms.

Solution:

Step 1: The prime factorization of 35 is $5 \cdot 7$. The prime factorization of 55 is $5 \cdot 11$.

Writing the fraction $\frac{35}{55}$ in prime factored form, we get $\frac{5 \cdot 7}{5 \cdot 11}$.

Step 2: Reduce out the common factor of 5. (Divide the numerator and the denominator by 5.)

This reduces the fraction to $\frac{\overset{1}{\cancel{5}} \cdot 7}{\underset{1}{\cancel{5}} \cdot 11}$ which simplifies into $\frac{7}{11}$.

$\frac{35}{55}$ becomes $\frac{7}{11}$ when written in lowest terms.

Example 12: Rewrite the fraction $\frac{30x}{42}$ in lowest terms.

Solution:

Step 1: Writing the fraction $\frac{30x}{42}$ in prime factored form, we get $\frac{2 \cdot 3 \cdot 5 \cdot x}{2 \cdot 3 \cdot 7}$.

Step 2: Reduce out the common factors of 2 and 3.

The fraction $\frac{\overset{1}{\cancel{2}} \cdot \overset{1}{\cancel{3}} \cdot 5 \cdot x}{\underset{1}{\cancel{2}} \cdot \underset{1}{\cancel{3}} \cdot 7}$ simplifies into $\frac{5x}{7}$.

$\frac{30x}{42}$ becomes $\frac{5x}{7}$ when written in lowest terms.

Note: Changing an improper fraction into a mixed number is not considered to be reducing the fraction, or writing the fraction in lowest terms.

When equivalent fractions are reduced to lowest terms, they are identical.

Example 13: Which of the following fractions are equivalent: $\frac{4}{9}, \frac{6}{18}, \frac{20}{45}, \frac{8}{18}$ and $\frac{10}{14}$?

Solution: Reduce each fraction to lowest terms in order to determine which fractions are equivalent. To do this, find the prime factorization of each fraction and then reduce out common factors.

$\frac{4}{9} = \frac{2 \cdot 2}{3 \cdot 3} = \frac{4}{9}$ since there are no common factors to reduce out.

$$\frac{6}{18} = \frac{2 \cdot 3}{2 \cdot 3 \cdot 3} = \frac{\overset{1}{\cancel{2}} \cdot \overset{1}{\cancel{3}}}{\underset{1}{\cancel{2}} \cdot \underset{1}{\cancel{3}} \cdot 3} = \frac{1}{3}$$

$$\frac{20}{45} = \frac{2 \cdot 2 \cdot 5}{3 \cdot 3 \cdot 5} = \frac{2 \cdot 2 \cdot \overset{1}{\cancel{5}}}{3 \cdot 3 \cdot \underset{1}{\cancel{5}}} = \frac{4}{9}$$

$$\frac{8}{18} = \frac{2 \cdot 2 \cdot 2}{2 \cdot 3 \cdot 3} = \frac{\overset{1}{\cancel{2}} \cdot 2 \cdot 2}{\underset{1}{\cancel{2}} \cdot 3 \cdot 3} = \frac{4}{9}$$

$$\frac{10}{14} = \frac{2 \cdot 5}{2 \cdot 7} = \frac{\overset{1}{\cancel{2}} \cdot 5}{\underset{1}{\cancel{2}} \cdot 7} = \frac{5}{7}$$

By looking at each fraction in lowest terms, we see that $\frac{4}{9}, \frac{20}{45}$, and $\frac{8}{18}$ are equivalent fractions.

Section 2 exercises. Identify each of the following numbers as a proper fraction, an improper fraction, or a mixed number.

1. $\frac{8}{9}$

2. $\frac{7}{1}$

3. $4\frac{2}{11}$

4. $\frac{3}{7}$

5. $\frac{9}{5}$

6. $7\frac{8}{13}$

7. $1\frac{2}{3}$

8. $\frac{6}{6}$

9. $\frac{5}{14}$

10. $5\frac{6}{17}$

11. $\frac{8}{7}$

12. $\frac{1}{4}$

Represent the shaded area in each drawing with the appropriate fraction.

13.

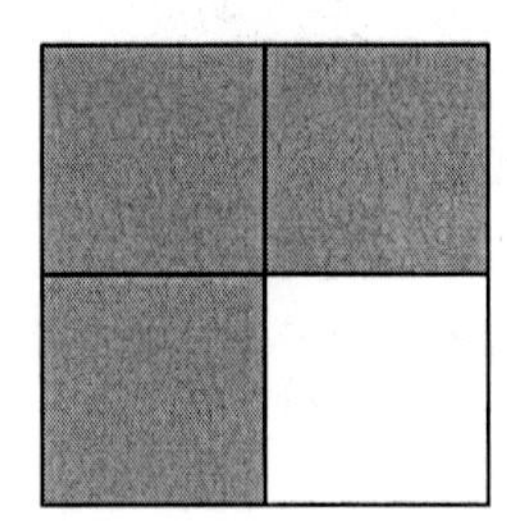

14.

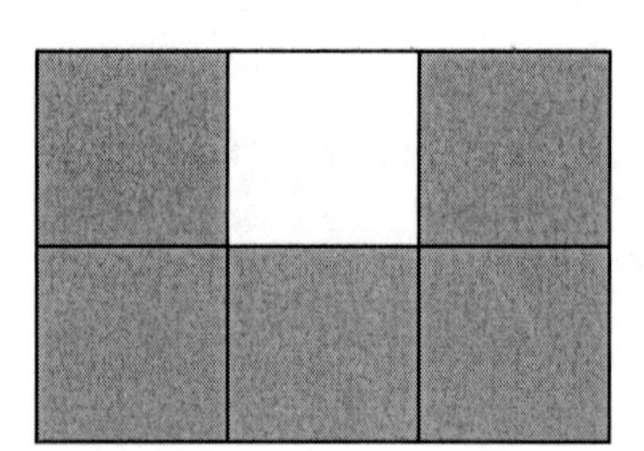

15.

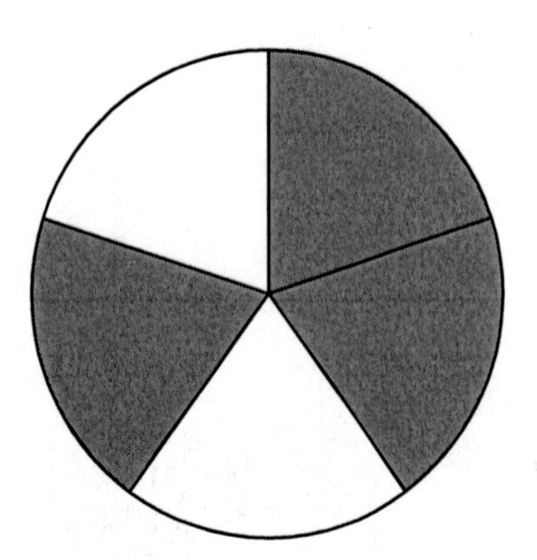

16.

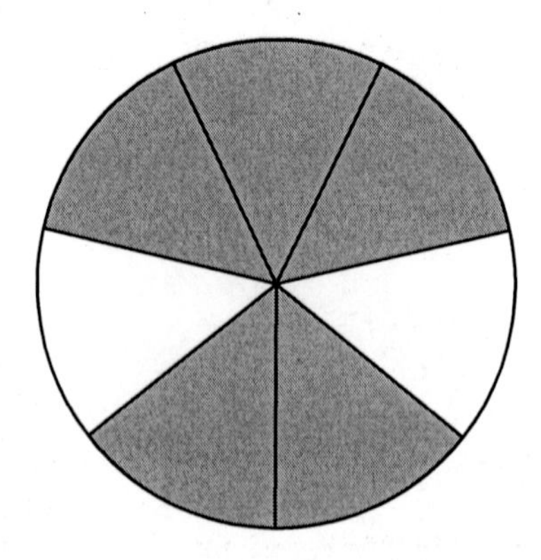

17.

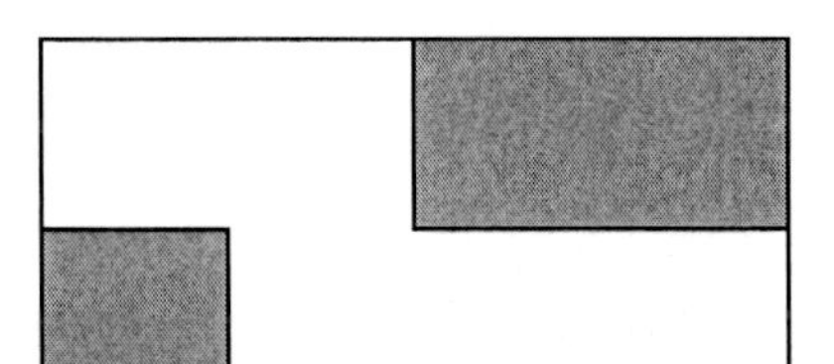

18.

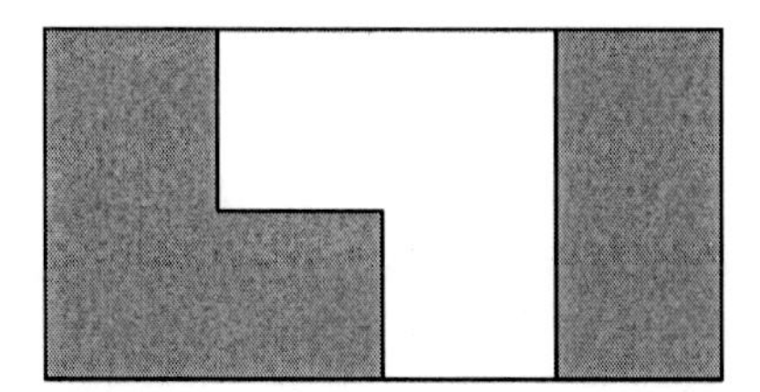

19.

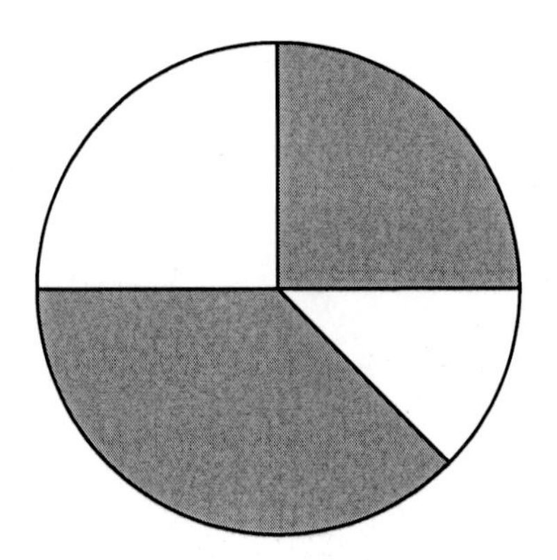

20.

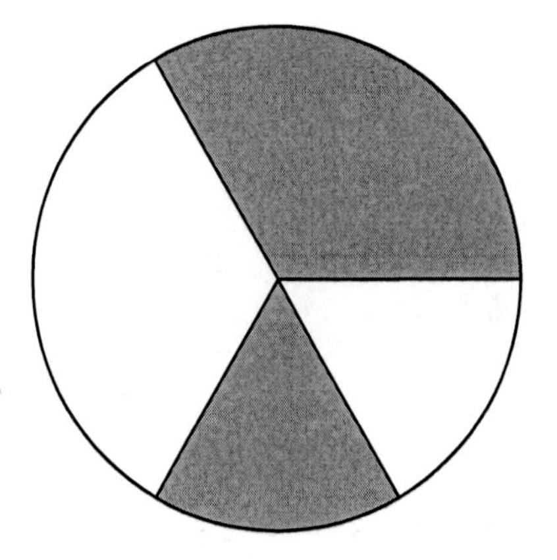

Represent the shaded area in each group of drawings as an improper fraction and then as a mixed number.

21.

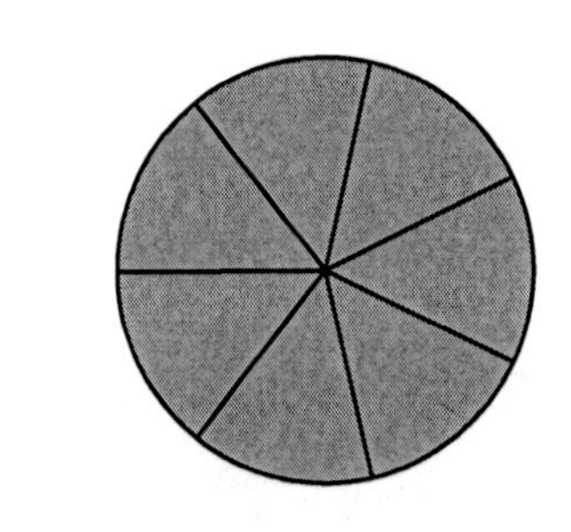

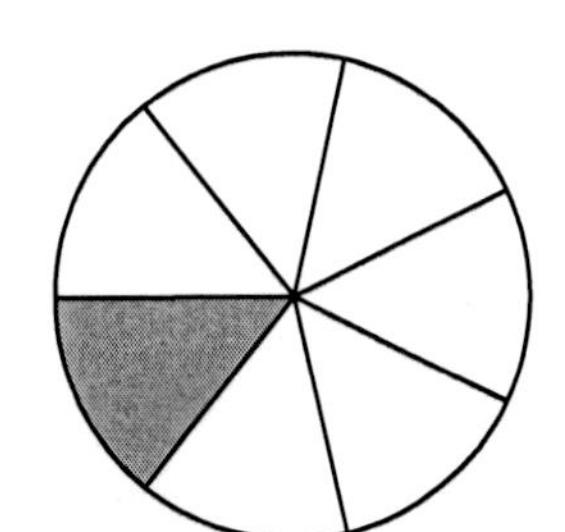

22.

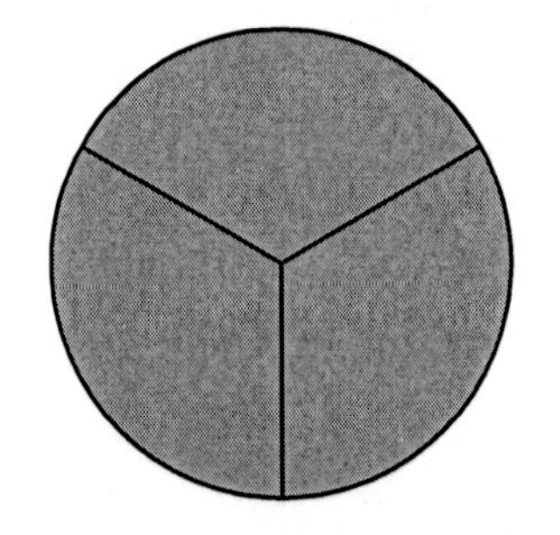

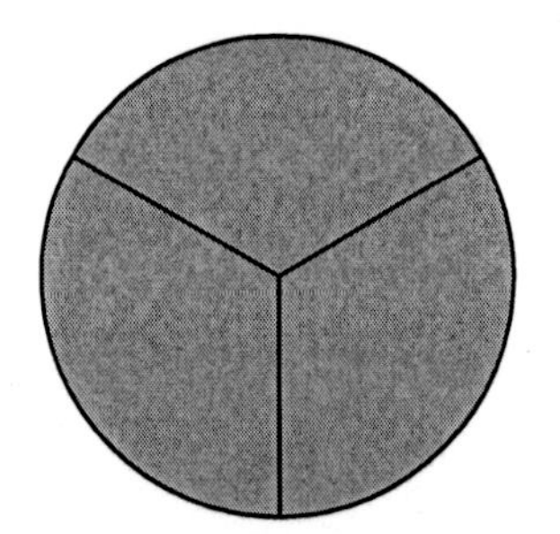

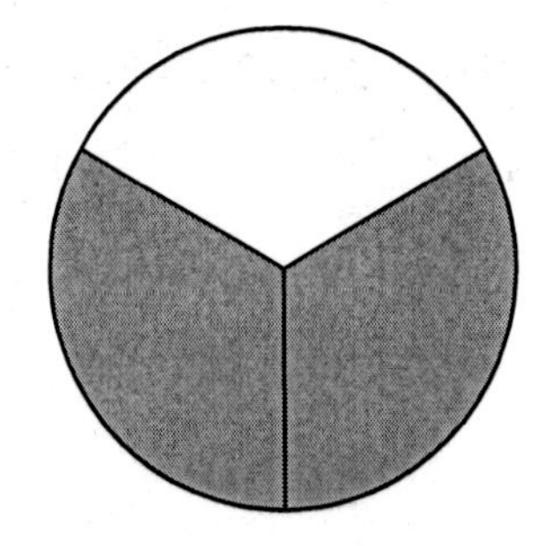

23.

24.

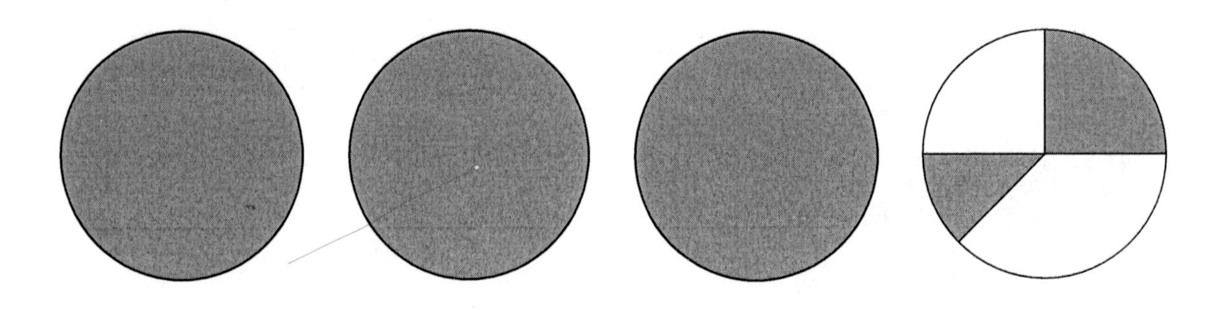

25. Draw a rectangle and shade $\frac{7}{12}$ of it.

26. Draw a rectangle and shade $\frac{5}{12}$ of it.

27. Draw a square and shade $\frac{3}{16}$ of it.

28. Draw a square and shade $\frac{9}{16}$ of it.

29. Draw a circle and shade $\frac{1}{4}$ of it.

30. Draw a circle and shade $\frac{3}{4}$ of it.

Write each fraction or mixed number in words.

31. $\frac{7}{9}$ **32.** $\frac{2}{5}$ **33.** $2\frac{3}{7}$ **34.** $4\frac{1}{6}$

35. $-\frac{8}{11}$ **36.** $-\frac{4}{3}$ **37.** $-6\frac{5}{6}$ **38.** $-10\frac{3}{10}$

39. $\frac{15}{2}$ **40.** $\frac{27}{4}$ **41.** $\frac{9}{8}$ **42.** $\frac{1}{25}$

Write each number using digits.

43. seven and nine tenths

44. five and four sevenths

45. negative nine fifteenths

46. negative three twentieths

47. three fourteenths

48. fourteen thirds

49. thirty-six fifths

50. two forty-ninths

51. twelve and one half

52. forty-one and seven eighths

53. one third

54. fifteen sixteenths

Change each improper fraction into a mixed number or whole number.

55. $\frac{16}{3}$ **56.** $\frac{12}{2}$ **57.** $\frac{19}{7}$ **58.** $\frac{17}{4}$ **59.** $\frac{6}{1}$

60. $\frac{14}{14}$ **61.** $\frac{37}{10}$ **62.** $\frac{37}{13}$ **63.** $\frac{15}{5}$ **64.** $\frac{29}{12}$

65. $\frac{51}{4}$ **66.** $\frac{18}{1}$ **67.** $\frac{24}{6}$ **68.** $\frac{36}{7}$ **69.** $\frac{25}{9}$

70. $\frac{28}{4}$ **71.** $\frac{49}{8}$ **72.** $\frac{53}{9}$ **73.** $\frac{13}{13}$ **74.** $\frac{73}{15}$

Change each mixed number or whole number into an improper fraction.

75. $7\frac{3}{4}$ **76.** $6\frac{5}{8}$ **77.** $9\frac{8}{11}$ **78.** $8\frac{7}{10}$ **79.** 6

80. $4\frac{2}{7}$ **81.** $5\frac{5}{9}$ **82.** $3\frac{13}{15}$ **83.** 48 **84.** $9\frac{4}{11}$

85. $10\frac{7}{8}$ **86.** 12 **87.** $6\frac{4}{5}$ **88.** $17\frac{1}{3}$ **89.** $12\frac{7}{10}$

90. $21\frac{3}{4}$ **91.** $33\frac{1}{3}$ **92.** 23 **93.** $1\frac{7}{13}$ **94.** $2\frac{71}{75}$

Write an equivalent fraction that has the given new denominator.

95. $\frac{2}{3}=\frac{?}{42}$ **96.** $\frac{3}{4}=\frac{?}{60}$ **97.** $\frac{9}{10}=\frac{?}{60}$ **98.** $\frac{2}{5}=\frac{?}{30}$

99. $\frac{3}{7}=\frac{?}{49}$ **100.** $3=\frac{?}{5}$ **101.** $\frac{8}{17}=\frac{?}{306}$ **102.** $\frac{4}{9}=\frac{?}{207}$

103. $\frac{5}{6}=\frac{?}{48}$ **104.** $\frac{5}{13}=\frac{?}{52}$ **105.** $4=\frac{?}{91}$ **106.** $\frac{7}{16}=\frac{?}{80}$

107. $8=\frac{?}{7}$ **108.** $\frac{2}{11}=\frac{?}{88}$ **109.** $\frac{5}{8}=\frac{?}{56}$ **110.** $10=\frac{?}{27}$

111. $\frac{4}{15}=\frac{?}{900}$ **112.** $\frac{7}{12}=\frac{?}{600}$ **113.** $\frac{13}{18}=\frac{?}{756}$ **114.** $\frac{3}{14}=\frac{?}{742}$

Write each fraction in lowest terms.

115. $\frac{105}{63}$ **116.** $\frac{36}{28}$ **117.** $\frac{285}{665}$ **118.** $\frac{4x}{18}$ **119.** $\frac{53}{53}$

120. $\frac{6}{60}$ **121.** $\frac{45w}{63}$ **122.** $\frac{147}{392}$ **123.** $\frac{0}{7}$ **124.** $\frac{24y}{48}$

125. $\frac{462}{616}$ **126.** $\frac{17}{17}$ **127.** $\frac{16m}{16}$ **128.** $\frac{168}{420}$ **129.** $\frac{476}{680}$

130. $\frac{21k}{21}$ **131.** $\frac{21}{77}$ **132.** $\frac{315}{540}$ **133.** $\frac{9p}{27}$ **134.** $\frac{0}{19}$

Determine whether each pair of fractions is equivalent by writing each fraction in lowest terms.

135. $\frac{21}{54}, \frac{34}{90}$

136. $\frac{36}{52}, \frac{45}{65}$

137. $\frac{28}{49}, \frac{36}{63}$

138. $\frac{40}{72}, \frac{32}{54}$

139. $\frac{56w}{21}, \frac{72w}{27}$

140. $\frac{30x}{21}, \frac{50x}{34}$

141. $\frac{40}{60}, \frac{22}{33}$

142. $\frac{9}{57}, \frac{21}{123}$

143. $\frac{51w}{12}, \frac{68x}{16}$

144. $\frac{26w}{16}, \frac{52y}{32}$

145. $\frac{27}{33}, \frac{63}{77}$

146. $\frac{35}{100}, \frac{21}{60}$

147. Can a mixed number be changed into a proper fraction? Explain your answer.

148. Can a proper fraction be changed into a mixed number? Explain your answer.

FRACTIONS

Section 3: Comparing Fractions

We can tell that $2 < 7$, since 2 is to the left of 7 on a number line. If two fractions have the same denominator, such as $\frac{2}{9}$ and $\frac{7}{9}$, then by comparing the numerators we can also tell that $\frac{2}{9} < \frac{7}{9}$ since $2 < 7$. It is relatively easy to compare two whole numbers or two fractions with the same denominator by using an inequality.

Now, suppose we want to graph the fractions $\frac{2}{9}$ and $\frac{7}{9}$ on a number line. Since both $\frac{2}{9}$ and $\frac{7}{9}$ are between 0 and 1, we take a small part of a number line and divide it into sections, each of which is $\frac{1}{9}$. Our number line graph looks like this:

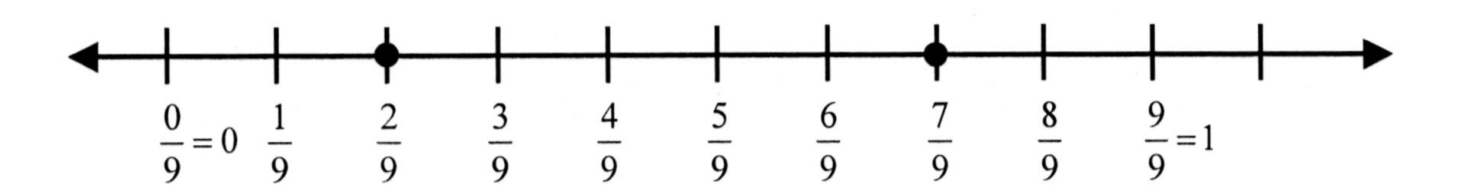

We can see from the graph that indeed, $\frac{2}{9} < \frac{7}{9}$. Suppose we want to graph the fraction $\frac{7}{3}$ on a number line. Since $\frac{7}{3}$ is an improper fraction, by changing it into a mixed number we can tell which two whole numbers it is located between on a number line. By using long division, we find that $\frac{7}{3}$ is equivalent to $2\frac{1}{3}$. So, $\frac{7}{3}$ is between 2 and 3 on a number line. We can take a number line and divide it into sections, each of which is $\frac{1}{3}$. Our number line graph looks like this:

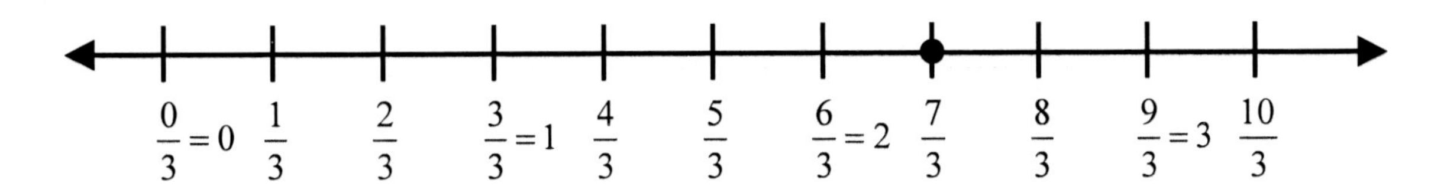

Example 1: Graph the mixed number $3\frac{1}{4}$ on a number line.

Solution: Since $3\frac{1}{4}$ is between 3 and 4 we will draw a number line that extends to the right up to the number 4. We will also divide the part of the number line that is between 3 and 4 into sections, each of which is $\frac{1}{4}$. Our number line graph looks like this:

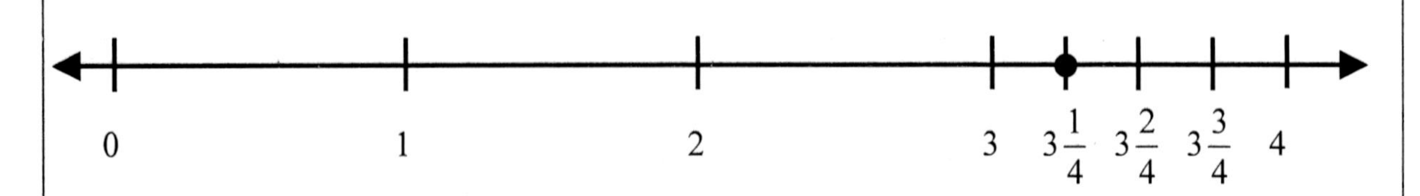

By the way, fractions and mixed numbers can be negative as well as positive.

Example 2: Graph the fraction $-\frac{4}{7}$ on a number line.

Solution: Since $-\frac{4}{7}$ is between -1 and 0, we take a small part of a number line and divide it into sections, each of which is $\frac{1}{7}$. Our number line graph looks like this:

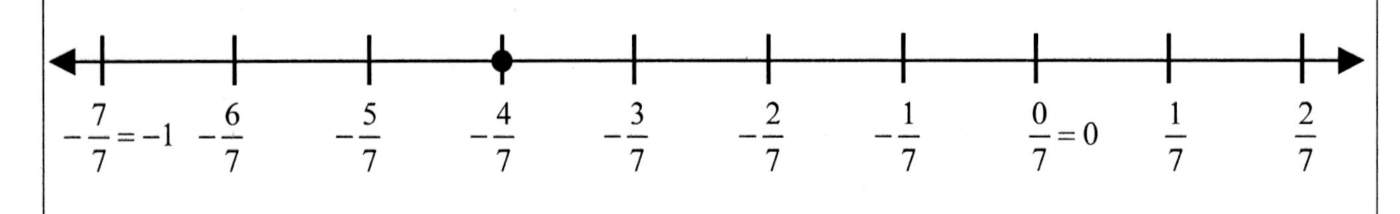

Example 3: Graph the mixed number $-2\frac{1}{5}$ on a number line.

Solution: Since $-2\frac{1}{5}$ is between -3 and -2 we will draw a number line that extends to the left up to the number -3. We will also divide the part of the number line that is between -3 and -2 into sections, each of which is $\frac{1}{5}$. Our number line graph looks like this:

-3 $-2\frac{4}{5}$ $-2\frac{3}{5}$ $-2\frac{2}{5}$ $-2\frac{1}{5}$ -2 -1 0

When mathematical tasks involving fractions are performed, it is often required for the fractions to have a common denominator. These tasks include comparing fractions as well as adding and subtracting them. It is often beneficial to have the denominators of these fractions as small as possible in order to make calculations easier. The combination of these two ideas, having a common denominator, and having the smallest denominator possible leads to the idea of what is called the **least common denominator,** or the **LCD**. At the beginning of this chapter, we looked at the idea of the **least common multiple** or the **LCM** of two or more numbers. Finding the least common denominator of two fractions is the same process as finding the least common multiple of the two denominators. Let's look at two examples and see how the two processes compare.

Example 4: Find the least common multiple of 4 and 6.

Solution:

Step 1: Find the prime factorization of each number. The prime factorization of 4 is 2^2 and the prime factorization of 6 is $2 \cdot 3$.

Step 2: Create a list of all the different prime factors in each of the original numbers. In this case, that would be 2 and 3.

Step 3: Raise each different prime factor to its highest power within any of the prime factorizations. In this case, it would be 2^2 and 3.

Step 4: Write these powers as a product: $2^2 \cdot 3$. Since $2^2 \cdot 3 = 12$, the least common multiple of 4 and 6 is 12.

Example 5: Find the least common denominator of $\frac{3}{4}$ and $\frac{5}{6}$.

Solution:

Step 1: Find the prime factorization of each denominator. The prime factorization of 4 is 2^2 and the prime factorization of 6 is $2 \cdot 3$.

Step 2: Create a list of all the different prime factors in each of the original denominators. In this case, that would be 2 and 3.

Step 3: Raise each different prime factor to its highest power within any of the prime factorizations. In this case, it would be 2^2 and 3.

Step 4: Write these powers as a product: $2^2 \cdot 3$. Since $2^2 \cdot 3 = 12$, the least common denominator of 4 and 6 is 12.

Now let's explore how to compare fractions with different denominators. Fractions with the same denominator can be compared just by considering their numerators. Fractions that have different denominators aren't as easy to compare, unless we change the fractions to equivalent fractions with the same denominator.

Compare the fractions: $\frac{1}{2}$ and $\frac{1}{3}$

Step 1: Find the least common denominator of $\frac{1}{2}$ and $\frac{1}{3}$. The least common denominator is 6.

Step 2: Change each fraction to an equivalent fraction with the least common denominator.

In other words, $\frac{1}{2}=\frac{?}{6}$ and $\frac{1}{3}=\frac{?}{6}$. Let's deal with finding the equivalent fractions one at a time.

First, $\frac{1}{2}=\frac{?}{6}$ Divide the new denominator by the old denominator. $6\div 2=3$.

Multiply both the numerator and the denominator of $\frac{1}{2}$ by the number 3.

$\frac{1\cdot 3}{2\cdot 3}=\frac{3}{6}$ So, $\frac{1}{2}$ becomes $\frac{3}{6}$.

Second, $\frac{1}{3}=\frac{?}{6}$ Divide the new denominator by the old denominator. $6\div 3=2$.

Multiply both the numerator and the denominator of $\frac{1}{3}$ by the number 2.

$\frac{1\cdot 2}{3\cdot 2}=\frac{2}{6}$ So, $\frac{1}{3}$ becomes $\frac{2}{6}$.

The pair of fractions $\frac{1}{2}$ and $\frac{1}{3}$, written as equivalent fractions with the LCD, are $\frac{3}{6}$ and $\frac{2}{6}$ respectively.

Now that there are two fractions with the same denominator, we can easily compare them.

Step 3: Compare the new fractions: $\frac{3}{6}>\frac{2}{6}$

Step 4: Compare the original fractions: $\frac{1}{2}>\frac{1}{3}$

Example 6: Compare the fractions: $\frac{7}{12}$ and $\frac{5}{8}$

Solution:

Step 1: Find the least common denominator of $\frac{7}{12}$ and $\frac{5}{8}$.

The prime factorization of 12 is $2^2 \cdot 3$ and the prime factorization of 8 is 2^3. Therefore, the LCD is $2^3 \cdot 3$ or 24.

Step 2: Change each fraction to an equivalent fraction with the least common denominator.

Since $24 \div 12 = 2$, then $\frac{7}{12} = \frac{7 \cdot 2}{12 \cdot 2} = \frac{14}{24}$ and since $24 \div 8 = 3$, then $\frac{5}{8} = \frac{5 \cdot 3}{8 \cdot 3} = \frac{15}{24}$.

Step 3: Compare the new fractions: $\frac{14}{24} < \frac{15}{24}$

Step 4: Compare the original fractions: $\frac{7}{12} < \frac{5}{8}$

Example 7: Compare the fractions: $\frac{7}{8}$ and $\frac{13}{15}$

Solution: Step 1: Find the least common denominator of $\frac{7}{8}$ and $\frac{13}{15}$.

The prime factorization of 8 is 2^3 and the prime factorization of 15 is $3 \cdot 5$. Therefore, the LCD is $2^3 \cdot 3 \cdot 5$ or 120.

Step 2: Change each fraction to an equivalent fraction with the least common denominator.

Since $120 \div 8 = 15$, then $\frac{7}{8} = \frac{7 \cdot 15}{8 \cdot 15} = \frac{105}{120}$ and since $120 \div 15 = 8$, then $\frac{13}{15} = \frac{13 \cdot 8}{15 \cdot 8} = \frac{104}{120}$.

Step 3: Compare the new fractions: $\frac{105}{120} > \frac{104}{120}$

Step 4: Compare the original fractions: $\frac{7}{8} > \frac{13}{15}$

Example 8: Compare the fractions: $-\frac{5}{6}$ and $-\frac{13}{15}$

Solution: Step 1: Find the least common denominator of $-\frac{5}{6}$ and $-\frac{13}{15}$.

The prime factorization of 6 is $2 \cdot 3$ and the prime factorization of 15 is $3 \cdot 5$. Therefore, the LCD is $2 \cdot 3 \cdot 5$ or 30.

Step 2: Change each fraction to an equivalent fraction with the least common denominator.

Since $30 \div 6 = 5$, then $-\frac{5}{6} = -\frac{5 \cdot 5}{6 \cdot 5} = -\frac{25}{30}$ and since $30 \div 15 = 2$, then $-\frac{13}{15} = -\frac{13 \cdot 2}{15 \cdot 2} = -\frac{26}{30}$.

Step 3: Compare the new fractions $-\frac{25}{30} > -\frac{26}{30}$

Step 4: Compare the original fractions $-\frac{5}{16} > -\frac{13}{15}$

Don't forget that $-\frac{25}{30}$ is to the right of $-\frac{26}{30}$ on a number line and therefore $-\frac{25}{30} > -\frac{26}{30}$.

Example 9: Compare the fractions: $-\frac{4}{11}$ and $\frac{8}{21}$

Solution: Since $-\frac{4}{11}$ is to the left of zero and $\frac{8}{21}$ is to the right of zero on a number line,

we can determine that $-\frac{4}{11} < \frac{8}{21}$ without finding the LCD of the two fractions.

Janet's Monthly Budget

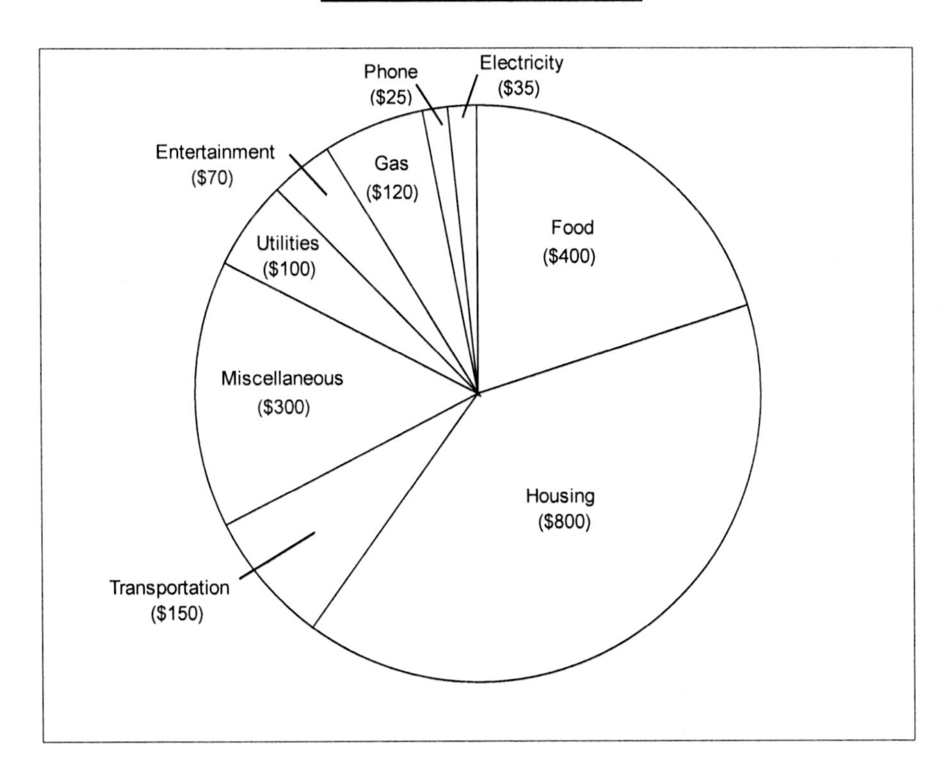

Example 10: Based on the pie chart above, what fraction of her monthly budget does Janet spend on housing?

Solution: Add the dollar amounts of all the segments to find Janet's total budget.

$\$800 + \$150 + \$300 + \$100 + \$70 + \$120 + \$25 + \$35 + \$400 = \$2{,}000$

Write a fraction with Janet's housing budget in the numerator and her total budget in the denominator. $\frac{\$800}{\$2{,}000}$ Reduce the fraction to lowest terms. Since both the numerator and the denominator of the fraction are multiples of 100, we could reduce out the 100 in the numerator and the denominator to get $\frac{\$8\cancel{00}}{\$2{,}0\cancel{00}}$. Now we can further reduce $\frac{\$8}{\$20}$ down to

$\frac{\overset{1}{\cancel{\$2}}\cdot\overset{1}{\cancel{2}}\cdot 2}{\underset{1}{\cancel{\$2}}\cdot\underset{1}{\cancel{2}}\cdot 5}$ or $\frac{2}{5}$. So, Janet spends $\frac{2}{5}$ of her monthly budget on housing.

Example 11: A case for an electric drill contains the following sized drill bits. Arrange them in order from smallest to largest.

$\frac{1}{8}$ in., $\frac{3}{16}$ in., $\frac{5}{32}$ in., $\frac{7}{32}$ in., $\frac{9}{64}$ in., and $\frac{11}{64}$ in.

Solution: To arrange the drill bits from smallest to largest we need to compare the fractions. To do this we need to have the same denominator for each fraction.

Step 1: Find the least common denominator of $\frac{1}{8}, \frac{3}{16}, \frac{5}{32}, \frac{7}{32}, \frac{9}{64}$, and $\frac{11}{64}$.

The prime factorization of 8 is 2^3. The prime factorization of 16 is 2^4. The prime factorization of 32 is 2^5. In addition, the prime factorization of 64 is 2^6. Therefore, the LCD is 2^6 or 64.

Step 2: Change each fraction to an equivalent fraction with the least common denominator.

Since $64 \div 8 = 8$, then $\frac{1}{8} = \frac{1 \cdot 8}{8 \cdot 8} = \frac{8}{64}$.

Since $64 \div 16 = 4$, then $\frac{3}{16} = \frac{3 \cdot 4}{16 \cdot 4} = \frac{12}{64}$.

Since $64 \div 32 = 2$, then $\frac{5}{32} = \frac{5 \cdot 2}{32 \cdot 2} = \frac{10}{64}$ and $\frac{7}{32} = \frac{7 \cdot 2}{32 \cdot 2} = \frac{14}{64}$.

$\frac{9}{64}$ and $\frac{11}{64}$ already have the LCD.

Step 3: Compare the new fractions: $\frac{8}{64} < \frac{9}{64} < \frac{10}{64} < \frac{11}{64} < \frac{12}{64} < \frac{14}{64}$

Step 4: Compare the original fractions: $\frac{1}{8} < \frac{9}{64} < \frac{5}{32} < \frac{11}{64} < \frac{3}{16} < \frac{7}{32}$

The arrangement of the drill bits from smallest to largest is as follows:

$\frac{1}{8}$ in., $\frac{9}{64}$ in., $\frac{5}{32}$ in., $\frac{11}{64}$ in., $\frac{3}{16}$ in., and $\frac{7}{32}$ in.

Section 3 exercises. For each of the following problems, draw a number line and graph the given number.

1. $\frac{2}{7}$
2. $-3\frac{1}{2}$
3. $-\frac{5}{2}$
4. $\frac{5}{4}$
5. $1\frac{3}{4}$
6. $-\frac{5}{6}$
7. $-\frac{1}{3}$
8. $1\frac{3}{5}$
9. $\frac{8}{5}$
10. $-\frac{11}{3}$
11. $-2\frac{5}{6}$
12. $\frac{5}{7}$

Find the least common denominator of each pair of fractions.

13. $\frac{2}{3}$ and $\frac{1}{4}$
14. $\frac{1}{2}$ and $\frac{3}{5}$
15. $\frac{9}{10}$ and $\frac{2}{15}$
16. $\frac{7}{6}$ and $\frac{3}{8}$
17. $\frac{3}{8}$ and $\frac{3}{4}$
18. $\frac{3}{10}$ and $\frac{3}{5}$
19. $\frac{4}{7}$ and $\frac{5}{12}$
20. $\frac{1}{3}$ and $\frac{9}{14}$
21. $\frac{2}{15}$ and $\frac{19}{40}$
22. $\frac{2}{25}$ and $\frac{13}{15}$
23. $\frac{3}{14}$ and $\frac{19}{21}$
24. $\frac{5}{6}$ and $\frac{1}{15}$

Compare the two fractions by placing either < or > between them.

25. $\frac{5}{12}$ $\frac{1}{2}$
26. $\frac{17}{35}$ $\frac{1}{2}$
27. $\frac{6}{11}$ $\frac{1}{2}$
28. $\frac{5}{8}$ $\frac{1}{2}$
29. $\frac{3}{4}$ $\frac{2}{5}$
30. $\frac{4}{9}$ $\frac{18}{35}$
31. $\frac{7}{16}$ $\frac{2}{3}$
32. $\frac{9}{17}$ $\frac{3}{7}$
33. $\frac{6}{13}$ $\frac{7}{12}$
34. $\frac{5}{11}$ $\frac{8}{15}$
35. $\frac{7}{30}$ $\frac{3}{70}$
36. $\frac{4}{50}$ $\frac{5}{40}$

37. $\frac{4}{7}$ $\frac{3}{5}$ **38.** $\frac{5}{8}$ $\frac{2}{3}$ **39.** $\frac{11}{14}$ $\frac{3}{4}$ **40.** $\frac{5}{6}$ $\frac{7}{9}$

41. $\frac{2}{3}$ $\frac{7}{11}$ **42.** $\frac{4}{15}$ $\frac{1}{4}$ **43.** $\frac{13}{24}$ $\frac{9}{16}$ **44.** $\frac{7}{16}$ $\frac{11}{24}$

45. $-\frac{2}{3}$ $-\frac{5}{7}$ **46.** $-\frac{3}{11}$ $-\frac{2}{7}$ **47.** $\frac{13}{17}$ $\frac{10}{13}$ **48.** $\frac{3}{4}$ $\frac{14}{19}$

49. $\frac{9}{7}$ $\frac{14}{11}$ **50.** $\frac{13}{9}$ $\frac{17}{12}$ **51.** $-\frac{7}{8}$ $\frac{3}{4}$ **52.** $-\frac{11}{12}$ $\frac{5}{6}$

53. $\frac{7}{15}$ $\frac{11}{25}$ **54.** $\frac{7}{10}$ $\frac{11}{15}$ **55.** $\frac{5}{3}$ $\frac{9}{5}$ **56.** $\frac{12}{7}$ $\frac{7}{4}$

57. $-\frac{4}{9}$ $-\frac{3}{7}$ **58.** $-\frac{7}{3}$ $-\frac{12}{5}$ **59.** $\frac{17}{24}$ $\frac{11}{16}$ **60.** $\frac{13}{20}$ $\frac{5}{8}$

61. If there are 3 feet in a yard then, 2 feet is what fraction of a yard?

62. If there are 12 inches in a foot, then 3 inches is what fraction of a foot?

63. If there are 60 minutes in an hour, then 25 minutes is what fraction of an hour?

64. If there are 60 seconds in a minute, then 18 seconds is what fraction of a minute?

65. If there are 12 months in a year, then 9 months is what fraction of a year?

66. If there are 4 quarters in a dollar, then 3 quarters is what fraction of a dollar?

67. What fraction of the days of the week contains the letter s?

68. What fraction of the days of the week contains the letter r?

69. What fraction of the days of the week contains both of the letters r and s?

70. What fraction of the days of the week contains either of the letters r or s?

71. What fraction of a dollar is 35 cents?

72. What fraction of a dollar is 45 cents?

Janet's Monthly Budget

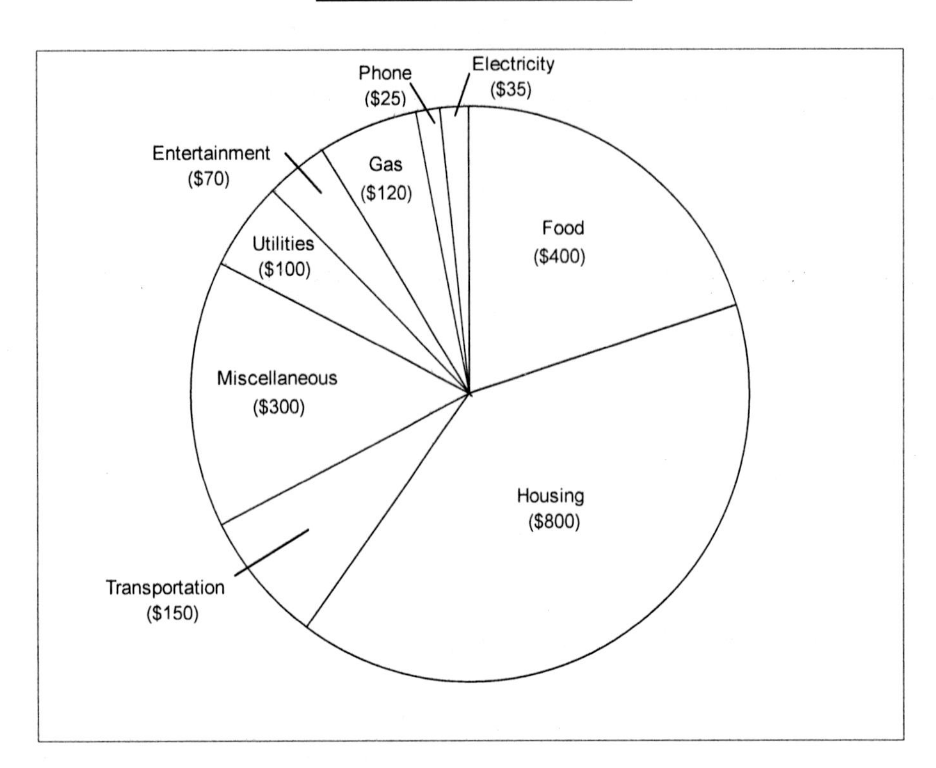

73. Based on the pie chart above, what fraction of her monthly budget does Janet spend on transportation?

74. Based on the pie chart above, what fraction of her monthly budget does Janet spend on utilities?

75. Based on the pie chart above, what fraction of her monthly budget does Janet spend on gas?

76. Based on the pie chart above, what fraction of her monthly budget does Janet spend on food?

77. Based on the pie chart above, what fraction of her monthly budget does Janet spend on entertainment and electricity?

78. Based on the pie chart above, what fraction of her monthly budget does Janet spend on phone and miscellaneous?

79. A toolbox contains the following sized wrenches. Arrange them in order from smallest to largest.

$\frac{1}{2}$ in., $\frac{3}{4}$ in., $\frac{3}{8}$ in., $\frac{5}{8}$ in., $\frac{7}{16}$ in., $\frac{9}{16}$ in., and $\frac{11}{16}$ in.

80. A socket set contains the following sized sockets. Arrange them in order from smallest to largest.

$\frac{1}{4}$ in., $\frac{3}{8}$ in., $\frac{3}{16}$ in., $\frac{5}{16}$ in., $\frac{7}{32}$ in., $\frac{9}{16}$ in., and $\frac{11}{32}$ in.

The table at the right shows the results of a recent survey conducted by Bogus University. College students were asked how many lattés they purchased on average during a typical week.

Responses to the question, "How many lattés do you purchase on average during a typical week?"

Number of lattés purchased	Fraction of students responding
0	$\frac{1}{10}$
1	$\frac{1}{5}$
2	$\frac{9}{25}$
3	$\frac{17}{50}$
4	$\frac{3}{25}$
5 or more	$\frac{2}{25}$

81. Which response was given most frequently?

82. Which response was given least frequently?

FRACTIONS

Section 4: Adding Fractions and Mixed Numbers

Grandma Pat made an apple pie and cut it into six equal pieces. Her granddaughter Jessica ate one piece of the pie for breakfast and two pieces of the pie for lunch. What fraction of the entire pie did she eat? Since the pie was cut into six pieces, then each piece was $\frac{1}{6}$ of the pie. Therefore, we have the following:

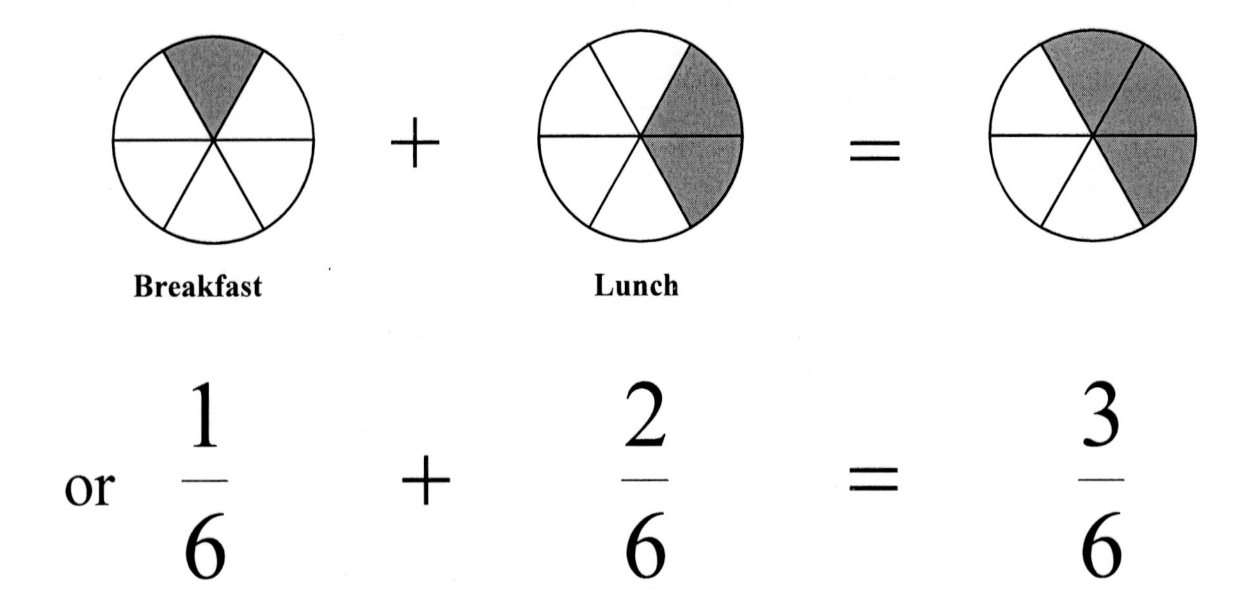

$$\text{or} \quad \frac{1}{6} + \frac{2}{6} = \frac{3}{6}$$

We can reduce the fraction $\frac{3}{6}$ to lowest terms and it becomes $\frac{1}{2}$. So, Jessica ate $\frac{1}{2}$ of the pie. We found the sum of these fractions by adding the numerators and putting them over the denominator, which was common to both fractions. This process is the same whenever fractions with a common denominator are being added.

To add fractions with a common denominator:

Step 1: Add the numerators and put their sum over the common denominator.

Step 2: Reduce this fraction to lowest terms (unless it's already in lowest terms).

Symbolically this process is: $\frac{a}{b} + \frac{c}{b} = \frac{a+c}{b}$, **where** $b \neq 0$.

Example 1: Add $\frac{7}{12}$ and $\frac{1}{12}$.

Solution: Since the fractions have the same denominator, we can follow the steps to add fractions with a common denominator.

Step 1: Add the numerators and put their sum over the common denominator.

$$\frac{7}{12}+\frac{1}{12}=\frac{7+1}{12}=\frac{8}{12}$$

Step 2: Reduce this fraction to lowest terms. $\frac{8}{12}=\frac{2\cdot2\cdot2}{2\cdot2\cdot3}=\frac{\overset{1}{\cancel{2}}\cdot\overset{1}{\cancel{2}}\cdot2}{\underset{1}{\cancel{2}}\cdot\underset{1}{\cancel{2}}\cdot3}=\frac{2}{3}$

So, $\frac{7}{12}+\frac{1}{12}=\frac{8}{12}=\frac{2}{3}$.

Example 2: Find the sum of $\frac{2}{9}$ and $\frac{-7}{9}$.

Solution: Since the fractions have the same denominator, we can follow the steps to add fractions with a common denominator.

Step 1: Add the numerators and put their sum over the common denominator.

$$\frac{2}{9}+\frac{-7}{9}=\frac{2+(-7)}{9}=\frac{-5}{9}$$

Step 2: This fraction is already in lowest terms.

So, $\frac{2}{9}+\frac{-7}{9}=\frac{-5}{9}$.

Note: $\frac{-5}{9}$ can also be written as $-\frac{5}{9}$ or $\frac{5}{-9}$. However, we don't usually leave a negative sign in the denominator of a fraction in lowest terms.

Example 3: Find $\frac{3}{w}+\frac{7}{w}$.

Solution: Since the fractions have the same denominator, we can follow the steps to add fractions with a common denominator.

Step 1: Add the numerators and put their sum over the common denominator.

$$\frac{3}{w}+\frac{7}{w}=\frac{3+7}{w}=\frac{10}{w}$$

Step 2: This fraction is already in lowest terms.

So, $\frac{3}{w}+\frac{7}{w}=\frac{10}{w}$.

Example 4: Find the sum of $\frac{5}{7}$ and $\frac{4}{7}$.

Solution: Since the fractions have the same denominator, we can follow the steps to add fractions with a common denominator.

Step 1: Add the numerators and put their sum over the common denominator.

$$\frac{5}{7}+\frac{4}{7}=\frac{5+4}{7}=\frac{9}{7}$$

Step 2: This fraction is already in lowest terms. We could change it into a mixed number if desired. That is, $\frac{9}{7}=1\frac{2}{7}$.

So, $\frac{5}{7}+\frac{4}{7}=\frac{9}{7}$ or $1\frac{2}{7}$.

Grandma Nancy made two cherry pies and cut one of them into three equal pieces while she cut the other one in half. Her grandson Sean ate one piece of each pie. What fraction of a pie did he eat? Since the first pie was cut into three pieces, then each piece was $\frac{1}{3}$ of the pie. Because the second pie was cut into two pieces, then each piece was $\frac{1}{2}$ of the pie. Therefore, we have the following:

First Pie **Second Pie**

$$\text{or} \quad \frac{1}{3} + \frac{1}{2} = ?$$

We can tell by looking at the final picture of pie that the answer is $\frac{5}{6}$. The question now is, how do we get to the answer? Suppose we take the two original pies and cut each one into six equal pieces. Now suppose that Sean eats the same amount of each pie as he did before, (not the same number of pieces, but the same amount of each pie). The new set of pictures would look like this:

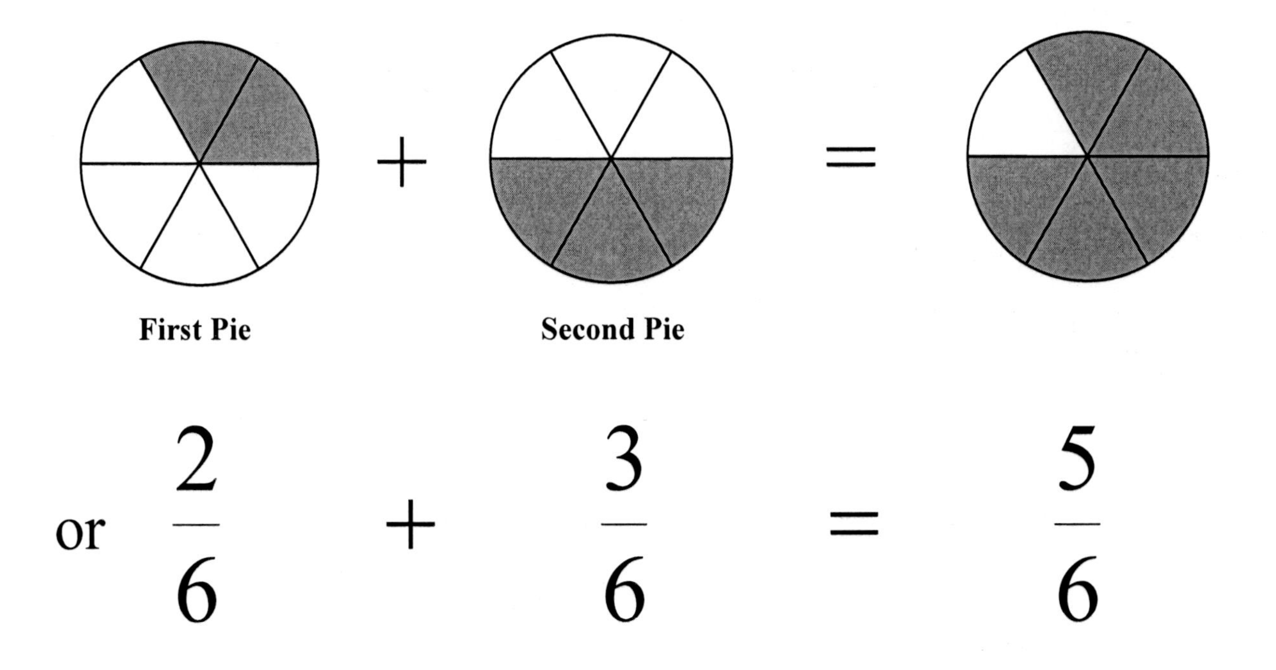

By cutting both pies into the same number of equal pieces, each piece is a fraction with the same denominator. Now we can add the numerators over the common denominator. Let's look at this same situation but without all the pie. To add $\frac{1}{3}$ and $\frac{1}{2}$, first determine what is the least common denominator of the two fractions. Next, change each fraction to an equivalent fraction that has the least common denominator (LCD). Then add the two fractions.

$\frac{1}{3}+\frac{1}{2}=?$ The LCD of $\frac{1}{3}$ and $\frac{1}{2}$ is 6. $\frac{1}{3}=\frac{1\cdot 2}{3\cdot 2}=\frac{2}{6}$ and $\frac{1}{2}=\frac{1\cdot 3}{2\cdot 3}=\frac{3}{6}$.

So, $\frac{1}{3}+\frac{1}{2}=\frac{2}{6}+\frac{3}{6}=\frac{5}{6}$.

<u>To add fractions with different denominators</u>:

Step 1: Find the LCD of the fractions.

Step 2: Change each fraction to an equivalent fraction with the LCD.

Step 3: Add the numerators of the new fractions and put their sum over the LCD.

Step 4: Reduce this fraction to lowest terms (unless it's already in lowest terms).

<u>Example 5:</u> Add: $\frac{1}{2}+\frac{2}{5}$

Solution:

Step 1: The LCD of $\frac{1}{2}$ and $\frac{2}{5}$ is 10.

Step 2: Change each fraction to an equivalent fraction with a denominator of 10.

$\frac{1}{2}=\frac{1\cdot 5}{2\cdot 5}=\frac{5}{10}$ and $\frac{2}{5}=\frac{2\cdot 2}{5\cdot 2}=\frac{4}{10}$. So, $\frac{1}{2}+\frac{2}{5}$ becomes $\frac{5}{10}+\frac{4}{10}$.

Step 3: Add the numerators and put their sum over the LCD.

$$\frac{5}{10}+\frac{4}{10}=\frac{4+5}{10}=\frac{9}{10}$$

Step 4: This fraction is already in lowest terms.

So, $\frac{1}{2}+\frac{2}{5}=\frac{5}{10}+\frac{4}{10}=\frac{9}{10}$.

Example 6: Add: $\frac{5}{6}+\frac{1}{4}$

Solution:

Step 1: The LCD of $\frac{5}{6}$ and $\frac{1}{4}$ is 12.

Step 2: Change each fraction to an equivalent fraction with a denominator of 12.

$\frac{5}{6}=\frac{5\cdot 2}{6\cdot 2}=\frac{10}{12}$ and $\frac{1}{4}=\frac{1\cdot 3}{4\cdot 3}=\frac{3}{12}$. So, $\frac{5}{6}+\frac{1}{4}$ becomes $\frac{10}{12}+\frac{3}{12}$.

Step 3: Add the numerators and put their sum over the LCD.

$$\frac{10}{12}+\frac{3}{12}=\frac{10+3}{12}=\frac{13}{12}$$

Step 4: This fraction is already in lowest terms. We could change it into a mixed number if desired. That is, $\frac{13}{12}=1\frac{1}{12}$.

So, $\frac{5}{6}+\frac{1}{4}=\frac{10}{12}+\frac{3}{12}=\frac{13}{12}$ or $1\frac{1}{12}$.

Example 7: Add: $-\frac{1}{8}+\left(-\frac{5}{6}\right)$

Solution:

Step 1: The LCD of $-\frac{1}{8}$ and $-\frac{5}{6}$ is 24.

Step 2: Change each fraction to an equivalent fraction with a denominator of 24.

$-\frac{1}{8}=-\frac{1\cdot 3}{8\cdot 3}=-\frac{3}{24}$ and $-\frac{5}{6}=-\frac{5\cdot 4}{6\cdot 4}=-\frac{20}{24}$. So, $-\frac{1}{8}+\left(-\frac{5}{6}\right)$ becomes $-\frac{3}{24}+\left(-\frac{20}{24}\right)$.

Step 3: Add the numerators and put their sum over the LCD.

$$-\frac{3}{24}+\left(-\frac{20}{24}\right)=\frac{-3+(-20)}{24}=-\frac{23}{24}$$

Step 4: This fraction is already in lowest terms.

So, $-\frac{1}{8}+\left(-\frac{5}{6}\right)=-\frac{3}{24}+\left(-\frac{20}{24}\right)=-\frac{23}{24}$.

In Chapter 1 we looked at adding whole numbers and in this chapter we've looked at adding fractions. Since mixed numbers are a combination of whole numbers and fractions, it makes sense that we can add them. When adding mixed numbers:

Step 1: Change the fraction part of each mixed number to an equivalent fraction with the LCD.

Step 2: Add the whole-number parts together and add the fraction parts together.

Step 3: If the resulting fraction is improper, change it into a mixed number and add the whole-number part to the whole number resulting from step 2.

Step 4: Reduce the fraction part to lowest terms if necessary. Then combine the whole number and the fraction to form the final mixed number.

Example 8: Add: $2\frac{4}{5}+4\frac{3}{4}$

Solution: Step 1: The LCD of $\frac{4}{5}$ and $\frac{3}{4}$ is 20.

$\frac{4}{5}=\frac{4\cdot 4}{5\cdot 4}=\frac{16}{20}$ and $\frac{3}{4}=\frac{3\cdot 5}{4\cdot 5}=\frac{15}{20}$. So, $2\frac{4}{5}+4\frac{3}{4}$ becomes $2\frac{16}{20}+4\frac{15}{20}$.

Step 2: Add the whole-number parts together and add the fraction parts together.

$2\frac{16}{20}+4\frac{15}{20}=6+\frac{31}{20}$

Step 3: Since $\frac{31}{20}$ is an improper fraction, change it into a mixed number. $\frac{31}{20}$ becomes $1\frac{11}{20}$.

Add the whole-number part to the whole number resulting from step 2.

$6+1\frac{11}{20}=7+\frac{11}{20}$

Step 4: Combine the whole number and the fraction to form the final mixed number.

$7+\frac{11}{20}=7\frac{11}{20}$

So, $2\frac{4}{5}+4\frac{3}{4}=2\frac{16}{20}+4\frac{15}{20}=6+\frac{31}{20}=6+1\frac{11}{20}=7+\frac{11}{20}=7\frac{11}{20}$. Or, $2\frac{4}{5}+4\frac{3}{4}=7\frac{11}{20}$.

Example 9: Add: $5\frac{2}{9}+3$

Solution: Step 1: Since there is only one fraction, we don't need to find an LCD.

Step 2: Add the whole-number parts together. $5\frac{2}{9}+3=8+\frac{2}{9}$

Step 3: Since $\frac{2}{9}$ is a proper fraction, go to step 4.

Step 4: Combine the whole number and the fraction to form the final mixed number.

$8+\frac{2}{9}=8\frac{2}{9}$ So, $5\frac{2}{9}+3=8+\frac{2}{9}=8\frac{2}{9}$.

Example 10: Add: $5\frac{3}{8}+11\frac{3}{4}$

Solution: Step 1: The LCD of $\frac{3}{8}$ and $\frac{3}{4}$ is 8.

$\frac{3}{8}$ remains unchanged and $\frac{3}{4}=\frac{3\cdot 2}{4\cdot 2}=\frac{6}{8}$. So, $5\frac{3}{8}+11\frac{3}{4}$ becomes $5\frac{3}{8}+11\frac{6}{8}$.

Step 2: Add the whole-number parts together and add the fraction parts together.

$5\frac{3}{8}+11\frac{6}{8}=16+\frac{9}{8}$

Step 3: Since $\frac{9}{8}$ is an improper fraction, change it into a mixed number. $\frac{9}{8}$ becomes $1\frac{1}{8}$.

Add the whole-number part to the whole number resulting from step 2.

$16+1\frac{1}{8}=17+\frac{1}{8}$

Step 4: Combine the whole number and the fraction to form the final mixed number.

$17+\frac{1}{8}=17\frac{1}{8}$

So, $5\frac{3}{8}+11\frac{3}{4}=5\frac{3}{8}+11\frac{6}{8}=16+\frac{9}{8}=16+1\frac{1}{8}=17+\frac{1}{8}=17\frac{1}{8}$. Or, $5\frac{3}{8}+11\frac{3}{4}=17\frac{1}{8}$.

Even though the process involves the same steps, students often prefer to add mixed numbers using a vertical format rather than a horizontal one. Consequently, we will look at the exact same problem as example 10, but this time we will add the mixed numbers vertically.

Example 10 Revisited: Add:

$$\begin{array}{r} 5\frac{3}{8} \\ +11\frac{3}{4} \\ \hline \end{array}$$

Solution: Step 1: The LCD of $\frac{3}{8}$ and $\frac{3}{4}$ is 8.

$\frac{3}{8}$ remains unchanged and $\frac{3}{4}=\frac{3\cdot 2}{4\cdot 2}=\frac{6}{8}$. So, $\begin{array}{r} 5\frac{3}{8} \\ +11\frac{3}{4} \\ \hline \end{array}$ becomes $\begin{array}{r} 5\frac{3}{8} \\ +11\frac{6}{8} \\ \hline \end{array}$.

Step 2: Add the whole-number parts together and add the fraction parts together.

$$\begin{array}{r} 5\frac{3}{8} \\ +11\frac{6}{8} \\ \hline 16\frac{9}{8} \end{array}$$

Step 3: Since $\frac{9}{8}$ is an improper fraction, change it into a mixed number. $\frac{9}{8}$ becomes $1\frac{1}{8}$.

Add the whole-number part to the whole number resulting from step 2.

$$\begin{array}{r} 16 \\ +1\frac{1}{8} \\ \hline 17\frac{1}{8} \end{array}$$

Step 4: The whole number and the fraction are already combined in the vertical addition process.

The final mixed number is $17\frac{1}{8}$.

In previous chapters, we evaluated variable expressions using whole numbers and integers. Now we will evaluate expressions involving addition of fractions and mixed numbers.

Example 11: Evaluate the expression for the given values of the variables:

$x + y$, where $x = \frac{2}{7}$ and $y = 4\frac{8}{21}$

Solution:

$x + y$ Substitute $\frac{2}{7}$ in the place of x and $4\frac{8}{21}$ in the place of y.

$\frac{2}{7} + 4\frac{8}{21}$ The LCD of $\frac{2}{7}$ and $\frac{8}{21}$ is 21.

$\frac{2}{7} = \frac{2 \cdot 3}{7 \cdot 3} = \frac{6}{21}$ and $\frac{8}{21}$ remains unchanged. So, $\frac{2}{7} + 4\frac{8}{21}$ becomes $\frac{6}{21} + 4\frac{8}{21}$.

Add the fraction parts together. $\frac{6}{21} + 4\frac{8}{21} = 4 + \frac{14}{21}$

Reduce the fraction part to lowest terms. $\frac{14}{21} = \frac{2 \cdot 7}{3 \cdot 7} = \frac{2 \cdot \overset{1}{\cancel{7}}}{3 \cdot \underset{1}{\cancel{7}}} = \frac{2}{3}$ So, $4 + \frac{14}{21}$ becomes $4 + \frac{2}{3}$.

Combine the whole number and the fraction to form the final mixed number.

$4 + \frac{2}{3} = 4\frac{2}{3}$

So, $\frac{2}{7} + 4\frac{8}{21} = \frac{6}{21} + 4\frac{8}{21} = 4 + \frac{14}{21} = 4 + \frac{2}{3} = 4\frac{2}{3}$. Or, $\frac{2}{7} + 4\frac{8}{21} = 4\frac{2}{3}$.

Applications involving fractions and mixed numbers

Example 12: Susie the seamstress sewed some skirts, which required several yards of fabric. The first skirt needed $2\frac{1}{3}$ yards, the second skirt called for $3\frac{1}{6}$ yards, and the third and final skirt was to be made from $5\frac{1}{4}$ yards of fabric. What was the total amount of fabric required by Susie to make the three skirts?

Solution: We need to add the mixed numbers.

$2\frac{1}{3}+3\frac{1}{6}+5\frac{1}{4}$ The LCD of $\frac{1}{3}$, $\frac{1}{6}$, and $\frac{1}{4}$ is 12.

$\frac{1}{3}=\frac{1\cdot 4}{3\cdot 4}=\frac{4}{12}$, $\frac{1}{6}=\frac{1\cdot 2}{6\cdot 2}=\frac{2}{12}$ and $\frac{1}{4}=\frac{1\cdot 3}{4\cdot 3}=\frac{3}{12}$.

So, $2\frac{1}{3}+3\frac{1}{6}+5\frac{1}{4}$ becomes $2\frac{4}{12}+3\frac{2}{12}+5\frac{3}{12}$.

Add the whole-number parts together and add the fraction parts together.

$10+\frac{9}{12}$

Reduce the fraction part to lowest terms. $\frac{9}{12}=\frac{3\cdot 3}{2\cdot 2\cdot 3}=\frac{3\cdot \overset{1}{\cancel{3}}}{2\cdot 2\cdot \underset{1}{\cancel{3}}}=\frac{3}{4}$

So, $10+\frac{9}{12}$ becomes $10+\frac{3}{4}$.

Combine the whole number and the fraction to form the final mixed number.

$10+\frac{3}{4}=10\frac{3}{4}$

The total amount of fabric required by Susie to make the three skirts is $10\frac{3}{4}$ yards.

Section 4 exercises. Add.

1. $\frac{2}{5}+\frac{1}{5}$ **2.** $\frac{3}{7}+\frac{2}{7}$ **3.** $\frac{9}{14}+\frac{5}{14}$ **4.** $\frac{8}{15}+\frac{7}{15}$

5. $-\frac{5}{9}+\left(-\frac{1}{9}\right)$ **6.** $-\frac{7}{12}+\left(-\frac{1}{12}\right)$ **7.** $-\frac{3}{11}+\frac{6}{11}$ **8.** $-\frac{2}{9}+\frac{4}{9}$

9. $\frac{8}{x}+\frac{3}{x}$ **10.** $\frac{9}{h}+\frac{4}{h}$ **11.** $\frac{6}{w}+\left(-\frac{7}{w}\right)$ **12.** $\frac{3}{y}+\left(-\frac{4}{y}\right)$

13. $\frac{3}{10}+\frac{9}{10}+\frac{7}{10}$ **14.** $\frac{8}{11}+\frac{2}{11}+\frac{5}{11}$ **15.** $\frac{7}{m}+\frac{8}{m}+\frac{3}{m}$ **16.** $\frac{6}{n}+\frac{5}{n}+\frac{9}{n}$

17. $8+6\frac{5}{8}$ **18.** $9+3\frac{4}{7}$ **19.** $7\frac{3}{4}+11$ **20.** $4\frac{1}{6}+5$

21. $6\frac{2}{3}+9\frac{1}{3}$ **22.** $6\frac{3}{5}+8\frac{2}{5}$ **23.** $3\frac{5}{7}+5\frac{1}{7}$ **24.** $9\frac{2}{9}+3\frac{4}{9}$

25. $-\frac{5}{7}+\left(-\frac{2}{3}\right)$ **26.** $-\frac{8}{9}+\left(-\frac{1}{2}\right)$ **27.** $\frac{7}{24}+\frac{11}{42}$ **28.** $\frac{9}{70}+\frac{4}{105}$

29. $\frac{1}{2}+\frac{3}{14}+\frac{5}{7}$ **30.** $\frac{1}{3}+\frac{11}{15}+\frac{3}{5}$ **31.** $-\frac{5}{36}+\frac{5}{28}$ **32.** $-\frac{5}{48}+\frac{7}{60}$

33. $\frac{7}{6}+\frac{7}{18}+\frac{7}{9}$ **34.** $\frac{11}{9}+\frac{11}{36}+\frac{11}{12}$ **35.** $\frac{4}{5}+\left(-\frac{5}{6}\right)$ **36.** $\frac{3}{4}+\left(-\frac{4}{5}\right)$

37. $-\frac{5}{6}+\frac{1}{2}+\frac{5}{8}$

38. $-\frac{3}{4}+\frac{13}{18}+\frac{1}{6}$

39. $7\frac{3}{56}+8\frac{5}{21}$

40. $4\frac{7}{48}+9\frac{4}{15}$

41. $-9\frac{3}{8}+\left(-7\frac{7}{12}\right)$

42. $-5\frac{10}{27}+\left(-3\frac{13}{18}\right)$

43. $4\frac{1}{2}+8\frac{1}{6}$

44. $-\frac{8}{9}+\frac{11}{15}+\left(-\frac{3}{35}\right)$

45. $-\frac{7}{10}+\frac{8}{15}+\left(-\frac{1}{16}\right)$

46. $7\frac{1}{2}+9\frac{3}{10}$

47. $7\frac{2}{3}+4\frac{3}{35}+9\frac{11}{15}$

48. $4\frac{1}{2}+3\frac{2}{35}+5\frac{3}{14}$

Evaluate each expression.

49. What is $1\frac{2}{3}$ increased by $4\frac{3}{8}$?

50. What is $2\frac{3}{4}$ added to $5\frac{2}{7}$?

51. Find the sum of $-\frac{7}{9}$ and $\frac{1}{9}$.

52. Find $-\frac{6}{11}$ increased by $-\frac{1}{4}$.

53. What is $2\frac{3}{5}$ more than $7\frac{5}{8}$?

54. Find the total of $6\frac{3}{10}$, $\frac{7}{20}$, and $7\frac{4}{25}$.

55. Find $-\frac{3}{40}$ added to $-\frac{3}{35}$.

56. What is the sum of $-\frac{5}{8}$ and $\frac{1}{8}$?

57. What is the total of $7\frac{1}{4}$, $\frac{3}{16}$, and $2\frac{5}{12}$?

58. Find $1\frac{1}{30}$ more than $3\frac{1}{42}$.

Evaluate the expression $a+b$ for the given values of a and b.

59. $a=\frac{5}{7};\ b=\frac{4}{7}$

60. $a=\frac{4}{5};\ b=\frac{3}{5}$

61. $a=-\frac{1}{63};\ b=-\frac{7}{18}$

62. $a=-\frac{1}{6};\ b=-\frac{3}{5}$

63. $a=3\frac{2}{9};\ b=-\frac{2}{9}$

64. $a=7\frac{3}{8};\ b=-\frac{3}{8}$

65. $a=4\frac{7}{10};\ b=3\frac{9}{22}$

66. $a=9\frac{3}{10};\ b=6\frac{11}{42}$

Evaluate the expression $a+b+c$ for the given values of a, b, and c.

67. $a=\frac{2}{3};\ b=\frac{2}{15};\ c=-\frac{4}{5}$

68. $a=\frac{3}{5};\ b=\frac{4}{35};\ c=-\frac{5}{7}$

69. $a=3\frac{4}{7};\ b=8\frac{7}{10};\ c=4\frac{8}{35}$

70. $a=2\frac{5}{9};\ b=6\frac{5}{6};\ c=7\frac{5}{8}$

Applications

71. If Joe eats $\frac{1}{3}$ of a pie, Bill eats $\frac{1}{4}$ of the same pie, and Julie eats $\frac{2}{5}$ of the same pie, what fraction of the pie have they eaten altogether? Who ate the most pie?

72. If John jogged $\frac{1}{4}$ of a mile on Monday, $\frac{1}{5}$ of a mile on Tuesday, and $\frac{2}{7}$ of a mile on Wednesday, what total fraction of a mile did John jog during the three days? On which day did John jog the furthest?

The table at the right shows the results of a recent survey conducted by Bogus University. College students were asked how many lattés they purchased on average during a typical week.

Responses to the question, "How many lattés do you purchase on average during a typical week?"

Number of lattés purchased	Fraction of students responding
0	$\frac{1}{10}$
1	$\frac{1}{5}$
2	$\frac{9}{25}$
3	$\frac{7}{50}$
4	$\frac{3}{25}$
5 or more	$\frac{2}{25}$

73. What fraction of students responded with purchasing 3 or more lattés per week?

74. What fraction of students responded with purchasing 2 or less lattés per week?

75. What is the perimeter (in feet) of the triangular garden shown below?

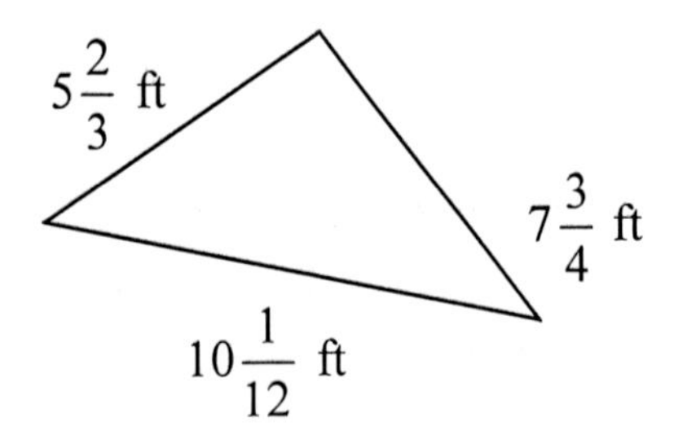

76. What is the perimeter (in meters) of the triangle shown below?

$4\frac{2}{5}$ m

$12\frac{3}{10}$ m

$9\frac{1}{2}$ m

FRACTIONS

Section 5: Subtracting Fractions and Mixed Numbers

Grandma Pat baked a peach pie and cut it into six equal pieces. Her granddaughter Jessica ate one piece of the pie for breakfast. What fraction of the entire pie remained? Since the pie was cut into six pieces, then each piece was $\frac{1}{6}$ of the pie. Therefore, we have the following:

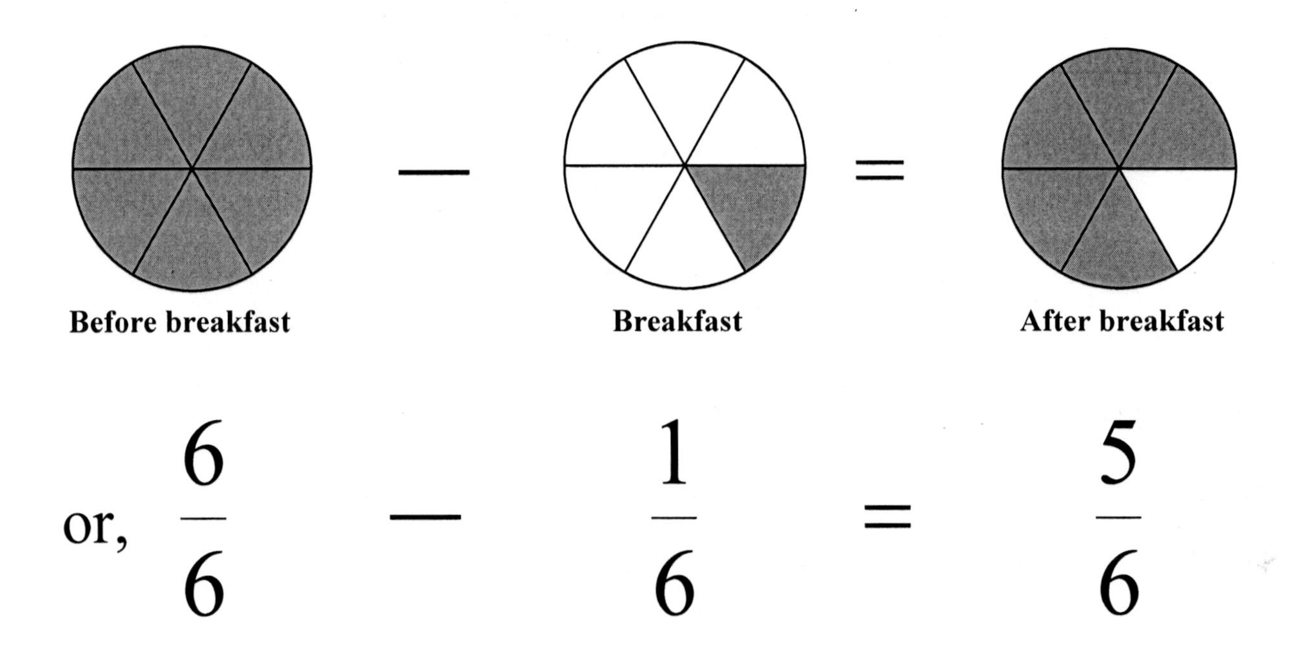

After that, $\frac{5}{6}$ of the pie remained. We found the difference of these fractions by subtracting the numerators and putting them over their common denominator. This process is the same whenever fractions with a common denominator are being subtracted.

To subtract fractions with a common denominator:

Step 1: Subtract the numerators and put their difference over the common denominator.

Step 2: Reduce this fraction to lowest terms (Unless it's already in lowest terms).

Symbolically, this process is: $\frac{a}{b} - \frac{c}{b} = \frac{a-c}{b}$, **where** $b \neq 0$.

Example 1: Find the difference of $\frac{7}{11}$ and $\frac{2}{11}$.

Solution: Since the fractions have the same denominator, we can follow the steps to subtract fractions with a common denominator.

Step 1: Subtract the numerators and put their difference over the common denominator.

$$\frac{7}{11}-\frac{2}{11}=\frac{7-2}{11}=\frac{5}{11}$$

Step 2: This fraction is already in lowest terms.

So, $\frac{7}{11}-\frac{2}{11}=\frac{5}{11}$.

Example 2: Subtract $\frac{1}{12}$ from $\frac{7}{12}$.

Solution: Since the fractions have the same denominator, we can follow the steps to subtract fractions with a common denominator.

Step 1: Subtract the numerators and put their difference over the common denominator.

$$\frac{7}{12}-\frac{1}{12}=\frac{7-1}{12}=\frac{6}{12}$$

Step 2: Reduce this fraction to lowest terms. $\frac{6}{12}=\frac{2\cdot 3}{2\cdot 2\cdot 3}=\frac{\overset{1}{\cancel{2}}\cdot\overset{1}{\cancel{3}}}{2\cdot\underset{1}{\cancel{2}}\cdot\underset{1}{\cancel{3}}}=\frac{1}{2}$

So, $\frac{7}{12}-\frac{1}{12}=\frac{6}{12}=\frac{1}{2}$.

Example 3: Find $\frac{4}{k}-\frac{7}{k}$.

Solution: Since the fractions have the same denominator, we can follow the steps to subtract fractions with a common denominator.

Step 1: Subtract the numerators and put their difference over the common denominator.

$$\frac{4}{k}-\frac{7}{k}=\frac{4-7}{k}=\frac{-3}{k} \text{ or, } -\frac{3}{k}.$$

Step 2: This fraction is already in lowest terms.

So, $\frac{4}{k}-\frac{7}{k}=\frac{-3}{k}$ or, $-\frac{3}{k}$.

Example 4: Subtract: $-\frac{4}{5}-\left(-\frac{3}{5}\right)$

Solution: Since the fractions have the same denominator, we can follow the steps to subtract fractions with a common denominator.

Step 1: Subtract the numerators and put their difference over the common denominator.

$$-\frac{4}{5}-\left(-\frac{3}{5}\right)=\frac{-4-(-3)}{5}=\frac{-4+(+3)}{5} \text{ or, } -\frac{1}{5}.$$

Step 2: This fraction is already in lowest terms.

So, $-\frac{4}{5}-\left(-\frac{3}{5}\right)=-\frac{1}{5}$.

Nancy made a banana cream pie and cut it into three equal pieces. Her son Don ate $\frac{1}{3}$ of the pie and then went home. Nancy put the remaining $\frac{2}{3}$ of the pie in the refrigerator overnight. During the night, her son Ben came in and ate $\frac{1}{2}$ of the original pie. After that, what fraction of the original pie was left? Starting with the pie in the refrigerator, we have the following:

Part of pie put in fridge — **Part of pie that Ben ate** = **Fraction of original pie that was left**

$$\text{or, } \frac{2}{3} - \frac{1}{2} = ?$$

We can tell by looking at the final picture of pie that the answer is $\frac{1}{6}$. The question now is, how do we get to the answer? Suppose we take the original pie and cut it into six equal pieces instead of three. The new set of pictures looks like this:

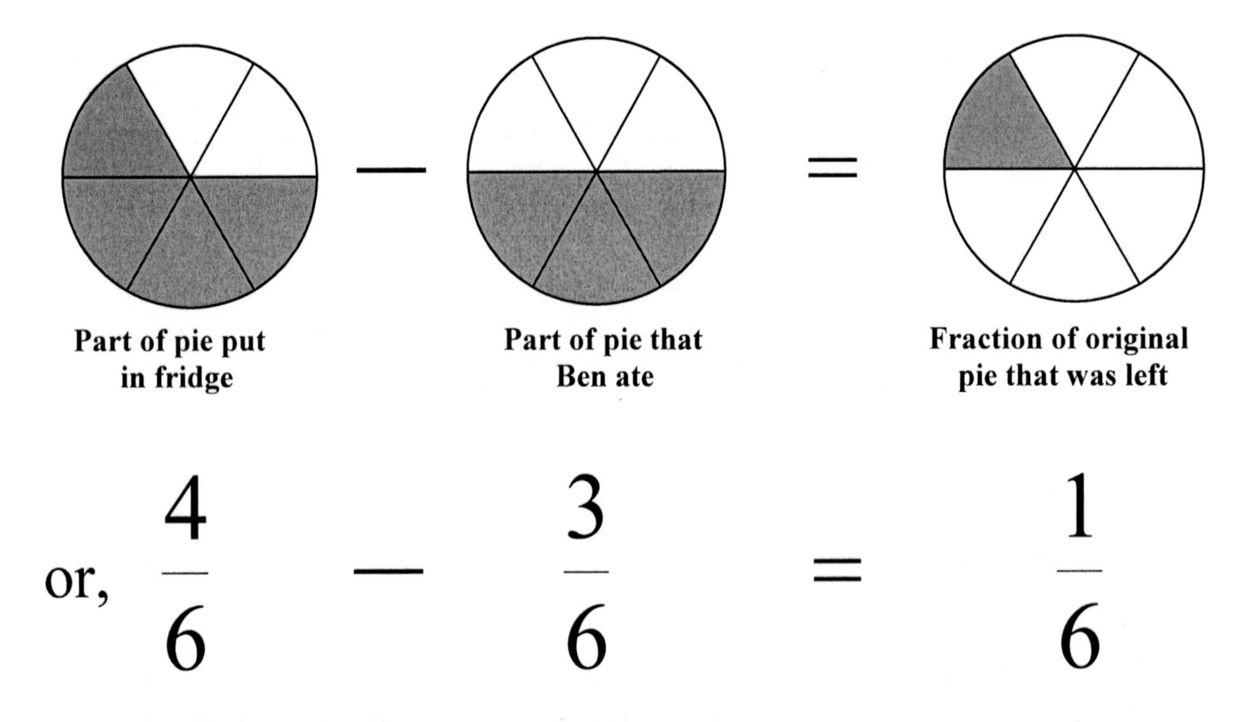

By using the fact that 6 is the least common multiple of 2 and 3, and then by cutting the pie into the same number of equal pieces, each of which was $\frac{1}{6}$, we are able to change the problem into a subtraction problem where each fraction has the same common denominator. This allows us to subtract the numerators over the common denominator. Let's look at this same situation but without all the pie. To find the difference of $\frac{2}{3}$ and $\frac{1}{2}$, first determine what is the least common denominator of the two fractions. Next, change each fraction to an equivalent fraction with the least common denominator (LCD). Then subtract the two fractions.

$\frac{2}{3}-\frac{1}{2}=?$ The LCD of $\frac{2}{3}$ and $\frac{1}{2}$ is 6. $\frac{2}{3}=\frac{2\cdot 2}{3\cdot 2}=\frac{4}{6}$ and $\frac{1}{2}=\frac{1\cdot 3}{2\cdot 3}=\frac{3}{6}$.

So, $\frac{2}{3} - \frac{1}{2} = \frac{4}{6} - \frac{3}{6} = \frac{1}{6}$.

To subtract fractions with different denominators:

Step 1: Find the LCD of the fractions.

Step 2: Change each fraction to an equivalent fraction with the LCD.

Step 3: Subtract the numerators of the new fractions and put their difference over the LCD.

Step 4: Reduce this fraction to lowest terms (unless it's already in lowest terms).

Example 5: Subtract: $\frac{1}{2}-\frac{2}{5}$

Solution:

Step 1: The LCD of $\frac{1}{2}$ and $\frac{2}{5}$ is 10.

Step 2: Change each fraction to an equivalent fraction with a denominator of 10.

$\frac{1}{2}=\frac{1\cdot 5}{2\cdot 5}=\frac{5}{10}$ and $\frac{2}{5}=\frac{2\cdot 2}{5\cdot 2}=\frac{4}{10}$. So, $\frac{1}{2}-\frac{2}{5}$ becomes $\frac{5}{10}-\frac{4}{10}$.

Step 3: Subtract the numerators and put their difference over the LCD.

$$\frac{5}{10}-\frac{4}{10}=\frac{5-4}{10}=\frac{1}{10}$$

Step 4: This fraction is already in lowest terms.

So, $\frac{1}{2}-\frac{2}{5}=\frac{5}{10}-\frac{4}{10}=\frac{1}{10}$.

Example 6: Find the difference of $-\frac{5}{6}$ and $\frac{1}{4}$.

Solution:

Step 1: The LCD of $-\frac{5}{6}$ and $\frac{1}{4}$ is 12.

Step 2: Change each fraction to an equivalent fraction with a denominator of 12.

$-\frac{5}{6}=-\frac{5\cdot 2}{6\cdot 2}=-\frac{10}{12}$ and $\frac{1}{4}=\frac{1\cdot 3}{4\cdot 3}=\frac{3}{12}$. So, $-\frac{5}{6}-\frac{1}{4}$ becomes $-\frac{10}{12}-\frac{3}{12}$.

Step 3: Subtract the numerators and put their difference over the LCD.

$-\frac{10}{12}-\frac{3}{12}=\frac{-10-3}{12}=\frac{-13}{12}$ or $-\frac{13}{12}$.

Step 4: This fraction is already in lowest terms. We could change it into a mixed number if desired. That is, $-\frac{13}{12}=-1\frac{1}{12}$.

So, $-\frac{5}{6}-\frac{1}{4}=-\frac{10}{12}-\frac{3}{12}=-\frac{13}{12}$ or $-1\frac{1}{12}$.

Example 7: Find $\frac{1}{6}$ minus $\frac{5}{8}$.

Solution:

Step 1: The LCD of $\frac{1}{6}$ and $\frac{5}{8}$ is 24.

Step 2: Change each fraction to an equivalent fraction with a denominator of 24.

$\frac{1}{6}=\frac{1\cdot 4}{6\cdot 4}=\frac{4}{24}$ and $\frac{5}{8}=\frac{5\cdot 3}{8\cdot 3}=\frac{15}{24}$. So, $\frac{1}{6}-\frac{5}{8}$ becomes $\frac{4}{24}-\frac{15}{24}$.

Step 3: Subtract the numerators and put their difference over the LCD.

$\frac{4}{24}-\frac{15}{24}=\frac{4-15}{24}=\frac{-11}{24}$ or $-\frac{11}{24}$.

Step 4: This fraction is already in lowest terms.

So, $\frac{1}{6}-\frac{5}{8}=\frac{4}{24}-\frac{15}{24}=-\frac{11}{24}$.

Since mixed numbers are a combination of whole numbers and fractions, it makes sense that we can subtract them. Before we proceed let's review some vocabulary words that will be used in this process. In the subtraction problem $3\frac{1}{2}-1\frac{2}{5}$, the first number $3\frac{1}{2}$ is called the **minuend** and the second number $1\frac{2}{5}$ is called the **subtrahend**. Therefore, $\frac{1}{2}$ is the fraction part of the minuend and $\frac{2}{5}$ is the fraction part of the subtrahend.

When subtracting mixed numbers:

Step 1: Change the fraction part of each mixed number to an equivalent fraction with the LCD.

Step 2: If the fraction part of the subtrahend is greater than the fraction part of the minuend, go to step 3. If the fraction part of the subtrahend is less than or equal to the fraction part of the minuend, then skip step 3 and go straight to step 4.

Step 3: If you are at step 3, this means that you will need to borrow a 1 from the whole-number part of the minuend in order to subtract the fraction parts. Take this 1 and turn it into an improper fraction with the numerator and the denominator matching the common denominator of the fraction parts of the problem. Now add this improper fraction to the fraction part of the minuend.

Step 4: Subtract the whole-number parts and subtract the fraction parts.

Step 5: Reduce the fraction part to lowest terms if necessary. Then combine the whole number and the fraction to form the final mixed number.

Example 8: Subtract: $7\frac{3}{5}-3\frac{2}{5}$

Solution: Step 1: The fraction part of each mixed number already has the same denominator.

Step 2. Since the fraction part of the subtrahend is less than the fraction part of the minuend, that is $\frac{2}{5}<\frac{3}{5}$, skip step 3 and go straight to step 4.

Step 4: Subtract the whole-number parts and subtract the fraction parts.

$7\frac{3}{5}-3\frac{2}{5}$ becomes $7-3=4$ and $\frac{3}{5}-\frac{2}{5}=\frac{1}{5}$.

Step 5: Combine the whole number and the fraction to form the final mixed number.

$4+\frac{1}{5}=4\frac{1}{5}$

So, $7\frac{3}{5}-3\frac{2}{5}=4\frac{1}{5}$.

Example 9: Subtract: $12\frac{3}{10}-3\frac{7}{10}$

Solution: Step 1: The fraction part of each mixed number already has the same denominator.

Step 2. Since the fraction part of the subtrahend is greater than the fraction part of the minuend, that is $\frac{7}{10}>\frac{3}{10}$, continue to step 3.

Step 3: Borrow a 1 from the whole-number part of the minuend in order to subtract the fraction parts.

$12\frac{3}{10}=12+\frac{3}{10}=11+1+\frac{3}{10}$ Take this 1 and turn it into an improper fraction with the numerator and the denominator matching the common denominator of the fraction parts of the problem.

$=11+\frac{10}{10}+\frac{3}{10}$ Add this improper fraction to the fraction part of the minuend.

$=11+\frac{13}{10}=11\frac{13}{10}$ So,

$12\frac{3}{10}=12+\frac{3}{10}=11+1+\frac{3}{10}=11+\frac{10}{10}+\frac{3}{10}=11+\frac{13}{10}=11\frac{13}{10}$. Or, $12\frac{3}{10}=11\frac{13}{10}$.

Step 4: Subtract the whole-number parts and subtract the fraction parts.

$12\frac{3}{10}-3\frac{7}{10}=11\frac{13}{10}-3\frac{7}{10}$ becomes $11-3=8$ and $\frac{13}{10}-\frac{7}{10}=\frac{6}{10}$.

Step 5: Reduce the fraction part to lowest terms. $\frac{6}{10}=\frac{2\cdot 3}{2\cdot 5}=\frac{\overset{1}{\cancel{2}}\cdot 3}{\underset{1}{\cancel{2}}\cdot 5}=\frac{3}{5}$

Combine the whole number and the fraction to form the final mixed number.

$8+\frac{3}{5}=8\frac{3}{5}$

So, $12\frac{3}{10}-3\frac{7}{10}=11\frac{13}{10}-3\frac{7}{10}=8+\frac{6}{10}=8+\frac{3}{5}=8\frac{3}{5}$. Or, $12\frac{3}{10}-3\frac{7}{10}=8\frac{3}{5}$.

Example 10: Subtract: $19\frac{5}{8}-5\frac{3}{4}$

Solution: Step 1: The LCD of $\frac{5}{8}$ and $\frac{3}{4}$ is 8.

$\frac{5}{8}$ remains unchanged and $\frac{3}{4}=\frac{3\cdot 2}{4\cdot 2}=\frac{6}{8}$. So, $19\frac{5}{8}-5\frac{3}{4}$ becomes $19\frac{5}{8}-5\frac{6}{8}$.

Step 2. Since the fraction part of the subtrahend is greater than the fraction part of the minuend, that is $\frac{6}{8}>\frac{5}{8}$, continue to step 3.

Step 3: Borrow a 1 from the whole-number part of the minuend in order to subtract the fraction parts.

$19\frac{5}{8}=19+\frac{5}{8}=18+1+\frac{5}{8}$

Take this 1 and turn it into an improper fraction with the numerator and the denominator matching the common denominator of the fraction parts of the problem.

$=18+\frac{8}{8}+\frac{5}{8}$

Add this improper fraction to the fraction part of the minuend.

$=18+\frac{13}{8}=18\frac{13}{8}$

So,

$19\frac{5}{8}=19+\frac{5}{8}=18+1+\frac{5}{8}=18+\frac{8}{8}+\frac{5}{8}=18+\frac{13}{8}=18\frac{13}{8}$. Or, $19\frac{5}{8}=18\frac{13}{8}$.

Step 4: Subtract the whole-number parts and subtract the fraction parts.

$19\frac{5}{8}-5\frac{6}{8}=18\frac{13}{8}-5\frac{6}{8}$ becomes $18-5=13$ and $\frac{13}{8}-\frac{6}{8}=\frac{7}{8}$.

Step 5: Combine the whole number and the fraction to form the final mixed number.

$13+\frac{7}{8}=13\frac{7}{8}$

So, $19\frac{5}{8}-5\frac{3}{4}=19\frac{5}{8}-5\frac{6}{8}=18\frac{13}{8}-5\frac{6}{8}=13\frac{7}{8}$. Or, $19\frac{5}{8}-5\frac{3}{4}=13\frac{7}{8}$.

Even though the process involves the same steps, students often prefer to subtract mixed numbers using a vertical format rather than a horizontal one. Let's look again at example 10, but this time we will subtract the mixed numbers vertically.

Example 10 Revisited: Subtract:

$$\begin{array}{r} 19\frac{5}{8} \\ -5\frac{3}{4} \\ \hline \end{array}$$

Solution: Step 1: The LCD of $\frac{5}{8}$ and $\frac{3}{4}$ is 8.

$\frac{5}{8}$ remains unchanged and $\frac{3}{4}=\frac{3\cdot 2}{4\cdot 2}=\frac{6}{8}$. So, $\begin{array}{r} 19\frac{5}{8} \\ -5\frac{3}{4} \\ \hline \end{array}$ becomes $\begin{array}{r} 19\frac{5}{8} \\ -5\frac{6}{8} \\ \hline \end{array}$.

Step 2. Since the fraction part of the subtrahend is greater than the fraction part of the minuend, that is $\frac{6}{8}>\frac{5}{8}$, continue to step 3.

Step 3: Borrow a 1 from the whole-number part of the minuend in order to subtract the fraction parts.

$19\frac{5}{8}=19+\frac{5}{8}=18+1+\frac{5}{8}$

Take this 1 and turn it into an improper fraction with the numerator and the denominator matching the common denominator of the fraction parts of the problem.

$=18+\frac{8}{8}+\frac{5}{8}$

Add this improper fraction to the fraction part of the minuend.

$=18+\frac{13}{8}=18\frac{13}{8}$

So, $19\frac{5}{8}=18\frac{13}{8}$ and $\begin{array}{r} 19\frac{5}{8} \\ -5\frac{6}{8} \\ \hline \end{array}$ becomes $\begin{array}{r} 18\frac{13}{8} \\ -5\frac{6}{8} \\ \hline \end{array}$.

Step 4: Subtract the whole-number parts and subtract the fraction parts.

$$\begin{array}{r} 18\frac{13}{8} \\ -5\frac{6}{8} \\ \hline 13\frac{7}{8} \end{array}$$

Step 5: The whole number and the fraction are already combined in the vertical subtraction process.

The final mixed number is $13\frac{7}{8}$.

Example 11: Subtract: $7-4\frac{1}{5}$

Solution: Step 1: Since the minuend doesn't contain a fraction part yet, there is no need to find a common denominator.

Step 2. Since the fraction part of the subtrahend is greater than the nonexistent fraction part of the minuend, that is $\frac{1}{5}>0$, continue to step 3.

Step 3: Borrow a 1 from the whole-number part of the minuend in order to subtract the fraction parts.

$7=6+1$ Take this 1 and turn it into an improper fraction with the numerator and the denominator matching the denominator of the fraction part of the subtrahend.

$=6+\frac{5}{5}$

$=6+\frac{5}{5}=6\frac{5}{5}$ So, $7=6+1=6+\frac{5}{5}=6\frac{5}{5}$. Or, $7=6\frac{5}{5}$.

Step 4: Subtract the whole-number parts and subtract the fraction parts.

$7-4\frac{1}{5}=6\frac{5}{5}-4\frac{1}{5}$ becomes $6-4=2$ and $\frac{5}{5}-\frac{1}{5}=\frac{4}{5}$.

Step 5: Combine the whole number and the fraction to form the final mixed number.

$2+\frac{4}{5}=2\frac{4}{5}$

So, $7-4\frac{1}{5}=6\frac{5}{5}-4\frac{1}{5}=2\frac{4}{5}$. Or, $7-4\frac{1}{5}=2\frac{4}{5}$.

In previous chapters, we evaluated variable expressions using whole numbers and integers. Now we will evaluate expressions involving subtraction of fractions and mixed numbers.

Example 12: Evaluate the expression for the given values of the variables:

$x - y$, where $x = 5\frac{1}{3}$ and $y = 4\frac{2}{3}$

Solution:

$x - y$ — Substitute $5\frac{1}{3}$ in the place of x and $4\frac{2}{3}$ in the place of y.

$5\frac{1}{3} - 4\frac{2}{3}$ — The fraction part of each mixed number already has the same denominator

Since the fraction part of the subtrahend is greater than the fraction part of the minuend, that is $\frac{2}{3} > \frac{1}{3}$, borrow a 1 from the whole-number part of the minuend in order to subtract the fraction parts.

$5\frac{1}{3} = 5 + \frac{1}{3} = 4 + 1 + \frac{1}{3}$ — Take this 1 and turn it into an improper fraction with the numerator and the denominator matching the common denominator of the fraction parts of the problem.

$= 4 + \frac{3}{3} + \frac{1}{3}$ — Now add this improper fraction to the fraction part of the minuend.

$= 4 + \frac{4}{3} = 4\frac{4}{3}$ — So,

$5\frac{1}{3} = 5 + \frac{1}{3} = 4 + 1 + \frac{1}{3} = 4 + \frac{3}{3} + \frac{1}{3} = 4 + \frac{4}{3} = 4\frac{4}{3}$. Or, $5\frac{1}{3} = 4\frac{4}{3}$.

Subtract the whole-number parts and subtract the fraction parts.

$5\frac{1}{3} - 4\frac{2}{3} = 4\frac{4}{3} - 4\frac{2}{3}$ becomes $4 - 4 = 0$ and $\frac{4}{3} - \frac{2}{3} = \frac{2}{3}$.

Since the whole number is 0, the final answer is the fraction $\frac{2}{3}$.

So, $5\frac{1}{3} - 4\frac{2}{3} = 4\frac{4}{3} - 4\frac{2}{3} = \frac{2}{3}$.

Applications involving fractions and mixed numbers

Example 13: Barb needs to exercise $6\frac{1}{2}$ hours per week in order to control her high cholesterol level. If she exercises for $2\frac{1}{4}$ hours on Monday and $1\frac{1}{6}$ hours on Wednesday, how many hours does she still need to exercise during the rest of the week?

Solution: We need to find the total amount that Barb has already exercised and then subtract that amount from the $6\frac{1}{2}$ hours she needs to exercise during the week. This will tell us how much time she still needs to exercise during the rest of the week.

$2\frac{1}{4}+1\frac{1}{6}$ — The LCD of $\frac{1}{4}$ and $\frac{1}{6}$ is 12. $\frac{1}{4}=\frac{1\cdot 3}{4\cdot 3}=\frac{3}{12}$ and $\frac{1}{6}=\frac{1\cdot 2}{6\cdot 2}=\frac{2}{12}$.

So, $2\frac{1}{4}+1\frac{1}{6}$ becomes

$2\frac{3}{12}+1\frac{2}{12}$. — Add the whole-number parts together and add the fraction parts together.

$3+\frac{5}{12}$ — Combine the whole number and the fraction to form the mixed number that represents the total amount Barb has already exercised.

$3+\frac{5}{12}=3\frac{5}{12}$ — Now subtract this amount from the $6\frac{1}{2}$ hours she needs to exercise during the week.

$6\frac{1}{2}-3\frac{5}{12}$ — The LCD of $\frac{1}{2}$ and $\frac{5}{12}$ is 12. $\frac{1}{2}=\frac{1\cdot 6}{2\cdot 6}=\frac{6}{12}$ and $\frac{5}{12}$ remains unchanged.

So, $6\frac{1}{2}-3\frac{5}{12}$ becomes

$6\frac{6}{12}-3\frac{5}{12}$. — Subtract the whole-number parts and subtract the fraction parts.

$6\frac{6}{12}-3\frac{5}{12}$ becomes $6-3=3$ and $\frac{6}{12}-\frac{5}{12}=\frac{1}{12}$.

$3+\frac{1}{12}$ — Combine the whole number and the fraction to form the final mixed number that represents the amount of hours she still needs to exercise during the rest of the week.

$3+\frac{1}{12}=3\frac{1}{12}$ — That amount is $3\frac{1}{12}$ hours.

Applications involving angles

Remember that the measure of angles can be added or subtracted. For instance, a $37\frac{1}{2}°$ angle and a $52\frac{1}{2}°$ angle can be added together to form a 90° angle. Or, a $22\frac{1}{3}°$ angle can be subtracted from a $48\frac{2}{3}°$ angle to form a $26\frac{1}{3}°$ angle.

Also, remember that when the sum of the measure of two angles is 90°, the angles are said to be a pair of **complementary angles** and when the sum of the measure of two angles is 180°, the angles are said to be a pair of **supplementary angles**.

Example 14: Given $\angle A = 53\frac{1}{4}°$ and $\angle B = 36\frac{3}{4}°$, are $\angle$ A and $\angle$ B a pair of complementary angles?

> Solution: Since $53\frac{1}{4}° + 36\frac{3}{4}° = 90°$, then $\angle$ A and $\angle$ B are a pair of complementary angles.

Example 15: Given $\angle C = 125\frac{2}{5}°$ and $\angle D = 54\frac{1}{5}°$, are $\angle$ C and $\angle$ D a pair of supplementary angles?

> Solution: Since $125\frac{2}{5}° + 54\frac{1}{5}° = 179\frac{3}{5}°$, then $\angle$ C and $\angle$ D are not a pair of supplementary angles.

Example 16: Given $\angle W = 34\frac{3}{7}°$, find $\angle$ X such that $\angle$ W and $\angle$ X are a pair of complementary angles.

> Solution: If $\angle$ W and $\angle$ X are a pair of complementary angles, then
>
> $\angle W + \angle X = 90°$. Since $\angle W = 34\frac{3}{7}°$, then
>
> ↓
>
> $34\frac{3}{7}° + \angle X = 90°$. By subtracting $34\frac{3}{7}°$ from both sides of the equation it becomes
>
> $34\frac{3}{7}° - 34\frac{3}{7}° + \angle X = \underbrace{90° - 34\frac{3}{7}°}$. Finally,
>
> $\angle X = 55\frac{4}{7}°$.

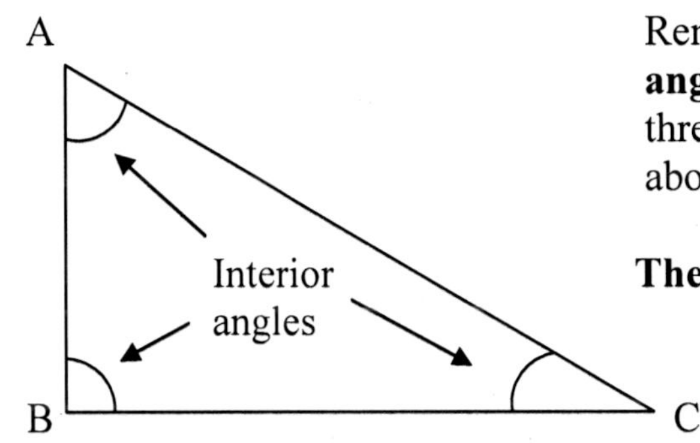

Remember that a triangle has what are called **interior angles**. Just like a tricycle has three wheels, a triangle has three interior angles. One of the things that is always true about a triangle is the following:

The sum of the three interior angles of a triangle is 180°.

So, for the triangle above, $\angle A + \angle B + \angle C = 180°$.

Example 17: A given triangle contains interior angles $\angle D$, $\angle E$ and $\angle F$. If $\angle D = 37\frac{2}{9}°$ and $\angle E = 69\frac{4}{9}°$, then find $\angle F$.

Solution: Since $\angle D$, $\angle E$ and $\angle F$ are the three interior angles of a triangle, then their sum is 180°. That is,

$\angle D + \angle E + \angle F = 180°$. Since $\angle D = 37\frac{2}{9}°$ and $\angle E = 69\frac{4}{9}°$, then

$37\frac{2}{9}° + 69\frac{4}{9}° + \angle F = 180°$. Adding together $37\frac{2}{9}° + 69\frac{4}{9}°$ the equation becomes

$106\frac{2}{3}° + \angle F = 180°$. By subtracting $106\frac{2}{3}°$ from both sides of the equation it becomes

$106\frac{2}{3}° - 106\frac{2}{3}° + \angle F = 180° - 106\frac{2}{3}°$. Finally,

$\angle F = 73\frac{1}{3}°$.

Section 5 exercises. Subtract.

1. $\frac{4}{5}-\frac{1}{5}$

2. $\frac{6}{7}-\frac{2}{7}$

3. $\frac{5}{9}-\frac{2}{9}$

4. $\frac{7}{12}-\frac{1}{12}$

5. $\frac{9}{14}-\frac{5}{14}$

6. $\frac{8}{15}-\frac{3}{15}$

7. $\frac{6}{11}-\left(-\frac{3}{11}\right)$

8. $\frac{4}{9}-\left(-\frac{2}{9}\right)$

9. $\frac{5}{m}-\frac{9}{m}$

10. $\frac{3}{k}-\frac{8}{k}$

11. $-\frac{5}{p}-\left(-\frac{7}{p}\right)$

12. $-\frac{3}{g}-\left(-\frac{9}{g}\right)$

13. $9\frac{3}{8}-7$

14. $11\frac{2}{3}-9$

15. $14\frac{7}{10}-14$

16. $6\frac{2}{9}-6$

17. $10-3\frac{7}{9}$

18. $8-4\frac{3}{7}$

19. $9-7\frac{1}{8}$

20. $12-6\frac{2}{5}$

21. $8\frac{3}{7}-3\frac{2}{7}$

22. $9\frac{8}{11}-4\frac{3}{11}$

23. $12\frac{7}{9}-10\frac{4}{9}$

24. $7\frac{8}{9}-2\frac{2}{9}$

25. $\frac{7}{9}-\frac{1}{2}$

26. $\frac{2}{3}-\frac{4}{7}$

27. $\frac{5}{6}-\frac{4}{9}$

28. $\frac{8}{15}-\frac{3}{10}$

29. $\frac{7}{72}-\frac{3}{40}$

30. $\frac{5}{36}-\frac{7}{60}$

31. $-\frac{1}{2}-\frac{5}{14}$

32. $-\frac{1}{3}-\frac{7}{15}$

33. $-\frac{9}{70}-\left(-\frac{11}{42}\right)$

34. $-\frac{3}{26}-\left(-\frac{14}{65}\right)$

35. $-\frac{1}{4}-\frac{4}{5}$

36. $-\frac{3}{5}-\frac{5}{6}$

37. $-\frac{3}{14}-\left(-\frac{8}{21}\right)$

38. $-\frac{7}{15}-\left(-\frac{9}{20}\right)$

39. $8\frac{2}{9}-5\frac{2}{3}$

40. $10\frac{3}{10}-6\frac{3}{5}$

41. $7\frac{5}{42}-2\frac{4}{15}$

42. $10\frac{5}{14}-6\frac{7}{15}$

43. $9\frac{3}{10}-3\frac{1}{2}$

44. $10\frac{1}{6}-5\frac{1}{2}$

Evaluate each expression.

45. What is $6\frac{3}{8}$ decreased by $4\frac{2}{3}$?

46. What is $5\frac{3}{4}$ subtracted from $6\frac{2}{7}$?

47. Find the difference of $-\frac{5}{7}$ and $\frac{2}{7}$.

48. Find 1 less $-\frac{2}{5}$.

49. What is $\frac{4}{5}$ less than 1?

50. What is $-\frac{5}{6}$ minus $\frac{1}{6}$?

Evaluate the expression $a-b$ for the given values of a and b.

51. $a=\frac{7}{9};\ b=\frac{8}{9}$

52. $a=\frac{9}{11};\ b=\frac{10}{11}$

53. $a=\frac{3}{5};\ b=-\frac{5}{6}$

54. $a=\frac{2}{5};\ b=-\frac{3}{4}$

55. $a=6\frac{5}{8};\ b=\frac{5}{8}$

56. $a=9\frac{4}{9};\ b=\frac{4}{9}$

57. $a = 8\frac{1}{3}$; $b = 1\frac{5}{6}$

58. $a = 7\frac{3}{5}$; $b = 4\frac{9}{10}$

59. $a = 5\frac{1}{45}$; $b = 3\frac{1}{20}$

60. $a = 3\frac{11}{42}$; $b = 2\frac{5}{24}$

61. $a = 10$; $b = \frac{6}{7}$

62. $a = 7$; $b = \frac{3}{10}$

63. $a = 8\frac{7}{15}$; $b = 5\frac{5}{9}$

64. $a = 5\frac{4}{15}$; $b = 2\frac{5}{6}$

65. $a = -\frac{11}{56}$; $b = \frac{9}{70}$

66. $a = -\frac{1}{52}$; $b = \frac{5}{78}$

67. $a = 2\frac{1}{3}$; $b = -\frac{3}{7}$

68. $a = 1\frac{3}{5}$; $b = -\frac{5}{8}$

Applications

69. Sam has a piece of land $1\frac{3}{16}$ acres in size. If he plants $\frac{5}{8}$ acre in corn, how much land does he have available to plant potatoes?

70. The dimensions of a painting are $32\frac{1}{6}$ inches long by $27\frac{1}{4}$ inches wide. How much longer is the painting than it is wide?

71. Mary takes $4\frac{2}{3}$ yards of material from a bolt of cloth to use on a sewing project. If there are still $11\frac{5}{6}$ yards of material left, how much was there to start with?

72. A fish tank contains $3\frac{9}{16}$ gallons of water. If another $1\frac{9}{16}$ gallons of water are added to the tank before it is full, then how much water will the fish tank hold?

73. If the grass was $3\frac{1}{2}$ inches long and Sean set the lawn mower to cut the top $1\frac{1}{4}$ inches off, how long was the grass when he finished cutting it?

74. Jim has a pair of dress pants that are $34\frac{1}{8}$ inches long. He has a pair of jeans that are $33\frac{1}{2}$ inches long. How much longer are the dress pants than the jeans?

75. A local triathlon consists of running, swimming, and biking. The total distance traveled in the triathlon is $6\frac{1}{5}$ miles. If the running distance is $2\frac{1}{2}$ miles, and the swimming distance is $\frac{5}{8}$ of a mile, how far is the biking distance?

76. A piece of property $24\frac{1}{3}$ acres in size is to be divided up between three heirs. If the first heir receives $8\frac{1}{2}$ acres and the second heir receives $8\frac{1}{4}$ acres, then how much land is left for the third heir to receive?

77. Restrictions on an overseas flight allow for a total luggage weight of $52\frac{1}{2}$ pounds. If a passenger has a suitcase weighing $28\frac{1}{8}$ pounds and a backpack weighing $15\frac{1}{3}$ pounds, how much weight are they still allowed for their final piece of luggage?

78. If Joyce eats $\frac{1}{5}$ of a pie and Bart eats $\frac{1}{4}$ of the same pie, how much of the pie is left for Mary to eat?

79. A board that is 10 feet long is cut into three pieces. If the length of the first piece is $4\frac{1}{8}$ feet and the length of the second piece is $2\frac{5}{12}$ feet, how long is the remaining piece of board?

80. To pay back a debt, Seth worked for his grandpa a total of 15 hours. The first day Seth worked $3\frac{1}{6}$ hours and on the second day he worked $5\frac{5}{12}$ hours. How much time remained for him to work in order to pay off his debt?

81. On May 1st a corn stock was $13\frac{5}{8}$ inches tall. By July 1st the same corn stock had grown another $7\frac{7}{8}$ inches. How tall was the corn stock on July 1st?

82. Jim is $66\frac{3}{8}$ inches tall. If Frank is $3\frac{7}{8}$ inches taller than Jim, then how tall is Frank?

83. An absentminded chef put $4\frac{1}{2}$ cups of flour in a mixing bowl. He then realized that the recipe he was fixing called for only $3\frac{2}{3}$ cups of flour. How much flour should he remove from the bowl before continuing to make the recipe?

84. A tank contains $46\frac{3}{10}$ gallons of heating oil. How much heating oil could a farmer use and still have $35\frac{1}{2}$ gallons left for the coming winter?

The table at the right shows the results of a recent survey conducted by Bogus University. College students were asked how many lattés they purchased on average during a typical week.

Responses to the question, "How many lattés do you purchase on average during a typical week?"

Number of lattés purchased	Fraction of students responding
0	$\frac{1}{10}$
1	$\frac{1}{5}$
2	$\frac{9}{25}$
3	$\frac{7}{50}$
4	$\frac{3}{25}$
5 or more	$\frac{2}{25}$

85. Find the difference between the fraction of students responding that they purchased no lattés during a typical week and the fraction of students responding that they purchased 5 or more lattés per week.

86. Find the difference between the fraction of students responding that they purchased 2 lattés during a typical week and the fraction of students responding that they purchased 3 lattés per week.

Applications involving angles

For each pair of angles, tell whether they are complementary, supplementary or neither one.

87. $\angle A = 123\frac{2}{7}°$, $\angle B = 56\frac{5}{7}°$

88. $\angle C = 164\frac{3}{5}°$, $\angle D = 15\frac{3}{10}°$

89. $\angle E = 85\frac{5}{6}°$, $\angle F = 5\frac{1}{6}°$

90. $\angle G = 38\frac{2}{3}°$, $\angle H = 51\frac{1}{3}°$

91. Given that $\angle X = 39\frac{4}{13}°$, find $\angle$ Y such that $\angle$ X and $\angle$ Y are complementary angles.

92. Given that $\angle A = 58\frac{7}{11}°$, find $\angle$ B such that $\angle$ A and $\angle$ B are complementary angles.

93. Given that $\angle C = 106\frac{5}{12}°$, find $\angle$ D such that $\angle$ C and $\angle$ D are supplementary angles.

94. Given that $\angle E = 44\frac{3}{8}°$, find $\angle$ F such that $\angle$ E and $\angle$ F are supplementary angles.

95. A given triangle contains interior angles $\angle$ D, $\angle$ E and $\angle$ F. If $\angle D = 30\frac{2}{3}°$ and $\angle E = 53\frac{4}{7}°$, then find $\angle$ F.

96. A given triangle contains interior angles $\angle$ M, $\angle$ N and $\angle$ P. If $\angle M = 119\frac{5}{6}°$ and $\angle N = 38\frac{2}{3}°$, then find $\angle$ P.

FRACTIONS

Section 6: Multiplying Fractions and Mixed Numbers

Just how much is $\frac{1}{2}$ of $\frac{1}{2}$ of a pie? Let's start by taking a whole pie and cutting it into 4 equal pieces.

Each piece is $\frac{1}{4}$ of the pie.

If we only had $\frac{1}{2}$ of the pie, it would look like this:

Now, suppose we only had $\frac{1}{2}$ of $\frac{1}{2}$ of the pie. That would look like this:

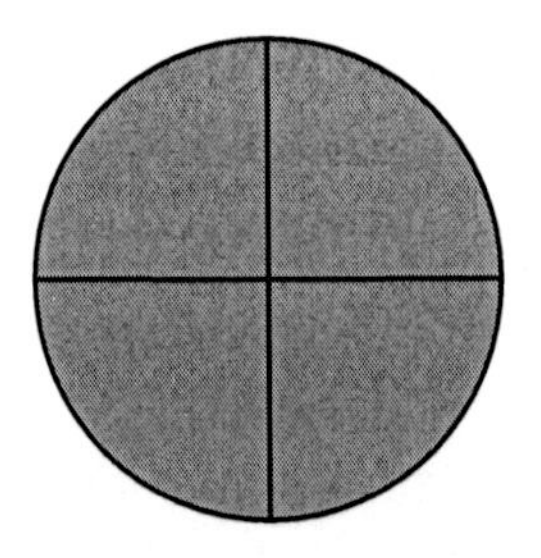

A whole pie cut into 4 equal pieces

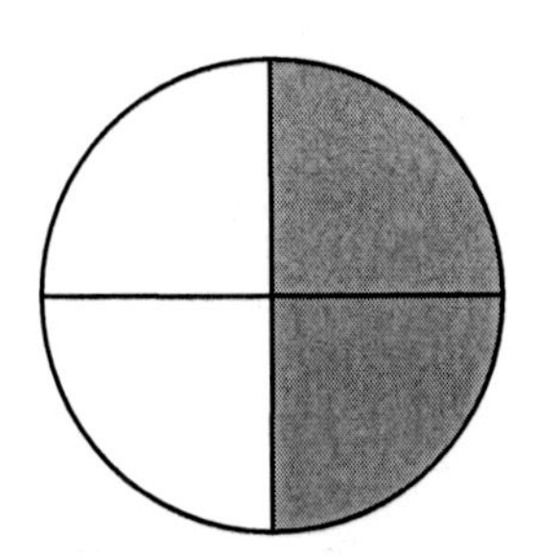

$\frac{1}{2}$ of a pie

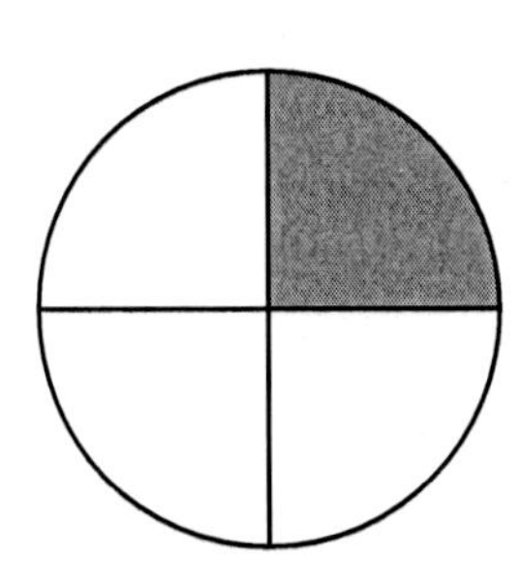

$\frac{1}{2}$ of $\frac{1}{2}$ of a pie

Notice from the picture of $\frac{1}{2}$ of $\frac{1}{2}$ a pie that this is also a picture of $\frac{1}{4}$ of a pie. This leads to the following statement. $\frac{1}{2}$ of $\frac{1}{2} = \frac{1}{4}$. Or to put it another way, $\frac{1}{2} \cdot \frac{1}{2} = \frac{1}{4}$. This is an example of multiplying fractions together. The numerator of the answer is the product of the numerators of the factors being multiplied while the denominator of the answer is the product of the denominators of the factors being multiplied. Put another way, when multiplying fractions together just multiply straight across.

<u>To multiply fractions:</u>

Step 1: Multiply the numerators. This becomes the numerator of the final product.

Step 2: Multiply the denominators. This becomes the denominator of the final product.

Step 3: Reduce the final product to lowest terms if necessary.

Symbolically this process is: $\frac{a}{b} \cdot \frac{c}{d} = \frac{ac}{bd}$, **where** $b \neq 0$ **and** $d \neq 0$.

Example 1: Find the product of $\frac{2}{3}$ and $\frac{5}{7}$.

Solution:

$$\frac{2}{3}\cdot\frac{5}{7}$$

Step 1: Multiply the numerators.

$$\frac{2}{3}\cdot\frac{5}{7}=\frac{2\cdot 5}{3\cdot 7}=\frac{10}{3\cdot 7}$$

Step 2: Multiply the denominators.

$$\frac{10}{3\cdot 7}=\frac{10}{21}$$

Step 3: The fraction is already in lowest terms.

So,

$$\frac{2}{3}\cdot\frac{5}{7}=\frac{10}{21}.$$

Example 2: Find the product of $\frac{4}{9}$ and $\frac{4}{5}$.

Solution:

$$\frac{4}{9}\cdot\frac{4}{5}$$

Step 1: Multiply the numerators.

$$\frac{4}{9}\cdot\frac{4}{5}=\frac{4\cdot 4}{9\cdot 5}=\frac{16}{9\cdot 5}$$

Step 2: Multiply the denominators.

$$\frac{16}{9\cdot 5}=\frac{16}{45}$$

Step 3: The fraction is already in lowest terms.

So,

$$\frac{4}{9}\cdot\frac{4}{5}=\frac{16}{45}.$$

Note: When multiplying fractions it is not necessary to find a common denominator.

Now that we've looked at several examples, let's review previously discussed ideas and how they relate to multiplying fractions. Fractions can be either positive or negative. The rules of multiplying positive and negative numbers apply to fractions in the same way that they apply to integers.

Multiplication of Fractions: When multiplying two fractions, apply the following rules:

1. **If the signs of the fractions are the same, both positive or both negative, then their product is a positive number.**

2. **If the signs of the fractions are opposites, one positive and one negative, then their product is a negative number.**

Example 3: Multiply $-\frac{4}{7}$ by $\frac{3}{5}$.

Solution: $-\frac{4}{7}\cdot\frac{3}{5}$ Step 1: Multiply the numerators.

$$-\frac{4}{7}\cdot\frac{3}{5}=-\frac{4\cdot 3}{7\cdot 5}=-\frac{12}{7\cdot 5}$$ Step 2: Multiply the denominators.

$$-\frac{12}{7\cdot 5}=-\frac{12}{35}$$ Step 3: The fraction is already in lowest terms.

So,

$$-\frac{4}{7}\cdot\frac{3}{5}=-\frac{12}{35}.$$

Note that the product of a negative fraction and a positive fraction is a negative number.

Example 4: Multiply $-\frac{7}{8}$ and $-\frac{1}{3}$.

Solution: $-\frac{7}{8}\cdot\left(-\frac{1}{3}\right)$ Step 1: Multiply the numerators.

$$-\frac{7}{8}\cdot\left(-\frac{1}{3}\right)=\frac{-7\cdot(-1)}{8\cdot 3}=\frac{7}{8\cdot 3}$$ Step 2: Multiply the denominators.

$$\frac{7}{8\cdot 3}=\frac{7}{24}$$ Step 3: The fraction is already in lowest terms.

So,

$$-\frac{7}{8}\cdot\left(-\frac{1}{3}\right)=\frac{7}{24}.$$

Note that the product of a negative fraction and a negative fraction is a positive number.

All of the properties, such as the commutative and associative properties of multiplication, apply to fractions as well as integers. The idea of opposites (also known as additive inverses) applies to fractions. For example, $\frac{2}{3}$ and $-\frac{2}{3}$ are opposites or additive inverses. Therefore, $\frac{2}{3}+\left(-\frac{2}{3}\right)=0$. When the product of two numbers equals 1, then those two numbers are called **multiplicative inverses** or **reciprocals**. This leads to the following property:

THE MULTIPLICATIVE INVERSE PROPERTY:

For any natural number a,

$$a\cdot\frac{1}{a}=1.$$

The product of a number and its multiplicative inverse (reciprocal) equals 1.

Example 5: What is the multiplicative inverse (reciprocal) of 6?

Solution: The multiplicative inverse of 6 is $\frac{1}{6}$.

We can verify this since $6\cdot\frac{1}{6}=\frac{6}{1}\cdot\frac{1}{6}=\frac{6}{6}=1$.

Example 6: Find the product of $\frac{3}{4}$ and $\frac{4}{3}$.

Solution: $\frac{3}{4}\cdot\frac{4}{3}$ Step 1: Multiply the numerators.

$\frac{3}{4}\cdot\frac{4}{3}=\frac{3\cdot 4}{4\cdot 3}=\frac{12}{4\cdot 3}$ Step 2: Multiply the denominators.

$\frac{12}{4\cdot 3}=\frac{12}{12}$ Step 3: The fraction can be reduced to lowest terms.

$\frac{\cancel{12}^{1}}{\cancel{12}_{1}}=1$ So, $\frac{3}{4}\cdot\frac{4}{3}=1$.

This means that $\frac{3}{4}$ and $\frac{4}{3}$ are reciprocals.

Example 6 shows that a pair of reciprocals doesn't have to be a natural number and a fraction consisting of 1 over that same natural number. A pair of reciprocals can consist of any fraction that does not contain a zero and a second fraction where the numerator and denominator are the reverse of the numerator and denominator of the first fraction.

Example 7: What is the reciprocal of $\frac{4}{9}$?

Solution: The reciprocal of $\frac{4}{9}$ is $\frac{9}{4}$. We can verify this since $\frac{4}{9}\cdot\frac{9}{4}=\frac{4\cdot 9}{9\cdot 4}=\frac{36}{36}=1$.

Example 8: What is the reciprocal of $-\frac{2}{7}$?

Solution: The reciprocal of $-\frac{2}{7}$ is $-\frac{7}{2}$. We can verify this since $-\frac{2}{7}\cdot\left(-\frac{7}{2}\right)=\frac{-2\cdot(-7)}{7\cdot 2}=\frac{14}{14}=1$.

Note: While opposites (or additive inverses) have opposite signs, reciprocals (or multiplicative inverses) have the same sign.

Example 9: What is the reciprocal of $\frac{0}{4}$?

Solution: The reciprocal of $\frac{0}{4}$ would be $\frac{4}{0}$.

However, because $\frac{4}{0}$ is undefined, $\frac{0}{4}$ (or just 0) has no reciprocal.

Example 10: What is the reciprocal of $2\frac{3}{5}$?

Solution: Change $2\frac{3}{5}$ into the improper fraction $\frac{13}{5}$.

The reciprocal of $\frac{13}{5}$ is $\frac{5}{13}$. We can verify this since $\frac{13}{5}\cdot\frac{5}{13}=\frac{13\cdot 5}{5\cdot 13}=\frac{65}{65}=1$.

Example 11: What is the reciprocal of x? (We are assuming that $x \neq 0$.)

Solution: Rewrite x as the improper fraction $\frac{x}{1}$

The reciprocal of $\frac{x}{1}$ is $\frac{1}{x}$. We can verify this since $\frac{x}{1}\cdot\frac{1}{x}=\frac{x\cdot 1}{1\cdot x}=\frac{x}{x}=1$.

Now let's look at two slightly different methods involving multiplication of fractions. In the first example, we will multiply the fractions and then reduce the answer to lowest terms at the end of the problem.

Example 12: Find the product of $\frac{7}{8}$ and $\frac{4}{21}$.

Solution: $\frac{7}{8}\cdot\frac{4}{21}$

Step 1: Multiply the numerators.

$$\frac{7}{8}\cdot\frac{4}{21}=\frac{7\cdot 4}{8\cdot 21}=\frac{28}{8\cdot 21}$$

Step 2: Multiply the denominators.

$$\frac{28}{8\cdot 21}=\frac{28}{168}$$

Step 3: The fraction can be reduced to lowest terms. Find any prime factorizations of the numerators and the denominators. Then, reduce out common factors.

$$\frac{28}{168}=\frac{2\cdot 2\cdot 7}{2\cdot 2\cdot 2\cdot 3\cdot 7}=\frac{\overset{1}{\cancel{2}}\cdot\overset{1}{\cancel{2}}\cdot\overset{1}{\cancel{7}}}{\underset{1}{\cancel{2}}\cdot\underset{1}{\cancel{2}}\cdot 2\cdot 3\cdot\underset{1}{\cancel{7}}}=\frac{1}{2\cdot 3}=\frac{1}{6}$$

So, $\frac{7}{8}\cdot\frac{4}{21}=\frac{1}{6}$.

In the second example, we will find the prime factorization of the numerators and the denominators at the beginning. Then we will reduce out common factors before multiplying the numerators together and the denominators together.

Example 12 Revisited: Find the product of $\frac{7}{8}$ and $\frac{4}{21}$.

Solution: $\frac{7}{8}\cdot\frac{4}{21}$

Find any prime factorizations of the numerators and the denominators. Then reduce out common factors.

$$\frac{7}{8}\cdot\frac{4}{21}=\frac{7}{2\cdot 2\cdot 2}\cdot\frac{2\cdot 2}{3\cdot 7}=\frac{\overset{1}{\cancel{7}}}{\underset{1}{\cancel{2}}\cdot\underset{1}{\cancel{2}}\cdot 2}\cdot\frac{\overset{1}{\cancel{2}}\cdot\overset{1}{\cancel{2}}}{3\cdot\underset{1}{\cancel{7}}}=\frac{1\cdot 1\cdot 1}{1\cdot 1\cdot 2\cdot 3\cdot 1}$$

Step 1: Multiply the numerators.

$$\frac{1\cdot 1\cdot 1}{1\cdot 1\cdot 2\cdot 3\cdot 1}=\frac{1}{1\cdot 1\cdot 2\cdot 3\cdot 1}$$

Step 2: Multiply the denominators.

$$\frac{1}{1\cdot 1\cdot 2\cdot 3\cdot 1}=\frac{1}{6}$$

So, $\frac{7}{8}\cdot\frac{4}{21}=\frac{1}{6}$.

Note: By reducing out common factors first, as in example 12 revisited, we didn't have to multiply large numbers together and then break them back down again.

Example 13: Multiply 4 by $-\frac{5}{6}$.

Solution: $4\cdot\left(-\frac{5}{6}\right)$

Find any prime factorizations of the numerators and the denominators. Then reduce out common factors.

$$4\cdot\left(-\frac{5}{6}\right)=\frac{4}{1}\cdot\left(-\frac{5}{6}\right)=\frac{2\cdot 2}{1}\cdot\frac{-5}{2\cdot 3}=\frac{\overset{1}{\cancel{2}}\cdot 2}{1}\cdot\frac{-5}{\underset{1}{\cancel{2}}\cdot 3}=\frac{1\cdot 2\cdot(-5)}{1\cdot 1\cdot 3}$$

Multiply the numerators.

$$\frac{1\cdot 2\cdot(-5)}{1\cdot 1\cdot 3}=\frac{-10}{1\cdot 1\cdot 3}$$

Multiply the denominators.

$$\frac{-10}{1\cdot 1\cdot 3}=\frac{-10}{3}=-\frac{10}{3}$$

The fraction is already in lowest terms.

We could change it into a mixed number if desired. That is, $-\frac{10}{3}=-3\frac{1}{3}$.

So, $4\cdot\left(-\frac{5}{6}\right)=-\frac{10}{3}$ or $-3\frac{1}{3}$.

Example 14: Find the product of $\frac{2}{x}$, $\frac{y}{5}$, and $\frac{3}{6}$.

Solution: $\frac{2}{x}\cdot\frac{y}{5}\cdot\frac{3}{6}$

Find any prime factorizations of the numerators and the denominators. Then reduce out common factors.

$$\frac{2}{x}\cdot\frac{y}{5}\cdot\frac{3}{6}=\frac{2}{x}\cdot\frac{y}{5}\cdot\frac{3}{2\cdot 3}=\frac{\overset{1}{\cancel{2}}}{x}\cdot\frac{y}{5}\cdot\frac{\overset{1}{\cancel{3}}}{\underset{1}{\cancel{2}}\cdot\underset{1}{\cancel{3}}}=\frac{1\cdot y\cdot 1}{x\cdot 5\cdot 1\cdot 1}$$

Step 1: Multiply the numerators.

$$\frac{1\cdot y\cdot 1}{x\cdot 5\cdot 1\cdot 1}=\frac{y}{x\cdot 5\cdot 1\cdot 1}$$

Step 2: Multiply the denominators.

$$\frac{y}{x\cdot 5\cdot 1\cdot 1}=\frac{y}{5x}$$

So, $\frac{2}{x}\cdot\frac{y}{5}\cdot\frac{3}{6}=\frac{y}{5x}$.

Example 15: Find the product of $2\frac{2}{3}$ and $2\frac{1}{4}$.

Solution: $2\frac{2}{3}\cdot 2\frac{1}{4}$

Change $2\frac{2}{3}$ into the improper fraction $\frac{8}{3}$ and change $2\frac{1}{4}$ into the improper fraction $\frac{9}{4}$.

$2\frac{2}{3}\cdot 2\frac{1}{4}=\frac{8}{3}\cdot\frac{9}{4}$

Find any prime factorizations of the numerators and the denominators. Then reduce out common factors.

$$\frac{8}{3}\cdot\frac{9}{4}=\frac{2\cdot 2\cdot 2}{3}\cdot\frac{3\cdot 3}{2\cdot 2}=\frac{\overset{1}{\cancel{2}}\cdot\overset{1}{\cancel{2}}\cdot 2}{\underset{1}{\cancel{3}}}\cdot\frac{\overset{1}{\cancel{3}}\cdot 3}{\underset{1}{\cancel{2}}\cdot\underset{1}{\cancel{2}}}=\frac{1\cdot 1\cdot 2\cdot 3\cdot 1}{1\cdot 1\cdot 1}$$

Multiply the numerators.

$$\frac{1\cdot 1\cdot 2\cdot 3\cdot 1}{1\cdot 1\cdot 1}=\frac{6}{1\cdot 1\cdot 1}$$

Multiply the denominators.

$$\frac{6}{1\cdot 1\cdot 1}=\frac{6}{1}$$

The fraction can be reduced to lowest terms.

$$\frac{6}{1}=6$$

So, $2\frac{2}{3}\cdot 2\frac{1}{4}=6$

Example 16: Find the product of $\frac{4}{7}$ and $\frac{5}{0}$.

Solution: $\frac{4}{7}\cdot\frac{5}{0}$ Since $\frac{5}{0}$ is undefined, we can't multiply it by any other number. So, $\frac{4}{7}\cdot\frac{5}{0}=$ undefined.

In previous chapters, we evaluated variable expressions using whole numbers and integers. Now we will evaluate expressions involving multiplication of fractions and mixed numbers.

Example 17: Evaluate the expression for the given values of the variables:

xy, where $x = \frac{1}{3}$ and $y = 4\frac{1}{2}$

Solution:

xy — Substitute $\frac{1}{3}$ in the place of x and $4\frac{1}{2}$ in the place of y.

$\frac{1}{3} \cdot \left(4\frac{1}{2}\right)$ — Change $4\frac{1}{2}$ into the improper fraction $\frac{9}{2}$.

$\frac{1}{3} \cdot \left(4\frac{1}{2}\right) = \frac{1}{3} \cdot \frac{9}{2}$ — Find any prime factorizations of the numerators and the denominators. Then reduce out common factors.

$\frac{1}{3} \cdot \frac{9}{2} = \frac{1}{3} \cdot \frac{3 \cdot 3}{2} = \frac{1}{\cancel{3}_1} \cdot \frac{\cancel{3}^1 \cdot 3}{2} = \frac{1 \cdot 1 \cdot 3}{1 \cdot 2}$ — Multiply the numerators and multiply the denominators.

$\frac{1 \cdot 1 \cdot 3}{1 \cdot 2} = \frac{3}{2}$ — The fraction is already in lowest terms.

We could change it into a mixed number if desired. That is, $\frac{3}{2} = 1\frac{1}{2}$.

So, $\frac{1}{3} \cdot \left(4\frac{1}{2}\right) = \frac{3}{2}$ or $1\frac{1}{2}$.

Applications involving fractions and mixed numbers

Example 18: If a bag of candy weighs $2\frac{3}{4}$ ounces, then what would $\frac{1}{2}$ of that bag weigh?

Solution: The question is, what is $\frac{1}{2}$ of $2\frac{3}{4}$ ounces?

In other words, what is $\frac{1}{2}\cdot\left(2\frac{3}{4}\right)$? Change $2\frac{3}{4}$ into the improper fraction $\frac{11}{4}$.

$\frac{1}{2}\cdot\left(2\frac{3}{4}\right)=\frac{1}{2}\cdot\frac{11}{4}$ Find any prime factorizations of the numerators and the denominators. Then reduce out common factors.

$\frac{1}{2}\cdot\frac{11}{4}=\frac{1}{2}\cdot\frac{11}{2\cdot 2}=\frac{1\cdot 11}{2\cdot 2\cdot 2}$ There are no common factors to reduce out. Multiply the numerators and multiply the denominators.

$\frac{1\cdot 11}{2\cdot 2\cdot 2}=\frac{11}{8}$ The fraction is already in lowest terms.

However, since it wouldn't be appropriate to describe the weight of the candy as $\frac{11}{8}$ ounces, we will change the answer into a mixed number. The final answer is $1\frac{3}{8}$ ounces.

Example 19: If $5\frac{1}{4}$ yards of material were required to make a dress, then how much material would be required to make 6 of the same dress?

Solution: The question is, what is 6 times $5\frac{1}{4}$ yards?

In other words, what is $6\cdot\left(5\frac{1}{4}\right)$? Change $5\frac{1}{4}$ into the improper fraction $\frac{21}{4}$.

$6\cdot\left(5\frac{1}{4}\right)=\frac{6}{1}\cdot\frac{21}{4}$ Find any prime factorizations of the numerators and the denominators. Then reduce out common factors.

$\frac{6}{1}\cdot\frac{21}{4}=\frac{2\cdot 3}{1}\cdot\frac{3\cdot 7}{2\cdot 2}=\frac{\overset{1}{\cancel{2}}\cdot 3}{1}\cdot\frac{3\cdot 7}{\underset{1}{\cancel{2}}\cdot 2}=\frac{1\cdot 3\cdot 3\cdot 7}{1\cdot 1\cdot 2}$ Multiply the numerators and multiply the denominators.

$\frac{1\cdot 3\cdot 3\cdot 7}{1\cdot 1\cdot 2}=\frac{63}{2}$ The fraction is already in lowest terms.

However, since it wouldn't be appropriate to describe the amount of fabric as $\frac{63}{2}$ yards, we will change the answer into a mixed number. The final answer is $31\frac{1}{2}$ yards.

Section 6 exercises. Multiply.

1. $\frac{3}{4}\cdot\frac{7}{9}$

2. $\frac{2}{3}\cdot\frac{6}{11}$

3. $\frac{1}{7}\cdot\frac{14}{6}$

4. $\frac{2}{9}\cdot\frac{12}{8}$

5. $-\frac{13}{10}\cdot\left(-\frac{6}{39}\right)$

6. $-\frac{14}{21}\cdot\left(-\frac{9}{20}\right)$

7. $\frac{8}{9}\cdot\frac{27}{12}$

8. $\frac{18}{25}\cdot\frac{75}{4}$

9. $\frac{3}{4}\cdot\frac{4}{11}$

10. $\frac{5}{7}\cdot\frac{7}{12}$

11. $-\frac{4}{7}\cdot\frac{0}{8}$

12. $-\frac{9}{11}\cdot\frac{0}{12}$

13. $\frac{g}{5}\cdot\frac{h}{4}$

14. $\frac{x}{2}\cdot\frac{y}{3}$

15. $\frac{6}{16}\cdot\frac{15}{20}$

16. $\frac{21}{81}\cdot\frac{15}{18}$

17. $-\frac{7}{8}\cdot\frac{13}{14}$

18. $-\frac{8}{9}\cdot\frac{11}{12}$

19. $\frac{6}{w}\cdot\frac{w}{2}$

20. $\frac{8}{n}\cdot\frac{n}{4}$

21. $\frac{6}{5}\cdot\frac{10}{0}$

22. $\frac{12}{0}\cdot\frac{1}{6}$

23. $\frac{2}{9}\cdot\left(-\frac{9}{2}\right)$

24. $\frac{3}{7}\cdot\left(-\frac{7}{3}\right)$

25. $\frac{11}{8}\cdot\frac{12}{9}$

26. $\frac{13}{7}\cdot\frac{14}{8}$

27. $-\frac{x}{7}\cdot\frac{14}{y}$

28. $-\frac{a}{3}\cdot\frac{6}{m}$

29. $-\frac{17}{41}\cdot\left(-\frac{51}{15}\right)$

30. $-\frac{13}{31}\cdot\left(-\frac{21}{12}\right)$

31. $7\cdot\frac{1}{14}$

32. $5\cdot\frac{1}{20}$

33. $4\cdot\left(-\frac{5}{8}\right)$

34. $6\cdot\left(-\frac{2}{9}\right)$

35. $\frac{1}{6}\cdot 3$

36. $\frac{1}{5}\cdot 10$

37. $-\frac{1}{9}\cdot(-12)$ **38.** $-\frac{1}{8}\cdot(-20)$ **39.** $0\cdot\left(-\frac{8}{9}\right)$ **40.** $0\cdot\left(-\frac{3}{7}\right)$

41. $\left(3\frac{1}{2}\right)\cdot\frac{1}{7}$ **42.** $\left(5\frac{2}{3}\right)\cdot\frac{2}{17}$ **43.** $\left(-2\frac{3}{8}\right)\cdot\frac{2}{19}$ **44.** $\left(-4\frac{1}{5}\right)\cdot\frac{3}{14}$

45. $6\cdot\left(2\frac{2}{9}\right)$ **46.** $3\cdot\left(4\frac{7}{12}\right)$ **47.** $\left(2\frac{5}{9}\right)\cdot\left(4\frac{1}{2}\right)$ **48.** $\left(4\frac{2}{7}\right)\cdot\left(3\frac{1}{2}\right)$

49. $\left(-6\frac{1}{8}\right)\cdot\left(-\frac{4}{7}\right)$ **50.** $\left(-8\frac{1}{6}\right)\cdot\left(-\frac{3}{7}\right)$ **51.** $\left(7\frac{2}{3}\right)\cdot\left(7\frac{1}{2}\right)$ **52.** $\left(6\frac{2}{5}\right)\cdot\left(2\frac{3}{4}\right)$

53. $\left(3\frac{1}{7}\right)\cdot\left(1\frac{13}{22}\right)$ **54.** $\left(8\frac{1}{4}\right)\cdot\left(3\frac{2}{11}\right)$ **55.** $\frac{22}{21}\cdot\frac{27}{10}\cdot\frac{60}{99}$ **56.** $\frac{10}{18}\cdot\frac{49}{5}\cdot\frac{6}{7}$

57. $\frac{2}{7}\cdot\left(-\frac{21}{10}\right)\cdot\frac{7}{3}$ **58.** $\frac{4}{5}\cdot\left(-\frac{7}{10}\right)\cdot\frac{5}{9}$ **59.** $-\frac{4}{21}\cdot\frac{14}{10}\cdot\left(-\frac{15}{4}\right)$

60. $-\frac{6}{25}\cdot\frac{35}{21}\cdot\left(-\frac{15}{7}\right)$ **61.** $\left(4\frac{1}{4}\right)\cdot\frac{8}{51}\cdot\left(4\frac{1}{3}\right)$ **62.** $\left(3\frac{1}{6}\right)\cdot\frac{12}{57}\cdot\left(1\frac{1}{2}\right)$

63. $\left(3\frac{1}{3}\right)\cdot\left(2\frac{1}{5}\right)\cdot\left(3\frac{3}{8}\right)$ **64.** $\left(6\frac{7}{8}\right)\cdot\left(1\frac{29}{33}\right)\cdot\left(2\frac{1}{5}\right)$ **65.** $\left(1\frac{2}{33}\right)\cdot\frac{4}{25}\cdot\left(5\frac{1}{2}\right)$

66. $\frac{14}{5}\cdot\frac{28}{38}\cdot\frac{57}{49}$ **67.** $\frac{3}{2}\cdot\frac{14}{7}\cdot\frac{15}{18}\cdot\frac{9}{28}$ **68.** $\frac{26}{18}\cdot\frac{54}{28}\cdot\frac{6}{39}\cdot\frac{8}{7}$

Determine whether or not the following pairs of numbers are reciprocals (multiplicative inverses).

69. $\frac{1}{8}; 8$

70. $-\frac{6}{7}; \frac{7}{6}$

71. $-3; -\frac{1}{3}$

72. $7; \frac{1}{7}$

73. $\frac{4}{9}; -\frac{4}{9}$

74. $\frac{2}{9}; -\frac{2}{9}$

75. $\frac{6}{9}; \frac{3}{2}$

76. $-5; -\frac{1}{5}$

77. $2x; \frac{1}{2x}$

78. $\frac{4}{5}; \frac{10}{8}$

79. $\frac{0}{7}; \frac{7}{0}$

80. $3x; \frac{1}{3}x$

81. $\frac{1}{3}; -\frac{1}{3}$

82. $\frac{3}{10}; 3\frac{1}{3}$

83. $\frac{7}{3}; \frac{3}{7}$

84. $2w; \frac{1}{2w}$

85. $4\frac{2}{5}; 4\frac{5}{2}$

86. $-\frac{6}{0}; -\frac{0}{6}$

87. $\frac{2}{9}; 4\frac{1}{2}$

88. $\frac{10}{13}; \frac{13}{10}$

89. $2y; \frac{1}{2}y$

90. $6\frac{7}{8}; 6\frac{8}{7}$

91. $\frac{10}{3}; \frac{3}{10}$

92. $\frac{9}{4}; \frac{4}{9}$

Find the reciprocal (multiplicative inverse) of each of the following numbers.

93. $\frac{3}{8}$

94. -7

95. $-\frac{5}{11}$

96. $\frac{14}{5}$

97. $\frac{1}{8}$

98. $7\frac{1}{4}$

99. 0

100. y

101. $2\frac{3}{5}$

102. -1

103. $\frac{7}{4}$

104. $-\frac{3}{13}$

105. x

106. $\frac{3}{0}$

107. -4

108. $\frac{2}{15}$

Evaluate each expression.

109. Find the product of $-\frac{16}{17}$ and $1\frac{5}{12}$.

110. Multiply $\frac{5}{6}$ by $\frac{21}{25}$.

111. Multiply $2\frac{1}{4}$ by $1\frac{7}{18}$.

112. What is $4\frac{1}{2}$ times $1\frac{31}{36}$?

113. What is $\frac{7}{8}$ times $\frac{20}{27}$?

114. Find the product of $-\frac{3}{8}$ and $-6\frac{2}{3}$.

Evaluate the expression ab for the given values of a and b.

115. $a = 2\frac{4}{7};\ b = 5\frac{1}{4}$

116. $a = 3\frac{1}{5};\ b = 3\frac{1}{8}$

117. $a = -5;\ b = 3\frac{3}{5}$

118. $a = -9;\ b = 3\frac{1}{9}$

119. $a = -2\frac{1}{7};\ b = -2\frac{1}{10}$

120. $a = -3\frac{9}{11};\ b = -4\frac{5}{7}$

121. $a = \frac{2}{8};\ b = \frac{9}{3}$

122. $a = \frac{5}{15};\ b = \frac{14}{7}$

Evaluate the expression abc for the given values of a, b, and c.

123. $a=\frac{3}{7};\ b=-1\frac{2}{3}\ ;\ c=1\frac{2}{5}$

124. $a=\frac{4}{9};\ b=-\frac{3}{14}\ ;\ c=10\frac{1}{2}$

125. $a=\frac{7}{38};\ b=2\ ;\ c=9\frac{1}{2}$

126. $a=\frac{5}{34};\ b=3\ ;\ c=5\frac{2}{3}$

127. $a=\frac{2}{5};\ b=\frac{0}{7}\ ;\ c=1\frac{2}{9}$

128. $a=\frac{3}{5};\ b=\frac{8}{0}\ ;\ c=2\frac{3}{16}$

Applications

129. If a batch of cookies uses $1\frac{2}{3}$ cups of sugar, then how much sugar is needed to make 5 batches of cookies?

130. If Lee can hike $7\frac{2}{3}$ miles in a day, how far could he hike in 6 days?

131. It took Sam $2\frac{1}{4}$ hours to walk to the store. Jason did it in $1\frac{1}{2}$ hours less time than it took Sam. How long did Jason take?

132. Joe makes $\$12\frac{3}{4}$ an hour working at a store. Mark makes $\$2\frac{1}{5}$ more than the amount Joe makes per hour. What is Mark's hourly wage?

133. Mary works at a café for $4\frac{1}{3}$ hours every day. How many hours a week does Mary work at the café?

134. An assembly plant that is open 24 hours a day produces $7\frac{1}{12}$ vehicles per hour. How many vehicles would the plant produce in a single day?

Using the formula $A = s^2$, find the area of the following squares.

135. $3\frac{1}{2}$ feet

$3\frac{1}{2}$ feet

136. $2\frac{1}{4}$ feet

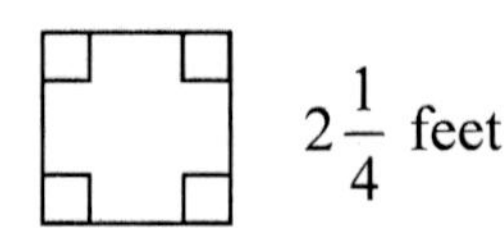

Using the formula $A = LW,$ find the area of the following rectangles.

137. $8\frac{2}{3}$ inches

$3\frac{1}{4}$ inches

138. $5\frac{1}{2}$ yards

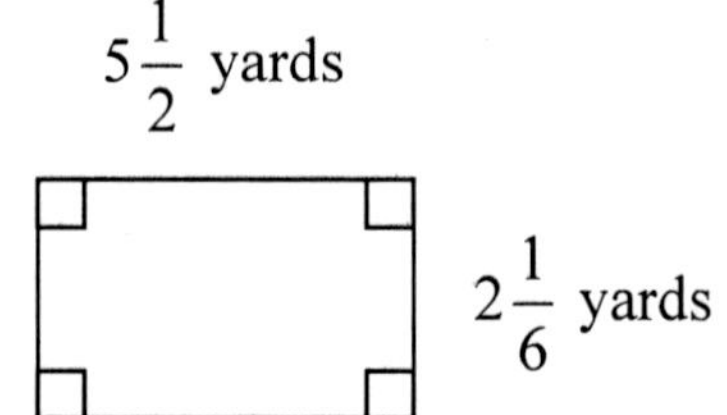

Using the formula $A = \frac{1}{2}bh$, find the area of the following triangles.

139.

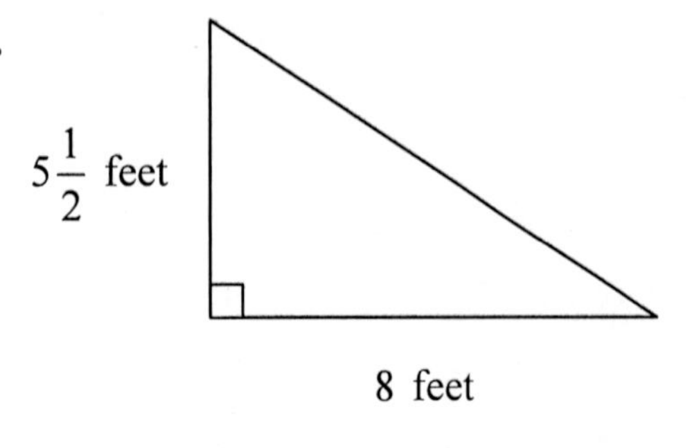

8 feet

140.

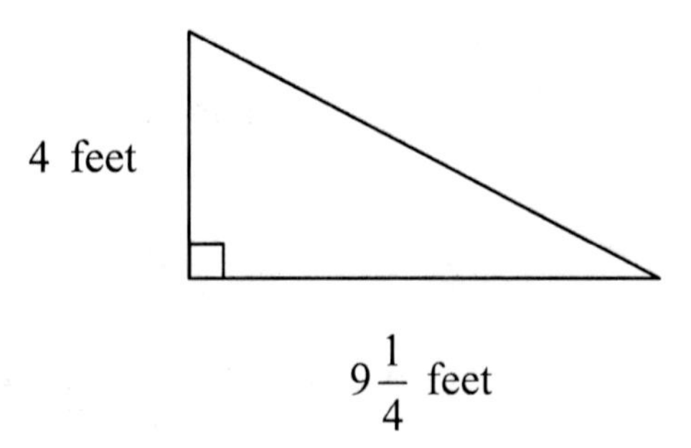

$9\frac{1}{4}$ feet

FRACTIONS

Section 7: Dividing Fractions and Mixed Numbers

Since $18 \div 2$ equals 9 and $18 \cdot \frac{1}{2}$ also equals 9, we can conclude that dividing by 2 produces the same result as multiplying by $\frac{1}{2}$. It should be noted that 2 and $\frac{1}{2}$ are reciprocals of one another. This leads to the following: Dividing by a number is the same as multiplying by the number's reciprocal.

To divide fractions:

Step 1: Instead of dividing, multiply by the reciprocal of the divisor.

Step 2: Find any prime factorizations of the numerators and the denominators. Reduce out common factors.

Step 3: Multiply the numerators and multiply the denominators.

Symbolically, this process is: $\frac{a}{b} \div \frac{c}{d} = \frac{a}{b} \cdot \frac{d}{c} = \frac{ad}{bc}$, **where** $b \neq 0$, $c \neq 0$, **and** $d \neq 0$.

Example 1: Find the quotient of $\frac{2}{3}$ and $\frac{4}{9}$.

Solution:

$\frac{2}{3} \div \frac{4}{9}$ Step 1: Instead of dividing, multiply by the reciprocal of the divisor.

$\frac{2}{3} \div \frac{4}{9} = \frac{2}{3} \cdot \frac{9}{4}$ Step 2: Find the prime factorization of the numerators and the denominators. Reduce out common factors.

$\frac{2}{3} \cdot \frac{9}{4} = \frac{2}{3} \cdot \frac{3 \cdot 3}{2 \cdot 2} = \frac{\overset{1}{\cancel{2}}}{\underset{1}{\cancel{3}}} \cdot \frac{\overset{1}{\cancel{3}} \cdot 3}{\underset{1}{\cancel{2}} \cdot 2} = \frac{1}{1} \cdot \frac{1 \cdot 3}{1 \cdot 2}$ Step 3: Multiply the numerators and multiply the denominators.

$\frac{1}{1} \cdot \frac{1 \cdot 3}{1 \cdot 2} = \frac{3}{2}$ This fraction is already in lowest terms.

We could change it into a mixed number if desired. $\frac{3}{2} = 1\frac{1}{2}$

So, $\frac{2}{3} \div \frac{4}{9} = \frac{3}{2}$ or $1\frac{1}{2}$.

Example 2: What is $\frac{5}{7}$ divided by $\frac{3}{14}$?

Solution:

$$\frac{5}{7} \div \frac{3}{14}$$

Step 1: Instead of dividing, multiply by the reciprocal of the divisor.

$$\frac{5}{7} \div \frac{3}{14} = \frac{5}{7} \cdot \frac{14}{3}$$

Step 2: Find any prime factorizations of the numerators and the denominators. Reduce out common factors.

$$\frac{5}{7} \cdot \frac{14}{3} = \frac{5}{7} \cdot \frac{2 \cdot 7}{3} = \frac{5}{\cancel{7}_1} \cdot \frac{2 \cdot \cancel{7}^1}{3} = \frac{5}{1} \cdot \frac{2 \cdot 1}{3}$$

Step 3: Multiply the numerators and multiply the denominators.

$$\frac{5}{1} \cdot \frac{2 \cdot 1}{3} = \frac{10}{3}$$

This fraction is already in lowest terms.

We could change it into a mixed number if desired. $\frac{10}{3} = 3\frac{1}{3}$

So, $\frac{5}{7} \div \frac{3}{14} = \frac{10}{3}$ or $3\frac{1}{3}$.

Note: When dividing fractions it is not necessary to find a common denominator.

Now that we've looked at several examples, let's review previously discussed ideas and how they relate to dividing fractions. Because fractions can be either positive or negative, the rules of dividing positive and negative numbers apply to fractions in the same way that they apply to integers.

Division of Fractions: When dividing two fractions, apply the following rules:

1. **If the signs of the fractions are the same, both positive or both negative, then their quotient is a positive number.**

2. **If the signs of the fractions are opposites, one positive and one negative, then their quotient is a negative number.**

Example 3: Divide $-\frac{2}{5}$ by $\frac{3}{7}$.

Solution:

$-\frac{2}{5} \div \frac{3}{7}$

Step 1: Instead of dividing, multiply by the reciprocal of the divisor.

$-\frac{2}{5} \div \frac{3}{7} = -\frac{2}{5} \cdot \frac{7}{3}$

Step 2: Find any prime factorizations of the numerators and the denominators. Reduce out common factors.

Since the numbers are all primes and there are no common factors, nothing can be reduced out.

Step 3: Multiply the numerators and multiply the denominators.

$-\frac{2}{5} \cdot \frac{7}{3} = -\frac{14}{15}$

This fraction is already in lowest terms.

So, $-\frac{2}{5} \div \frac{3}{7} = -\frac{14}{15}$.

Note that the quotient of a negative fraction and a positive fraction is a negative number.

Example 4: What is the quotient of $-\frac{5}{8}$ and $-\frac{3}{4}$?

Solution:

$-\frac{5}{8} \div \left(-\frac{3}{4}\right)$

Step 1: Instead of dividing, multiply by the reciprocal of the divisor.

$-\frac{5}{8} \div \left(-\frac{3}{4}\right) = -\frac{5}{8} \cdot \left(-\frac{4}{3}\right)$

Step 2: Find any prime factorizations of the numerators and the denominators. Reduce out common factors.

$$-\frac{5}{8} \cdot \left(-\frac{4}{3}\right) = -\frac{5}{2 \cdot 2 \cdot 2} \cdot \left(-\frac{2 \cdot 2}{3}\right) = -\frac{5}{\cancel{2}^{1} \cdot \cancel{2}^{1} \cdot 2} \cdot \left(-\frac{\cancel{2}^{1} \cdot \cancel{2}^{1}}{3}\right) = -\frac{5}{1 \cdot 1 \cdot 2} \cdot \left(-\frac{1 \cdot 1}{3}\right)$$

Step 3: Multiply the numerators and multiply the denominators.

$-\frac{5}{1 \cdot 1 \cdot 2} \cdot \left(-\frac{1 \cdot 1}{3}\right) = \frac{5}{6}$

This fraction is already in lowest terms.

So, $-\frac{5}{8} \div \left(-\frac{3}{4}\right) = \frac{5}{6}$.

Note that the quotient of a negative fraction and a negative fraction is a positive number.

Example 5: Find the quotient of $5\frac{1}{3}$ and $3\frac{1}{9}$.

Solution: $\left(5\frac{1}{3}\right)\div\left(3\frac{1}{9}\right)$

Change $5\frac{1}{3}$ into the improper fraction $\frac{16}{3}$ and change $3\frac{1}{9}$ into the improper fraction $\frac{28}{9}$.

$\left(5\frac{1}{3}\right)\div\left(3\frac{1}{9}\right)=\frac{16}{3}\div\frac{28}{9}$

Step 1: Instead of dividing, multiply by the reciprocal of the divisor.

$\frac{16}{3}\div\frac{28}{9}=\frac{16}{3}\cdot\frac{9}{28}$

Step 2: Find any prime factorizations of the numerators and the denominators. Reduce out common factors.

$$\frac{16}{3}\cdot\frac{9}{28}=\frac{2\cdot2\cdot2\cdot2}{3}\cdot\frac{3\cdot3}{2\cdot2\cdot7}=\frac{\overset{1}{\cancel{2}}\cdot\overset{1}{\cancel{2}}\cdot2\cdot2}{\underset{1}{\cancel{3}}}\cdot\frac{\overset{1}{\cancel{3}}\cdot3}{\underset{1}{\cancel{2}}\cdot\underset{1}{\cancel{2}}\cdot7}=\frac{1\cdot1\cdot2\cdot2}{1}\cdot\frac{1\cdot3}{1\cdot1\cdot7}$$

Step 3: Multiply the numerators and multiply the denominators.

$\frac{1\cdot1\cdot2\cdot2}{1}\cdot\frac{1\cdot3}{1\cdot1\cdot7}=\frac{12}{7}$

This fraction is already in lowest terms.

We could change it into a mixed number if desired. $\frac{12}{7}=1\frac{5}{7}$

So, $\left(5\frac{1}{3}\right)\div\left(3\frac{1}{9}\right)=\frac{12}{7}$ or $1\frac{5}{7}$.

Example 6: Find the quotient of $\frac{2}{9}$ and 0.

Solution: $\frac{2}{9}\div0$

Dividing by 0 is not possible. The answer is undefined.

So, $\frac{2}{9}\div0=$ undefined.

In previous chapters, we evaluated variable expressions using whole numbers and integers. Now we will evaluate expressions involving division of fractions and mixed numbers.

Example 7: Evaluate the expression for the given values of the variables:

$x \div y$, where $x = \frac{4}{15}$ and $y = 1\frac{3}{5}$

Solution:

$x \div y$ — Substitute $\frac{4}{15}$ in the place of x and $1\frac{3}{5}$ in the place of y.

$\frac{4}{15} \div \left(1\frac{3}{5}\right)$ — Change $1\frac{3}{5}$ into the improper fraction $\frac{8}{5}$.

$\frac{4}{15} \div \left(1\frac{3}{5}\right) = \frac{4}{15} \div \frac{8}{5}$ — Instead of dividing, multiply by the reciprocal of the divisor.

$\frac{4}{15} \div \frac{8}{5} = \frac{4}{15} \cdot \frac{5}{8}$ — Find any prime factorizations of the numerators and the denominators. Reduce out common factors.

$$\frac{4}{15} \cdot \frac{5}{8} = \frac{2 \cdot 2}{3 \cdot 5} \cdot \frac{5}{2 \cdot 2 \cdot 2} = \frac{\overset{1}{\cancel{2}} \cdot \overset{1}{\cancel{2}}}{3 \cdot \underset{1}{\cancel{5}}} \cdot \frac{\overset{1}{\cancel{5}}}{\underset{1}{\cancel{2}} \cdot \underset{1}{\cancel{2}} \cdot 2} = \frac{1 \cdot 1}{3 \cdot 1} \cdot \frac{1}{1 \cdot 1 \cdot 2}$$

Multiply the numerators and multiply the denominators.

$\frac{1 \cdot 1}{3 \cdot 1} \cdot \frac{1}{1 \cdot 1 \cdot 2} = \frac{1}{6}$ — This fraction is already in lowest terms.

So, $\frac{4}{15} \div \left(1\frac{3}{5}\right) = \frac{1}{6}$.

Applications involving fractions and mixed numbers

Example 8: How many $1\frac{1}{2}$ cup servings are in a box which contains 24 cups of breakfast cereal?

Solution: The question is, how many times does $1\frac{1}{2}$ cups go into 24 cups or, what is 24 cups divided by $1\frac{1}{2}$ cups? In other words,

what is $24 \div \left(1\frac{1}{2}\right)$? Change $1\frac{1}{2}$ into the improper fraction $\frac{3}{2}$.

$24 \div \left(1\frac{1}{2}\right) = \frac{24}{1} \div \frac{3}{2}$ Instead of dividing, multiply by the reciprocal of the divisor.

$\frac{24}{1} \div \frac{3}{2} = \frac{24}{1} \cdot \frac{2}{3}$ Find any prime factorizations of the numerators and the denominators. Reduce out common factors.

$$\frac{24}{1} \cdot \frac{2}{3} = \frac{2 \cdot 2 \cdot 2 \cdot 3}{1} \cdot \frac{2}{3} = \frac{2 \cdot 2 \cdot 2 \cdot \overset{1}{\cancel{3}}}{1} \cdot \frac{2}{\underset{1}{\cancel{3}}} = \frac{2 \cdot 2 \cdot 2 \cdot 1}{1} \cdot \frac{2}{1}$$

Multiply the numerators and multiply the denominators.

$\frac{2 \cdot 2 \cdot 2 \cdot 1}{1} \cdot \frac{2}{1} = \frac{16}{1}$ This fraction can be reduced to lowest terms.

$\frac{16}{1} = 16$ The final answer is 16 servings.

Section 7 exercises. Divide.

1. $\frac{2}{5} \div \frac{4}{15}$

2. $\frac{3}{10} \div \frac{9}{20}$

3. $7 \div \frac{14}{25}$

4. $9 \div \frac{18}{23}$

5. $-\frac{3}{8} \div \left(-\frac{3}{8}\right)$

6. $-\frac{2}{7} \div \left(-\frac{2}{7}\right)$

7. $\frac{9}{10} \div \frac{10}{9}$

8. $\frac{7}{11} \div \frac{11}{7}$

9. $\frac{3}{14} \div \left(-\frac{9}{28}\right)$

10. $\frac{5}{11} \div \left(-\frac{15}{44}\right)$

11. $0 \div \frac{7}{10}$

12. $0 \div \frac{5}{8}$

13. $\frac{8}{11} \div (-16)$

14. $\frac{6}{7} \div (-18)$

15. $\frac{3}{2} \div \frac{6}{9}$

16. $\frac{5}{2} \div \frac{10}{15}$

17. $\left(2\frac{1}{2}\right) \div \frac{1}{4}$

18. $\left(3\frac{1}{3}\right) \div \frac{1}{6}$

19. $-\frac{6}{11} \div 0$

20. $-\frac{3}{5} \div 0$

21. $\left(-7\frac{2}{7}\right) \div \left(1\frac{3}{14}\right)$

22. $\left(-5\frac{2}{3}\right) \div \left(7\frac{5}{9}\right)$

23. $\left(8\frac{2}{3}\right) \div 13$

24. $\left(7\frac{1}{2}\right) \div 5$

25. $8 \div \left(3\frac{3}{4}\right)$

26. $6 \div \left(2\frac{1}{3}\right)$

27. $1 \div \left(3\frac{1}{2}\right)$

28. $-1 \div \left(8\frac{1}{6}\right)$

29. $\frac{x}{6} \div \frac{3}{y}$

30. $\frac{m}{8} \div \frac{4}{p}$

31. $\left(4\frac{1}{8}\right) \div \left(5\frac{1}{2}\right)$

32. $\left(7\frac{1}{7}\right) \div \left(1\frac{11}{14}\right)$

33. $-14 \div \left(-1\frac{3}{4}\right)$

34. $-8 \div \left(-1\frac{1}{3}\right)$

35. $\frac{w}{10} \div \frac{0}{z}$

36. $\frac{c}{12} \div \frac{f}{0}$

Evaluate each expression.

37. Find the quotient of $\frac{1}{4}$ and $-\frac{3}{16}$.

38. Divide $-\frac{5}{6}$ by $1\frac{1}{24}$.

39. What is $1\frac{7}{18}$ divided by $2\frac{1}{4}$?

40. What is the quotient of $3\frac{1}{8}$ and $6\frac{1}{4}$?

41. Divide $\frac{3}{8}$ by $\frac{15}{16}$.

42. Find the quotient of $-\frac{1}{5}$ and $\frac{4}{15}$.

43. What is the quotient of $-2\frac{1}{4}$ and $4\frac{1}{2}$?

44. What is $3\frac{1}{2}$ divided by $4\frac{3}{8}$?

Evaluate the expression $a \div b$ for the given values of a and b.

45. $a = \frac{5}{8};\ b = 1\frac{1}{6}$

46. $a = \frac{3}{4};\ b = \frac{9}{10}$

47. $a = 7\frac{7}{11};\ b = \frac{21}{44}$

48. $a = 5\frac{4}{9};\ b = \frac{14}{27}$

49. $a = -18;\ b = 1\frac{1}{35}$

50. $a = -19;\ b = 1\frac{3}{35}$

51. $a = 4\frac{1}{4};\ b = -2\frac{5}{6}$

52. $a = 5\frac{5}{6};\ b = -7\frac{7}{9}$

53. $a = \frac{0}{7};\ b = \frac{3}{7}$

54. $a = -\frac{3}{5};\ b = \frac{8}{0}$

55. $a = \frac{4}{19};\ b = 2$

56. $a = \frac{6}{17};\ b = 3$

Applications

57. If a batch of cookies uses $2\frac{1}{3}$ cups of sugar, then how many batches of cookies can be made using 21 cups of sugar?

58. If Marvin can hike $8\frac{1}{4}$ miles in a day, how many days should it take him to hike 66 miles?

59. It took Joe $2\frac{1}{4}$ hours to walk to the mall. James did it in $\frac{1}{3}$ of the time it took Joe. How long did James take?

60. On June 1st a sunflower was $27\frac{1}{8}$ inches tall. On August 1st the same sunflower was $33\frac{5}{6}$ inches tall. How much did the sunflower grow between June 1st and August 1st?

61. How many ceramic tiles with dimensions of $3\frac{1}{2}$ inches by $3\frac{1}{2}$ inches are necessary to cover a bathroom counter with a total area of 392 square inches? (Assume no spacing between the tiles.)

62. How many pieces of carpet with dimensions of $2\frac{1}{4}$ feet by $2\frac{1}{4}$ feet are necessary to cover a family room floor with a total area of 243 square feet?

63. Gina purchased three packages of bacon from the butcher. The first package weighed $3\frac{5}{16}$ pounds, the second package weighed $2\frac{9}{16}$ pounds, and the third package weighed $3\frac{3}{8}$ pounds. What was the total weight of the three packages?

64. Seth makes $\$12\frac{3}{4}$ an hour working at a store. Marvin makes $2\frac{2}{5}$ times the amount Seth makes per hour. What is Marvin's hourly wage?

65. Use the formula $R = p \div h$ (where R is the rate of pay, p is the total amount of pay, and h is the number of hours worked), to find the rate of pay for a person that earns $52 in $3\frac{1}{4}$ hours.

66. Use the formula $R = p \div h$ (where R is the rate of pay, p is the total amount of pay, and h is the number of hours worked), to find the rate of pay for a person that earns $93 in $5\frac{1}{6}$ hours.

67. Steven eats $7\frac{1}{2}$ ounces of a chocolate bar weighing a total of $14\frac{1}{8}$ ounces. How much of the chocolate bar is still left?

68. Carmen jogged $1\frac{1}{2}$ miles on Monday, $2\frac{1}{3}$ miles on Tuesday, and $2\frac{4}{5}$ miles on Wednesday. How far did she jog during the three days?

69. Use the formula $r = d \div t$ (where r is rate of speed, d is distance, and t is the time spent traveling), to determine how fast a truck is going if it travels 207 miles in $3\frac{3}{4}$ hours.

70. Use the formula $r = d \div t$ (where r is rate of speed, d is distance, and t is the time spent traveling), to determine how fast a motorcycle is going if it travels 132 miles in $2\frac{1}{2}$ hours.

FRACTIONS

Section 8: Order of Operations with Fractions

In Chapter 1, we established the order of operations for whole numbers, which consisted of four main steps. In Chapter 2, the order of operations for integers contained the same four steps. The first step, however, needed to be expanded. Instead of just using parentheses, we needed to include all "grouping symbols." Among those included were parentheses as well as absolute value bars. With the introduction of fractions we need to introduce the fraction bar as another grouping symbol. The fraction bar groups together the numerator separately from the denominator. So, when simplifying a fraction, first simplify the numerator completely and then simplify the denominator completely.

Order of Operations: When simplifying a mathematical expression, do the following operations in the order that they are listed.

1. **Perform all calculations within grouping symbols.**
2. **Evaluate all exponential expressions.**
3. **Do all multiplication and division in order from left to right.**
4. **Do all addition and subtraction in order from left to right.**

Example 1: Simplify the expression: $\frac{2+5}{3+6}$

Solution:

$\frac{2+5}{3+6}$ Simplify the numerator.
Add.

$\frac{7}{3+6}$ Simplify the denominator.
Add.

$\frac{7}{9}$ This fraction is already in lowest terms.

So, $\frac{2+5}{3+6}=\frac{7}{9}$.

Example 2: Simplify the expression: $\frac{4+5\cdot 2}{10-3}$

Solution:

$\frac{4+5\cdot 2}{10-3}$	Simplify the numerator. Multiply.
$\frac{4+10}{10-3}$	Add.
$\frac{14}{10-3}$	Simplify the denominator. Subtract.
$\frac{14}{7}$	Divide the numerator by the denominator.
$\frac{14}{7}=2$	So, $\frac{4+5\cdot 2}{10-3}=2$.

Example 3: Simplify the expression: $\frac{5(3+1)}{\lvert 2-7\rvert}$

Solution:

$\frac{5(3+1)}{\lvert 2-7\rvert}$	Simplify the numerator. Add inside the parentheses.
$\frac{5(4)}{\lvert 2-7\rvert}$	Multiply.
$\frac{20}{\lvert 2-7\rvert}$	Simplify the denominator. Subtract inside the absolute value bars.
$\frac{20}{\lvert -5\rvert}$	Take the absolute value of -5.
$\frac{20}{5}$	Divide the numerator by the denominator.
$\frac{20}{5}=4$	So, $\frac{5(3+1)}{7-2}=4$.

We also need to look at how fractions work with exponents. For example, if we want to use an exponent as a way to indicate $\frac{2}{3}\cdot\frac{2}{3}\cdot\frac{2}{3}$ then we need to write the expression as $\left(\frac{2}{3}\right)^3$. That is, the entire fraction needs to be grouped such that the exponent applies to both the numerator and the denominator. If the expression is written as $\frac{2^3}{3}$, then the exponent only applies to the numerator and the expression would become $\frac{2\cdot 2\cdot 2}{3}$ or $\frac{8}{3}$.

As with integers, if a fraction with a negative sign is being raised to a power then the sign must be included as part of the base. Let's clarify the difference between two sets of notation.

For example, $\left(-\frac{3}{5}\right)^2$ and $-\left(\frac{3}{5}\right)^2$. In the first instance, $\left(-\frac{3}{5}\right)^2$, the base is $-\frac{3}{5}$.

The entire base is being squared, so $\left(-\frac{3}{5}\right)^2=\left(-\frac{3}{5}\right)\cdot\left(-\frac{3}{5}\right)=\frac{(-3)\cdot(-3)}{5\cdot 5}=\frac{9}{25}$.

In the second instance, $-\left(\frac{3}{5}\right)^2$, the base is just the $\frac{3}{5}$ and the negative sign is attached to the $\left(\frac{3}{5}\right)^2$. So, $-\left(\frac{3}{5}\right)^2=-\left(\frac{3}{5}\right)\cdot\left(\frac{3}{5}\right)=-\frac{3\cdot 3}{5\cdot 5}=-\frac{9}{25}$.

Here are several more examples involving fractions and exponents.

Example 4: Simplify the expression: $\frac{2+1}{5^2}$

Solution:

$\frac{2+1}{5^2}$	Simplify the numerator. Add.
$\frac{3}{5^2}$	Simplify the denominator. Apply the exponent in the denominator.
$\frac{3}{5\cdot 5}$	Multiply the factors in the denominator.
$\frac{3}{25}$	So, $\frac{2+1}{5^2}=\frac{3}{25}$.

Example 5: Simplify the expression: $\frac{2^3}{7^2}$

Solution:

$\frac{2^3}{7^2}$ Simplify the numerator.

Apply the exponent in the numerator.

$\frac{2 \cdot 2 \cdot 2}{7^2}$ Multiply the factors in the numerator.

$\frac{8}{7^2}$ Simplify the denominator.

Apply the exponent in the denominator.

$\frac{8}{7 \cdot 7}$ Multiply the factors in the denominator.

$\frac{8}{49}$ So, $\frac{2^3}{7^2} = \frac{8}{49}$.

Example 6: Simplify the expression: $\left(\frac{1}{5}\right)^3$

Solution:

$\left(\frac{1}{5}\right)^3$ Apply the exponent to the entire fraction.

$\left(\frac{1}{5}\right) \cdot \left(\frac{1}{5}\right) \cdot \left(\frac{1}{5}\right)$ Multiply the fractions together.

$\frac{1 \cdot 1 \cdot 1}{5 \cdot 5 \cdot 5}$ Multiply the factors in the numerator.

$\frac{1}{5 \cdot 5 \cdot 5}$ Multiply the factors in the denominator.

$\frac{1}{125}$ So, $\left(\frac{1}{5}\right)^3 = \frac{1}{125}$.

Example 7: Simplify the expression: $\left(-\frac{1}{2}\right)^4$

Solution:

$\left(-\frac{1}{2}\right)^4$	Apply the exponent to the entire fraction.
$\left(-\frac{1}{2}\right)\cdot\left(-\frac{1}{2}\right)\cdot\left(-\frac{1}{2}\right)\cdot\left(-\frac{1}{2}\right)$	Multiply the fractions together.
$\frac{(-1)\cdot(-1)\cdot(-1)\cdot(-1)}{2\cdot 2\cdot 2\cdot 2}$	Multiply the factors in the numerator.
$\frac{1}{2\cdot 2\cdot 2\cdot 2}$	Multiply the factors in the denominator.
$\frac{1}{16}$	So, $\left(-\frac{1}{2}\right)^4 = \frac{1}{16}$.

Example 8: Simplify the expression: $-\left(\frac{1}{3}\right)^4$

Solution:

$-\left(\frac{1}{3}\right)^4$	Apply the exponent to the entire fraction.
$-\left(\frac{1}{3}\right)\cdot\left(\frac{1}{3}\right)\cdot\left(\frac{1}{3}\right)\cdot\left(\frac{1}{3}\right)$	Multiply the fractions together.
$-\frac{1\cdot 1\cdot 1\cdot 1}{3\cdot 3\cdot 3\cdot 3}$	Multiply the factors in the numerator.
$-\frac{1}{3\cdot 3\cdot 3\cdot 3}$	Multiply the factors in the denominator.
$-\frac{1}{81}$	So, $-\left(\frac{1}{3}\right)^4 = -\frac{1}{81}$.

Suppose we mix together $2\frac{5}{8}$ cups of peanut butter, $\frac{1}{4}$ cup of chocolate and $\frac{1}{8}$ cup of finely crushed walnuts. Then we divide the mix into a dozen equally sized, no-bake cookies. What would be the size (in terms of cups) of each cookie? To answer the question, we would first add $2\frac{5}{8}$, $\frac{1}{4}$ and $\frac{1}{8}$. Then we would divide the total by 12. Writing this whole process as a single expression could look like this: $\left(2\frac{5}{8}+\frac{1}{4}+\frac{1}{8}\right)\div 12$. Remember that a fraction bar is a division symbol. Therefore, we could also write this expression as follows:

$$\frac{2\frac{5}{8}+\frac{1}{4}+\frac{1}{8}}{12}$$

We wouldn't need parentheses around the mixed number and fractions because the fraction bar is already a grouping symbol. By following order of operations, we would simplify the numerator first, and then divide by the denominator.

This expression $\frac{2\frac{5}{8}+\frac{1}{4}+\frac{1}{8}}{12}$ is called a **complex fraction**. A **complex fraction is a fraction in which either the numerator, the denominator, or both contain at least one fraction or mixed number.**

Here are some examples of complex fractions: $\frac{\frac{1}{2}}{\frac{7}{8}}$, $\frac{2-7}{1\frac{2}{3}}$, $\frac{\frac{3}{8}+\frac{1}{4}}{\frac{3}{4}}$

When asked to simplify a complex fraction, it needs to be written with no more than one fraction bar. **A fraction with only one fraction bar is called a simple fraction.**

Here are some examples of simple fractions. $\frac{3}{7}$, $\frac{w}{2}$, $\frac{3+6}{7^2}$

Example 9: Simplify the complex fraction: $\dfrac{\frac{1}{2}}{\frac{7}{8}}$

Solution: $\dfrac{\frac{1}{2}}{\frac{7}{8}}$ The numerator and denominator are already simplified.

$\dfrac{\frac{1}{2}}{\frac{7}{8}}$ ← To divide the numerator by the denominator, rewrite the complex fraction, changing the **main fraction bar** into a division sign. The complex fraction becomes

$\frac{1}{2} \div \frac{7}{8}$. Instead of dividing, multiply by the reciprocal of the divisor.

$\frac{1}{2} \div \frac{7}{8} = \frac{1}{2} \cdot \frac{8}{7}$ Find any prime factorizations of the numerators and the denominators. Reduce out common factors.

$\frac{1}{2} \cdot \frac{8}{7} = \frac{1}{2} \cdot \frac{2 \cdot 2 \cdot 2}{7} = \frac{1}{\cancel{2}_{1}} \cdot \frac{\cancel{2}^{1} \cdot 2 \cdot 2}{7} = \frac{1}{1} \cdot \frac{1 \cdot 2 \cdot 2}{7}$ Multiply the numerators and multiply the denominators.

$\frac{1}{1} \cdot \frac{1 \cdot 2 \cdot 2}{7} = \frac{4}{7}$ This fraction is already in lowest terms.

So, $\dfrac{\frac{1}{2}}{\frac{7}{8}} = \frac{4}{7}$.

Example 10: Simplify the complex fraction: $\dfrac{2-7}{1\frac{2}{3}}$

Solution: $\dfrac{2-7}{1\frac{2}{3}}$ Simplify the numerator.

Subtract.

$\dfrac{-5}{1\frac{2}{3}}$ Simplify the denominator.

Change the mixed number in the denominator into an improper fraction.

$\dfrac{-5}{\frac{5}{3}}$

To divide the numerator by the denominator, rewrite the complex fraction, changing the main fraction bar into a division sign. The complex fraction becomes

$-\dfrac{5}{1} \div \dfrac{5}{3}.$ Instead of dividing, multiply by the reciprocal of the divisor.

$-\dfrac{5}{1} \div \dfrac{5}{3} = -\dfrac{5}{1} \cdot \dfrac{3}{5}$ Reduce out common factors.

$-\dfrac{5}{1} \cdot \dfrac{3}{5} = -\dfrac{\overset{1}{\cancel{5}}}{1} \cdot \dfrac{3}{\underset{1}{\cancel{5}}} = -\dfrac{1}{1} \cdot \dfrac{3}{1}$ Multiply the numerators and multiply the denominators.

$-\dfrac{1}{1} \cdot \dfrac{3}{1} = -\dfrac{3}{1}$ This fraction can be reduced to lowest terms.

$-\dfrac{3}{1} = -3$ So, $\dfrac{2-7}{1\frac{2}{3}} = -3$.

Example 11: Simplify the complex fraction: $\dfrac{\frac{3}{8}+\frac{1}{4}}{\frac{3}{4}}$

Solution: $\dfrac{\frac{3}{8}+\frac{1}{4}}{\frac{3}{4}}$ Simplify the numerator.

The LCD of $\frac{3}{8}$ and $\frac{1}{4}$ is 8.

Change each fraction to an equivalent fraction with a denominator of 8.

$\frac{3}{8}$ remains unchanged and $\frac{1}{4}=\frac{1\cdot 2}{4\cdot 2}=\frac{2}{8}$. So, $\frac{3}{8}+\frac{1}{4}$ becomes $\frac{3}{8}+\frac{2}{8}$ and

$\dfrac{\frac{3}{8}+\frac{1}{4}}{\frac{3}{4}}=\dfrac{\frac{3}{8}+\frac{2}{8}}{\frac{3}{4}}$. Add the numerators and put their sum over the LCD. $\frac{3}{8}+\frac{2}{8}=\frac{3+2}{8}=\frac{5}{8}$

$\dfrac{\frac{3}{8}+\frac{2}{8}}{\frac{3}{4}}=\dfrac{\frac{5}{8}}{\frac{3}{4}}$ To divide the numerator by the denominator, rewrite the complex fraction, changing the main fraction bar into a division sign. The complex fraction becomes

$\frac{5}{8}\div\frac{3}{4}$. Instead of dividing, multiply by the reciprocal of the divisor.

$\frac{5}{8}\div\frac{3}{4}=\frac{5}{8}\cdot\frac{4}{3}$ Find any prime factorizations of the numerators and the denominators. Reduce out common factors.

$\frac{5}{8}\cdot\frac{4}{3}=\frac{5}{2\cdot 2\cdot 2}\cdot\frac{2\cdot 2}{3}=\frac{5}{\overset{1}{\cancel{2}}\cdot\overset{1}{\cancel{2}}\cdot 2}\cdot\frac{\overset{1}{\cancel{2}}\cdot\overset{1}{\cancel{2}}}{3}=\frac{5}{1\cdot 1\cdot 2}\cdot\frac{1\cdot 1}{3}$ Multiply the numerators and multiply the denominators.

$\frac{5}{1\cdot 1\cdot 2}\cdot\frac{1\cdot 1}{3}=\frac{5}{6}$ This fraction is already in lowest terms.

So, $\dfrac{\frac{3}{8}+\frac{1}{4}}{\frac{3}{4}}=\frac{5}{6}$.

Example 12: Simplify the complex fraction: $\dfrac{2\frac{5}{8}+\frac{1}{4}+\frac{1}{8}}{12}$

Solution: $\dfrac{2\frac{5}{8}+\frac{1}{4}+\frac{1}{8}}{12}$ Simplify the numerator.

The LCD of $2\frac{5}{8}$, $\frac{1}{4}$ and $\frac{1}{8}$ is 8.

The fraction part of $2\frac{5}{8}$ remains unchanged, while $\frac{1}{4}=\frac{1\cdot 2}{4\cdot 2}=\frac{2}{8}$. $\frac{1}{8}$ also remains unchanged.

So, $2\frac{5}{8}+\frac{1}{4}+\frac{1}{8}$ becomes $2\frac{5}{8}+\frac{2}{8}+\frac{1}{8}$ and

$\dfrac{2\frac{5}{8}+\frac{1}{4}+\frac{1}{8}}{12}=\dfrac{2\frac{5}{8}+\frac{2}{8}+\frac{1}{8}}{12}$. Add the fraction parts together. $2\frac{5}{8}+\frac{2}{8}+\frac{1}{8}=2+\frac{8}{8}=2+1=3$

$\dfrac{2\frac{5}{8}+\frac{2}{8}+\frac{1}{8}}{12}=\dfrac{3}{12}$ Find any prime factorizations of the numerator and the denominator. Reduce out common factors.

$\dfrac{3}{12}=\dfrac{3}{2\cdot 2\cdot 3}=\dfrac{\overset{1}{\cancel{3}}}{2\cdot 2\cdot \underset{1}{\cancel{3}}}=\dfrac{1}{2\cdot 2\cdot 1}$ Multiply the numerators and multiply the denominators.

$\dfrac{1}{2\cdot 2\cdot 1}=\dfrac{1}{4}$ This fraction is already in lowest terms.

So, $\dfrac{2\frac{5}{8}+\frac{1}{4}+\frac{1}{8}}{12}=\dfrac{1}{4}$.

This is the no-bake cookie problem. The size of each cookie would be $\frac{1}{4}$ cup.

Example 13: Simplify the complex fraction: $\dfrac{\frac{1}{6}+\left(\frac{1}{2}\right)^2}{-\frac{7}{18}}$

Solution: $\dfrac{\frac{1}{6}+\left(\frac{1}{2}\right)^2}{-\frac{7}{18}}$

Simplify the numerator.

Evaluate the exponential expression. $\left(\frac{1}{2}\right)^2=\frac{1}{2}\cdot\frac{1}{2}=\frac{1}{4}$

$\dfrac{\frac{1}{6}+\left(\frac{1}{2}\right)^2}{-\frac{7}{18}}=\dfrac{\frac{1}{6}+\frac{1}{4}}{-\frac{7}{18}}$

The LCD of $\frac{1}{6}$ and $\frac{1}{4}$ is 12. Change each fraction to an equivalent fraction with a denominator of 12.

$\frac{1}{6}=\frac{1\cdot 2}{6\cdot 2}=\frac{2}{12}$ and $\frac{1}{4}=\frac{1\cdot 3}{4\cdot 3}=\frac{3}{12}$. So, $\frac{1}{6}+\frac{1}{4}$ becomes $\frac{2}{12}+\frac{3}{12}$ and

$\dfrac{\frac{1}{6}+\frac{1}{4}}{-\frac{7}{18}}=\dfrac{\frac{2}{12}+\frac{3}{12}}{-\frac{7}{18}}$.

Add the fractions. $\frac{2}{12}+\frac{3}{12}=\frac{5}{12}$

$\dfrac{\frac{2}{12}+\frac{3}{12}}{-\frac{7}{18}}=\dfrac{\frac{5}{12}}{-\frac{7}{18}}$

To divide the numerator by the denominator, rewrite the complex fraction, changing the main fraction bar into a division sign. The complex fraction becomes

$\frac{5}{12}\div\left(-\frac{7}{18}\right)$.

Instead of dividing, multiply by the reciprocal of the divisor.

$\frac{5}{12}\div\left(-\frac{7}{18}\right)=\frac{5}{12}\cdot\left(-\frac{18}{7}\right)$

Find any prime factorizations of the numerators and the denominators. Reduce out common factors.

$\frac{5}{12}\cdot\left(-\frac{18}{7}\right)=\frac{5}{2\cdot 2\cdot 3}\cdot\left(-\frac{2\cdot 3\cdot 3}{7}\right)=\frac{5}{\cancel{2}^{1}\cdot 2\cdot\cancel{3}^{1}}\cdot\left(-\frac{\cancel{2}^{1}\cdot\cancel{3}^{1}\cdot 3}{7}\right)=\frac{5}{1\cdot 2\cdot 1}\cdot\left(-\frac{1\cdot 1\cdot 3}{7}\right)$

Multiply the numerators and multiply the denominators.

$\frac{5}{1\cdot 2\cdot 1}\cdot\left(-\frac{1\cdot 1\cdot 3}{7}\right)=-\frac{15}{14}$

This fraction is already in lowest terms. We could change it into a mixed number if desired. $-\frac{15}{14}=-1\frac{1}{14}$

Remember that following "order of operations" is necessary when evaluating algebraic expressions, since the process involves simplifying a mathematical expression.

Example 14: Evaluate the expression for the given values of the variables: $x^3 y^2$, where $x = 1\frac{4}{5}$ and $y = 3\frac{1}{3}$

Solution:

$x^3 y^2$ Substitute $1\frac{4}{5}$ in the place of x and $3\frac{1}{3}$ in the place of y.

$\left(1\frac{4}{5}\right)^3 \cdot \left(3\frac{1}{3}\right)^2$ Change each mixed number into an improper fraction.

$\left(\frac{9}{5}\right)^3 \cdot \left(\frac{10}{3}\right)^2$ Apply the exponents.

$\frac{9}{5} \cdot \frac{9}{5} \cdot \frac{9}{5} \cdot \frac{10}{3} \cdot \frac{10}{3}$ Find any prime factorizations of the numerators and the denominators. Reduce out common factors.

$$\frac{9}{5} \cdot \frac{9}{5} \cdot \frac{9}{5} \cdot \frac{10}{3} \cdot \frac{10}{3} = \frac{3\cdot3}{5} \cdot \frac{3\cdot3}{5} \cdot \frac{3\cdot3}{5} \cdot \frac{2\cdot5}{3} \cdot \frac{2\cdot5}{3} = \frac{\overset{1}{\cancel{3}}\cdot\overset{1}{\cancel{3}}}{\underset{1}{\cancel{5}}} \cdot \frac{3\cdot3}{\underset{1}{\cancel{5}}} \cdot \frac{3\cdot3}{5} \cdot \frac{2\cdot\overset{1}{\cancel{5}}}{\underset{1}{\cancel{3}}} \cdot \frac{2\cdot\overset{1}{\cancel{5}}}{\underset{1}{\cancel{3}}} = \frac{1\cdot1}{1} \cdot \frac{3\cdot3}{1} \cdot \frac{3\cdot3}{5} \cdot \frac{2\cdot1}{1} \cdot \frac{2\cdot1}{1}$$

Multiply the numerators and multiply the denominators.

$$\frac{1\cdot1}{1} \cdot \frac{3\cdot3}{1} \cdot \frac{3\cdot3}{5} \cdot \frac{2\cdot1}{1} \cdot \frac{2\cdot1}{1} = \frac{324}{5}$$

This fraction is already in lowest terms. We could change it into a mixed number if desired. $\frac{324}{5} = 64\frac{4}{5}$

When $x = 1\frac{4}{5}$ and $y = 3\frac{1}{3}$, the value of $x^3 y^2$ is $\frac{324}{5}$ or $64\frac{4}{5}$.

Example 15: Evaluate the expression for the given values of the variables: $\dfrac{x^2}{y+z}$,

where $x=-1\frac{1}{2}$, $y=4\frac{1}{2}$ and $z=\frac{3}{8}$

Solution:

$\dfrac{x^2}{y+z}$

Substitute $-1\frac{1}{2}$ in the place of x, $4\frac{1}{2}$ in the place of y and $\frac{3}{8}$ in the place of z.

$\dfrac{\left(-1\frac{1}{2}\right)^2}{4\frac{1}{2}+\frac{3}{8}}$

Simplify the numerator. Change the mixed number into an improper fraction.

$\dfrac{\left(-\frac{3}{2}\right)^2}{4\frac{1}{2}+\frac{3}{8}}$

Apply the exponent. $\left(-\frac{3}{2}\right)\cdot\left(-\frac{3}{2}\right)=\frac{9}{4}$

$\dfrac{\left(-\frac{3}{2}\right)^2}{4\frac{1}{2}+\frac{3}{8}}=\dfrac{\frac{9}{4}}{4\frac{1}{2}+\frac{3}{8}}$

Simplify the denominator. The LCD of $\frac{1}{2}$ and $\frac{3}{8}$ is 8.

$\frac{1}{2}=\frac{1\cdot 4}{2\cdot 4}=\frac{4}{8}$. $\frac{3}{8}$ remains unchanged.

So, $4\frac{1}{2}+\frac{3}{8}$ becomes $4\frac{4}{8}+\frac{3}{8}$ and

$\dfrac{\frac{9}{4}}{4\frac{1}{2}+\frac{3}{8}}=\dfrac{\frac{9}{4}}{4\frac{4}{8}+\frac{3}{8}}$.

Add the fraction parts together. $4\frac{4}{8}+\frac{3}{8}=4+\frac{7}{8}=4\frac{7}{8}$

Example 15 is continued on the next page.

Example 15 continued from previous page.

$$\frac{\frac{9}{4}}{4\frac{4}{8}+\frac{3}{8}}=\frac{\frac{9}{4}}{4\frac{7}{8}}$$

Change the mixed number into an improper fraction.

$$\frac{\frac{9}{4}}{4\frac{7}{8}}=\frac{\frac{9}{4}}{\frac{39}{8}}$$

To divide the numerator by the denominator, rewrite the complex fraction, changing the main fraction bar into a division sign. The complex fraction becomes

$$\frac{9}{4}\div\frac{39}{8}.$$

Instead of dividing, multiply by the reciprocal of the divisor.

$$\frac{9}{4}\div\frac{39}{8}=\frac{9}{4}\cdot\frac{8}{39}$$

Find any prime factorizations of the numerators and the denominators. Reduce out common factors.

$$\frac{9}{4}\cdot\frac{8}{39}=\frac{3\cdot3}{2\cdot2}\cdot\frac{2\cdot2\cdot2}{3\cdot13}=\frac{\overset{1}{\cancel{3}}\cdot3}{\underset{1}{\cancel{2}}\cdot\underset{1}{\cancel{2}}}\cdot\frac{\overset{1}{\cancel{2}}\cdot\overset{1}{\cancel{2}}\cdot2}{\underset{1}{\cancel{3}}\cdot13}=\frac{1\cdot3}{1\cdot1}\cdot\frac{1\cdot1\cdot2}{1\cdot13}$$

Multiply the numerators and multiply the denominators.

$$\frac{1\cdot3}{1\cdot1}\cdot\frac{1\cdot1\cdot2}{1\cdot13}=\frac{6}{13}$$

This fraction is already in lowest terms.

When $x=-1\frac{1}{2}$, $y=4\frac{1}{2}$, and $z=\frac{3}{8}$, the value of $\frac{x^2}{y+z}$ is $\frac{6}{13}$.

Section 8 exercises. Simplify each expression.

1. $\left(\frac{4}{7}\right)^2$

2. $\left(\frac{5}{9}\right)^2$

3. $\left(-\frac{2}{3}\right)^2$

4. $\left(-\frac{4}{5}\right)^2$

5. $\left(\frac{3}{4}\right)^3 \cdot \left(\frac{8}{9}\right)^2$

6. $\left(\frac{5}{6}\right)^4 \cdot \left(\frac{9}{25}\right)^3$

7. $-\left(\frac{2}{3}\right)^2$

8. $-\left(\frac{4}{5}\right)^2$

9. $\left(-\frac{3}{10}\right)^3 \cdot \left(\frac{5}{12}\right)^2$

10. $\left(-\frac{6}{7}\right)^3 \cdot \left(\frac{14}{15}\right)^2$

11. $\left(-\frac{1}{5}\right)^3$

12. $\left(-\frac{3}{4}\right)^3$

13. $\left(\frac{4}{15}\right)^3 \cdot \left(\frac{5}{8}\right)^2$

14. $\left(\frac{2}{9}\right)^2 \cdot \left(\frac{3}{10}\right)^3$

15. $\left(2\frac{1}{5}\right)^2$

16. $\left(4\frac{1}{2}\right)^2$

17. $\left(1\frac{2}{5}\right)^4 \cdot \left(\frac{5}{7}\right)^4$

18. $\left(2\frac{3}{7}\right)^3 \cdot \left(\frac{7}{17}\right)^3$

19. $\left(-2\frac{1}{3}\right)^2$

20. $\left(-1\frac{1}{4}\right)^2$

21. $8^3 \cdot \left(\frac{1}{6}\right)^3 \cdot \left(\frac{9}{16}\right)^2$

22. $6^2 \cdot \left(\frac{5}{6}\right)^3 \cdot \left(\frac{12}{25}\right)^2$

Simplify each complex fraction.

23. $\dfrac{\frac{5}{8}}{\frac{15}{16}}$

24. $\dfrac{\frac{3}{7}}{\frac{9}{14}}$

25. $\dfrac{\frac{7}{12}}{\frac{5}{9}}$

26. $\dfrac{\frac{6}{11}}{\frac{15}{22}}$

27. $\dfrac{-\frac{2}{13}}{\frac{22}{39}}$

28. $\dfrac{\frac{7}{8}}{-\frac{21}{32}}$

29. $\dfrac{\frac{7}{18}}{-\frac{11}{12}}$

30. $\dfrac{-\frac{3}{16}}{\frac{17}{24}}$

31. $\dfrac{3+\frac{3}{5}}{6}$

32. $\dfrac{4+\frac{5}{11}}{7}$

33. $\dfrac{-2\frac{1}{4}}{\frac{7}{8}-\frac{3}{4}}$

34. $\dfrac{-3\frac{1}{5}}{\frac{3}{20}-\frac{1}{10}}$

35. $\dfrac{\frac{7}{8}-\frac{7}{10}}{\frac{7}{12}}$

36. $\dfrac{\frac{5}{7}-\frac{5}{9}}{\frac{5}{11}}$

37. $\dfrac{\frac{3}{4}-\frac{2}{3}}{\frac{7}{9}}$

38. $\dfrac{\frac{5}{6}-\frac{4}{5}}{\frac{9}{10}}$

39. $\dfrac{\frac{1}{2}+\frac{1}{3}}{\frac{1}{4}+\frac{1}{5}}$

40. $\dfrac{\frac{1}{6}+\frac{1}{5}}{\frac{1}{4}+\frac{1}{3}}$

41. $\dfrac{3\frac{2}{9}-1\frac{2}{3}}{4\frac{1}{8}-2\frac{3}{8}}$

42. $\dfrac{5\frac{1}{4}-3\frac{1}{2}}{2\frac{1}{6}-1\frac{3}{4}}$

43. $\dfrac{\left(\frac{1}{3}\right)^2+2\frac{1}{4}}{4\frac{1}{3}+\left(\frac{1}{2}\right)^2}$

44. $\dfrac{\left(\frac{2}{5}\right)^2+2\frac{3}{4}}{2\frac{4}{25}+\left(\frac{3}{5}\right)^2}$

45. $\dfrac{\frac{7}{10}-\left(\frac{3}{5}\right)^2}{\left(\frac{1}{2}\right)^3-\frac{5}{6}}$

46. $\dfrac{\frac{7}{12}-\left(\frac{2}{3}\right)^2}{\left(\frac{1}{4}\right)^2-\frac{13}{16}}$

Simplify each expression.

47. $\frac{2}{5}\cdot\frac{7}{8}+\frac{9}{10}$

48. $\frac{4}{9}\cdot\frac{3}{8}+\frac{1}{3}$

49. $\frac{7}{12}-\frac{6}{11}\div\frac{3}{22}$

50. $\frac{5}{9}-\frac{7}{10}\div\frac{21}{40}$

51. $\frac{5}{6}-\frac{4}{5}\cdot\left(\frac{3}{8}+\frac{1}{4}\right)$

52. $\frac{2}{3}+\frac{4}{9}\cdot\left(\frac{1}{2}-\frac{1}{3}\right)$

53. $\left(\frac{2}{5}\right)^2\div\left(2-\frac{2}{5}\right)-\frac{1}{10}$

54. $\left(\frac{1}{2}\right)^3-\left(8\div\frac{2}{3}\right)\cdot\frac{1}{6}$

55. $\left(\frac{1}{3}\right)^3+\frac{6^2-2}{1+2^4}\div\frac{4}{5}$

56. $\frac{(6-4)^2}{7^2-5\cdot 8}\cdot\left(\frac{3}{4}\right)^2-\frac{1}{5}$

57. $\left(3\frac{1}{4}-1\frac{1}{2}\right)\cdot\left(\frac{2}{3}\right)^2+\left(\frac{8}{9}+\frac{1}{3}\right)$

58. $\left(4\frac{5}{8}-2\frac{3}{4}\right)\cdot\left(\frac{1}{3}\right)^2+\left(\frac{11}{12}+\frac{7}{8}\right)$

59. $\left(\frac{3-1\frac{1}{8}}{2-1\frac{1}{4}}\right)\cdot\left(\frac{5-4\frac{3}{7}}{4-2\frac{4}{7}}\right)$

60. $\left(\frac{4+2\frac{1}{6}}{10-1\frac{7}{9}}\right)\cdot\left(\frac{6-3\frac{2}{3}}{3-2\frac{3}{7}}\right)$

Evaluate each expression for the given value of the variable.

61. a^2, where $a=-\frac{1}{2}$

62. b^2, where $b=-\frac{2}{3}$

63. c^2, where $c=\frac{3}{5}$

64. d^2, where $d=\frac{4}{9}$

65. g^3, where $g=-\frac{1}{3}$

66. h^3, where $h=-\frac{1}{4}$

67. m^4, where $m=-\frac{2}{5}$

68. n^4, where $n=-\frac{3}{2}$

Evaluate each expression for the given values of the variables.

69. x^2y^3, where $x = 1\frac{3}{5}$ and $y = \frac{3}{4}$

70. w^3z^2, where $w = 1\frac{1}{6}$ and $z = \frac{3}{14}$

71. a^3b^4, where $a = -\frac{2}{9}$ and $b = 2\frac{1}{4}$

72. k^2m^4, where $k = -\frac{5}{12}$ and $m = \frac{3}{10}$

73. $\frac{xy}{y \div x}$, where $x = 2\frac{1}{2}$ and $y = 1\frac{7}{8}$

74. $\frac{x \div y}{x - y}$, where $x = 2\frac{1}{2}$ and $y = 1\frac{7}{8}$

75. $\frac{x - y}{y + x}$, where $x = 2\frac{1}{2}$ and $y = 1\frac{7}{8}$

76. $\frac{x + y}{yx}$, where $x = 2\frac{1}{2}$ and $y = 1\frac{7}{8}$

77. c^3df^2, where $c = 1\frac{1}{3}$, $d = -7$, and $f = 1\frac{1}{8}$

78. hn^3p^2, where $h = -14$, $n = \frac{1}{2}$, and $p = 1\frac{3}{7}$

79. $\frac{x^2}{y - z} + \frac{y}{z^2}$, where $x = \frac{3}{8}$, $y = 1\frac{1}{4}$, and $z = \frac{5}{6}$

80. $\frac{z - x}{y^2} + \frac{y - x}{z^2}$, where $x = \frac{3}{8}$, $y = 1\frac{1}{4}$, and $z = \frac{5}{6}$

81. $x^2 \div y^2 \cdot z^2$, where $x = \frac{1}{4}$, $y = 1\frac{1}{3}$, and $z = \frac{8}{9}$

82. $y^2 \div z^2 \cdot x^2$, where $x = \frac{1}{4}$, $y = 1\frac{1}{3}$, and $z = \frac{8}{9}$

Create a complex fraction based on the information given. Then simplify the complex fraction and answer the question.

83. $3\frac{1}{2}$ cups of flour, $2\frac{3}{4}$ cups of sugar and $4\frac{1}{6}$ cups of salt are mixed together in a bowl. Then the contents are divided equally and placed in 5 jars. How many cups of the mixture are in each jar?

84. $3\frac{1}{16}$ ounces of dark chocolate, $2\frac{1}{8}$ ounces of bittersweet chocolate and 1 ounce of milk chocolate are mixed together in a bowl. Then the contents are divided equally between 3 chocoholics. How many ounces of the mixture does each one get?

85. How many $\frac{1}{4}$ pound brass medallions can be produced from a mixture of $1\frac{1}{2}$ pounds of copper and $\frac{3}{4}$ pound of zinc?

86. How many $\frac{1}{3}$ pound bronze medallions can be produced from a mixture of $2\frac{2}{3}$ pounds of copper and $\frac{2}{3}$ pound of tin?

87. How many $6\frac{1}{8}$ fl oz bottles of sparkling apple-grape juice can be made by mixing $26\frac{1}{8}$ fl oz. of apple juice, $15\frac{1}{4}$ fl oz of grape juice, and $13\frac{3}{4}$ fl oz of pear juice?

88. How many $25\frac{2}{5}$ fl oz bottles of sparkling apple-cherry juice can be made by mixing $111\frac{4}{5}$ fl oz. of apple juice, $60\frac{4}{5}$ fl oz of cherry juice, and $30\frac{3}{5}$ fl oz pear juice?

89. A trail mix consists of $8\frac{1}{2}$ oz of sunflower seeds, $10\frac{3}{4}$ oz of raisins, $5\frac{1}{8}$ oz of walnuts, and $7\frac{3}{16}$ oz of soybeans. If the mix is split equally between five hikers, how much would each one get?

90. A trail mix consists of $5\frac{7}{16}$ oz of dried strawberries, $9\frac{1}{4}$ oz of golden raisins, $8\frac{13}{16}$ oz of cranberries, and $6\frac{1}{2}$ oz of almonds. If the mix is split equally between eight climbers, how much would each one get?

FRACTIONS

Section 9: Solving Equations with Fractions

Let's look at possible solutions of equations, using fractions and mixed numbers.

Example 1: Is $1\frac{8}{9}$ a solution of the equation $2\frac{7}{9} + y = 4\frac{2}{3}$?

Solution:

$2\frac{7}{9} + y = 4\frac{2}{3}$	Substitute $1\frac{8}{9}$ in the place of y.
$2\frac{7}{9} + 1\frac{8}{9} \stackrel{?}{=} 4\frac{2}{3}$	Simplify the left side of the equation. Add the whole-number parts together and add the fraction parts together.
$3 + \frac{15}{9} \stackrel{?}{=} 4\frac{2}{3}$	Since $\frac{15}{9}$ is an improper fraction, change it into a mixed number. $\frac{15}{9}$ becomes $1\frac{6}{9}$.
$3 + 1\frac{6}{9} \stackrel{?}{=} 4\frac{2}{3}$	Reduce the fraction part to lowest terms. $\frac{6}{9} = \frac{2 \cdot 3}{3 \cdot 3} = \frac{2 \cdot \cancel{3}^{1}}{3 \cdot \cancel{3}_{1}} = \frac{2}{3}$ So, $1\frac{6}{9}$ becomes $1\frac{2}{3}$.
$3 + 1\frac{2}{3} \stackrel{?}{=} 4\frac{2}{3}$	Add the whole-number part together.
$4 + \frac{2}{3} \stackrel{?}{=} 4\frac{2}{3}$	Combine the whole number and the fraction to form the final mixed number.
$4\frac{2}{3} \stackrel{\checkmark}{=} 4\frac{2}{3}$	This is a true statement. Consequently, $1\frac{8}{9}$ is a solution.

Example 2: Is $3\frac{1}{3}$ a solution of the equation $8\frac{1}{2} - x = 5\frac{1}{4}$?

Solution:

$8\frac{1}{2} - x = 5\frac{1}{4}$

Substitute $3\frac{1}{3}$ in the place of x.

$8\frac{1}{2} - 3\frac{1}{3} \stackrel{?}{=} 5\frac{1}{4}$

Simplify the left side of the equation.

The LCD of $\frac{1}{2}$ and $\frac{1}{3}$ is 6.

$\frac{1}{2} = \frac{1\cdot 3}{2\cdot 3} = \frac{3}{6}$ and $\frac{1}{3} = \frac{1\cdot 2}{3\cdot 2} = \frac{2}{6}$. So, $8\frac{1}{2} - 3\frac{1}{3} = 5\frac{1}{4}$ becomes

$8\frac{3}{6} - 3\frac{2}{6} \stackrel{?}{=} 5\frac{1}{4}$.

Subtract the whole-number parts and subtract the fraction parts.

$8\frac{3}{6} - 3\frac{2}{6}$ becomes $8 - 3 = 5$ and $\frac{3}{6} - \frac{2}{6} = \frac{1}{6}$.

Combine the mixed number and the fraction to form the final mixed number.

$5 + \frac{1}{6} = 5\frac{1}{6}$ So, $8\frac{3}{6} - 3\frac{2}{6} = 5\frac{1}{6}$.

$5\frac{1}{6} \stackrel{?}{=} 5\frac{1}{4}$

However,

$5\frac{1}{6} \neq 5\frac{1}{4}$.

This is a false statement. Consequently, $3\frac{1}{3}$ is not a solution.

Example 3: Is $24\frac{3}{4}$ a solution of the equation $\frac{2}{9}x = 5\frac{1}{2}$?

Solution:

$\frac{2}{9}x = 5\frac{1}{2}$

Substitute $24\frac{3}{4}$ in the place of x.

$\frac{2}{9}\cdot\left(24\frac{3}{4}\right) \stackrel{?}{=} 5\frac{1}{2}$

Simplify the left side of the equation.

Change $24\frac{3}{4}$ into the improper fraction $\frac{99}{4}$.

$\frac{2}{9}\cdot\frac{99}{4} \stackrel{?}{=} 5\frac{1}{2}$

Find any prime factorizations of the numerators and the denominators. Then reduce out common factors.

$$\frac{2}{9}\cdot\frac{99}{4} = \frac{2}{3\cdot 3}\cdot\frac{3\cdot 3\cdot 11}{2\cdot 2} = \frac{\overset{1}{\cancel{2}}}{\underset{1}{\cancel{3}}\cdot\underset{1}{\cancel{3}}}\cdot\frac{\overset{1}{\cancel{3}}\cdot\overset{1}{\cancel{3}}\cdot 11}{\underset{1}{\cancel{2}}\cdot 2} = \frac{1\cdot 1\cdot 1\cdot 11}{1\cdot 1\cdot 1\cdot 2} \stackrel{?}{=} 5\frac{1}{2}$$

Multiply the numerators and multiply the denominators.

$\frac{1\cdot 1\cdot 1\cdot 11}{1\cdot 1\cdot 1\cdot 2} = \frac{11}{2} \stackrel{?}{=} 5\frac{1}{2}$

The fraction is already in lowest terms. However, if we change it into a mixed number, the left side of the equation becomes $5\frac{1}{2}$. So the equation becomes

$5\frac{1}{2} \stackrel{\checkmark}{=} 5\frac{1}{2}$.

This is a true statement. Consequently, $24\frac{3}{4}$ is a solution.

Example 4: Is $\frac{2}{7}$ a solution of the equation $\frac{6}{7} \div x = 3$?

Solution:

$\frac{6}{7} \div x = 3$	Substitute $\frac{2}{7}$ in the place of x.
$\frac{6}{7} \div \frac{2}{7} \stackrel{?}{=} 3$	Simplify the left side of the equation.
	Instead of dividing, multiply by the reciprocal of the divisor.
$\frac{6}{7} \cdot \frac{7}{2} \stackrel{?}{=} 3$	Find any prime factorizations of the numerators and the denominators.
$\frac{2 \cdot 3}{7} \cdot \frac{7}{2} \stackrel{?}{=} 3$	Reduce out common factors.
$\frac{\overset{1}{\cancel{2}} \cdot 3}{\underset{1}{\cancel{7}}} \cdot \frac{\overset{1}{\cancel{7}}}{\underset{1}{\cancel{2}}} \stackrel{?}{=} 3$	
$\frac{1 \cdot 3}{1} \cdot \frac{1}{1} \stackrel{?}{=} 3$	Multiply the numerators and multiply the denominators.
$\frac{3}{1} \stackrel{?}{=} 3$	This fraction can be reduced to lowest terms.
$3 \stackrel{\checkmark}{=} 3$	This is a true statement. Consequently, $\frac{2}{7}$ is a solution.

Let's look at possible solutions of equations, using fractions with exponents and/or complex fractions.

Example 5: Is $\frac{1}{2}$ a solution of the equation $\frac{x^3}{3-x}=\frac{1}{20}$?

Solution:

$\frac{x^3}{3-x}=\frac{1}{20}$ — Substitute $\frac{1}{2}$ in the place of x.

$\frac{\left(\frac{1}{2}\right)^3}{3-\frac{1}{2}} \stackrel{?}{=} \frac{1}{20}$ — Simplify the left side of the equation.

Simplify the numerator.

Evaluate the exponential expression. $\left(\frac{1}{2}\right)^3=\frac{1}{2}\cdot\frac{1}{2}\cdot\frac{1}{2}=\frac{1}{8}$

$\frac{\frac{1}{8}}{3-\frac{1}{2}} \stackrel{?}{=} \frac{1}{20}$ — Simplify the denominator.

Subtract. $3-\frac{1}{2}=2\frac{2}{2}-\frac{1}{2}=2\frac{1}{2}$

$\frac{\frac{1}{8}}{2\frac{1}{2}} \stackrel{?}{=} \frac{1}{20}$ — Change the mixed number $2\frac{1}{2}$ into an improper fraction $\frac{5}{2}$.

$\frac{\frac{1}{8}}{\frac{5}{2}} \stackrel{?}{=} \frac{1}{20}$ — To divide the numerator by the denominator, rewrite the complex fraction, changing the main fraction bar into a division sign. The complex fraction becomes

$\frac{1}{8}\div\frac{5}{2} \stackrel{?}{=} \frac{1}{20}.$ — Instead of dividing, multiply by the reciprocal of the divisor.

$\frac{1}{8}\cdot\frac{2}{5} \stackrel{?}{=} \frac{1}{20}$ — Find any prime factorizations of the numerators and the denominators. Reduce out common factors.

$\frac{1}{2\cdot 2\cdot 2}\cdot\frac{2}{5}=\frac{1}{\cancel{2}^{1}\cdot 2\cdot 2}\cdot\frac{\cancel{2}^{1}}{5}=\frac{1}{1\cdot 2\cdot 2}\cdot\frac{1}{5} \stackrel{?}{=} \frac{1}{20}$ — Multiply the numerators and multiply the denominators.

$\frac{1}{20} \stackrel{\checkmark}{=} \frac{1}{20}$ — This is a true statement. Consequently, $\frac{1}{2}$ is a solution.

In Chapter 1 we established properties that are used to solve equations with whole numbers. In Chapter 2 we used those same properties to solve equations with integers. In this chapter we will use those properties to solve equations that involve fractions. Let's review those properties along with an example of how each property is used with fractions.

THE ADDITION PROPERTY OF EQUALITY:

When a, b, and c are real numbers, the following is true:

If $\mathrm{a} = \mathrm{b}$ then $\mathrm{a} + \mathrm{c} = \mathrm{b} + \mathrm{c}$.

If the same quantity is added to both sides of an equation, the new equation is equivalent to the old equation. That is, both equations have the same solution.

Example 6: Solve the equation: $x - \frac{2}{3} = \frac{5}{6}$

Solution:

$x - \frac{2}{3} = \frac{5}{6}$ Use the addition property of equality by adding $\frac{2}{3}$ to both sides of the equation.

$x - \frac{2}{3} + \frac{2}{3} = \frac{5}{6} + \frac{2}{3}$ Simplify the left side of the equation.

$x = \frac{5}{6} + \frac{2}{3}$ Simplify the right side of the equation.

The LCD of $\frac{5}{6}$ and $\frac{2}{3}$ is 6.

Change each fraction to an equivalent fraction with a denominator of 6.

$\frac{5}{6}$ remains unchanged and $\frac{2}{3} = \frac{2 \cdot 2}{3 \cdot 2} = \frac{4}{6}$. So, $x = \frac{5}{6} + \frac{2}{3}$ becomes $x = \frac{5}{6} + \frac{4}{6}$.

Add the numerators and put their sum over the LCD.

$x = \frac{5}{6} + \frac{4}{6} = \frac{5+4}{6} = \frac{9}{6}$ So, $x = \frac{9}{6}$.

Example 6 is continued on the next page.

Example 6 continued from previous page.

Reduce this fraction to lowest terms.

Find any prime factorizations of the numerator and the denominator. Reduce out common factors.

$$x = \frac{9}{6} = \frac{3 \cdot 3}{2 \cdot 3} = \frac{\overset{1}{\cancel{3}} \cdot 3}{2 \cdot \underset{1}{\cancel{3}}} = \frac{1 \cdot 3}{2 \cdot 1} = \frac{3}{2}.$$

The solution is $x = \frac{3}{2}$.

To check the solution, substitute it back into the original equation in place of the variable.

$x - \frac{2}{3} = \frac{5}{6}$ becomes

$\frac{3}{2} - \frac{2}{3} \overset{?}{=} \frac{5}{6}$. Simplify the left side of the equation.

The LCD of $\frac{3}{2}$ and $\frac{2}{3}$ is 6.

Change each fraction to an equivalent fraction with a denominator of 6.

$\frac{3}{2} = \frac{3 \cdot 3}{2 \cdot 3} = \frac{9}{6}$ and $\frac{2}{3} = \frac{2 \cdot 2}{3 \cdot 2} = \frac{4}{6}$. So, $\frac{3}{2} - \frac{2}{3} \overset{?}{=} \frac{5}{6}$ becomes $\frac{9}{6} - \frac{4}{6} \overset{?}{=} \frac{5}{6}$,

which simplifies to

$\frac{5}{6} \overset{\checkmark}{=} \frac{5}{6}$. The statement is true, therefore the solution is correct.

THE SUBTRACTION PROPERTY OF EQUALITY:

When a, b, and c are real numbers, the following is true:

If $a = b$ then $a - c = b - c$.

If the same quantity is subtracted from both sides of an equation, the new equation is equivalent to the old equation. That is, both equations have the same solution.

Example 7: Solve: $\frac{3}{4} = y + \frac{1}{4}$

Solution:

$\frac{3}{4} = y + \frac{1}{4}$ Use the subtraction property of equality by subtracting $\frac{1}{4}$ from both sides of the equation.

$\frac{3}{4} - \frac{1}{4} = y + \frac{1}{4} - \frac{1}{4}$ Simplify the left side of the equation.

$\frac{2}{4} = y + \frac{1}{4} - \frac{1}{4}$ Simplify the right side of the equation.

$\frac{2}{4} = y$ So, $y = \frac{2}{4}$.

Reduce this fraction to lowest terms.

Find any prime factorizations of the numerator and the denominator. Reduce out common factors.

$$y = \frac{2}{4} = \frac{2}{2 \cdot 2} = \frac{\overset{1}{\cancel{2}}}{\underset{1}{\cancel{2}} \cdot 2} = \frac{1}{2}$$

The solution is $y = \frac{1}{2}$.

Example 7 is continued on the next page.

Example 7 continued from previous page.

To check the solution, substitute it back into the original equation in place of the variable.

$\frac{3}{4} = y + \frac{1}{4}$ becomes

$\frac{3}{4} \stackrel{?}{=} \frac{1}{2} + \frac{1}{4}$. Simplify the right side of the equation.

The LCD of $\frac{1}{2}$ and $\frac{1}{4}$ is 4.

Change each fraction to an equivalent fraction with a denominator of 4.

$\frac{1}{2} = \frac{1 \cdot 2}{2 \cdot 2} = \frac{2}{4}$ and $\frac{1}{4}$ remains unchanged. So, $\frac{3}{4} \stackrel{?}{=} \frac{1}{2} + \frac{1}{4}$ becomes $\frac{3}{4} \stackrel{?}{=} \frac{2}{4} + \frac{1}{4}$,

which simplifies to

$\frac{3}{4} \stackrel{\checkmark}{=} \frac{3}{4}$. The statement is true, therefore the solution is correct.

THE DIVISION PROPERTY OF EQUALITY:

When a, b, and c are real numbers with $c \neq 0$, the following is true:

$$\text{If} \quad a = b \quad \text{then} \quad \frac{a}{c} = \frac{b}{c}.$$

If both sides of the equation are divided by the same non-zero quantity, the new equation is equivalent to the old equation. That is, both equations have the same solution.

Example 8: Solve: $\frac{2}{5}x = 6$

Solution:

$\frac{2}{5}x = 6$ — Use the division property of equality by dividing both sides of the equation by $\frac{2}{5}$.

$\frac{\frac{2}{5}x}{\frac{2}{5}} = \frac{6}{\frac{2}{5}}$ — Simplify the left side of the equation.

Instead of dividing by $\frac{2}{5}$, multiply by its reciprocal, which is $\frac{5}{2}$.

$\frac{2}{5}x \cdot \frac{5}{2} = \frac{6}{\frac{2}{5}}$ — Reduce out common factors.

$\frac{\cancel{2}^{1}}{\cancel{5}_{1}}x \cdot \frac{\cancel{5}^{1}}{\cancel{2}_{1}} = \frac{6}{\frac{2}{5}}$ — Simplify the right side of the equation.

Instead of dividing by $\frac{2}{5}$, multiply by its reciprocal, which is $\frac{5}{2}$.

$x = \frac{6}{1} \cdot \frac{5}{2}$ — Find any prime factorizations of the numerators and the denominators. Reduce out common factors.

Example 8 is continued on the next page.

Example 8 continued from previous page.

$$x = \frac{6}{1} \cdot \frac{5}{2} = \frac{2 \cdot 3}{1} \cdot \frac{5}{2} = \frac{\overset{1}{\cancel{2}} \cdot 3}{1} \cdot \frac{5}{\underset{1}{\cancel{2}}} = \frac{1 \cdot 3}{1} \cdot \frac{5}{1}$$

Multiply the numerators and multiply the denominators.

$$x = \frac{1 \cdot 3}{1} \cdot \frac{5}{1} = \frac{15}{1}$$

This fraction can be reduced to lowest terms.

$$x = \frac{15}{1} = 15$$

The solution is $x = 15$.

To check the solution, substitute it back into the original equation in place of the variable.

$$\frac{2}{5}x = 6$$

becomes

$$\frac{2}{5} \cdot 15 \stackrel{?}{=} 6.$$

Simplify the left side of the equation.

Find any prime factorizations of the numerators and the denominators.

$$\frac{2}{5} \cdot \frac{3 \cdot 5}{1} \stackrel{?}{=} 6$$

Reduce out common factors.

$$\frac{2}{\underset{1}{\cancel{5}}} \cdot \frac{3 \cdot \overset{1}{\cancel{5}}}{1} \stackrel{?}{=} 6$$

Multiply the numerators and multiply the denominators.

$$\frac{6}{1} \stackrel{?}{=} 6$$

This fraction can be reduced to lowest terms.

$$6 \stackrel{\checkmark}{=} 6$$

The statement is true. Consequently, the solution is correct.

With the introduction of fractions, there is another property that needs to be discussed. Sometimes solving an equation requires removing a number from the denominator of a fraction in order to isolate the variable. To do this we use what is called **The Multiplication Property of Equality**.

THE MULTIPLICATION PROPERTY OF EQUALITY:

When a, b, and c are real numbers with $c \neq 0$, the following is true:

If $a = b$ then $a \cdot c = b \cdot c$.

If the same non-zero quantity is multiplied by both sides of an equation, the new equation is equivalent to the old equation. That is, both equations have the same solution.

Example 9: Solve: $\frac{x}{6} = 5$

Solution:

$\frac{x}{6} = 5$ Use the multiplication property of equality by multiplying both sides of the equation by 6.

$\frac{x}{6} \cdot 6 = 5 \cdot 6$ Simplify the left side of the equation.

$\frac{x}{\cancel{6}_1} \cdot \cancel{6}^1 = 5 \cdot 6$ Simplify the right side of the equation.

$x = 30$ The solution is $x = 30$.

To check the solution, substitute it back into the original equation in place of the variable.

$\frac{x}{6} = 5$ becomes

$\frac{30}{6} \stackrel{?}{=} 5$. Simplify the left side of the equation.

$5 \stackrel{\checkmark}{=} 5$ The statement is true. Consequently, the solution is correct.

Example 10: Solve: $-\frac{m}{3}=4$

Solution:

$-\frac{m}{3}=4$	Rewrite the left side of the equation attaching the negative sign to the denominator.
$\frac{m}{-3}=4$	Use the multiplication property of equality by multiplying both sides of the equation by -3.
$\frac{m}{-3}\cdot(-3)=4\cdot(-3)$	Simplify the left side of the equation.
$\frac{m}{\cancel{-3}_{1}}\cdot(\cancel{-3})^{1}=4\cdot(-3)$	Simplify the right side of the equation.
$m=-12$	The solution is $m=-12$.

To check the solution, substitute it back into the original equation in place of the variable.

$-\frac{m}{3}=4$	becomes
$-\frac{-12}{3}\overset{?}{=}4$.	Rewrite the left side of the equation attaching the negative sign to the denominator.
$\frac{-12}{-3}\overset{?}{=}4$	Simplify the left side of the equation.
$4\overset{\checkmark}{=}4$	The statement is true. Consequently, the solution is correct.

Now that we have introduced the multiplication property of equality, let's look again at example 8. In example 8 we started by dividing both sides of the equation by the fraction $\frac{2}{5}$. As we simplified each side of the equation, instead of dividing by $\frac{2}{5}$, we multiplied each side by its reciprocal, $\frac{5}{2}$. This leads to the following: **When the coefficient of the variable is a fraction, instead of dividing both sides of the equation by this fraction, multiply both sides by its reciprocal instead.**

Example 8 Revisited: Solve: $\frac{2}{5}x = 6$

Solution:

$\frac{2}{5}x = 6$ Use the division property of equality by dividing both sides of the equation by $\frac{2}{5}$.

Instead of dividing by $\frac{2}{5}$, multiply by its reciprocal, which is $\frac{5}{2}$.

$\frac{2}{5}x \cdot \frac{5}{2} = 6 \cdot \frac{5}{2}$ Simplify the left side of the equation.

Reduce out common factors.

$\frac{\overset{1}{\cancel{2}}}{\underset{1}{\cancel{5}}}x \cdot \frac{\overset{1}{\cancel{5}}}{\underset{1}{\cancel{2}}} = 6 \cdot \frac{5}{2}$ Simplify the right side of the equation.

$x = \frac{6}{1} \cdot \frac{5}{2}$ Find any prime factorizations of the numerators and the denominators. Reduce out common factors.

$$x = \frac{6}{1} \cdot \frac{5}{2} = \frac{2 \cdot 3}{1} \cdot \frac{5}{2} = \frac{\overset{1}{\cancel{2}} \cdot 3}{1} \cdot \frac{5}{\underset{1}{\cancel{2}}} = \frac{1 \cdot 3}{1} \cdot \frac{5}{1}$$

Multiply the numerators and multiply the denominators.

$x = \frac{1 \cdot 3}{1} \cdot \frac{5}{1} = \frac{15}{1}$ This fraction can be reduced to lowest terms.

$x = \frac{15}{1} = 15$ The solution is $x = 15$.

We already checked the solution in the original example 3.

Example 11: Solve: $-\frac{3}{8}x = 9$

Solution:

$$-\frac{3}{8}x = 9$$

The coefficient of the variable is a fraction. Use the multiplication property of equality by multiplying both sides of the equation by the reciprocal of $-\frac{3}{8}$ which is $-\frac{8}{3}$ or $\frac{-8}{3}$.

$$\frac{-3}{8}x \cdot \frac{-8}{3} = \frac{9}{1} \cdot \frac{-8}{3}$$

Simplify the left side of the equation.

Reduce out common factors.

$$\frac{\overset{-1}{\cancel{-3}}}{\underset{1}{\cancel{8}}}x \cdot \frac{\overset{-1}{\cancel{-8}}}{\underset{1}{\cancel{3}}} = \frac{9}{1} \cdot \frac{-8}{3}$$

Since $-1 \cdot (-1) = 1$, the left side simplifies further to just x.

$$x = \frac{9}{1} \cdot \frac{-8}{3}$$

Simplify the right side of the equation.

Find any prime factorizations of the numerators and the denominators.

To find the prime factorization of a negative number such as -8, first factor out a -1; that is, -8 becomes $-1 \cdot 8$. Then, factor the remaining natural number. $-8 = -1 \cdot 8 = -1 \cdot 2 \cdot 2 \cdot 2$.

$$x = \frac{3 \cdot 3}{1} \cdot \frac{-1 \cdot 2 \cdot 2 \cdot 2}{3}$$

Reduce out common factors.

$$x = \frac{\overset{1}{\cancel{3}} \cdot 3}{1} \cdot \frac{-1 \cdot 2 \cdot 2 \cdot 2}{\underset{1}{\cancel{3}}}$$

Multiply the numerators and multiply the denominators.

$$x = \frac{-24}{1}$$

This fraction can be reduced to lowest terms.

$$x = -24$$

The solution is $x = -24$.

Example 11 is continued on the next page.

Example 11 continued from previous page.

To check the solution, substitute it back into the original equation in place of the variable.

$-\frac{3}{8}x=9$	becomes
$\frac{-3}{8}(-24)\stackrel{?}{=}9.$	Simplify the left side of the equation. Find any prime factorizations of the numerators and the denominators.
$\frac{-1\cdot3}{2\cdot2\cdot2}\cdot\frac{-1\cdot2\cdot2\cdot2\cdot3}{1}\stackrel{?}{=}9$	Reduce out common factors.
$\frac{-1\cdot3}{\cancel{2}_1\cdot\cancel{2}_1\cdot\cancel{2}_1}\cdot\frac{-1\cdot\cancel{2}^1\cdot\cancel{2}^1\cdot\cancel{2}^1\cdot3}{1}\stackrel{?}{=}9$	Multiply the numerators and multiply the denominators.
$\frac{9}{1}\stackrel{?}{=}9$	This fraction can be reduced to lowest terms.
$9\stackrel{\checkmark}{=}9$	The statement is true, therefore the solution is correct.

Example 12: Translate the following expression into an equation using mathematical symbols. Then, solve the equation and answer the question.
The sum of a number and one fifth is one fourth. What is the number?

Solution: First we need to choose a variable to represent the unknown quantity. Since the unknown quantity is "a number" let's use the letter N. The statement

"The sum of	a number	and	one fifth	is	one fourth"	translates into
add	the unknown "N"		$\frac{1}{5}$	equals	$\frac{1}{4}$	

which becomes the equation: $N \quad + \quad \frac{1}{5} \quad = \quad \frac{1}{4}$

Now we can solve the equation.

$N+\frac{1}{5}=\frac{1}{4}$ Use the subtraction property of equality by subtracting $\frac{1}{5}$ from both sides of the equation.

$N+\frac{1}{5}-\frac{1}{5}=\frac{1}{4}-\frac{1}{5}$ Simplify the left side of the equation.

$N=\frac{1}{4}-\frac{1}{5}$ Simplify the right side of the equation.

The LCD of $\frac{1}{4}$ and $\frac{1}{5}$ is 20.

Change each fraction to an equivalent fraction with a denominator of 20.

$\frac{1}{4}=\frac{1\cdot 5}{4\cdot 5}=\frac{5}{20}$ and $\frac{1}{5}=\frac{1\cdot 4}{5\cdot 4}=\frac{4}{20}$. So, $N=\frac{1}{4}-\frac{1}{5}$ becomes $N=\frac{5}{20}-\frac{4}{20}$.

Subtract the numerators and put their difference over the LCD.

$$N=\frac{5}{20}-\frac{4}{20}=\frac{5-4}{20}=\frac{1}{20}$$

This fraction is already in lowest terms.

So, $N=\frac{1}{20}$. The solution is $\frac{1}{20}$, therefore, the number is $\frac{1}{20}$.

We'll leave verifying the solution up to you.

Example 13: Translate the following expression into an equation using mathematical symbols. Then, solve the equation and answer the question.
The product of negative three fifths and a number is equal to two. What is the number?

Solution: First we need to choose a variable to represent the unknown quantity. Since the unknown quantity is "a number" let's use the letter N. The statement

"The product of negative three fifths and a number is equal to two" translates into

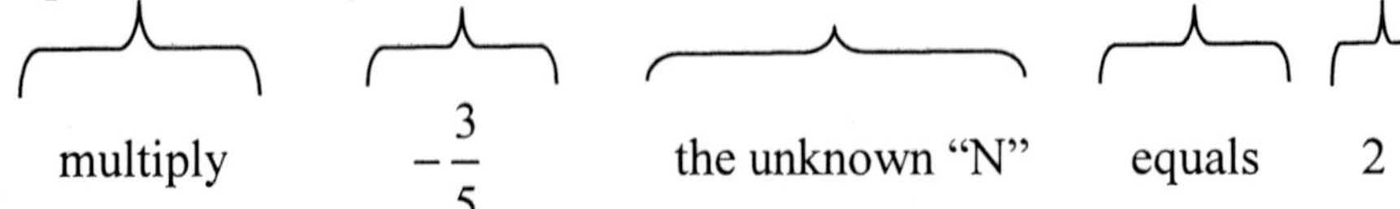

multiply $-\frac{3}{5}$ the unknown "N" equals 2

which becomes the equation: $-\frac{3}{5}N = 2$

Now we can solve the equation.

$-\frac{3}{5}N = 2$ The coefficient of the variable is a fraction. Use the multiplication property of equality by multiplying both sides of the equation by the reciprocal of $-\frac{3}{5}$ which is $-\frac{5}{3}$ or $\frac{-5}{3}$.

$\frac{-3}{5}N \cdot \frac{-5}{3} = \frac{2}{1} \cdot \frac{-5}{3}$ Simplify the left side of the equation.

Reduce out common factors.

$\frac{\overset{-1}{\cancel{-3}}}{\underset{1}{\cancel{5}}}N \cdot \frac{\overset{-1}{\cancel{-5}}}{\underset{1}{\cancel{3}}} = \frac{2}{1} \cdot \frac{-5}{3}$ Since $-1 \cdot (-1) = 1$, the left side simplifies further to just *N*.

$N = \frac{2}{1} \cdot \frac{-5}{3}$ Simplify the right side of the equation.

Multiply the numerators and multiply the denominators.

$N = -\frac{10}{3}$ This fraction is in lowest terms.

So, $N = -\frac{10}{3}$ or $-3\frac{1}{3}$. The solution and, therefore, the number is $-\frac{10}{3}$ or $-3\frac{1}{3}$. We'll leave verifying the solution up to you.

Example 14: Translate the following situation into an equation using mathematical symbols. Then, solve the equation and answer the question.
The white cat weighs three fifths of a pound more than the black cat. If the white cat weighs four and two fifths pounds, how much does the black cat weigh?

Solution: The letter B is used to represent the unknown quantity, which is "how much does the black cat weigh." The statement "The white cat weighs three fifths of a pound more than the black cat" becomes: $\text{white cat} = B + \frac{3}{5}$. The statement "the white cat weighs four and two fifths pounds" becomes: $\text{white cat} = 4\frac{2}{5}$. Since $\text{white cat} = B + \frac{3}{5}$ and $\text{white cat} = 4\frac{2}{5}$, by putting these two statements together, we get the equation $B + \frac{3}{5} = 4\frac{2}{5}$.

Now we can solve the equation.

$$B + \frac{3}{5} = 4\frac{2}{5}$$

Use the subtraction property of equality by subtracting $\frac{3}{5}$ from both sides of the equation.

$$B + \frac{3}{5} - \frac{3}{5} = 4\frac{2}{5} - \frac{3}{5}$$

Simplify the left side of the equation.

$$B = 4\frac{2}{5} - \frac{3}{5}$$

Simplify the right side of the equation.

Borrow a 1 from the whole-number part of the minuend in order to subtract the fraction parts.

$$B = \left(4\frac{2}{5}\right) - \frac{3}{5} = \left(3 + 1 + \frac{2}{5}\right) - \frac{3}{5}$$

Take this 1 and turn it into an improper fraction with the numerator and the denominator matching the common denominator of the fraction parts of the problem.

$$B = \left(3 + \frac{5}{5} + \frac{2}{5}\right) - \frac{3}{5}$$

Add this improper fraction to the fraction part of the minuend.

$$B = \left(3 + \frac{7}{5}\right) - \frac{3}{5}$$

$$B = 3\frac{7}{5} - \frac{3}{5}$$

Subtract the fraction parts.

$$B = 3\frac{4}{5}$$

The solution is $3\frac{4}{5}$. Therefore, the black cat weighs $3\frac{4}{5}$ pounds.

We'll leave verifying the solution up to you.

Example 15: Translate the following situation into an equation using mathematical symbols. Then, solve the equation and answer the question.
Joe is one third as old as Donald. If Joe is eight years old, how old is Donald?

Solution: The letter D is used to represent the unknown quantity, which is "how old is Donald?" The statement "Joe is one third as old as Donald" becomes: $\text{Joe} = \frac{1}{3}\text{D}$. The statement "Joe is eight years old" becomes: $\text{Joe} = 8$. Since $\text{Joe} = \frac{1}{3}\text{D}$ and $\text{Joe} = 8$, by putting these two statements together, we get the equation $\frac{1}{3}\text{D} = 8$.

Now we can solve the equation.

$$\frac{1}{3}\text{D} = 8$$

The coefficient of the variable is a fraction. Use the multiplication property of equality by multiplying both sides of the equation by the reciprocal of $\frac{1}{3}$ which is $\frac{3}{1}$ or just 3.

$$\frac{1}{3}\text{D}\cdot\frac{3}{1} = \frac{8}{1}\cdot\frac{3}{1}$$

Simplify the left side of the equation.

Reduce out common factors.

$$\frac{1}{\cancel{3}_1}\text{D}\cdot\frac{\cancel{3}^1}{1} = \frac{8}{1}\cdot\frac{3}{1}$$

$$\text{D} = \frac{8}{1}\cdot\frac{3}{1}$$

Simplify the right side of the equation.

Multiply the numerators and multiply the denominators.

$$\text{D} = \frac{24}{1}$$

This fraction can be reduced to lowest terms.

$$\text{D} = 24$$

The solution is 24, therefore, Donald is 24 years old.

We'll leave verifying the solution up to you.

Section 9 exercises. Check the solutions.

1. Is $\frac{7}{9}$ a solution of the equation $x+\frac{7}{18}=1\frac{1}{6}$?

2. Is $\frac{6}{7}$ a solution of the equation $y+\frac{9}{14}=1\frac{1}{2}$?

3. Is $3\frac{1}{4}$ a solution of the equation $x-\frac{7}{16}=2\frac{7}{8}$?

4. Is $2\frac{1}{5}$ a solution of the equation $y-\frac{7}{15}=1\frac{11}{15}$?

5. Is $-\frac{4}{9}$ a solution of the equation $3\frac{1}{4}-a=3\frac{2}{3}$?

6. Is $-\frac{7}{16}$ a solution of the equation $7\frac{1}{3}-w=7\frac{3}{4}$?

7. Is $\frac{3}{16}$ a solution of the equation $4x=\frac{3}{4}$?

8. Is $\frac{5}{14}$ a solution of the equation $7y=2\frac{1}{2}$?

9. Is $3\frac{1}{3}$ a solution of the equation $\frac{9}{22}n=1\frac{1}{4}$?

10. Is $2\frac{4}{5}$ a solution of the equation $\frac{10}{21}z = \frac{2}{3}$?

11. Is $1\frac{22}{27}$ a solution of the equation $2\frac{1}{3} \div n = \frac{7}{9}$?

12. Is $2\frac{1}{4}$ a solution of the equation $3\frac{1}{6} \div m = \frac{27}{38}$?

13. Is $3\frac{2}{11}$ a solution of the equation $w \div \frac{7}{22} = 10$?

14. Is $7\frac{1}{5}$ a solution of the equation $z \div \frac{9}{10} = 8$?

15. Is $-\frac{2}{3}$ a solution of the equation $\frac{3x}{x - \frac{4}{5}} = 1\frac{4}{11}$?

16. Is $\frac{7}{8}$ a solution of the equation $\frac{4y}{y^2 - \frac{3}{4}} = 222$?

17. Is $\frac{4}{5}$ a solution of the equation $\frac{x}{2\frac{7}{15} - x} + x^2 = \frac{24}{25}$?

18. Is $-\frac{1}{3}$ a solution of the equation $x^2 + \frac{x}{\frac{2}{3}} = -\frac{7}{18}$?

Solve each of the following equations.

19. $\frac{x}{2}=7$

20. $y+\frac{1}{5}=\frac{1}{15}$

21. $x+\frac{1}{2}=\frac{1}{8}$

22. $\frac{y}{5}=9$

23. $2x=\frac{1}{4}$

24. $y-\frac{1}{5}=-\frac{1}{10}$

25. $x-\frac{1}{2}=-\frac{1}{6}$

26. $5y=\frac{1}{3}$

27. $\frac{1}{4}m=6$

28. $\frac{1}{9}n=3$

29. $-2=\frac{w}{6}$

30. $-9=\frac{h}{5}$

31. $-2k=-\frac{8}{13}$

32. $-3h=\frac{6}{11}$

33. $-\frac{m}{6}=-\frac{2}{9}$

34. $-\frac{n}{4}=-\frac{3}{8}$

35. $-\frac{3}{7}w=6$

36. $-\frac{2}{9}y=8$

37. $-\frac{2}{3}=\frac{2}{9}k$

38. $-\frac{3}{4}=\frac{3}{8}m$

39. $\frac{3}{7}a=-\frac{6}{11}$

40. $\frac{5}{9}z=-\frac{10}{13}$

41. $-\frac{2}{5}+n=\frac{3}{5}$

42. $-\frac{3}{7}+d=\frac{4}{7}$

43. $-4x = 18$

44. $-6y = 21$

45. $6w = 10$

46. $8m = 14$

47. $-\frac{5}{6}z = -\frac{7}{18}$

48. $-\frac{2}{9}h = \frac{8}{3}$

49. Verify the solution to example 12.

50. Verify the solution to example 13.

51. Verify the solution to example 14.

52. Verify the solution to example 15.

Translate each of the following expressions into an equation using mathematical symbols. Then, solve the equation and answer the question.

53. The product of a number and eight elevenths equals negative four sevenths. What is the number?

54. Seven twelfths added to a number is equal to five sixths. What is the number?

55. Four ninths subtracted from a number is negative two fifths. What is the number?

56. Twice a number equals negative three sevenths. What is the number?

57. Seven ninths more than a number is equal to eight. What is the number?

58. Four and two thirds increased by a number is seven and one third. What is the number?

59. Negative five eighths multiplied by a number is three fourths. What is the number?

60. The total of a number and seven eighths is equal to zero. What is the number?

61. A number minus one sixth is one twelfth. What is the number?

62. A number decreased by three fourths equals three eighths. What is the number?

63. The sum of a number and one half equals seven fourths. What is the number?

64. A number less four fifths equals negative two fifteenths. What is the number?

65. Seven tenths less than a number is negative seven thirtieths. What is the number?

66. Negative nine tenths times a number is equal to three fifths. What is the number?

67. A number plus two and three eighths is six and one eighth. What is the number?

68. The difference of a number and five sevenths is equal to three fourths. What is the number?

69. The quotient of a number and negative three equals eight. What is the number?

70. Three divided into a number is negative six. What is the number?

71. A number divided by seven is nine. What is the number?

72. A number divided by five is seventeen. What is the number?

Translate each of the following expressions into an equation using mathematical symbols. Then, solve the equation and answer the question.

73. The width of a rectangle is $\frac{1}{5}$ the length. If the width is 6 meters, what is the length?

74. Sarah is $\frac{1}{3}$ of a foot taller than Jim. If Sarah is $4\frac{1}{5}$ feet tall, how tall is Jim?

75. Ralph weighs $\frac{1}{4}$ of a kilogram less than Monty. If Ralph weighs $72\frac{1}{8}$ kilograms, how much does Monty weigh?

76. Bob's salary is $\frac{7}{8}$ as much as Judy's salary. If Bob's salary is $42,000, what is Judy's salary?

77. A lab technician working for Laboratory Associates Medical Enterprises makes $\frac{1}{12}$ as much money as the company's C.E.O. If the lab technician makes $23,000, how much does the C.E.O. make?

78. Janet's phone bill is $\frac{1}{6}$ her transportation bill. If her phone bill is $25, how much is her transportation bill?

79. The birch tree is $\frac{3}{5}$ of a yard taller than the pine tree. If the birch tree is $8\frac{1}{2}$ yards tall, how tall is the pine tree?

80. John can run a mile in $\frac{2}{5}$ of a minute less than Charlie. If John can run a mile in $5\frac{1}{4}$ minutes, how long does it take Charlie to run a mile?

81. Use the formula $R = \frac{p}{h}$ (where R is the rate of pay, p is the total amount of pay, and h is the number of hours worked), to find the total amount of pay a person makes if they earn $18 per hour and work for 7 hours.

82. Use the formula $R = \frac{p}{h}$ (where R is the rate of pay, p is the total amount of pay, and h is the number of hours worked), to find the total amount of pay a person makes if they earn $23 per hour and work for 8 hours.

FRACTIONS

Chapter Review

Section 1: The Least Common Multiple and The Greatest Common Factor

Review Exercises: Find the Least Common Multiple (LCM) of the group of numbers.

1. 21, 24, and 50

Find the Greatest Common Factor (GCF) of the group of numbers.

2. 30, 36, and 54

Solve the following application problem.

3. Oatmeal cookies come in boxes of 64 and boxes of 96. If the cookies are sealed in several plastic bags inside of the boxes, what's the largest amount of cookies that the manufacturer can put in each bag so that they can be used in either box?

Section 2: An Introduction to Fractions

Review Exercises: Identify the following number as a proper fraction, an improper fraction, or a mixed number.

4. $\frac{19}{1}$

Represent the shaded area in the group of drawings as an improper fraction and as a mixed number.

5.

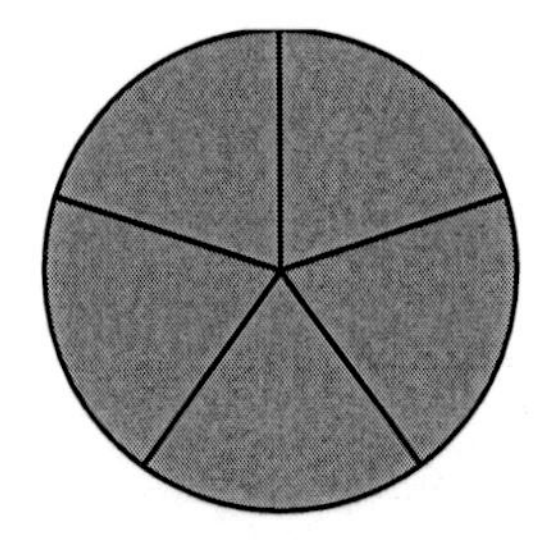 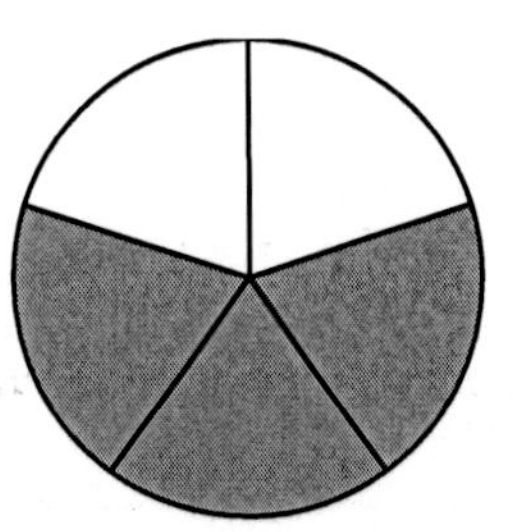

Change the improper fraction into a mixed number or whole number.

6. $\frac{42}{13}$

Change the mixed number into an improper fraction.

7. $6\frac{2}{7}$

Write an equivalent fraction that has the given new denominator.

8. $4 = \frac{?}{4}$

Determine whether the pair of fractions is equivalent by writing each fraction in lowest terms.

9. $\frac{45}{72}, \frac{32}{48}$

Section 3: Comparing Fractions

Review Exercises: For the following problem, draw a number line and graph the given number.

10. $1\frac{1}{6}$

Compare the two fractions by placing either $<$ or $>$ between them.

11. $\frac{8}{7} \quad \frac{9}{8}$

12. If there are 60 minutes in an hour, then 28 minutes is what fraction of an hour?

Section 4: Adding Fractions and Mixed Numbers

Review Exercises: Add.

13. $6\frac{5}{12}+2\frac{7}{9}$

Evaluate the expression.

14. Find $-\frac{8}{9}$ increased by $-\frac{4}{5}$.

Evaluate the expression $a+b+c$ for the given values of a, b, and c.

15. $a=\frac{1}{2}$; $b=\frac{9}{14}$; $c=-\frac{5}{7}$

Solve the following application problem.

16. If Pete eats $\frac{1}{3}$ of a cake, Bruce eats $\frac{1}{5}$ of the same cake, and Jim eats $\frac{4}{15}$ of the same cake, what fraction of the cake have they eaten altogether? Who ate the most cake?

17. What is the perimeter (in yards) of the triangle shown below?

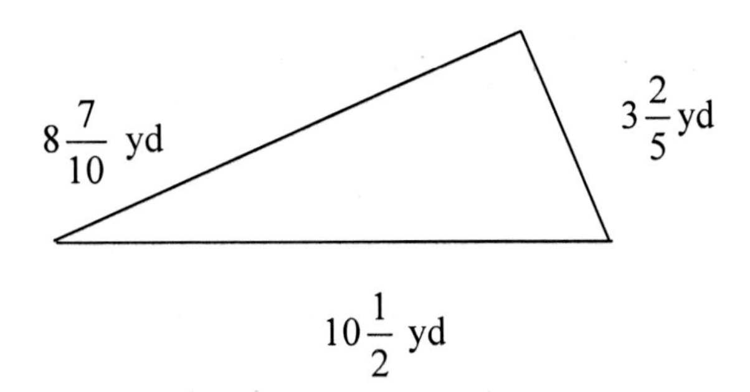

Section 5: Subtracting Fractions and Mixed Numbers

Review Exercises: Subtract.

18. $\frac{3}{4}-\left(-\frac{1}{6}\right)$

Evaluate the expression.

19. What is $3\frac{3}{4}$ subtracted from $5\frac{1}{7}$?

Evaluate the expression $a-b$ for the given values of a and b.

20. $a=-\frac{1}{2}$; $b=-\frac{5}{6}$

Solve the following application problems.

21. The dimensions of a table are $35\frac{1}{6}$ inches long by $26\frac{1}{3}$ inches wide. How much longer is the table than it is wide?

22. A local triathlon consists of running, swimming, and biking. The total distance traveled in the triathlon is $5\frac{2}{5}$ miles. If the running distance is $2\frac{1}{4}$ miles, and the swimming distance is $\frac{3}{8}$ of a mile, how far is the biking distance?

23. A given triangle contains interior angles $\angle M$, $\angle N$ and $\angle P$. If $\angle M = 117\frac{1}{6}°$ and $\angle N = 29\frac{1}{3}°$, then find $\angle P$.

Section 6: Multiplying Fractions and Mixed Numbers

Review Exercises: Multiply.

24. $7 \cdot \left(2\frac{5}{14}\right)$

25. $\left(4\frac{3}{8}\right) \cdot \frac{4}{21} \cdot \left(2\frac{2}{5}\right)$

Determine whether the following numbers are a pair of reciprocals (multiplicative inverses) or not.

26. $2\frac{1}{3}; \frac{3}{7}$

Find the reciprocal (multiplicative inverse) of the following number.

27. -3

Evaluate the expression.

28. Find the product of $-\frac{7}{24}$ and $2\frac{2}{5}$.

Evaluate the expression ab for the given values of a and b.

29. $a = -8$; $b = 4\frac{1}{8}$

Solve the following application problem.

30. It took Joey $1\frac{5}{8}$ hours to walk to the mall. Matt did it in $\frac{1}{2}$ of the time it took Joey. How long did Matt take?

Using the formula $A = \frac{1}{2}bh$, find the area of the following triangle.

31.

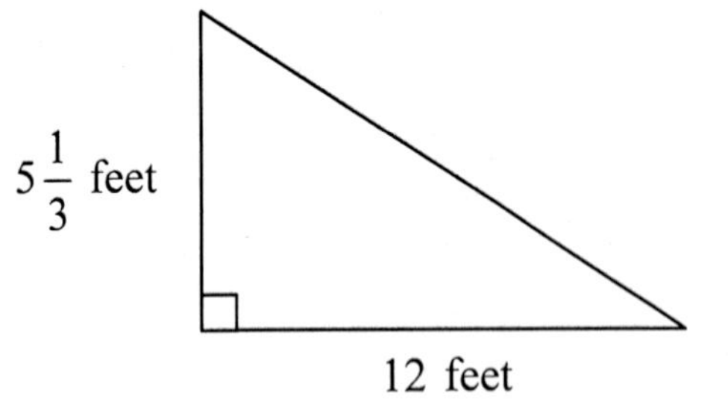

Section 7: Dividing Fractions and Mixed Numbers

Review Exercises: Divide.

32. $-\frac{7}{12} \div 0$

Evaluate the expression.

33. Find the quotient of $-\frac{2}{7}$ and $\frac{3}{14}$.

Evaluate the expression $a \div b$ for the given values of a and b.

34. $a = 6\frac{2}{9}$; $b = \frac{7}{18}$

Solve the following application problem.

35. How many ceramic tiles with dimensions of $2\frac{1}{4}$ inches by $2\frac{1}{4}$ inches are necessary to cover a bathroom counter with a total area of 405 square inches? (Assume no spacing between the tiles.)

Section 8: Order of Operations With Fractions

Review Exercises: Simplify the expression.

36. $\left(-\frac{5}{9}\right)^3 \cdot \left(1\frac{1}{5}\right)^2$

Simplify the complex fraction.

37. $\dfrac{4\frac{1}{4}-2\frac{2}{5}}{3\frac{1}{3}-1\frac{1}{2}}$

Simplify the expression.

38. $\frac{8}{15}-\frac{9}{20}\div\frac{3}{4}$

Evaluate each expression for the given values of the variables.

39. $\frac{x \div y}{y-x}$, where $x = 1\frac{1}{2}$ and $y = 2\frac{1}{3}$

40. hn^3p^2, where $h = -6$, $n = \frac{1}{3}$, and $p = 2\frac{1}{4}$

41. $\frac{z-x}{y^2}+\frac{y-x}{z^2}$, where $x = \frac{1}{2}$, $y = 1\frac{1}{3}$, and $z = 2$

Section 9: Solving Equations with Fractions

Review Exercises: Check the solution.

42. Is $3\frac{1}{8}$ a solution of the equation $7\frac{3}{7} = 4\frac{5}{14} + w$?

Solve each of the following equations.

43. $y + \frac{1}{6} = \frac{1}{12}$

44. $-\frac{5}{8}z = \frac{5}{16}$

Translate each of the following expressions into an equation using mathematical symbols. Then, solve the equation and answer the question.

45. A number decreased by one fifth equals seven tenths. What is the number?

46. Janet's phone bill is $\frac{1}{16}$ her food bill. If her phone bill is \$25, how much is her food bill?

47. Use the formula $R = \frac{p}{h}$ (where R is the rate of pay, p is the total amount of pay, and h is the number of hours worked) to find the total amount of pay a person makes if they earn \$15 per hour and work for 12 hours.

FRACTIONS

Chapter Test

Find the Least Common Multiple (LCM) of the group of numbers.

1. 14, 21, and 30

Find the Greatest Common Factor (GCF) of the group of numbers.

2. 14, 35, and 91

Change the improper fraction into a mixed number or whole number.

3. $\frac{63}{14}$

Change the mixed number into an improper fraction.

4. $3\frac{7}{11}$

Determine whether the pair of fractions is equivalent by writing each fraction in lowest terms.

5. $\frac{44}{77}, \frac{32}{56}$

Compare the two fractions by placing either $<$ or $>$ between them.

6. $\frac{11}{13} \quad \frac{17}{20}$

7. If there are 12 inches in a foot, then 9 inches is what fraction of a foot?

Add.

8. $3\frac{5}{9}+4\frac{7}{9}$

Evaluate the expression.

9. What is $\frac{7}{10}$ more than $-\frac{4}{5}$.

Evaluate the expression $m+p+w$ for the given values of *m, p,* and *w*.

10. $m=\frac{1}{3}$; $p=-\frac{7}{12}$; $w=\frac{4}{9}$

Evaluate the expression.

11. Find the difference of $11\frac{1}{6}$ and $5\frac{1}{3}$.

Solve the following application problems.

12. The dimensions of a picture frame are $36\frac{1}{4}$ inches long by $25\frac{1}{2}$ inches wide. How much longer is the picture frame than it is wide?

13. John jogs $12\frac{1}{2}$ miles every week to keep in shape. If John jogs $3\frac{2}{5}$ miles on Monday and $4\frac{1}{5}$ miles on Tuesday, how far does John still have to jog the rest of the week?

Multiply.

14. $\frac{14}{25} \cdot \left(3\frac{3}{4}\right) \cdot \frac{10}{21}$

Evaluate the expression.

15. What is $3\frac{1}{8}$ times $-\frac{4}{5}$.

Evaluate the expression ab for the given values of a and b.

16. $a = 7$; $b = -1\frac{6}{7}$

Solve the following application problem.

17. If Tom can build $5\frac{1}{2}$ doghouses in 1 day, how many doghouses can Tom build in $\frac{1}{3}$ of a day?

Using the formula $A = \frac{1}{2}bh$, find the area of the following triangle.

18.

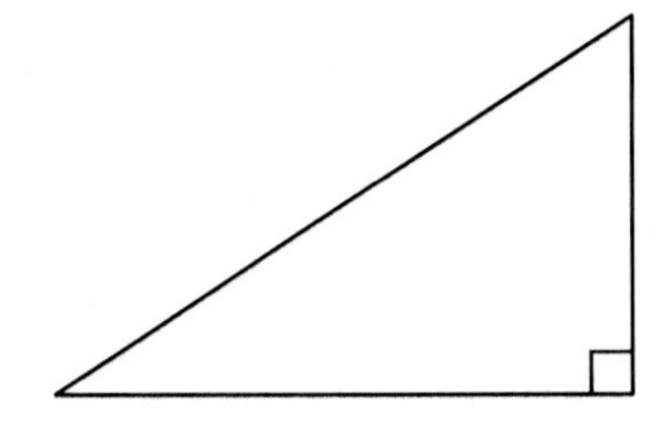

$10\frac{1}{4}$ inches

16 inches

Divide.

19. $0 \div \left(-\frac{4}{9}\right)$

Evaluate the expression.

20. What is the quotient of $-\frac{3}{8}$ and $\frac{7}{12}$?

Evaluate the expression $a \div b$ for the given values of a and b.

21. $a = 7\frac{5}{7};\ b = \frac{9}{14}$

Solve the following application problem.

22. How many pieces of carpet with dimensions of 3 feet by $4\frac{1}{4}$ feet are necessary to cover a living room floor with a total area of 408 square feet?

Simplify the complex fraction.

23. $$\frac{\left(\frac{1}{5}\right)^2 - \frac{3}{10}}{1\frac{3}{4} + 3\frac{1}{8}}$$

Simplify the expression.

24. $\left(\frac{3}{4}\right)^2 + \left(8 - \frac{7}{8}\right) \div \left(4\frac{3}{4}\right)$

Evaluate each expression for the given values of the variables.

25. $\frac{x-y}{xy}$, where $x = 3\frac{1}{4}$ and $y = 2\frac{1}{2}$

26. n^3p^2, where $n = \frac{2}{7}$ and $p = 3\frac{1}{2}$

Check the solution.

27. Is $4\frac{3}{4}$ a solution of the equation $8\frac{5}{12} = x + 3\frac{2}{3}$?

Solve the following equation.

28. $\frac{4}{9}x = -\frac{8}{45}$

Translate the expression into an equation using mathematical symbols. Then, solve the equation and answer the question.

29. A number increased by two sevenths equals five fourteenths. What is the number?

30. Use the formula $R = \frac{p}{h}$ (where R is the rate of pay, p is the total amount of pay, and h is the number of hours worked) to find the total amount of pay a person makes if they earn \$26 per hour and work for 9 hours.

CHAPTER 4

DECIMAL NUMBERS

Section 1: An Introduction to Decimal Numbers

Decimal Numbers
Place Value
Writing Decimal Numbers in Words
Changing Decimal Numbers into Fractions or Mixed Numbers
Changing Fractions or Mixed Numbers into Decimal Numbers
Inequalities
The Number Line
Rounding
Applications

Section 2: Adding and Subtracting Decimal Numbers

Addition of Decimal Numbers
Subtraction of Decimal Numbers
Evaluating Variable Expressions
Applications

Section 3: Multiplying Decimal Numbers

Multiplication of Decimal Numbers
Multiplying by Powers of 10
Evaluating Variable Expressions
Applications

Section 4: Dividing Decimal Numbers

Division of Decimal Numbers
Division by Powers of 10
Evaluating Variable Expressions
Applications

Section 5: Converting and Comparing Fractions and Decimal Numbers

Converting a Fraction or Mixed Number into a Decimal Number
Repeating Decimal Numbers
Comparing Fractions and Decimals
Applications

Section 6: Order of Operations with Decimal Numbers

Rules of Order of Operations
Evaluating Variable Expressions using Order of Operations
Applications

Section 7: Solving Equations with Decimal Numbers

The Addition Property of Equality
The Subtraction Property of Equality
The Multiplication Property of Equality
The Division Property of Equality
Applications

Section 8: Estimating

Section 9: Roots

Square Roots
Perfect Squares
Evaluating Variable Expressions
Other Roots
Applications
The Pythagorean Theorem

Section 10: Real Numbers

Rational Numbers
Irrational Numbers
Real Numbers
Graphing Real Numbers
Applications

DECIMAL NUMBERS

Section 1: An Introduction to Decimal Numbers

Steven called two different automotive shops to get an estimate on how long it would take to fix his car. The first shop's estimate was $3\frac{3}{4}$ hours. The second shop's estimate was 3.75 hours. Were the estimates for the same amount of time? To answer this question, let's review some of what we've already learned about mixed numbers. A mixed number is made up of two types of numbers: a whole number part, and a fraction part. The fraction part represents a number less than one. In the mixed number $3\frac{3}{4}$, the whole number part is 3 and the fraction part is $\frac{3}{4}$.

Whole Number Part ⟶ $3\frac{3}{4}$ ⟵ **Fraction Part**

The number 3.75 is called a **decimal number**. A decimal number is also made up of two types of numbers, a whole number part, and a decimal part. The decimal part represents a number less than one. The two parts of a decimal number are separated by a dot called a **decimal point**. In the decimal number 3.75, 3 is the whole number part and 0.75 is the decimal part.

Note: When a decimal number contains no whole number part, we put a zero in front of the decimal point. So, .75 is written as 0.75, in order to draw our attention to the decimal point.

Whole Number Part ⟶ **3.75** ⟵ **Decimal Part**

Decimal Point

Since both the mixed number and the decimal number contain a 3 as the whole number part, does the fraction part $\frac{3}{4}$ equal the decimal part 0.75? The best way to compare these two numbers is to have them written in the same form, both as fractions or both as decimal numbers. We can change a fraction into a decimal number, or a decimal number into a fraction. To change a decimal number into a fraction, we need to know the decimal number's place value. We will come back to this problem after a discussion of placeholders similar to that in Chapter 1.

The chart below shows the names of the place values on both sides of the decimal point. To the left of the decimal point, the name of each place value is the same as it was in Chapter 1 when we limited our study to whole numbers. To the right of the decimal point, the name of each place value corresponds to the denominator that is created by changing the decimal number in that column into a fraction.

Hundred-thousands	***Ten-thousands***	***Thousands***	***Hundreds***	***Tens***	***Ones***	***Tenths***	***Hundredths***	***Thousandths***	***Ten-thousandths***	***Hundred-thousandths***	***Millionths***
1	**5**	**4,**	**2**	**0**	**5 .**	**3**	**7**	**9**	**1**	**6**	**8**

In the chart above, the 3 is in the ***tenths*** column, so we would say that there are three tenths. Three tenths written as a decimal number is 0.3. Three tenths written as a fraction is $\frac{3}{10}$. Note that the numerator is a whole number and the denominator is a **ten**.

In the chart above, the 7 is in the ***hundredths*** column, so we would say that there are seven hundredths. Seven hundredths written as a decimal number is 0.07. Seven hundredths written as a fraction is $\frac{7}{100}$. Note that the numerator is a whole number and the denominator is a **hundred**.

In the chart above, the 9 is in the ***thousandths*** column, so we would say that there are nine thousandths. Nine thousandths written as a decimal number is 0.009. Nine thousandths written as a fraction is $\frac{9}{1{,}000}$. Note that the numerator is a whole number and the denominator is a **thousand**.

At the beginning of Chapter 1, when we looked at how to write numbers using words, we were careful to avoid the use of the word "**and**". This was because "**and**" is used to indicate the location of the decimal point in a decimal number. For instance, the number 127 is written in words as one hundred twenty-seven. On the other hand, the number 1.27 is written in words as one and twenty-seven hundredths.

Note: not only are the decimal number 1.27 and the mixed number $1\frac{27}{100}$ equal, but both can be described in words as one and twenty-seven hundredths.

Example 1: Write the decimal number 620.1 in words.

Solution: Six hundred twenty and one tenth

Example 2: Write the decimal number 6.201 in words.

Solution: Six and two hundred one thousandths

Example 3: Write the decimal number 8,010.0073 in words.

Solution: Eight thousand, ten and seventy-three ten-thousandths

A whole number that is written out using any combination of the digits 0 through 9 is said to be in **standard form.** The same is true of decimal numbers.

Example 4: Write eighteen and four hundredths as a decimal number in standard form.

Solution: 18.04

Example 5: Write thirty-eight thousand, four hundred seven and seven hundred four thousandths as a decimal number in standard form.

Solution: 38,407.704

Example 6: Write seven hundred fifty-nine million, five thousand, seventeen and three thousand, forty-two ten-thousandths as a decimal number in standard form.

Solution: 759,005,017.3042

Referring to the place value chart you saw earlier, consider the number made from two consecutive digits to the right of the decimal point, the number 0.37, for example. To change this decimal number into a fraction, rewrite it as a whole number and place it in the numerator. Then use the denominator that corresponds to the farthest digit to the right that is being included.

For the number 0.37, the 7 is farthest to the right and the 7 is in the ***hundredths*** column, so 0.37 written as a fraction is $\frac{37}{100}$. That is, $0.37 = \frac{37}{100}$.

For the number 0.379, the 9 is farthest to the right and the 9 is in the ***thousandths*** column, so 0.379 written as a fraction is $\frac{379}{1{,}000}$. That is, $0.379 = \frac{379}{1{,}000}$.

For the number 0.3791, the 1 is farthest to the right and the 1 is in the ***ten-thousandths*** column, so 0.3791 written as a fraction is $\frac{3{,}791}{10{,}000}$. That is, $0.3791 = \frac{3{,}791}{10{,}000}$.

We are now ready to answer the question we asked previously, that is, does the fraction part $\frac{3}{4}$ equal the decimal part 0.75?

Using your knowledge of the position of the placeholders, for the number 0.75, the 5 is farthest to the right and the 5 is in the ***hundredths*** column.

So 0.75 written as a fraction is $\frac{75}{100}$, that is, $0.75 = \frac{75}{100}$.

Using the techniques we learned in Chapter 3 about reducing a fraction to lowest terms,

$\frac{75}{100} = \frac{3 \cdot 5 \cdot 5}{2 \cdot 2 \cdot 5 \cdot 5} = \frac{3 \cdot \overset{1}{\cancel{5}} \cdot \overset{1}{\cancel{5}}}{2 \cdot 2 \cdot \underset{1}{\cancel{5}} \cdot \underset{1}{\cancel{5}}} = \frac{3}{4}$. Since $0.75 = \frac{75}{100}$ and $\frac{75}{100} = \frac{3}{4}$, then $0.75 = \frac{3}{4}$ and

$3\frac{3}{4}\text{ hours} = 3.75\text{ hours}$. So, the estimated times were the same amount.

Example 7: Change the decimal number 0.0041 into a fraction.

Solution: Rewrite 0.0041 as the whole number **41**. This becomes the numerator of the fraction.

For the number 0.0041, the 1 is farthest to the right and the 1 is in the ***ten-thousandths*** column.

Therefore, the denominator becomes **10,000**.

The entire fraction is $\frac{41}{10{,}000}$. Thus, $0.0041 = \frac{41}{10{,}000}$.

Example 8: Change the decimal number 4.07 into a mixed number.

Solution: The whole number part of 4.07, which is the 4, becomes the whole number part of the mixed number answer. The decimal part of 4.07, which is the 0.07, needs to be changed into the fraction part of the mixed number. To change 0.07 into a fraction, rewrite 0.07 as the whole number **7**. This becomes the numerator of the fraction.

For the number 4.07, the 7 is farthest to the right and the 7 is in the ***hundredths*** column.

Therefore, the denominator becomes **100**, and the fraction part becomes $\frac{7}{100}$.

The entire mixed number is $4\frac{7}{100}$. Thus, $4.07 = 4\frac{7}{100}$.

Let's look at another way of changing a decimal number into a fraction. By looking at several decimal numbers and their fraction equivalents, we can establish a pattern.

$0.37 = \frac{37}{100}$ The decimal number has **2** digits to the right of the decimal point, the numerator of the fraction is a whole number, and the denominator of the fraction is a 1 followed by **2** zeros.

$0.379 = \frac{379}{1{,}000}$ The decimal number has **3** digits to the right of the decimal point, the numerator of the fraction is a whole number, and the denominator of the fraction is a 1 followed by **3** zeros.

Example 9: Change the decimal number 0.069 into a fraction.

Solution: Rewrite 0.069 as the whole number **69**. This becomes the numerator of the fraction.

0.069 has **3** digits to the right of the decimal point. The denominator of the fraction is a 1 followed by **3** zeros, which is **1,000**.

The entire fraction is $\frac{69}{1{,}000}$. Thus, $0.069 = \frac{69}{1{,}000}$.

Another way of looking at this process is as follows:

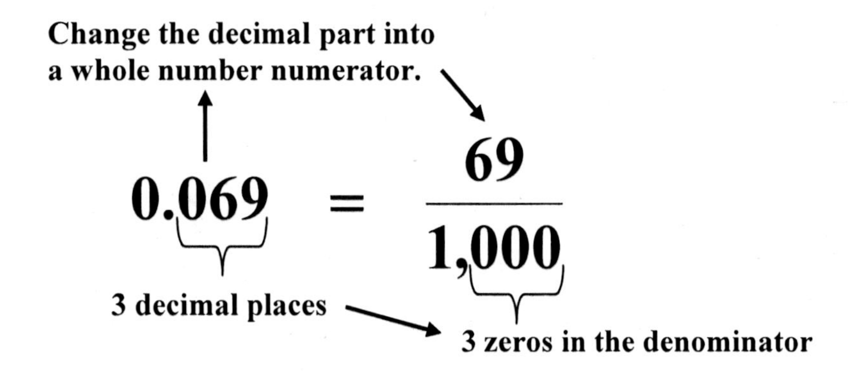

Example 10: Change the decimal number 3.71 into a mixed number.

Solution:

Change the decimal part into a whole number numerator.

$$3.71 = 3\frac{71}{100}$$

2 decimal places → **2 zeros in the denominator**

Note: The whole number part of decimal number becomes the whole number part of the mixed number.

When we change a decimal number into a fraction, the denominator is always a power of 10, such as 100 or 1,000 etc. It's easy to change a fraction into a decimal number when the fraction has a denominator that is a power of 10. First, however, let's talk about the location of an **implied decimal point**. A whole number has an implied decimal point to the right of its smallest place value. For example, the number forty-six can be written as 46 or as 46., but either way the number has the same value.

Implied decimal point

We previously established that $0.37 = \frac{37}{100}$. So, $0.37 = \frac{37.}{100}$.

Since $0.37 = \frac{37.}{100}$, then $\frac{37.}{100} = 0.37$ is also true.

The net result is that when dividing 37. by 100 (which is a 1 followed by **2** zeros) the decimal point gets moved **2** places to the left which creates the decimal number 0.37.

$$\frac{\mathbf{37.}}{\mathbf{100}} = \mathbf{.37} = \mathbf{0.37}$$

2 1

2 zeros

Move the decimal point 2 places to the left.

Implied decimal point

We previously established that $0.379 = \frac{379}{1{,}000}$. So, $0.379 = \frac{379.}{1{,}000}$.

Since $0.379 = \frac{379.}{1{,}000}$, then $\frac{379.}{1{,}000} = 0.379$ is also true.

The net result is that when dividing 379. by 1,000 (which is a 1 followed by **3** zeros) the decimal point gets moved **3** places to the left which creates the decimal number 0.379.

$$\frac{\mathbf{379.}}{\mathbf{1{,}000}} = \mathbf{.379} = \mathbf{0.379}$$

3 2 1

3 zeros

Move the decimal point 3 places to the left.

Example11: Change the fraction $\frac{83}{10,000}$ into a decimal number.

Solution:

Rewrite the numerator with the implied decimal point.

$$\frac{83}{10,000} = \frac{83.}{10,000}$$

Change the whole number in the numerator into a decimal number.

$$\frac{83.}{10,000} = 0.0083$$

4 3 2 1

4 zeros → **Move the decimal point 4 places to the left.**

Final answer: $\frac{83}{10,000} = 0.0083$

Example 12: Change the mixed number $6\frac{29}{100}$ into a decimal number.

Solution:

Rewrite the numerator of the fraction part with the implied decimal point.

$$6\frac{29}{100} = 6\frac{29.}{100}$$

Change the whole number in the numerator into the decimal part of the decimal number.

$$6\frac{29.}{100} = 6.29$$

2 1

2 zeros → **Move the decimal point 2 places to the left.**

Note: The whole number part of the mixed number becomes the whole number part of the decimal number.

Final answer: $6\frac{29}{100} = 6.29$

Let's look at another way to change a fraction into a decimal number. By saying the name of the fraction we can determine how to write it as a decimal number. For example, $\frac{27}{100}$ is twenty-seven ***hundredths***. This tells us that the digit farthest to the right in the numerator of the fraction will be the digit in the ***hundredths*** place of the decimal number.

Twenty-seven *hundredths* ⟶ $\frac{27}{100} = 0.27$

***hundredths* place**

Example 13: Change the fraction $\frac{51}{10{,}000}$ into a decimal number.

Solution: $\frac{51}{10{,}000}$ is fifty-one ***ten-thousandths***. This tells us that the digit farthest to the right in the numerator of the fraction will be the digit in the ***ten-thousandths*** place of the decimal number.

Fifty-one *ten-thousandths* ⟶ $\frac{51}{10{,}000} = 0.0051$

***ten-thousandths* place**

Example 14: Change the mixed number $17\frac{9}{10}$ into a decimal number.

Solution: $17\frac{9}{10}$ is seventeen and nine ***tenths***. This tells us that the digit farthest to the right in the numerator of the fraction will be the digit in the ***tenths*** place of the decimal number.

Seventeen and nine *tenths* ⟶ $17\frac{9}{10} = 17.9$

***tenths* place**

Note: The whole number part of the mixed number becomes the whole number part of the decimal number.

Inequality symbols such as $<$ or $>$ can be used to compare decimal numbers in the same way that they are used to compare whole numbers, integers, or fractions. Eighteen dollars and four cents is more money than just eighteen dollars. That is $\$18.04 > \$18$. However, suppose we want to compare 18.003 and 18.03. Write both numbers such that they have the same number of digits to the right of the decimal point. Can we do this without changing the value of either number? Consider this example. Is \$18 the same amount as \$18.00? Of course it is. We can add zeros on the right side of the decimal point if they are also to the right of the smallest place value currently represented. So, in comparing 18.003 and 18.03, write them as 18.003 and 18.030. Next, line the numbers up vertically by their decimal points.

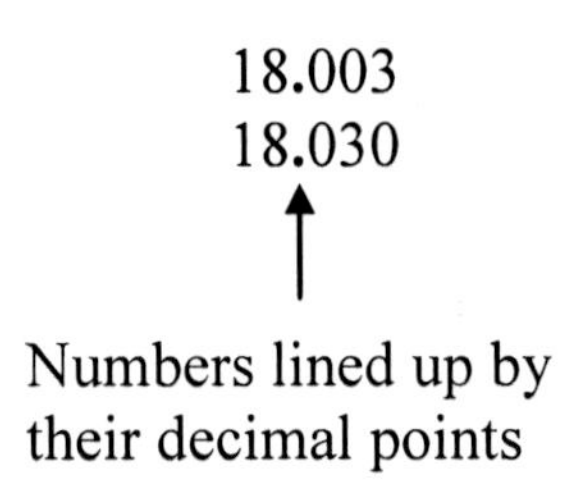

Note: By lining the numbers up by their decimal points they are also lined up by the same place values.

Now, starting at the left end, compare each place value until one is reached where the numbers are not identical. At this place value, the number with the larger digit is the larger number; likewise, the number with the smaller digit is the smaller number.

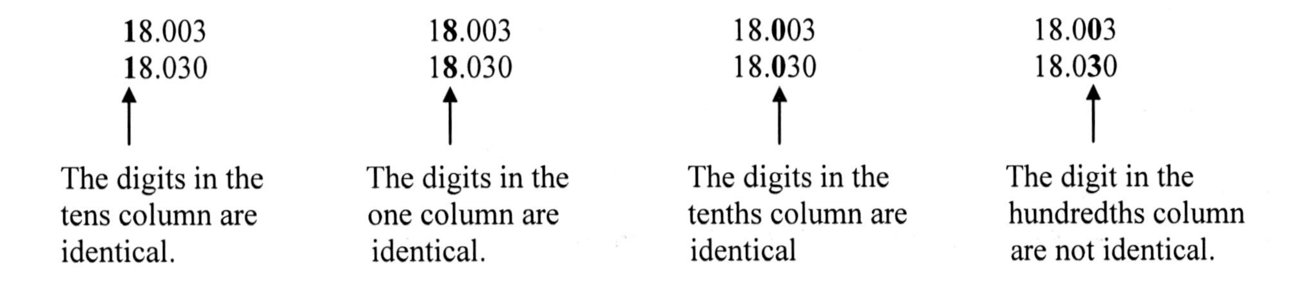

Since $0 < 3$, then $18.003 < 18.030$.

Example 15: Compare the following decimal numbers, and then write them in order from smallest to largest: 62.097, 629.7, 62.907, and 602.97

Solution: Rewrite each decimal number such that it has the same number of digits to the right of the decimal point.

62.097 stays the same.

629.7 becomes 629.700.

62.907 stays the same.

602.97 becomes 602.970.

Line the numbers up vertically by their decimal points. Starting at the left end, compare each place value until one is reached where the numbers are not identical.

```
 62.097
629.700
 62.907
602.970
↑
```

The digits in the hundreds column are not identical. The two numbers that contain a 6 in the hundreds column are larger that the two numbers that have no digit in this column. Based on this information we will split the numbers into two groups. 62.097 and 62.907 are in the group of smaller numbers and 629.700 and 602.970 are in the group of larger numbers. Since our goal is to write the numbers in order from smallest to largest, we need to find out which number is smallest. We will compare the two numbers 62.097 and 62.907.

Start at the left end, and compare each place value until one is reached where the numbers are not identical.

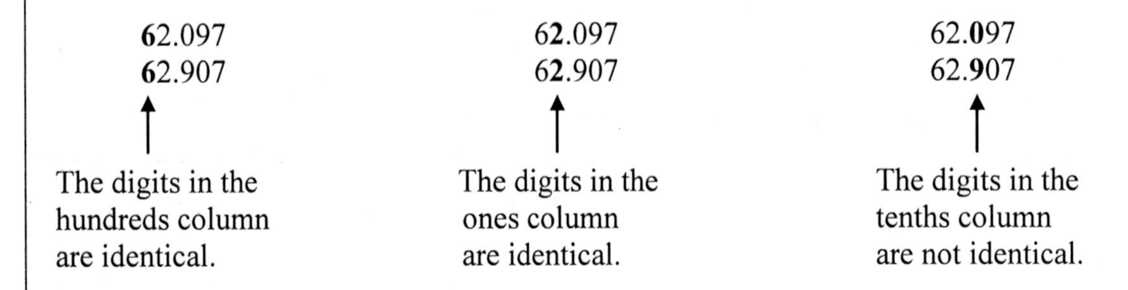

Since $0 < 9$, then $62.097 < 62.907$.

Now we need to compare 629.700 and 602.970. Start at the left end, and compare each place value until one is reached where the numbers are not identical.

```
629.700        629.700
602.970        602.970
↑               ↑
```

The digits in the hundreds column are identical.

The digits in the tens column are not identical.

Since $2 > 0$, the top number is greater than the bottom number. That is $629.700 > 602.970$ or $602.970 < 629.700$.

So, $62.097 < 62.907 < 602.970 < 629.700$. The decimal numbers written in order from smallest to largest are **62.097, 62.907, 602.97, and 629.7**.

Decimal numbers can be graphed on a number line in much the way that whole numbers, integers, and fractions are graphed. The scale on the bottom of the number line is determined by the smallest placeholder in the numbers that are to be graphed. For instance, when graphing the decimal numbers 0.4, 0.8, and 1.1 we use a scale that is divided up into units of 0.1 or one tenth.

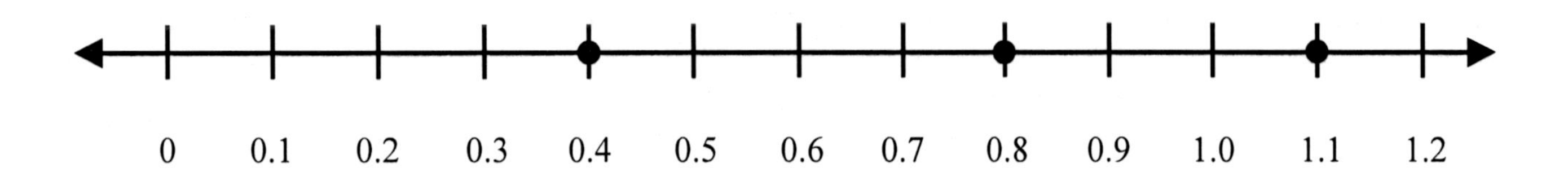

When graphing the decimal numbers 0.02, 0.07, and 0.12 we use a scale that is divided up into units of 0.01 or one hundredth.

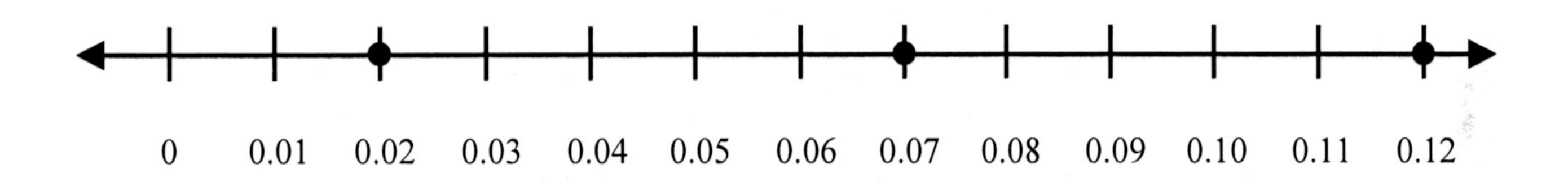

Note: As with integers and fractions, decimal numbers can be positive or negative.

Example 16: Graph the following decimal numbers: -0.5, 0.6, 0.2, and -0.1

Solution: Use a scale that is divided up into units of 0.1 or one tenth and that extends at least as far as -0.5 to the left and at least as far as 0.6 to the right.

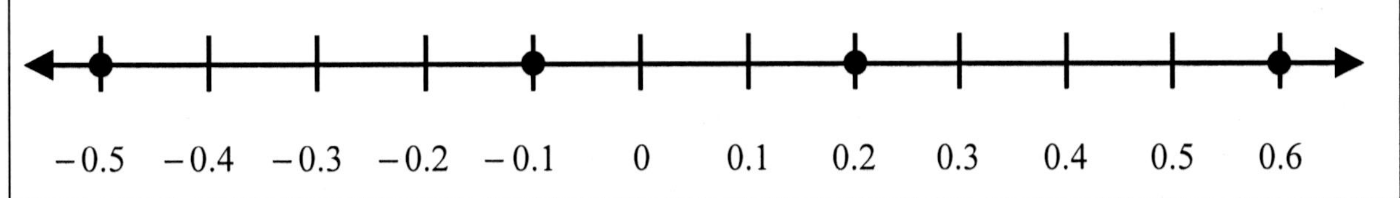

Example 17: By using a number line, determine the correct inequality symbol, $>$ or $<$, to place between the pair of decimal numbers -0.3 and -0.7.

Solution: Use a scale that is divided up into units of 0.1 or one tenth and that extends at least as far as -0.7 to the left and at least as far as -0.3 to the right.

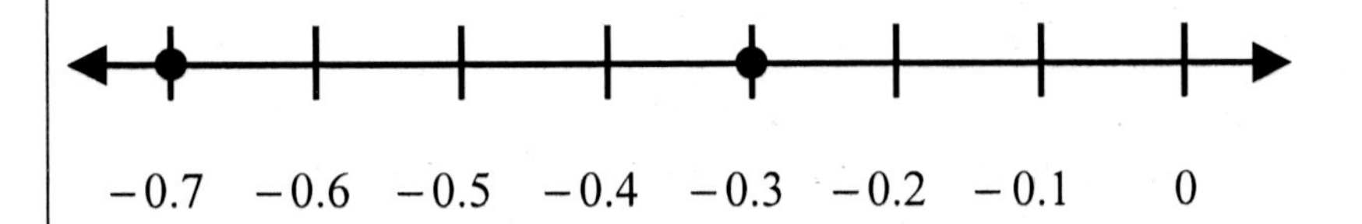

Since numbers get larger to the right on the number line, $-0.3 > -0.7$.

Sometimes it is convenient to use **rounding** on decimal numbers, such as when adding up the cost of items in a grocery store, to make sure you don't exceed your budget.

Rounding to the left of the decimal point

When rounding a decimal number to a certain place value on the left side of the decimal point, all digits to the right of that place value become zeros until reaching the decimal point. At that point, (no pun intended), all digits to the right of the decimal point should be removed. In other words, any decimal number that is rounded at a place value to the left of the decimal point should be written as a whole number.

Rounding to the right of the decimal point

When rounding a decimal number to a certain place value on the right side of the decimal point, all digits to the right of that place value should be removed.

Example 18: Round 2,763.42 to the nearest hundred.

Solution: Place value to be rounded

↓

2,763.42

↑

First digit to the right

The first digit to the right of the hundreds place value is a 6. Since 6 is greater than 5, we will round up. Consequently, the 7 in the hundreds place will increase in value by one (it becomes an 8). All digits to the right of that place value become zeros until reaching the decimal point. At that point, all digits to the right of the decimal point should be removed.

2,763.42 rounded to the nearest hundred becomes **2,800**.

Example 19: Round 16.0973 to the nearest tenth.

Solution: Place value to be rounded

↓

16.0973

↑

First digit to the right

The first digit to the right of the tenths place value is a 9. Since 9 is greater than 5, we will round up. Consequently, the 0 in the tenths place will increase in value by one (it becomes a 1). All digits to the right of that place value should be removed.

16.0973 rounded to the nearest tenth becomes **16.1**.

Example 20: Round 423.2678 to the nearest whole number.

Solution: To round a number to the nearest whole number, round at the ones place value.

Place value to be rounded

423.2678

First digit to the right

The first digit to the right of the ones place value is a 2. Since 2 is less than 5, we will round down. Consequently, the 3 in the ones place will remain unchanged. All digits to the right of the decimal point should be removed.

423.2678 rounded to the nearest whole number becomes **423**.

Example 21: Round 67.398 to the nearest hundredth.

Solution: Place value to be rounded

67.398

First digit to the right

The first digit to the right of the hundredths place value is an 8. Since 8 is greater than 5, we will round up. Consequently, the 9 in the hundredths place will increase in value by one. However, this would create a 10 in the hundredths place, so we put a 0 in the hundredths place and carry a 1 over to the tenths place. This makes the tenths place a 4. Now we have a 4 in the tenths place, a 0 in the hundredths place and all remaining digits to the right are removed.

67.398 rounded to the nearest hundredth becomes **67.40**.

Note: Even though the digit to the far right of the answer is a 0, it should not be removed because we are to give an answer that is to the nearest hundredth. Therefore, in this case, the 0 is necessary.

Applications

Example 22: In converting American units of measure into metric units of measure, 1 inch is equal to 2.54 centimeters. Round 2.54 centimeters to the nearest tenth of a centimeter.

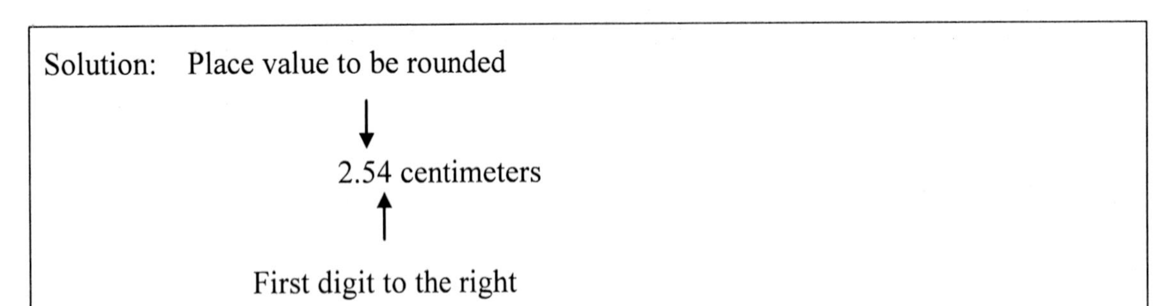

The first digit to the right of the tenths place value is a 4. Since 4 is less than 5, we will round down. Consequently, the 5 in the tenths place will remain unchanged. All digits to the right of that place value should be removed.

2.54 centimeters rounded to the nearest tenth of a centimeter becomes **2.5 centimeters**.

Decimal numbers often appear on charts and graphs. The following is an example of this.

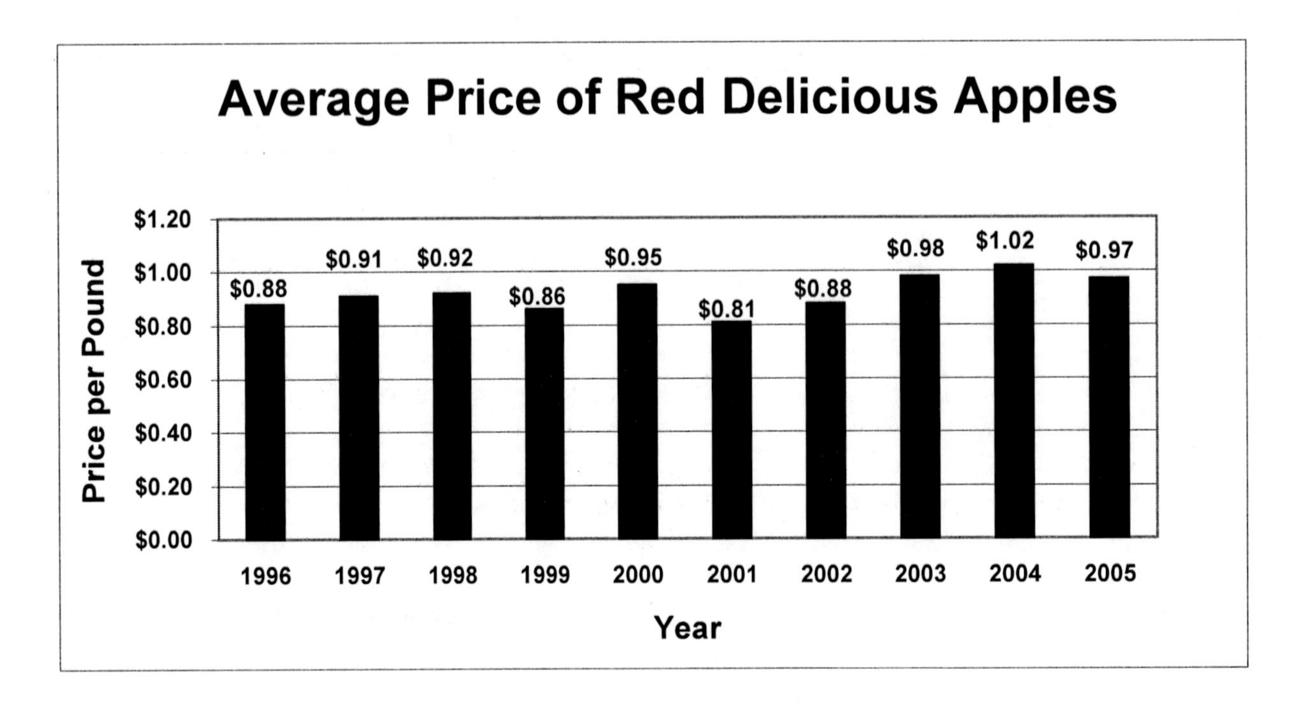

Example 23: Based on the bar graph of the average price of red delicious apples, in which years was the price greater than $0.88 per pound and less than $0.97 per pound?

Solution: The amounts of money that are greater than $0.88 and less than $0.97 are $0.91, which corresponds to 1997, $0.92, which corresponds to 1998, and $0.95, which corresponds to 2000. Consequently, the answer is 1997,1998, and 2000.

Section 1 exercises.

1. For the number 324.87615 what digit is in the hundredths column?

2. For the number 307,968.0245 what number is in the thousands column?

3. For the number 12,089.124 what number is in the hundreds column?

4. For the number 976.84315 what digit is in the tenths column?

5. For the number 23,968,250.00045783 what digit is in the millionths column?

6. For the number 1,442.78034 what digit is in the thousandths column?

7. For the number 671.93 what number is in the tens column?

8. For the number 762.5348 what digit is in the hundredths column?

9. For the number 823.0941 what digit is in the tenths column?

10. For the number 324,324.16789 what digit is in the ten-thousandths column?

11. For the number 2,687.49375 what digit is in the thousandths column?

12. For the number 7,328.79 what number is in the tens column?

13. For the number 82,384.583972 what digit is in the ten-thousandths column?

14. For the number 742.247 what number is in the hundreds column?

15. For the number 12,387.0089 what number is in the thousands column?

16. For the number 2,457,952.6843791 what digit is in the hundred-thousandths column?

Write each number in words.

17. 46.3 **18.** 8.71 **19.** 407.035 **20.** 3,200.0411

21. 28,015.071 **22.** 457,091.32 **23.** 300.03 **24.** 7,077.077

25. 60.0708 **26.** 0.9 **27.** 0.4385 **28.** 0.7269

Write each number as a decimal number in standard form.

29. seventy-three and sixteen thousandths **30.** four hundred and three hundredths

31. ten thousand, five and five ten-thousandths **32.** thirty-two and six tenths

33. seventeen and one hundred twenty-three thousandths **34.** sixty-two millionths

35. thirty-eight and one hundred-thousandth **36.** nine hundred twelve thousandths

37. two tenths **38.** eighty-nine hundredths

39. six thousand, four and seventeen ten-thousandths

40. eight hundred ninety-four and five hundred-thousandths

Change each decimal number into a fraction or mixed number.

41. 9.7 **42.** 0.27 **43.** 0.43 **44.** 2.1

45. 5.01 **46.** 7.0033 **47.** 0.0009 **48.** 0.731

49. 0.419 **50.** 7.09 **51.** 341.83 **52.** 0.3

Change each fraction or mixed number into a decimal number.

53. $\frac{9}{10}$ **54.** $4\frac{1}{10}$ **55.** $5\frac{3}{100}$ **56.** $\frac{93}{1,000}$

57. $\frac{409}{1,000}$ **58.** $\frac{7}{100}$ **59.** $\frac{63}{10,000}$ **60.** $98\frac{91}{100}$

61. $72\frac{73}{100}$ **62.** $7\frac{77}{10,000}$ **63.** $3\frac{81}{1,000}$ **64.** $\frac{487}{1,000}$

Compare each pair of numbers by putting the correct symbol $<$, $>$, or $=$ between them.

65. 7.01 7.10 **66.** 6.90 6.09 **67.** 81.2 81.20

68. 2.703 2.073 **69.** 42.036 42.306 **70.** 97.50 97.5

71. 7.008 7.0008 **72.** 6.0005 6.005 **73.** 10.42 10.246

74. 4.97083 4.9807 **75.** 50.6 56.05 **76.** 6.42 6.24

Compare each group of numbers, and then write them in order from smallest to largest.

77. 4.68 0.4068 0.68 **78.** 0.9087 9.87 9.087

79. 0.409 0.0049 0.49 0.049 **80.** 7.30 0.073 37.03 0.0703

81. 0.08 0.008 0.0081 0.079 **82.** 42.09 41.9 42.19 41.01

Graph each set of numbers on a number line.

83. -0.6, 0.3, 0.1, -0.4

84. 0.4, -0.1, -0.3, 0.6

85. -1.1, -0.1, -0.7

86. -0.8, -1.0, -0.2

87. -0.04, 0.01, -0.11

88. -0.03, 0.04, -0.07

By using a number line, determine the correct inequality symbol > or < to place between each pair of numbers.

89. 0.3, -0.4

90. -0.2, 0.5

91. -1.2, -1.6

92. -0.8, -0.6

93. -0.12, -0.09

94. -0.11, -0.07

Round each number to the given place value.

95. 357.016 Hundredths

96. 7,230.04545 Thousandths

97. 374,937.002 Thousands

98. 24,756.829 Tens

99. 0.00080194 Millionths

100. 21.349958 Hundred-thousandths

101. 842.6391 Whole number

102. 34,837.092 Hundreds

103. 10.95 Tenths

104. 4,961.38 Whole number

105. 3,483.012 Thousandths

106. 610.789454 Ten-thousandths

107. 3,475.984 Tens

108. 718.203 Hundredths

109. 643.8799673 Ten-thousandths

110. 2,470.0056 Thousands

111. 2,398.9087 Hundreds

112. 17.5 Tenths

Applications

113. In converting metric units into American units, 1 Liter is approximately 0.264 gallon. Round 0.264 gallon to the nearest tenth of a gallon.

114. In converting metric units into American units, 1 gram is approximately 0.035 ounce. Round 0.035 ounce to the nearest tenth of an ounce.

115. In converting American units into metric units, 1 pint is approximately 0.473 Liter. Round 0.473 Liter to the nearest hundredth of a Liter.

116. In converting American units into metric units, 1 gallon is approximately 3.785 Liters. Round 3.785 Liters to the nearest hundredth of a Liter.

117. In converting American units into metric units, 1 pound is approximately 0.454 kilogram. Round 0.454 kilogram to the nearest whole kilogram.

118. In converting metric units into American units, 1 Liter is approximately 33.8 fluid ounces. Round 33.8 fluid ounces to the nearest whole fluid ounce.

119. An insurance company awards student drivers "good student" discounts if their G.P.A. (grade point average) is 3.0 or better. If students were allowed to round their G.P.A. to the nearest tenth, would a student with a G.P.A. of 2.984 be eligible to receive a "good student" discount?

120. To pass a math class, students must get a 73% or better. If students were allowed to round their grade to the nearest tenth of a percent, would a student with a 72.54% pass the class?

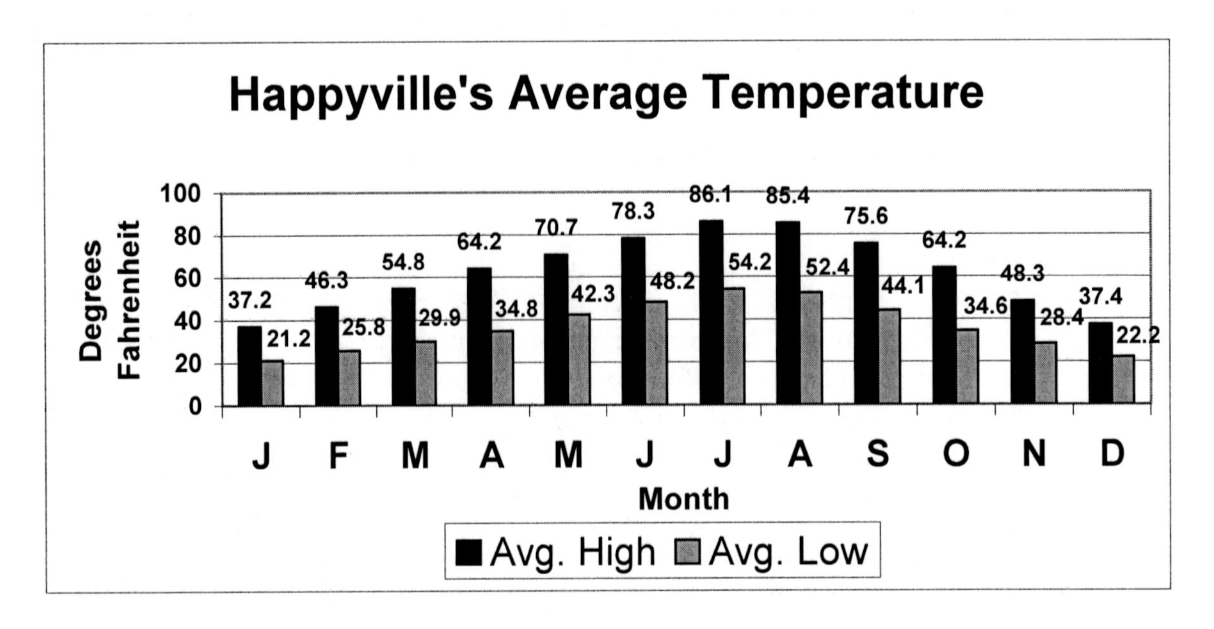

Use the double bar graph above to answer the following questions.

121. During which month(s) is Happyville's average high temperature greater than 47.5° F and less than 75.6° F?

122. During which month(s) is Happyville's average low temperature less than 44.1° F and greater than 25.6° F?

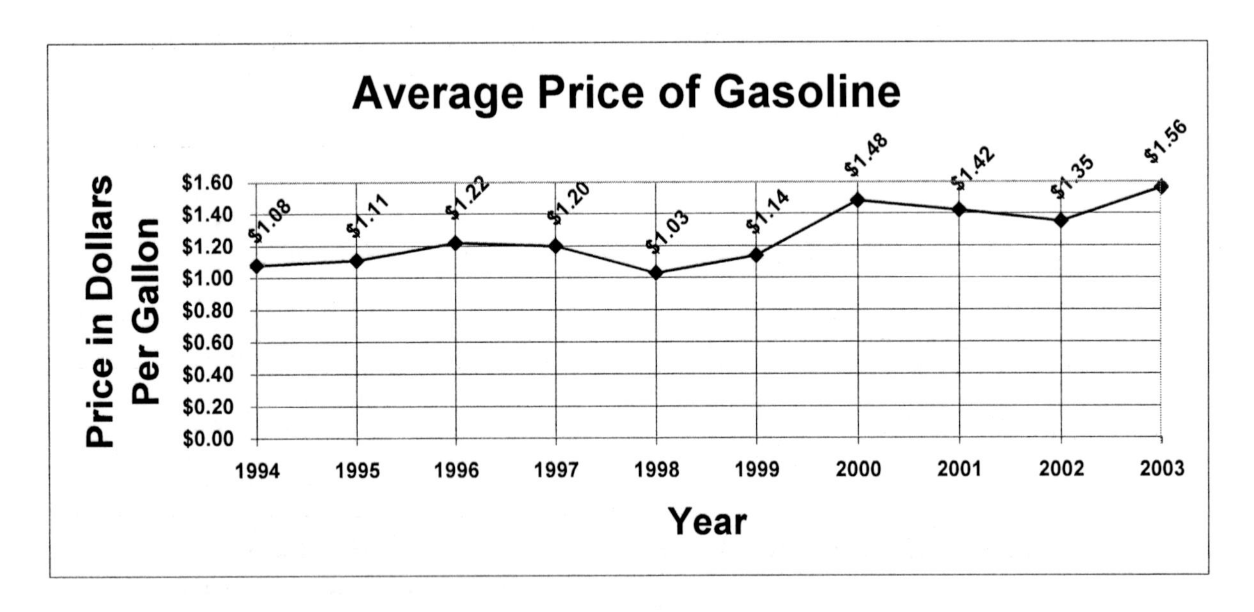

Use the broken-line graph above to answer the following questions.

123. Did the average price of gasoline increase or decrease between 1996 and 1997?

124. Did the average price of gasoline increase or decrease between 1994 and 1995?

DECIMAL NUMBERS

Section 2: Adding and Subtracting Decimal Numbers

One of the places that decimal numbers are frequently used is in the area of finances. When you make purchases at a store, decimal numbers (in the form of dollars and cents) are added together. When you balance a checkbook, decimal numbers are added or subtracted to reflect deposits or checks written. As with whole numbers, when decimal numbers are added or subtracted they need to be lined up by their place values. The quickest way to accomplish this is by lining up the decimal point in each number vertically.

Example 1: Add: 36.405 + 2.14

Solution: Line up the numbers vertically in columns according to their place values. Do this by lining up the decimal point in each number.

36.45 + 2.14 becomes

```
  36.405
+  2.14
--------
```

Now, starting at the far right end, add the numbers in each column and write the result at the bottom of that column below the solid line.

```
  36.405
+  2.14
--------
  38 545
```

Finally, put a decimal point in the answer such that it lines up vertically with the decimal point in each of the numbers being added or subtracted.

```
  36.405
+  2.14
--------
  38.545
    ↑
```

Decimal point in answer

Example 2: Add: 489.073 + 56.88

Solution: 489.073 + 56.88 becomes

```
  489.073
+  56.88
---------
```

If it is necessary, carry a number to the top of the next column to the left.

```
  11  1
  489.073
+  56.88
---------
  545.953
     ↑
```

Decimal point in answer

Example 3: Subtract: $34.56 - 8.23$

Solution: Line up the numbers vertically in columns according to their place values. Do this by lining up the decimal point in each number.

$34.56 - 8.23$ becomes

$$\begin{array}{r} 34.56 \\ -\ \ 8.23 \\ \hline \end{array}$$

Now, starting at the far right end, subtract the numbers in each column and write the result at the bottom of that column below the solid line. If it becomes necessary, borrow from the column immediately to the left of the one that is being subtracted.

$$\begin{array}{r} {\scriptstyle 2\ 14} \\ \not{3}\not{4}.56 \\ -\ \ 8.23 \\ \hline 26.33 \end{array}$$

↑

Decimal point in answer

Example 4: Subtract: $42 - 31.75$

Solution: Line up the numbers vertically in columns according to their place values. Do this by lining up the decimal point in each number.

$42 - 31.75$ becomes

$$\begin{array}{r} 42 \\ -\ 31.75 \\ \hline \end{array}$$

Put the implied decimal point followed by zeros in the minuend so that it has the same number of decimal places as the subtrahend.

$$\begin{array}{r} 42.00 \\ -\ 31.75 \\ \hline \end{array}$$

Now, starting at the far right end, subtract the numbers in each column and write the result at the bottom of that column below the solid line. If it becomes necessary, borrow from the column immediately to the left of the one that is being subtracted.

$$\begin{array}{r} {\scriptstyle 1\ \ 9\ 10} \\ 4\not{2}.\not{0}\not{0} \\ -\ 31.75 \\ \hline 10.25 \end{array}$$

↑

Decimal point in answer

When it comes to adding or subtracting positive or negative numbers, the rules that apply to integers also apply to decimal numbers.

Example 5: Add: $-2.35+(-4.08)$

Solution: When adding two decimal numbers with the same sign, add their absolute values.

$|-2.35|+|-4.08| = 2.35+4.08$

2.35 + 4.08 becomes $\begin{array}{r} 2.35 \\ +\,4.08 \\ \hline \end{array}$ the sum of which is $\begin{array}{r} {}^{1} \\ 2.35 \\ +\,4.08 \\ \hline 6.43 \end{array}$

Now attach their common sign (negative) to the resulting sum. The final answer becomes

-6.43. $-2.35+(-4.08)=-6.43$

Example 6: Subtract: $2.67-18.25$

Solution: Change subtraction to addition of the opposite.
$2.67-18.25$ becomes $2.67+(-18.25)$.

When adding two decimal numbers with opposite signs, subtract the smaller absolute value from the larger absolute value.

$|2.67| = 2.67$ and $|-18.25| = 18.25$.

Since 2.67 is smaller than 18.25, we subtract it from 18.25.

$$\begin{array}{r} 7\ 11\ 15 \\ 1\not{8}.\not{2}\not{5} \\ -\ \ 2.67 \\ \hline 15.58 \end{array}$$

Finally, attach the sign of the number with the larger absolute value to the resulting difference. Since -18.25 has the largest absolute value, attach a negative sign to the 15.58 and the final answer becomes -15.58. $2.67-18.25=-15.58$

In previous chapters, we evaluated variable expressions using whole numbers, integers, and fractions. Now we will evaluate expressions involving addition and subtraction of decimal numbers.

Example 7: Evaluate the expression for the given values of the variables: $x-y$, when $x=-1.7$ and $y=-2.3$

Solution: $x-y$	Substitute -1.7 in the place of x and -2.3 in the place of y.
$-1.7-(-2.3)$	Change subtraction to addition of the opposite.
$-1.7+2.3$	When adding two decimal numbers with opposite signs, subtract the smaller absolute value from the larger absolute value.
$\lvert -1.7\rvert = 1.7$ and	
$\lvert 2.3\rvert = 2.3$.	Since 1.7 is smaller than 2.3, we subtract it from 2.3.
$\begin{array}{r} \overset{1\ 13}{\not{2}.\not{3}} \\ -1.7 \\ \hline 0.6 \end{array}$	Finally, attach the sign of the number with the larger absolute value to the resulting difference. Since 2.3 has the larger absolute value, attach a positive sign to the 0.6 and the final answer becomes
$+0.6$ or just 0.6.	When $x=-1.7$ and $y=-2.3$ the value of $x-y$ is 0.6.

Applications

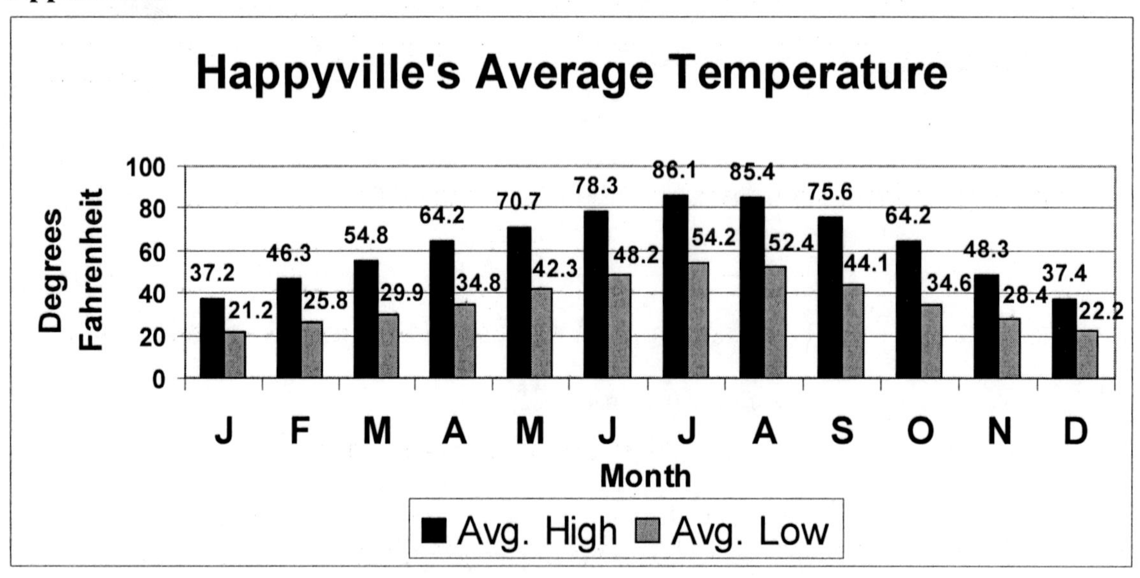

Example 8: Based on the double bar graph above, find the difference between the highest average monthly temperature and the lowest average monthly temperature.

Solution: The highest average monthly temperature is 86.1°F while the lowest average monthly temperature is 21.2°F. In this case, subtract the smaller amount from the larger amount to find the difference.

$$\begin{array}{r} \overset{5\ 11}{8\not{6}.\not{1}} \\ -21.2 \\ \hline 64.9 \end{array}$$

The difference between the highest average monthly temperature and the lowest average monthly temperature is 64.9°F.

Remember that when the sum of the measure of two angles is 90°, the angles are said to be a pair of **complementary angles** and when the sum of the measure of two angles is 180°, the angles are said to be a pair of **supplementary angles**.

Example 9: Given $\angle W = 29.6°$, find $\angle$ X such that $\angle$ W and $\angle$ X are a pair of complementary angles.

Solution: If $\angle$ W and $\angle$ X are a pair of complementary angles, then

$\angle W + \angle X = 90°$. Since $\angle W = 29.6°$, then

$29.6° + \angle X = 90°$. By subtracting 29.6° from both sides of the equation it becomes

$29.6° - 29.6° + \angle X = 90° - 29.6°$. Since $\begin{array}{r} \overset{8\ 9\ 10}{\not{9}\not{0}.\not{0}} \\ -29.6 \\ \hline 60.4 \end{array}$

then $\angle X = 60.4°$.

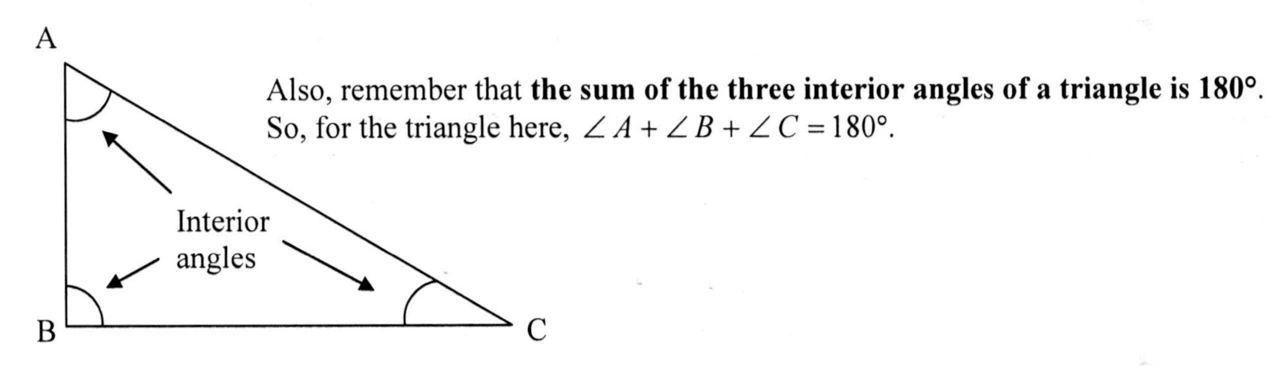

Also, remember that **the sum of the three interior angles of a triangle is 180°**. So, for the triangle here, $\angle A + \angle B + \angle C = 180°$.

Example 10: A given triangle contains interior angles $\angle$ D, $\angle$ E and $\angle$ F. If $\angle D = 42.3°$ and $\angle E = 64.9°$, then find $\angle$ F.

Solution: Since $\angle$ D, $\angle$ E and $\angle$ F are the three interior angles of a triangle, then their sum is 180°. That is,

$\angle D + \angle E + \angle F = 180°$. Since $\angle D = 42.3°$ and $\angle E = 64.9°$, then

$42.3° + 64.9° + \angle F = 180°$. Since $\begin{array}{r} 42.3° \\ +64.9° \\ \hline 107.2° \end{array}$ the equation becomes

$107.2° + \angle F = 180°$. By subtracting 107.2° from both sides of the equation it becomes

$107.2° - 107.2° + \angle F = 180° - 107.2°$. Since $\begin{array}{r} 180.0 \\ -107.2 \\ \hline 72.8 \end{array}$

then $\angle F = 72.8°$.

Section 2 exercises. Add or subtract.

1. $34.9 + 4.85$

2. $45.7 + 2.96$

3. $28.4 - 19.3$

4. $87.5 - 46.8$

5. $7.89 + 24.5 + 5$

6. $51.8 + 7 + 4.38$

7. $18.7 - 26.4$

8. $43.6 - 52.3$

9. $-31.17 + (-92.5)$

10. $-48.93 + (-72.581)$

11. $76.4 - (-35.7)$

12. $49.03 - (-38.506)$

13. $-48.6 + 37.85$

14. $-84.6 + 28.39$

15. $4 - 0.0037$

16. $9 - 0.0807$

17. $-29.094 - 3.0482$

18. $-17.805 - 0.2307$

19. $46.9 - 63.47 + 72.06$

20. $27.08 - 38.62 + 74.8$

21. $-0.95 - (-9.03)$

22. $-0.304 - (-2.22)$

23. $48.6 - 39.7$

24. $52.1 - 28.3$

Evaluate each expression.

25. What is 3.009 minus 12.9?

26. Find 23.9 less 39.03.

27. What is 17 more than 34.06?

28. What is 16.8 increased by 12?

29. Find the sum of 0.00773 and 3.0394.

30. Find 62.043 decreased by 9.017.

31. What is 0.42 less than 73.06?

32. Find the difference of 0.705 and 23.

Translate each phrase into mathematical symbols using decimal numbers. Then determine the result in each case.

33. What is forty-nine and seven tenths plus twelve and three hundredths?

34. Find the difference between eight hundred seven thousandths and three and sixty-one ten-thousandths.

35. What is two hundred seven thousandths added to three and four tenths?

36. How much greater is seventy-five and six hundredths than negative four and five tenths?

37. What is negative fifteen and seventy-two hundredths subtracted from negative eighteen hundredths?

38. Find the total of four hundred seven thousandths and sixty-two hundredths.

Evaluate the expression $x + y$ for the given values of x and y.

39. $x = 1.5;\ y = 0.72$

40. $x = 4.6;\ y = 0.91$

41. $x = 51.7;\ y = 2.89$

42. $x = 6.73;\ y = 15.6$

43. $x = 0.698;\ y = 0.5025$

44. $x = 0.0427;\ y = 0.348$

Evaluate the expression $x - y$ for the given values of x and y.

45. $x = 0.86;\ y = 2.7$

46. $x = 0.53;\ y = 3.4$

47. $x = 6.62;\ y = 59.5$

48. $x = 6.03;\ y = 28.8$

49. $x = 80.2;\ y = 0.04$

50. $x = 56.3;\ y = 0.05$

Evaluate the expression $x + y + z$ for the given values of x, y, and z.

51. $x = 30.8;\ y = -45.9;\ z = 5.71$

52. $x = 27.8;\ y = 4.26;\ z = -37.1$

53. $x = 8.063;\ y = 69.10;\ z = 587.7$

54. $x = 4.137;\ y = 20.16;\ z = 780.9$

Applications

55. Complete the following checkbook ledger.

NUMBER OR CODE	DATE	TRANSACTION DESCRIPTION	PAYMENT, FEE, WITHDRAWAL (-)		DEPOSIT, CREDIT (+)		BALANCE $112 . 96	
17488	3/04/08	Clothes	$42	18			$42	18
17489	3/07/08	Food	$63	85			$63	85
	3/10/08	Deposit			$378	93	$378	93
17490	3/14/08	Electric bill	$43	78			$43	78
17491	3/26/08	Video rental	$5	41			$5	41
	3/30/08	Deposit			$38	50	$38	50

56. Complete the following checkbook ledger.

NUMBER OR CODE	DATE	TRANSACTION DESCRIPTION	PAYMENT, FEE, WITHDRAWAL (-)		DEPOSIT, CREDIT (+)		BALANCE $209 . 46	
12855	5/09/08	Phone bill	$23	57			$23	57
12856	5/12/08	Medicine	$52	99			$52	99
	5/16/08	Deposit			$250	00	$250	00
12857	5/18/08	Food	$97	85			$97	85
12858	5/22/08	Movie tickets	$14	50			$14	50
	5/27/08	Deposit			$29	85	$29	85

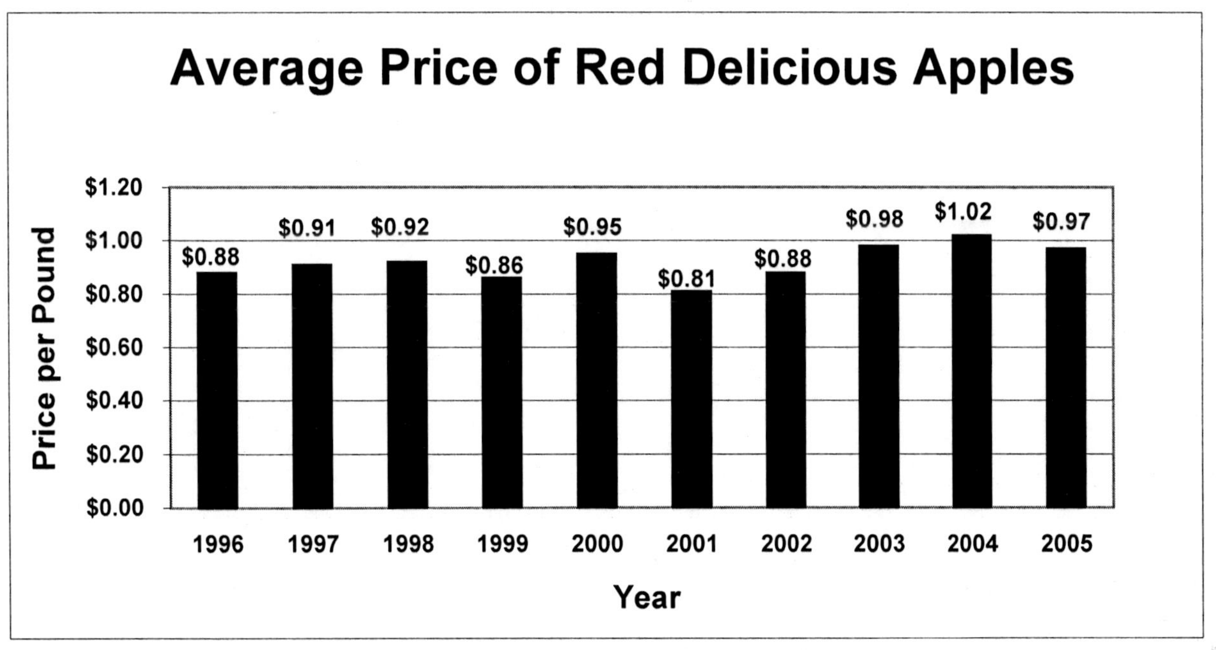

Use the bar graph above to answer the following questions.

57. What's the difference between the price per pound of apples in 2005 and the price per pound of apples in 1996?

58. What's the difference between the price per pound of apples in 2004 and the price per pound of apples in 1999?

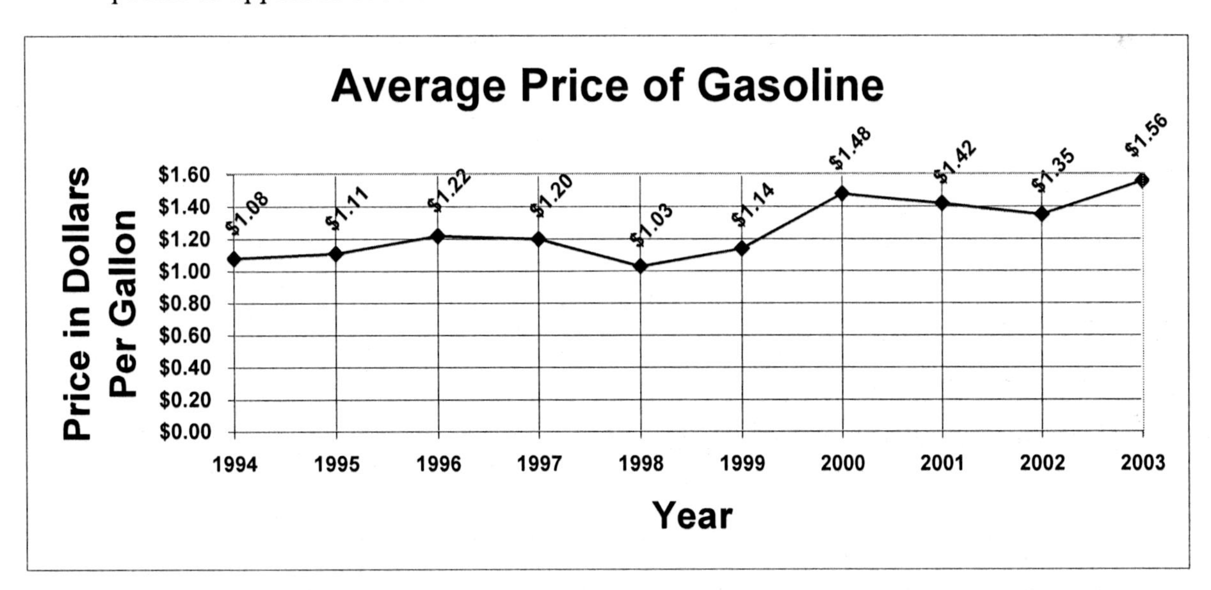

Use the broken-line graph above to answer the following questions.

59. Did the price per gallon of gasoline increase more between 1995 and 1996 or between 2002 and 2003?

60. Did the price per gallon of gasoline decrease more between 1997 and 1998 or between 2001 and 2002?

61. A set of six medium gauge bronze acoustic guitar stings consists of the following sizes:

E-1st string............................ 0.013 inch
B-2nd string............................ 0.017 inch
G-3rd string............................ 0.026 inch
D-4th string............................ 0.035 inch
A-5th string............................ 0.045 inch
E-6th string............................ 0.056 inch

What is the difference in size between the E-6th string and the E-1st string?

62. A set of six medium gauge bronze acoustic guitar stings consists of the following sizes:

E-1st string....................... 0.33 millimeter
B-2nd string....................... 0.43 millimeter
G-3rd string....................... 0.66 millimeter
D-4th string....................... 0.89 millimeter
A-5th string....................... 1.14 millimeter
E-6th string....................... 1.42 millimeter

What is the difference in size between the A-5th string and the E-1st string?

63. Given that $\angle X = 41.7°$, find $\angle$ Y such that $\angle$ X and $\angle$ Y are complementary angles.

64. Given that $\angle A = 33.8°$, find $\angle$ B such that $\angle$ A and $\angle$ B are complementary angles.

65. Given that $\angle C = 123.81°$, find $\angle$ D such that $\angle$ C and $\angle$ D are supplementary angles.

66. Given that $\angle E = 77.53°$, find $\angle$ F such that $\angle$ E and $\angle$ F are supplementary angles.

67. A given triangle contains interior angles $\angle$ D, $\angle$ E and $\angle$ F. If $\angle D = 92.06°$ and $\angle E = 15.36°$, then find $\angle$ F.

68. A given triangle contains interior angles $\angle$ M, $\angle$ N and $\angle$ P. If $\angle M = 12.7°$ and $\angle N = 53°$, then find $\angle$ P.

69. A given triangle contains interior angles $\angle$ X, $\angle$ Y and $\angle$ Z. If $\angle X = 14.8°$ and $\angle Y = 25°$, then find $\angle$ Z.

70. A given triangle contains interior angles $\angle$ R, $\angle$ K and $\angle$ W. If $\angle R = 40.07°$ and $\angle K = 33.33°$, then find $\angle$ W.

DECIMAL NUMBERS

Section 3: Multiplying Decimal Numbers

Unless you live in a state such as Oregon, when you purchase non-food items you usually have to pay sales tax. Sales tax is based on a percent of the cost of the items being purchased. Sales tax is calculated by multiplying the sales tax rate by the purchase price of items. For instance, if the local sales tax rate is 8%, then to calculate the amount of tax on an item, multiply the cost of the item by 0.08. (A discussion on how we got from 8% to 0.08 will be presented in a later course). Suppose for example, you wish to calculate the amount of sales tax on a CD player that costs $50. To do this, you must multiply 50 by 0.08. Setting up the multiplication vertically as we would with whole numbers, we get the following:

$$\begin{array}{r} 50 \\ \times\ 0.08 \\ \hline 400 \end{array}$$

It appears that the answer is $400. Does it seem reasonable that the tax on a $50 item is $400? That's because it isn't correct.

When multiplying numbers involving decimals, apply the following steps:

Step 1: Multiply the numbers together in the same manner that you would multiply whole numbers.

Step 2: Count the total number of digits to the right of the decimal point in both of the numbers being multiplied.

Step 3: Move the implied decimal point in the answer to the left the same number of decimal places as the total in step 2.

Now let's apply these steps to the problem.

$$\begin{array}{r} 50 \\ \times\ 0.08 \\ \hline 400 \end{array}$$

50 ← There are no digits to the right of the implied decimal point in this number.
× 0.08 ← There are 2 digits to the right of the decimal point in this number.

So, the total number of digits to the right of the decimal point in both numbers is 2.

Move the implied decimal point in the answer to the left the same number of decimal places as the total in step 2.

$$\begin{array}{r} 50 \\ \times\ 0.08 \\ \hline 4\,00. \end{array}$$

4 00. ← **Implied decimal point** (places counted 2 1)

Location of final decimal point (between 4 and 00)

The final answer is 4.00, or just 4, as in $4 sales tax.

Example 1: Multiply 1.25 and 8.3.

Solution: Line up the numbers vertically in columns. When multiplying decimal numbers it is not necessary to line the numbers up by their decimal points. Rather, just line them up by their lowest place values.

```
   1.25
×   8.3
```

Step 1: Multiply the numbers together in the same manner that you would multiply whole numbers.

Step 2: Count the total number of digits to the right of the decimal point in both of the numbers being multiplied.

```
    2 4
     1
   1.25  ←— There are 2 digits to the right of the decimal point in this number.
×   8.3  ←— There is 1 digit to the right of the decimal point in this number.
    375
+ 10000
  10375
```

Step 3: Since the total number of digits to the right of the decimal point in both numbers is 3, move the implied decimal point 3 places to the left.

10.375 is the final answer.

Example 2: Find the product of 7.34 and 2.05.

Solution: Line up the numbers vertically by their lowest place values and then multiply.

```
     2 4
     1 2
    7.34  ←— There are 2 digits to the right of the decimal point in this number.
×   2.05  ←— There are 2 digits to the right of the decimal point in this number.
    3670
+ 146800
  150470
```

Since the total number of digits to the right of the decimal point for both numbers is 4, move the implied decimal point 4 places to the left.

15.047 is the final answer.

Note: The zero to the right of the 7 was removed because it wasn't necessary in the final answer.

When it comes to multiplying positive or negative numbers, the rules that apply to integers also apply to decimal numbers.

Example 3: Multiply -2.6 and 4.

Solution: Line up the numbers vertically by their lowest place values and then multiply. The operation to be performed is multiplication. To avoid confusing the negative sign in front of the 2.6 with a subtraction sign, leave the negative sign off during the multiplication process. **However, don't forget to make the final answer negative since a negative number times a positive number is a negative product.**

```
   2
  2.6  ←— There is 1 digit to the right of the decimal point in this number.
×   4  ←— There are no digits to the right of the decimal point in this number.
 10.4
```

Since the total number of digits to the right of the decimal point for both numbers is 1, move the implied decimal point 1 place to the left.

-10.4 is the final answer.

Example 4: Find the product of -12.3 and -0.59.

Solution: Line up the numbers vertically by their lowest place values and then multiply. The operation to be performed is multiplication. To avoid confusing the negative signs with subtraction signs, leave the negative signs off during the multiplication process. **However, don't forget to make the final answer positive since a negative number times a negative number is a positive product.**

```
   11
   ~~11~~
   12.3  ←— There is 1 digit to the right of the decimal point in this number.
 × 0.59  ←— There are 2 digits to the right of the decimal point in this number.
   1107
 + 6150
  7.257
```

Since the total number of digits to the right of the decimal point for both numbers is 3, move the implied decimal point 3 places to the left.

7.257 is the final answer.

We've looked at multiplying decimal numbers. Now let's look at a pattern involving multiplying by powers of 10. In Chapter 1 we established that to multiply a whole number by 10, just put a zero at the right end of the original number. For instance, $34 \times 10 = 340$. Or, when multiplying a whole number by 100, just put 2 zeros at the right end of the original number. For instance, $756 \times 100 = 75{,}600$.

Let's look at these same two scenarios, but from a slightly different perspective. Let's think in terms of the decimal point in each number. 34 has an implied decimal point after the 4 and 340 has an implied decimal point after the 0. So, $34 \times 10 = 340$ becomes $34. \times 10 = 340.$ When 34. was multiplied by 10, the decimal point moved 1 place to the right to produce the answer 340. 756 has an implied decimal point after the 6 and 75,600 has an implied decimal point after the 0. So, $756 \times 100 = 75{,}600$ becomes $756. \times 100 = 75{,}600.$ When 756 was multiplied by 100, the decimal point moved 2 places to the right to produce the answer 75,600.

Conclusion: to multiply a number by 10, move the decimal point 1 place to the right. To multiply a number by 100 or 10^2, move the decimal point 2 places to the right.

To multiply a decimal number by 10 raised to a power, move the decimal point 1 place to the right for each factor of 10 in the power.

Example 5: Find the product of 20.3 and 10^4.

Solution: Move the decimal point 4 places to the right.

2 0 . 3 0 0 0 becomes 203,000.   So, $(20.3)(10^4) = 203{,}000$.

1 2 3 4

Example 6: Find the product of 23.78 and 1,000.

Solution: Since $1{,}000 = 10^3$ move the decimal point 3 places to the right.

2 3 . 7 8 0 becomes 23,780.   So, $(23.78)(1{,}000) = 23{,}780$.

1 2 3

Note: 1,000 has 3 zeros, so move the decimal point 3 places to the right.

Example 7: Find the product of 0.0036 and 100.

Solution: Since $100 = 10^2$ move the decimal point 2 places to the right.

0 . 0 0 3 6 becomes 0.36.   So, $(0.0036)(100) = 0.36$.

1 2

Note: 100 has 2 zeros, so move the decimal point 2 places to the right.

In previous chapters, we evaluated variable expressions using whole numbers, integers, and fractions. Now we will evaluate expressions involving multiplication of decimal numbers.

Example 8: Evaluate the expression for the given values of the variables: xy, when $x = 3.42$ and $y = 6.8$

Solution: xy Substitute 3.42 in the place of x and 6.8 in the place of y.

(3.42)(6.8) becomes

$$\begin{array}{r} \scriptstyle 2\,1 \\ \scriptstyle \not{3}\,\not{1} \\ 3.42 \\ \times\quad 6.8 \\ \hline 2736 \\ +\ 20520 \\ \hline 23.256 \end{array}$$

and 23.256 is the final answer.

Applications involving decimal numbers

Example 9: If your monthly cable bill is \$45.30, how much does one year of cable cost?

Solution: Since there are twelve months in a year, multiply the cost of one month of cable by twelve.

$$\begin{array}{r} \scriptstyle 1 \\ \$45.30 \\ \times\quad 12 \\ \hline 9060 \\ +\ 45300 \\ \hline \$543.60 \end{array}$$

The cost of one year of cable is \$543.60.

Example 10: Using the formula $P = 2L + 2W$, find the perimeter of the following rectangle.

7.6 inches

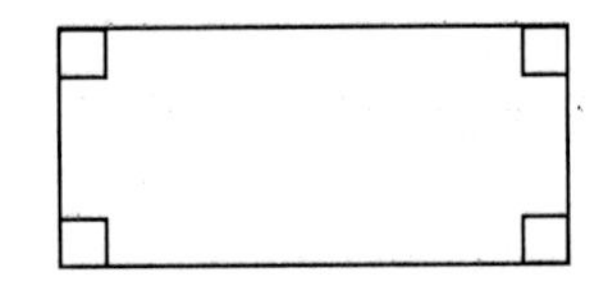

2.3 inches

Solution: Use the formula for the perimeter of a rectangle.	
$P = 2L + 2W$	Substitute 7.6 inches in the place of L and 2.3 inches in the place of W.
$P = 2(7.6\text{ in.}) + 2(2.3\text{ in.})$	Simplify the right side of the equation using order of operations.
	Multiply.
$P = 15.2\text{ in.} + 4.6\text{ in.}$	Add.
$P = 19.8\text{ in.}$	The perimeter of the rectangle is 19.8 inches.

Example 11: Using the formula $A = LW$, find the area of the following rectangle.

7.5 inches

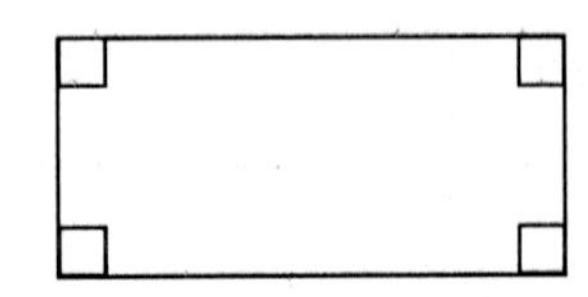

2.6 inches

Solution: Use the formula for the area of a rectangle.	
$A = LW$	Substitute 7.5 inches in the place of L and 2.6 inches in the place of W.
$A = (7.5\text{ in.})(2.6\text{ in.})$	Simplify the right side of the equation.
$\begin{array}{r} 1 \\ \not{3} \\ 7.5 \\ \times\ 2.6 \\ \hline 450 \\ 1500 \\ \hline 19.50 \end{array}$	Multiply.
$A = 19.5\text{ in}^2.$	The area of the rectangle is 19.5 square inches.

Section 3 exercises. Multiply.

1. $0.7(0.03)$

2. $0.4(0.06)$

3. $7.813(10^3)$

4. $92.05(10^4)$

5. $(-0.83)(-3.08)$

6. $(-0.74)(-6.03)$

7. $10(0.017)$

8. $100(6.9)$

9. $(0.2)(-0.3)(4)$

10. $(0.6)(5)(-0.2)$

11. $(0.0005)1,000$

12. $10(487.92)$

13. $(8.42)(0.0041)$

14. $(7.36)(0.0053)$

15. $10^2(-6.85)$

16. $10^5(0.0043)$

17. $(38.001)(0.04002)$

18. $(16.003)(0.00509)$

19. $4.94(10^5)$

20. $(32.741)10,000$

21. $(10^3)(100)(0.0042)$

22. $(1,000)(10^2)(0.0715)$

23. $10,000(68.92)$

24. $-0.807(10^2)$

Evaluate each expression.

25. What is 1.07 times 0.25?

26. Find the product of -0.44 and 5.3.

27. What is -8.24 multiplied by 10^4?

28. What is 2.08 times 0.57?

29. Find the product of -0.55 and 2.3.

30. What is -7.3 multiplied by 10^3?

Evaluate the expression xy for the given values of x and y.

31. $x = 25.4;\ y = 7.3$

32. $x = 19.6;\ y = 3.8$

33. $x = -6;\ y = 0.037$

34. $x = -8;\ y = 0.019$

35. $x = 42.8;\ y = 80.05$

36. $x = 16.7;\ y = 30.08$

37. $x = -0.16;\ y = -2.8$

38. $x = -0.37;\ y = -5.2$

39. $x = 100;\ y = -7.342$

40. $x = -84.91;\ y = 1{,}000$

41. $x = -3.3;\ y = 4.7$

42. $x = -5.5;\ y = 1.2$

Applications

43. If a monthly internet bill is $37.25, how much does one year of internet cost?

44. If a monthly newspaper bill is $12.40, how much does one year of newspaper cost?

45. If it costs an average of $1.24 per day to run an air conditioner, approximately how much would it cost to run it for one week?

46. If it costs an average of $2.16 per day to heat a hot water heater, approximately how much would it cost to heat it for one week?

47. If is costs \$2.49 to rent a DVD from a local video store, how much would it cost to rent five DVDs from the same store?

48. If a gallon of milk costs \$3.49 at a local mini-mart, how much would three gallons of milk cost from the same mini-mart?

49. If a chocolate bar costs \$0.35, how much would a dozen chocolate bars cost?

50. If a car can travel 24.3 miles on a gallon of gas, then how far could it travel on 8.6 gallons of gas? Round your answer to the nearest tenth of a mile.

51. If a gallon of gas costs \$2.09, then how much does 12.48 gallons of gas cost? Round your answer to the nearest cent.

52. If sugar costs \$0.79 per pound, how much would a 7.5 pound bag of sugar cost? Round your answer to the nearest cent.

53. If frozen lemonade costs 6.3¢ per fluid ounce, then how much would a 12.5 fluid ounce can of frozen lemonade cost? Round your answer to the nearest cent.

54. If the average American family has 2.7 children, then how many children would eight families have? Round your answer to the nearest whole child.

Using the formula $P = 4s$, find the perimeter of the following squares.

55.

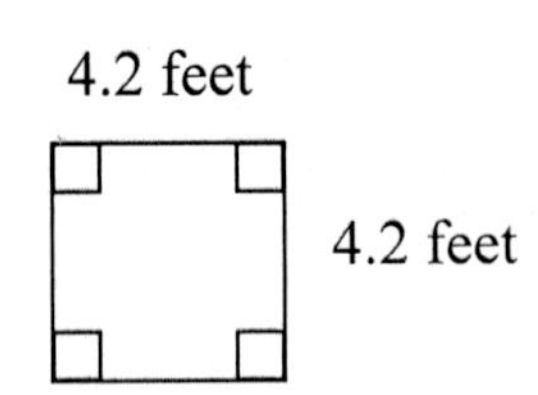

56.

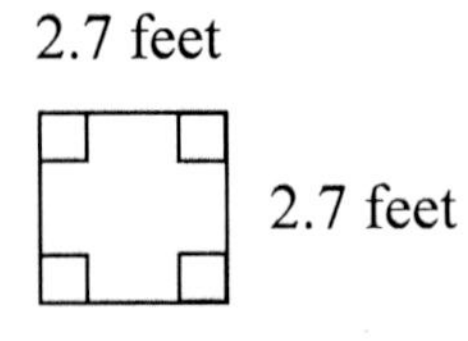

Using the formula $P = 2L + 2W$, find the perimeter of the following rectangles.

57.

8.5 inches

3.25 inches

58.

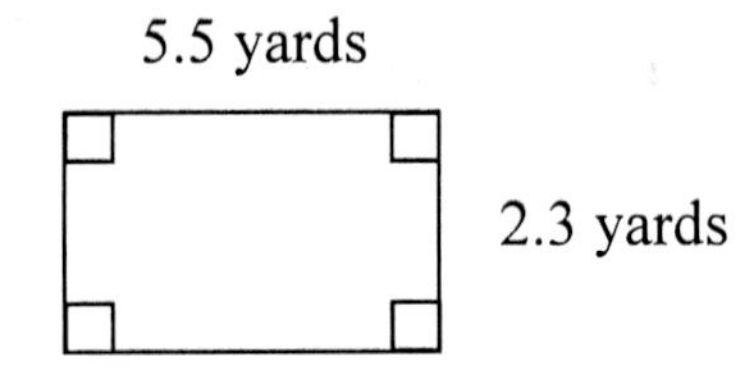

Using the formula $A = s^2$, find the area of the following squares.

59.

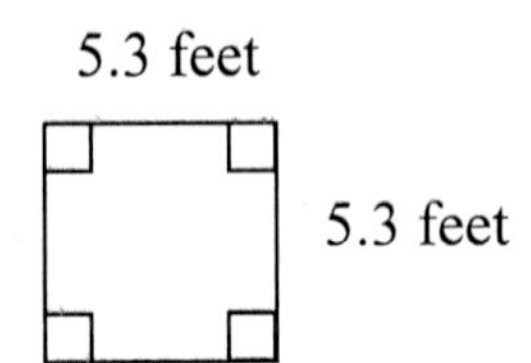

60.

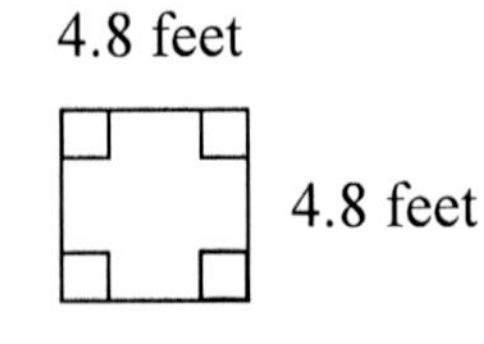

Using the formula $A = LW$, find the area of the following rectangles.

61.

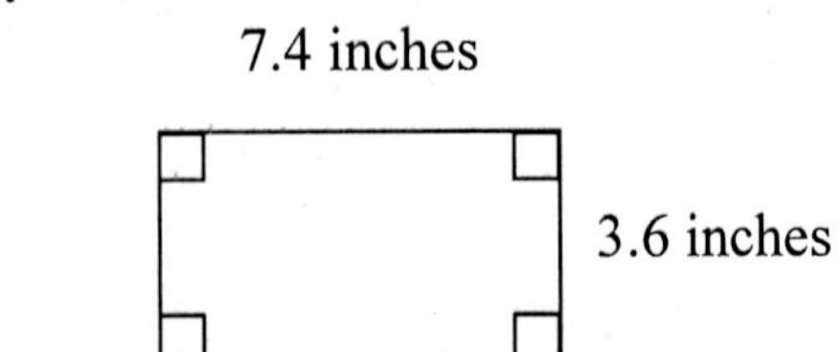

62.

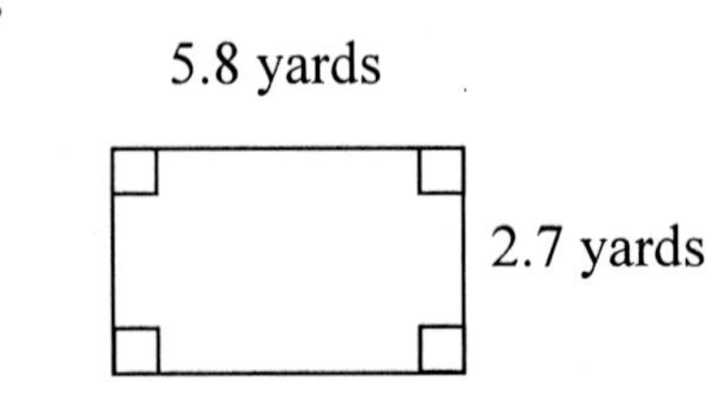

63. Explain the difference between 59¢ and 0.59¢.

64. Explain the difference between \$0.59 and 0.59¢.

DECIMAL NUMBERS

Section 4: Dividing Decimal Numbers

Division of decimal numbers involves careful manipulation of the decimal point in the dividend and the divisor, before the division process is completed. For example, when dividing 22.26 by 5.3, or $\frac{22.26}{5.3}$ if written as a fraction, the first thing to do is put the problem in long division form. $5.3\overline{)22.26}$ Now, turn the divisor into a whole number. In this example it's done by moving the decimal point 1 place to the right. Also, move the decimal point of the dividend the same number of places to the right. $5.3\overline{)22.26}$ becomes $53.\overline{)222.6}$ Now put a decimal point straight above the decimal point in the dividend where the quotient will be. $53\overline{)222.6}$ Finally, divide just like you would divide whole numbers.

$$\begin{array}{r} 4.2 \\ 53\overline{)222.6} \\ -\,212 \\ \hline 10\,6 \\ -\;10\,6 \\ \hline 0 \end{array}$$

So, $22.26 \div 5.3 = 4.2$, or $\frac{22.26}{5.3} = 4.2$.

When dividing numbers involving decimals, apply the following steps:

Step 1: Rewrite the problem in long division form.

Step 2: Move the decimal point to the right the necessary number of places to turn the divisor into a whole number. Also move the decimal point of the dividend to the right the same number of places.

Step 3: Put a decimal point straight above the decimal point in the dividend where the quotient will be.

Step 4: Divide.

Example 1: Divide 0.72 by 1.8.

Solution:	Step 1: Rewrite the problem in long division form.
$0.72 \div 1.8$ becomes $1.8\overline{)0.72}$.	Step 2: Move the decimal point to the right the necessary number of places to turn the divisor into a whole number. Also move the decimal point of the dividend to the right the same number of places.
$1.8\overline{)0.72}$ becomes $18\overline{)7.2}$.	Step 3: Put a decimal point straight above the decimal point in the dividend where the quotient will be.
$18\overline{)7.2}$ becomes $18\overline{)7.2}$.	Step 4: Divide.
$\begin{array}{r} 0.4 \\ 18\overline{)7.2} \\ -\,7\,2 \\ \hline 0 \end{array}$	So, $0.72 \div 1.8 = 0.4$.

Example 2: Find the quotient of -0.03825 and -1.53.

Solution: To avoid confusion we will leave the negative signs off during the long division process. **However, don't forget to make the final answer positive since a negative number divided by a negative number is a positive quotient.**

$-0.03825 \div (-1.53)$ becomes $1.53\overline{)0.03825}$.

$1.53\overline{)0.03825}$ becomes $153\overline{)3.825}$.

$153\overline{)3.825}$ becomes $153\overline{)3\dot{.}825}$.

$$\begin{array}{r} 0.025 \\ 153\overline{)3.825} \\ -\ 3\,06 \\ \hline 765 \\ -\ 765 \\ \hline 0 \end{array}$$

So, $-0.03825 \div (-1.53) = 0.025$.

Example 3: Find the quotient of -4 and 20.

Solution: To avoid confusion we will leave the negative sign off during the long division process. **However, don't forget to make the final answer negative since a negative number divided by a positive number is a negative quotient.**

$-4 \div 20$ becomes $20\overline{)4}$. In the past, we might have said that 20 can't be divided into 4. However, remember that 4 is the same as 4.0, or 4.00 for that matter. So, we can rewrite the long division problem as follows:

$20\overline{)4}$ becomes $20\overline{)4.0}$.

$20\overline{)4.0}$ becomes $20\overline{)4\dot{.}0}$.

$$\begin{array}{r} 0.2 \\ 20\overline{)4.0} \\ -\ 4\,0 \\ \hline 0 \end{array}$$

So, $-4 \div 20 = -0.2$.

Since division is basically undoing multiplication, it should be no surprise that when dividing by a power of 10 the decimal point gets moved to the left instead of the right.

To divide a decimal number by 10 raised to a power, move the decimal point 1 place to the left for each factor of 10 in the power.

Example 4: Find the quotient of 49.23 and 10^5.

Solution: Move the decimal point 5 places to the left.

0 0 0 4 9 . 2 3 becomes 0.0004923. So, $49.23 \div 10^5 = 0.0004923$.

5 4 3 2 1

Example 5: Find the quotient of 4,873 and 100.

Solution: Since $100 = 10^2$ move the decimal point 2 places to the left.

4, 8 7 3 becomes 48.73. So, $4{,}873 \div 100 = 48.73$.

2 1

Note: 100 has 2 zeros, so move the decimal point 2 places to the left.

Example 6: Find the quotient of 32,875 and 10.

Solution: Since $10 = 10^1$ move the decimal point 1 place to the left.

3 2, 8 7 5 becomes 3,287.5. So, $32{,}875 \div 10 = 3{,}287.5$.

1

Note: 10 has 1 zero, so move the decimal point 1 place to the left.

Example 7: Divide 0.078 by 10^3.

Solution: Move the decimal point 3 places to the left.

0 0 0 . 0 7 8 becomes 0.000078. So, $0.078 \div 10^3 = 0.000078$.

3 2 1

In previous chapters, we evaluated variable expressions using whole numbers, integers, and fractions. Now we will evaluate expressions involving multiplication and division of decimal numbers.

Example 8: Evaluate the expression for the given values of the variables: $x \div y$, when $x = 22.68$ and $y = 6.3$

> Solution: $x \div y$ Substitute 22.68 in the place of x and 6.3 in the place of y.
>
> $22.68 \div 6.3$ becomes $6.3\overline{)22.68}$.
>
> $6.3\overline{)22.68}$ becomes $63\overline{)226.8}$.
>
> $63\overline{)226.8}$ becomes $63\overline{)226\dot{.}8}$.
>
> $$\begin{array}{r} 3.6 \\ 63\overline{)226.8} \\ -\underline{189} \\ 37\,8 \\ -\underline{37\,8} \\ 0 \end{array}$$
>
> So, $22.68 \div 6.3 = 3.6$.

When dividing decimal numbers, the answer can continue out for quite a few decimal places. In some situations, being this accurate isn't necessary. In these situations, we may round the answer to a predetermined place value.

Example 9: Divide 16 by 0.14. Round the quotient to the nearest tenth.

> Solution: The process is the same as before, except that the final answer will be rounded at the tenth place value.
>
> $16 \div 0.14$ becomes $0.14\overline{)16}$.
>
> $0.14\overline{)16}$ becomes $14\overline{)1{,}600}$.
>
> $14\overline{)1{,}600}$ becomes $14\overline{)1{,}600\dot{.}}$.
>
> Since the answer is to be rounded to the nearest tenth, we only need to carry out the division process to the hundredths place value. This will allow us to see whether to round up or down.
>
> $$\begin{array}{r} 114.28 \\ 14\overline{)1{,}600.00} \\ -\underline{14} \\ 20 \\ -\underline{14} \\ 60 \\ -\underline{56} \\ 40 \\ -\underline{28} \\ 120 \\ -\underline{112} \\ 8 \end{array}$$
>
> Since the place value in the hundredths column is an 8, we round up which makes the 2 in the tenths place becomes a 3.
>
> So, 16 divided by 0.14 is approximately 114.3, or
>
> $16 \div 0.14 \approx 114.3$.

Applications

Sometimes when we buy in bulk, we still want to know the cost of a single item so that we can easily compare the cost with similar items.

Example 10: If a 6-pack of soda is on sale for 89¢, how much would a single can of soda cost during the sale? Give the answer in cost per can and round it to the nearest tenth of a cent.

Solution: We want to know the cost per can therefore we need a fraction that is $\frac{\text{cost}}{\text{can}}$. In other words, $\frac{89¢}{6\text{ cans}}$. Now we need to divide 89 by 6.

$\frac{89}{6}$ becomes $6\overline{)89}$ which then becomes $6\overline{)89.}$.

$$\begin{array}{r} 14.83 \\ 6\overline{)89.00} \\ -\ 6 \\ \hline 29 \\ -\ 24 \\ \hline 5\,0 \\ -\ 4\,8 \\ \hline 20 \\ -\ 18 \\ \hline 2 \end{array}$$

Even though the long division process isn't finished, we only need to go out to the hundredths place value in order to know how to round the decimal answer to the nearest tenth. Since the number in the hundredths place is a 3 we will round down. The final answer to the nearest tenth of a cent is 14.8¢ per can of soda pop.

To find the "average" for a set of numbers, add the numbers together and then divide the total by how many numbers there are in the set.

Example 11: The daily low temperatures for a 7 day period were as follows: $-5°F$, $7°F$, $8°F$, $-2°F$, $-4°F$, $7°F$ and $-2°F$. What was the average daily low temperature for the 7-day period? Give the answer to the nearest tenth of a degree Fahrenheit.

Solution:
To find the average daily low temperature, add the 7 temperatures and divide the total by 7.
$-5°F + 7°F + 8°F + (-2°F) + (-4°F) + 7°F + (-2°F) = 9°F$

$9 \div 7$ becomes $7\overline{)9}$ which then becomes $7\overline{)9.}$.

$$\begin{array}{r} 1.28 \\ 7\overline{)9.00} \\ -\ 7 \\ \hline 2\,0 \\ -\ 1\,4 \\ \hline 60 \\ -\ 56 \\ \hline 4 \end{array}$$

Even though the long division process isn't finished, we only need to go out to the hundredths place value in order to know how to round the decimal answer to the nearest tenth. Since the number in the hundredths place is an 8 we will round up. The final answer to the nearest tenth of a degree is $1.3°F$.

The average daily low temperature for the 7-day period was $1.3°F$ or 1.3 degrees Fahrenheit.

Section 4 exercises. Divide.

1. $0.45 \div 9$ **2.** $0.42 \div 6$ **3.** $7.234 \div 100$

4. $68.5 \div 10$ **5.** $-72.8 \div (-0.008)$ **6.** $-4.38 \div (-0.006)$

7. $7{,}276 \div 10^3$ **8.** $42.8 \div 10^4$ **9.** $448.8 \div 0.374$

10. $144.67 \div 0.629$ **11.** $482 \div 10$ **12.** $1{,}000 \div 10^5$

13. $100 \div 10^2$ **14.** $1{,}000 \div 10^4$ **15.** $-7 \div 28$

16. $3 \div (-24)$ **17.** $-16 \div 0.0032$ **18.** $1 \div 0.016$

19. $-57{,}003 \div 10^5$ **20.** $100{,}000 \div 100$ **21.** $3.14 \div 10^3$

22. $-100 \div 10^6$ **23.** $0.252 \div 4.2$ **24.** $0.441 \div (-6.3)$

25. $2{,}718.28 \div 100{,}000$ **26.** $80{,}764.3 \div 100{,}000$ **27.** $0.004 \div 10{,}000$

28. $-10 \div 1{,}000$ **29.** $27.18 \div 0.0009$ **30.** $84.96 \div 0.0012$

Evaluate each expression.

31. What is 23.8 divided by 1,000?

32. What is 8.7 divided into 0.04263?

33. What is 7.6 divided into 0.0266?

34. What is 0.62 divided by 10^2?

35. What is the quotient of 252.42 and 4.2?

36. What is the quotient of 85.1 and 3.7?

Evaluate the expression $x \div y$ for the given values of x and y.

37. $x = 5.44;\ y = -1.6$

38. $x = 17.1;\ y = -4.5$

39. $x = 7.456;\ y = 3.2$

40. $x = 45.54;\ y = 1.8$

41. $x = -1.17;\ y = 26$

42. $x = -0.928;\ y = 32$

43. $x = 34.888;\ y = 0.56$

44. $x = 25.104;\ y = 0.48$

Divide. Round each quotient to the nearest tenth.

45. $36.85 \div 4.2$

46. $52.95 \div 5.6$

47. $-7.05 \div 26.3$

48. $-8.49 \div 56.3$

49. $0.067 \div 0.0085$

50. $0.058 \div 0.0037$

Divide. Round each quotient to the nearest hundredth.

51. $-6.948 \div 7$

52. $-9.362 \div 13$

53. $9 \div 7$

54. $13 \div 8$

55. $-10 \div (-5.636)$

56. $-37.32 \div (-4.9)$

Applications

Using the formula $P = a + b + c$, find the perimeter of the following triangles.

57.

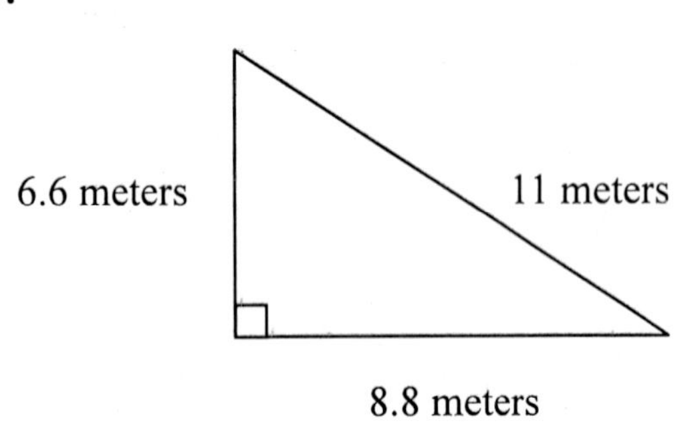

58.

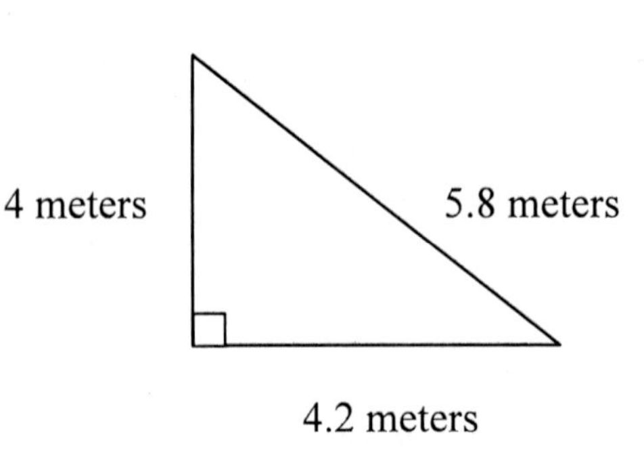

Using the formula $A = \frac{1}{2}bh$, find the area of the following triangles.

59.

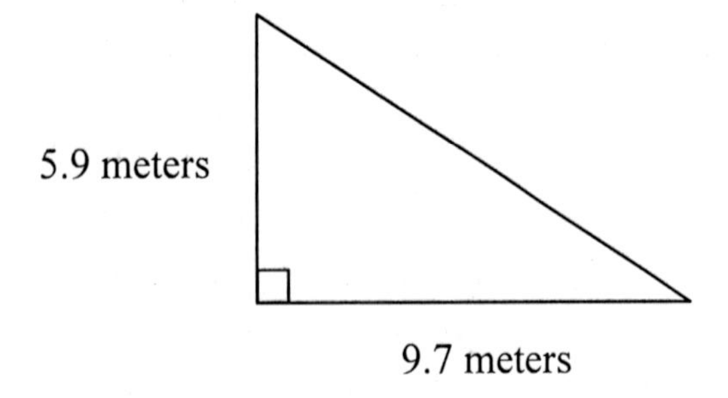

60.

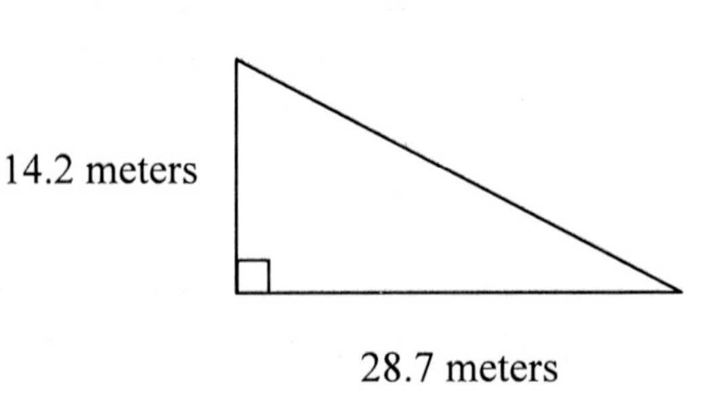

61. If 6 eggs sell for 98¢, how much would a single egg sell for? Give your answer in cost per egg and round it to the nearest tenth of a cent.

62. If a dozen candy canes sell for 99¢, how much would a single candy cane sell for? Give your answer in cost per candy cane and round it to the nearest tenth of a cent.

63. If a car travels 160 miles while using 5.6 gallons of gasoline, how many miles could it travel on 1 gallon of gasoline? Give your answer in miles per gallon and round it to the nearest tenth of a mile.

64. If a tank holding 500 gallons of water takes 74 minutes to drain, how many gallons of water would drain from the tank in 1 minute? Give your answer in gallons per minute and round it to the nearest tenth of a gallon.

65. If 12,000 people live in an area of 314 square miles, what is the population density of this area? Give your answer in terms of people per square mile and round it to the nearest tenth of a person.

66. If 4.3 pounds of hamburger costs $8.19, what is the price of a pound of hamburger? Give your answer in dollars per pound and round it to the nearest cent.

67. If a company charges $175 to spray 16 acres of land with a chemical treatment, what would they charge to spray 1 acre? Give your answer in dollars per acre and round it to the nearest cent.

68. If a runner travels 1,320 feet in 56 seconds, how far would they travel in 1 second? Give your answer in feet per second and round it to the nearest hundredth of a foot.

69. If 0.45 pound of sliced turkey has a cost of $4.04, what is the price of a pound of sliced turkey? Give your answer in dollars per pound and round it to the nearest cent.

70. If a 10.75 ounce can of mushroom soup costs 88¢, what is the price of 1 ounce of mushroom soup? Give your answer in cents per ounce and round it to the nearest tenth of a cent.

71. Seth received the following scores on his history tests: 93%, 85%, 79%, and 98%. What percent was his average test score? Round your answer to the nearest hundredth of a percent.

72. Mollie works at a delicatessen. She sliced 14 pounds of turkey on Saturday, 9 pounds of turkey on Monday, 10 pounds of turkey on Tuesday, and 12 pounds of turkey on Wednesday. How many pounds of turkey did Mollie slice per day on average? Round your answer to the nearest hundredth of a pound.

73. Jamie jogged 2.4 miles on Monday, 4.5 miles on Tuesday, 5.3 miles on Wednesday, and 6.3 miles on Thursday. How many miles did Jamie jog per day on average? Round your answer to the nearest hundredth of a mile.

74. Mike baled 3.4 acres of hay on Monday, 4.1 acres of hay on Tuesday, and 5.2 acres of hay on Wednesday. How many acres of hay did Mike bale per day on average? Round your answer to the nearest hundredth of an acre.

Multiply or divide.

75. $98.6 \div 10^2$

76. $0.004 \div 10{,}000$

77. $(48.313)(7.0007)$

78. $(83.274)(5.005)$

79. $0.04186 \div 9.1$

80. $0.05029 \div 4.7$

81. $10^3(6.00805)$

82. $10^4(78.0034)$

83. $-70.2 \div 0.0072$

84. $-30.6 \div 0.036$

85. $13.701(10{,}000)$

86. $99.0908(100{,}000)$

87. $-8.403 \div 100$

88. $80{,}496 \div 1{,}000$

89. $(2.5)(400)(0.765)$

90. $(0.05)(2{,}000)(0.044)$

91. $0.0408 \div 10{,}000$

92. $0.8 \div 10^3$

93. $(-0.05)(-0.4)(-0.003)$

94. $(-0.6)(-0.03)(-0.002)$

95. $100 \div 1{,}000$

96. $10{,}000 \div 10^3$

97. $3.1(1{,}000)(10^2)$

98. $4.9(10{,}000)(10^2)$

99. $4{,}086.3 \div 10$

100. $10 \div 2{,}500$

101. $100 \div 80{,}000$

102. $-2{,}241 \div 0.083$

103. $-0.00075(-56{,}000)$

104. $-6{,}700(-0.0043)$

DECIMAL NUMBERS

Section 5: Converting and Comparing Fractions and Decimal Numbers

Earlier in this chapter, we examined two different ways to go about converting decimals into fractions. One of these methods is illustrated in example 1 below.

Example 1: Convert the decimal number 0.039 into a fraction.

Solution: Rewrite 0.039 as the whole number **39**. This becomes the numerator of the fraction.

For the number 0.039, the 9 is farthest to the right and the 9 is in the ***thousandths*** column.

Therefore, the denominator becomes **1,000**.

The entire fraction is $\frac{39}{1,000}$. Thus, $0.039 = \frac{39}{1,000}$.

We also looked at converting fractions with denominators made up of powers of 10 into decimal numbers. Now let's discuss changing fractions in general into decimal numbers. We already have all the tools we need by using long division and the implied decimal point.

Example 2: Convert $\frac{7}{8}$ into a decimal number.

Solution:

$\frac{7}{8}$ becomes $8\overline{)7}$ which then becomes $8\overline{)7.}$.

$$\begin{array}{r} 0.875 \\ 8\overline{)7.000} \\ -\ 6\ 4 \\ \hline 60 \\ -\ 56 \\ \hline 40 \\ -\ 40 \\ \hline 0 \end{array}$$

So, $\frac{7}{8} = 0.875$.

Example 3: Convert $4\frac{3}{5}$ into a decimal number.

Solution: The whole number part of the mixed number will become the whole number part of the decimal number. So, we only need to convert the fraction into a decimal number and then add the whole number 4 to the results.

$\frac{3}{5}$ becomes $5\overline{)3}$ which then becomes $5\overline{)3.}$.

$$\begin{array}{r} 0.6 \\ 5\overline{)3.0} \\ -\ 3\ 0 \\ \hline 0 \end{array}$$

Now, adding the 4

we get $4\frac{3}{5} = 4.6$.

Sometimes, dividing two numbers results in a decimal number that just goes on and on and on. Let's look at an example of this.

Example 4: Convert $\frac{1}{3}$ into a decimal number.

Solution:

$\frac{1}{3}$ becomes $3\overline{)1}$ which then becomes $3\overline{)1.}$.

$$\begin{array}{r} 0.3333 \\ 3\overline{)1.0000} \\ -\ 9 \\ \hline 10 \\ -\ \ 9 \\ \hline 10 \\ -\ \ \ 9 \\ \hline 10 \\ -\ \ \ \ 9 \\ \hline 1 \end{array}$$

Notice that the problem isn't finished. However, if we were to go on with the problem, we would continue to get 3's in our answer. This is what is known as a **repeating decimal number**. There is a special notation that is used to indicate a repeating decimal number. We put a bar above the number or block of numbers that is repeating. In this case, it is just the single number 3. Enlarged, the answer looks like this:

$0.\overline{3}$ ← **This line is called a repeating bar.**

Example 5: Convert $8\frac{2}{11}$ into a decimal number.

Solution: We only need to convert the fraction into a decimal number and then add the whole number 8 to the results.

$\frac{2}{11}$ becomes $11\overline{)2}$ which then becomes $11\overline{)2.}$.

$$\begin{array}{r} 0.1818 \\ 11\overline{)2.0000} \\ -\ 1\ 1 \\ \hline 90 \\ -\ \ 88 \\ \hline 20 \\ -\ \ \ 11 \\ \hline 90 \\ -\ \ \ \ 88 \\ \hline 2 \end{array}$$

The problem isn't finished. However, if we were to go on with the problem, we would continue to get 181818 etc. in our answer. Enlarged, the answer looks like this:

$\mathbf{8.\overline{18}}$

We put a bar above the block of numbers that is repeating. However, since a repeating bar is not to be written across a decimal point, we couldn't write the answer as $\overline{8.1}$.

We have looked at how to compare fractions by getting a common denominator. We have also looked at comparing decimal numbers by lining them up vertically. However, what about comparing a fraction with a decimal number?

Example 6: Compare the two numbers 0.33 and $\frac{1}{3}$ by placing either < or > between them.

Solution: We can work two different ways on this problem. We can either write both numbers as decimal numbers, or write both numbers as fractions.

To write them both as decimal numbers, we need to change $\frac{1}{3}$ into a decimal number. In a previous example, we established that $\frac{1}{3} = 0.\overline{3}$. So, now we need to compare 0.33 and $0.\overline{3}$.

If we line them up vertically, it looks like this.

$$\begin{array}{l} 0.33 \\ 0.\overline{3} \end{array}$$

Keep in mind that $0.\overline{3}$ means 0.3333 with the 3's continuing on forever. If we extend 0.33 out to the thousandths place value, we get 0.330. If we extend $0.\overline{3}$ out to the thousandths place value, we get 0.333. Now the comparison looks like this:

$$\begin{array}{l} 0.33\mathbf{0} \\ 0.33\mathbf{3} \end{array}$$

By comparing the digits in the thousandths place we see that 0.330 < 0.333

$$\text{Therefore } 0.33 < \frac{1}{3}.$$

Now let's do the problem by writing both numbers as fractions. In this case, we need to rewrite 0.33 as a fraction. $0.33 = \frac{33}{100}$ So, now we need to compare $\frac{33}{100}$ with $\frac{1}{3}$. To do this we need to find a common denominator. The common denominator of 100 and 3 is 300.

$$\frac{33}{100} = \frac{33 \cdot 3}{100 \cdot 3} = \frac{99}{300} \text{ and } \frac{1}{3} = \frac{1 \cdot 100}{3 \cdot 100} = \frac{100}{300}.$$

$$\text{Since } \frac{99}{300} < \frac{100}{300} \text{ then } 0.33 < \frac{1}{3}.$$

Either way we do the problem, the answer is the same.

Applications involving decimal numbers

Often baseball players are compared to each other by their batting average. A baseball player's batting average is calculated by taking the number of hits the player has, and dividing it by the number of times the player has been up to bat. A player's batting average is usually given as a decimal number, rounded to the nearest thousandth.

As a formula it looks like this: $\text{Batting Average} = \dfrac{\text{Number of Hits}}{\text{Number of Times at Bat}}$

Example 7: Harley Griswold had 17 hits in 48 times at bat. What was Harley's batting average?

Solution: Using the formula, $\text{Batting Average} = \dfrac{\text{Number of Hits}}{\text{Number of Times at Bat}}$, we get

$\text{Batting Average} = \dfrac{17}{48}$. Convert this fraction into a decimal number using long division,

rounding at the thousandths place value. $\dfrac{17}{48}$ becomes $48\overline{)17}$ which then becomes $48\overline{)17.}$.

$$\begin{array}{r} 0.3541 \\ 48\overline{)17.0000} \\ -\ 144 \\ \hline 260 \\ -\ 240 \\ \hline 200 \\ -\ 192 \\ \hline 80 \\ -\ 48 \\ \hline 32 \end{array}$$

Even though the long division process isn't finished, we only need to go out to the ten-thousandths place value in order to know how to round the decimal answer to the nearest thousandth. Since the number in the ten-thousandths place is a 1 we will round down. The final answer to the nearest thousandth is 0.354. **Harley Griswold's batting average was 0.354.**

In the sports world, people would say that Harvey was batting three fifty-four, although technically he was batting three hundred fifty-four thousandths.

Baseball pitchers are compared by a statistic called E.R.A. (earned run average). A pitcher's E.R.A. is calculated by taking the number of earned runs he has given up, multiplied by 9, and then divided by the number of innings he has pitched. E.R.A. is usually given as a decimal number, rounded to the nearest hundredth.

As a formula it looks like this: $\text{E.R.A.} = \dfrac{(\text{Number of Earned Runs}) \times 9}{\text{Number of Innings Pitched}}$

Example 8: Last year Andy Johnston gave up 25 earned runs in 62 innings pitched. What was his E.R.A. last year?

Solution: Using the formula $\text{E.R.A.} = \dfrac{(\text{Number of Earned Runs}) \times 9}{\text{Number of Innings Pitched}}$, we get

$\text{E.R.A.} = \dfrac{(25)(9)}{62}$. Simplify the right side of the equation using order of operations.

Multiply.

$\text{E.R.A.} = \dfrac{225}{62}$ Divide.

$$\begin{array}{r} 3.629 \\ 62\overline{)225.000} \\ -\ 186 \\ \hline 390 \\ -\ 372 \\ \hline 180 \\ -\ 124 \\ \hline 560 \\ -\ 558 \\ \hline 2 \end{array}$$

Since the number in the thousandths place is a 9, we will round up. The final answer to the nearest hundredth is 3.63. **Last year, Andy Johnston's E.R.A. was 3.63.**

Section 5 exercises.

Convert each decimal number into a fraction or mixed number. Be sure to write answers in lowest terms.

1. 0.96 **2.** 4.44 **3.** 7.38 **4.** 0.45

5. 9.4 **6.** 3.6 **7.** 0.516 **8.** 0.425

9. 0.475 **10.** 0.524 **11.** 0.389 **12.** 0.451

13. 87.492 **14.** 73.908 **15.** 16.0605 **16.** 33.2002

Convert each fraction or mixed number into a decimal number. Use a repeating bar in your answers when necessary.

17. $\frac{2}{5}$ **18.** $\frac{5}{8}$ **19.** $\frac{2}{9}$ **20.** $\frac{2}{3}$

21. $3\frac{5}{6}$ **22.** $2\frac{3}{11}$ **23.** $6\frac{7}{10}$ **24.** $4\frac{17}{20}$

25. $\frac{4}{11}$ **26.** $\frac{5}{11}$ **27.** $\frac{11}{4}$ **28.** $\frac{11}{5}$

29. $\frac{7}{3}$ **30.** $\frac{7}{6}$ **31.** $5\frac{7}{12}$ **32.** $6\frac{4}{15}$

Compare each pair of numbers by placing either < or > between them.

33. $0.6 \quad \frac{2}{3}$

34. $0.3 \quad \frac{1}{3}$

35. $\frac{3}{4} \quad 0.74$

36. $\frac{7}{8} \quad 0.876$

37. $0.636 \quad \frac{7}{11}$

38. $0.833 \quad \frac{5}{6}$

39. $\frac{8}{17} \quad 0.471$

40. $\frac{6}{7} \quad 0.857$

41. $\frac{13}{24} \quad 0.5416$

42. $\frac{17}{24} \quad 0.7084$

43. $0.\overline{56} \quad \frac{14}{25}$

44. $0.\overline{34} \quad \frac{17}{50}$

45. $3\frac{2}{3} \quad 3.67$

46. $4\frac{1}{6} \quad 4.16$

Applications

47. \$0.85 is what fraction of a dollar?

48. 0.76 lb is what fraction of a pound?

49. Write $6\frac{3}{8}$ pounds using a decimal number.

50. Write \$$4\frac{2}{5}$ using a decimal number.

51. One Liter is approximately 0.264 gallon. What fraction of a gallon is 0.264 gallon?

52. One gram is approximately 0.035 ounces. What fraction of an ounce is 0.035 ounce?

53. One gallon is approximately $3\frac{157}{200}$ Liters. Write $3\frac{157}{200}$ Liters using a decimal number.

54. One pound is approximately $\frac{227}{500}$ kilogram. Write $\frac{227}{500}$ kilogram using a decimal number.

For problems 55-60 use the formula: $\text{Batting Average} = \dfrac{\text{Number of Hits}}{\text{Number of Times at Bat}}$ to calculate each baseball player's batting average. (Round answers to the nearest thousandth).

55. Ivan Suzuki had 210 hits in 678 times at bat.

56. Rudy Bendacourt had 151 hits in 552 times at bat.

57. Ron Ibanez had 186 hits in 627 times at bat.

58. John Lopez had 189 hits in 636 times at bat.

59. Sam Gariko had 131 hits in 486 times at bat.

60. Andre Belltree had 148 hits in 556 times at bat.

For problems 61-64 use the formula: $\text{E.R.A.} = \dfrac{(\text{Number of Earned Runs}) \times 9}{\text{Number of Innings Pitched}}$ to calculate each baseball pitcher's earned run average. (Round answers to the nearest hundredth).

61. Frank Hernandez gave up 76 earned runs in 193 innings pitched.

62. Billy Washtub gave up 79 earned runs in 153 innings pitched.

63. Kelly Battleground gave up 80 earned runs in 115 innings pitched.

64. Johnny Silver gave up 110 earned runs in 154 innings pitched.

DECIMAL NUMBERS

Section 6: Order of Operations with Decimal Numbers

Order of operations for decimal numbers is the same as it was for whole numbers, integers, and fractions. Below are the rules, followed by examples of how to apply them.

Order of Operations: When simplifying a mathematical expression, do the following operations in the order that they are listed.

1. **Perform all calculations within grouping symbols.**
2. **Evaluate all exponential expressions.**
3. **Do all multiplication and division in order from left to right.**
4. **Do all addition and subtraction in order from left to right.**

Example 1: Simplify the expression: $1.2+(3.5)(4.2)$

Solution:

$1.2+(3.5)(4.2)$	Multiply.
$1.2 + 14.7$	Add.
15.9	**15.9** is the final answer.

Example 2: Simplify the expression: $(6.1-3.7)^2-5.32$

Solution:

$(6.1-3.7)^2-5.32$	Perform all calculations within grouping symbols.
$(2.4)^2-5.32$	Evaluate the exponential expression.
$5.76-5.32$	Subtract.
0.44	**0.44** is the final answer.

Example 3: Simplify the expression: $|4.2-7.19|$

Solution:

$\lvert 4.2-7.19\rvert$	Perform all operations within grouping symbols. Subtract.
$\lvert -2.99\rvert$	Take the absolute value of -2.99.
2.99	**2.99** is the final answer.

Example 4: Simplify the expression: $\dfrac{3.9\div1.3(4)}{3.9\div\left((1.3)(4)\right)}$

Solution:

$\dfrac{3.9\div1.3(4)}{3.9\div\left((1.3)(4)\right)}$	Simplify the numerator. Divide.
$\dfrac{3(4)}{3.9\div\left((1.3)(4)\right)}$	Multiply.
$\dfrac{12}{3.9\div\left((1.3)(4)\right)}$	Simplify the denominator. Multiply inside the parentheses.
$\dfrac{12}{3.9\div5.2}$	Divide.
$\dfrac{12}{0.75}$	Divide the numerator by the denominator.
16	**16** is the final answer.

Remember that following "order of operations" is necessary when evaluating algebraic expressions, since the process involves simplifying a mathematical expression.

Example 5: Evaluate the expression for the given values of the variables: $x^2(y+z)$, where $x=-0.5$, $y=3.4$, and $z=2.1$

Solution:	
$x^2(y+z)$	Substitute -0.5 in the place of x, 3.4 in the place of y, and 2.1 in the place of z.
$(-0.5)^2((3.4)+(2.1))$	Evaluate the expression using order of operations.
	Perform all calculations within grouping symbols.
$(-0.5)^2(5.5)$	Evaluate the exponential expressions.
$(-0.5)(-0.5)(5.5)$	Finally, multiply.
$(0.25)(5.5)$	Continue multiplying.
1.375	When $x=-0.5$, $y=3.4$, and $z=2.1$, the value of $x^2(y+z)$ is **1.375**.

Example 6: Evaluate the expression for the given values of the variables: $\frac{x+y}{x-y}$, where $x=2.1$ and $y=1.2$

Solution:	
$\frac{x+y}{x-y}$	Substitute 2.1 in the place of x and 1.2 in the place of y.
$\frac{2.1+1.2}{2.1-1.2}$	Evaluate the expression using order of operations.
	Simplify the numerator.
	Add.
$\frac{3.3}{2.1-1.2}$	Simplify the denominator.
	Subtract.
$\frac{3.3}{0.9}$	Finally, divide.
$\mathbf{3.\overline{6}}$	When x = 2.1 and y = 1.2, the value of $x^2(y+z)$ is $\mathbf{3.\overline{6}}$.

Applications

Solving an application problem often involves more than one operation. When this is true it is important to know what order to do the operations in. Here are several examples of this kind of situation.

Example 7: If carpet costs \$2.39 per 1 square foot, how much would it cost to carpet a rectangular room that is 13 feet wide by 15.5 feet long? Round your answer to the nearest cent.

Solution: To determine the total cost of the carpet, first find the area that is to be carpeted. Since the room is rectangular shaped, use the formula for the area of a rectangle, $A = LW$.

From this we get Area = (15.5 feet)(13 feet), or 201.5 square feet.

Next, multiply the area by the cost per square foot. $(201.5 \text{ square feet})\left(\dfrac{\$2.39}{1 \text{ square foot}}\right)$

The units of square feet reduce out of both factors. $(201.5 \cancel{\text{square feet}})\left(\dfrac{\$2.39}{1 \cancel{\text{square foot}}}\right)$

This leave us with (201.5)(\$2.39) which equals \$481.585.

Rounding to the nearest cent, the total cost is \$481.59.

Example 8: If floor molding costs \$1.25 per foot, how much would it cost to put molding around the perimeter of a rectangular area that is 15 feet long by 8.5 feet wide? Round your answer to the nearest dollar.

Solution: To determine the total cost of the molding, first find the perimeter of the area that is to be covered. Since the room is rectangular shaped, use the formula for the perimeter of a rectangle, $P = 2L + 2W$.

From this we get Perimeter = 2(15 feet) + 2(8.5 feet), or 47 feet.

Next, multiply the perimeter by the cost per foot. $(47 \text{ feet})\left(\dfrac{\$1.25}{1 \text{ foot}}\right)$

The units of feet reduce out of both factors. $(47 \cancel{\text{feet}})\left(\dfrac{\$1.25}{1 \cancel{\text{foot}}}\right)$

This leave us with (47)(\$1.25) which equals \$58.75.

Rounding to the nearest dollar, the total cost is \$59.

In the past we have dealt with perimeter and area of triangles, squares, and rectangles. Now, with the introduction of decimal numbers, we are ready to consider circles as well.

A **circle** is the set of all points in a plane that are the same distance from a point called the **center** of the circle. This distance from the center to a point on the circle is called the **radius** of the circle. A line segment that passes through the center of a circle and extends to two points on the circle is called the **diameter** of the circle. The length of the diameter of a circle is 2 times the length of its radius.

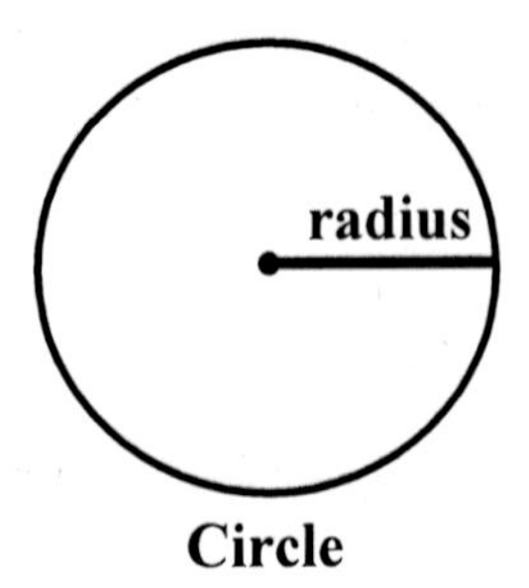

Circle

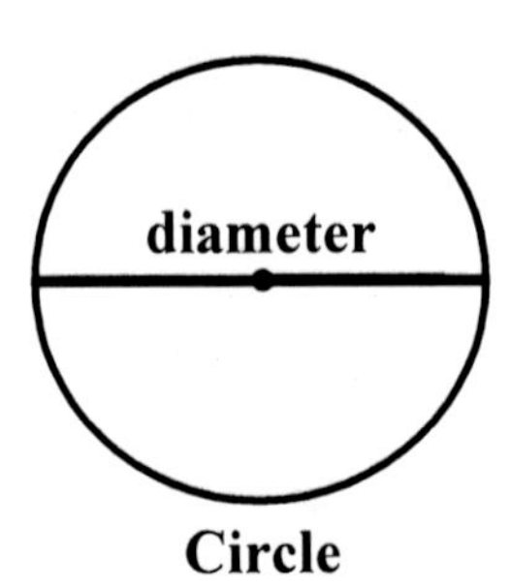

Circle

While the distance around a rectangle or a square is called the perimeter, the distance around a circle is called the **circumference**. When the circumference of a circle is divided by its diameter, no matter what size the circle is, the result always comes out to be the same number. This number is slightly larger than three and is known in the mathematics world as **π (pi).** π is an irrational number. This means that π can't be written exactly as a fraction or a decimal number. The best we can do is to approximate it. For the purpose of calculations, use the symbol π in answers that are to be exact. We will use the fact that $\pi \approx 3.14$ for answers that are to be approximations. The symbol $\approx$ means "**is approximately equal to**." This all leads to the following formula.

> *FORMULA FOR THE CIRCUMFERENCE OF A CIRCLE:*
>
> $$\boldsymbol{C = 2\pi r}$$
>
> where $\boldsymbol{C}$ is the circumference and $\boldsymbol{r}$ is the length of the radius.

Example 9: Find the approximate circumference of the following circle using the fact that $\pi \approx 3.14$.

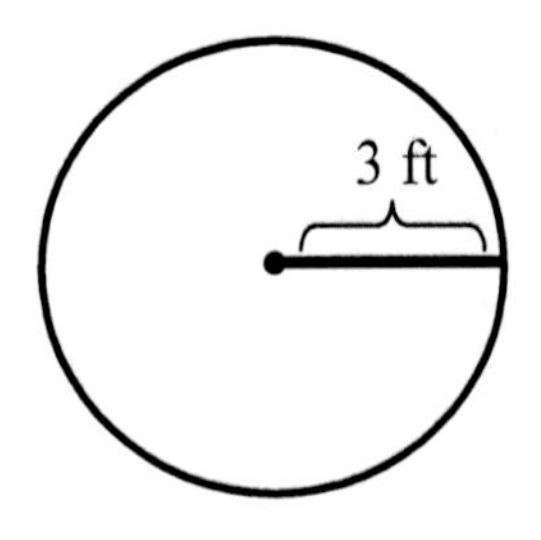

> Solution: Since the radius of the circle is 3 ft, using the formula for the circumference of a circle,
>
> $C = 2\pi r$ gives us
>
> $C = 2\pi(3 \text{ ft})$ or $C = 6\pi$ ft.
>
> Using the fact that $\pi \approx 3.14$,
>
> $C \approx (6)(3.14)$ ft. Since $(6)(3.14)$ ft $= 18.84$ ft, then
>
> $C \approx 18.84$ ft. Consequently,
>
> **the approximate circumference of the circle is 18.84 feet.**

FORMULA FOR THE AREA OF A CIRCLE:

$$\boldsymbol{A = \pi r^2}$$

where $\boldsymbol{A}$ is the area and $\boldsymbol{r}$ is the length of the radius.

Example 10: Find the approximate area of the following circle using the fact that $\pi \approx 3.14$.

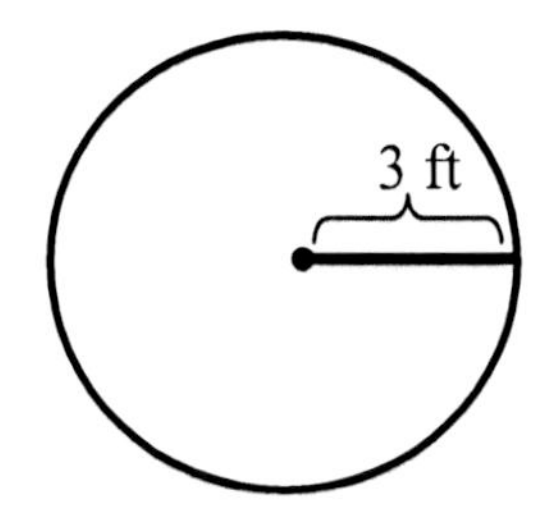

Solution: Since the radius of the circle is 3 ft, using the formula for the area of a circle,

$A = \pi r^2$ gives us

$A = \pi (3 \text{ ft})^2$ or $A = 9\pi \text{ ft}^2$.

Using the fact that $\pi \approx 3.14$,

$A \approx (9)(3.14) \text{ ft}^2$. Since $(9)(3.14) \text{ ft}^2 = 28.26 \text{ ft}^2$, then

$\text{A} \approx 28.26 \text{ ft}^2$. Consequently,

the approximate area of the circle is 28.26 square feet or $\mathbf{28.26 \text{ ft}^2}$.

Example 11: Find the approximate area of the following circle using the fact that $\pi \approx 3.14$.

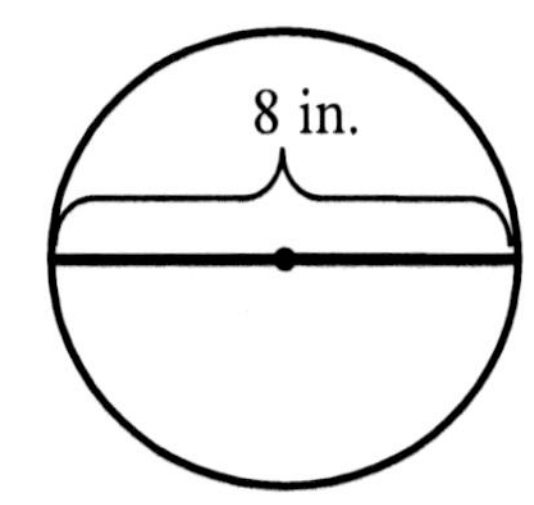

Solution: Since the radius of the circle is one half of the diameter and the diameter is 8 in., then the radius is 4 in. Using the formula for the area of a circle,

$A = \pi r^2$ gives us

$A = \pi (4 \text{ in.})^2$ or $A = 16\pi \text{ in.}^2$

Using the fact that $\pi \approx 3.14$,

$A \approx (16)(3.14) \text{ in.}^2$. Since $(16)(3.14) \text{ in.}^2 = 50.24 \text{ in.}^2$ then,

$A \approx 50.24 \text{ in.}^2$. Consequently,

the approximate area of the circle is 50.24 square inches or $\mathbf{50.24 \text{ in.}^2}$.

Students are compared using their grade point average (GPA). Students may get scholarships, make the dean's list, or even be accepted into a prestigious college based on their GPA. The process of determining a student's GPA is a bit more complicated than determining batting averages or earned run averages. It involves multiplication, followed by addition, followed by division of decimal numbers. Each letter grade that is assigned has a grade point value. These may differ from school to school but we will use the following information for the GPA problems in this book:

Grade	Grade point value
A	4.0
A−	3.7
B+	3.3
B	3.0
B−	2.7
C+	2.3
C	2.0
C−	1.7
D+	1.3
D	1.0
F	0.0

The grade points for a course are determined by multiplying the grade point value of the letter grade by the number of credits in the course. For example, the grade points for a four-credit course with a grade of C+ would be

$$\begin{array}{rl} 2.3 & \leftarrow \text{Grade point value} \\ \times\ 4 & \leftarrow \text{Number of credits in the course} \\ \hline 8.6 & \leftarrow \text{Grade points} \end{array}$$

The grade point average of a student is determined by adding up the grade points a student received and then dividing this sum by the total number of credit hours for which this student received a letter grade. GPA is usually given as a decimal number, rounded to the nearest hundredth.

Example 12: What was Jane Doe's GPA for fall quarter of 2007, if her transcript was as follows:

FALL QUARTER 2007

Course	Letter Grade	Credits
ENGL 101	C	5
HLTH 130	A	2
HIST 197	C+	3
MUS 130	A	3
WPE 131	A−	2

Example 12 is continued on the next page.

Example 12 continued from previous page.

Solution: Determine the grade points for each course.

ENGL 101	HLTH 130	HIST 130	MUS 130	WPE 131
C = 2.0	A = 4.0	C + = 2.3	A = 4.0	A− = 3.7
$2.0 \times 5 = 10.0$	$4.0 \times 2 = 8.0$	$2.3 \times 3 = 6.9$	$4.0 \times 3 = 12.0$	$\overset{1}{3.7} \times 2 = 7.4$

Add the grade points for each course.

$$\begin{array}{r} 10.0 \\ 8.0 \\ 6.9 \\ 12.0 \\ +\ 7.4 \\ \hline 44.3 \end{array}$$

Determine the total number of credit hours for which this student received a letter grade.

$5 + 2 + 3 + 3 + 2 = 15$

Divide the sum of the grade points by the total number of credit hours for which the student received a letter grade.

$$\begin{array}{r} 2.953 \\ 15\overline{)44.300} \\ -\ 30 \\ \hline 143 \\ -\ 135 \\ \hline 80 \\ -\ 75 \\ \hline 50 \\ -\ 45 \\ \hline 5 \end{array}$$

Even though the long division process isn't finished, we only need to go out to the thousandths place value in order to know how to round the decimal answer to the nearest hundredth. Since the number in the thousandths place is a 3, we will round down. The final answer to the nearest hundredth is 2.95. **Jane Doe's GPA for fall quarter 2007 was 2.95.**

Section 6 exercises. Simplify each expression.

1. $4.6 \div 2(4)$

2. $6.9 \div 3(12)$

3. $\frac{4.6(4)}{2}$

4. $\frac{6.9(12)}{3}$

5. $2.3 - 1.3(7.4 - 4.7)$

6. $4.5 - 2.5(9.3 - 3.9)$

7. -0.4^2

8. -0.3^2

9. $(-0.4)^2$

10. $(-0.3)^2$

11. $(3 - 4.2)(2.7 - 5.6)$

12. $(6 - 8.5)(1.3 - 4.1)$

13. $(0.2)^3$

14. $(0.4)^3$

15. $-(3.7 + 4.5)$

16. $-(8.3 + 7.9)$

17. $|31.6 - 42.8|$

18. $|57.3 - 83.4|$

19. $\frac{3.4 - 2^3}{3^2 - 6.7}$

20. $\frac{13.9 - 4^2}{5^2 - 24.3}$

21. $\frac{|3.4 - 6.7|}{|6.7 - 3.4|}$

22. $\frac{|8.6 - 5.2|}{|5.2 - 8.6|}$

23. $0.2(1.3 + 4.5)^2$

24. $0.4(2.5 + 1.7)^2$

25. $3.2 + (4.5 - 2) - |-0.7|$

26. $7.4 + (8.3 - 5) - |-0.9|$

27. $-0.5^2 - (-0.5)^2$

28. $-0.6^2 - (-0.6)^2$

Put the correct symbol <, >, or = in the box between each pair of expressions.

29. $|7-2.1|-(-0.2)(1.5)+4.1 \; \square \; -6.3-4.2\div 7(5)$

30. $|4.6-3|-(1.2)(-0.5)-0.18 \; \square \; -3.5+17.6\div 8(5)$

31. $(0.1)^4(100)^2-1 \; \square \; 173\div 10^2-0.06(10)-(1.1)^2+0.08$

32. $(0.1)^5(10)^6-1 \; \square \; 248\div 10^2+0.08(100)-(1.3)^2+0.21$

33. $-4.5-(0.3)^2-(4-6.2) \; \square \; -(0.4)^2+0.51-(-0.5)^3$

34. $-9.6+(1.2)^2-(4.2-8.4) \; \square \; -(1.5)^2-1.74-(-0.3)^3$

Evaluate each expression for the given values of the variables.

35. $7x-3y$, where $x=-0.05$ and $y=-0.6$

36. $6d-8f$, where $d=-0.3$ and $f=-0.09$

37. $a^2\div b^2+c^3$, where $a=-0.9$, $b=-3$, and $c=-0.2$

38. $m^2\div p^3-z^2$, where $m=-0.4$, $p=-2$, and $z=-0.7$

39. $-|x-7y|+|-5z|$, where $x=-6.7$, $y=-3.9$, and $z=-2.05$

40. $-|2a+3b|-|-7c|$, where $a=-4.7$, $b=-3.8$, and $c=-0.06$

Convert.

41. Using the formula $F=\frac{9}{5}C+32$, convert $9°$ C into degrees Fahrenheit.

42. Using the formula $F=\frac{9}{5}C+32$, convert $16°$ C into degrees Fahrenheit.

43. Using the formula $F=\frac{9}{5}C+32$, convert $-18.4°$ C into degrees Fahrenheit.

44. Using the formula $C=\frac{5(F-32)}{9}$, convert $9.86°$ F into degrees Celsius.

45. Using the formula $C=\frac{5(F-32)}{9}$, convert $54.14°$ F into degrees Celsius.

46. Using the formula $C=\frac{5(F-32)}{9}$, convert $62.96°$ F into degrees Celsius.

47. If tile costs \$3.27 per square foot how much would it cost to tile a counter top that is 3 feet wide by 5.5 feet long? Round your answer to the nearest cent.

48. If linoleum costs \$1.15 per square foot, how much would it cost to cover a room that is 9 feet wide by 12.5 feet long? Round your answer to the nearest cent.

49. If wood paneling costs \$2.59 per square foot, how much would it cost to panel a wall that is 21 feet long by 8 feet high? Round your answer to the nearest dollar.

50. If it costs \$0.89 per square yard to paint a ceiling, how much would it cost to paint a ceiling that is 11 yards long by 8 yards wide? Round your answer to the nearest dollar.

51. If gold soldering costs \$5.29 per inch, how much would it cost to put it around the perimeter of a stained glass window that is 3 feet high by 2.5 feet wide? Round your answer to the nearest dollar.

52. If oak framing costs \$0.24 per inch, how much would it cost to put a frame around a picture that is 20 inches long by 30.5 inches high? Round your answer to the nearest dollar.

Find the approximate circumference and area of each of the following circles.

53.

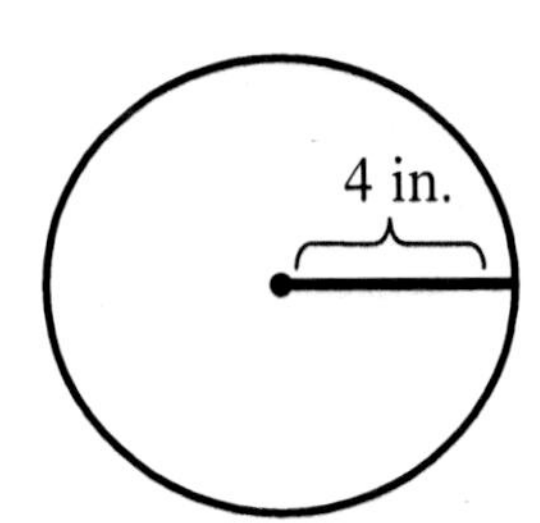

54.

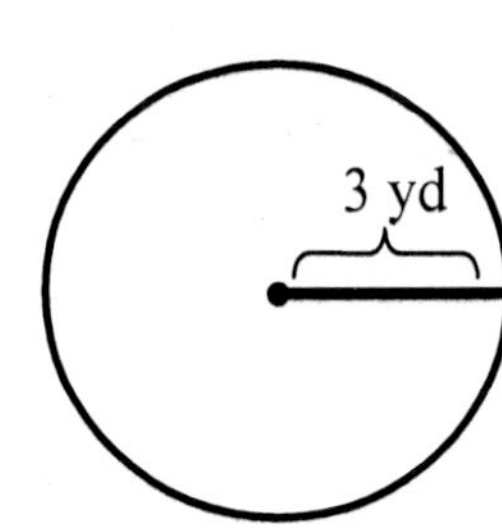

55.

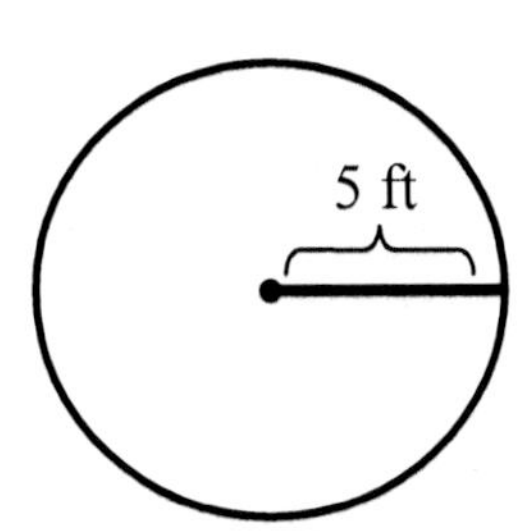

56.

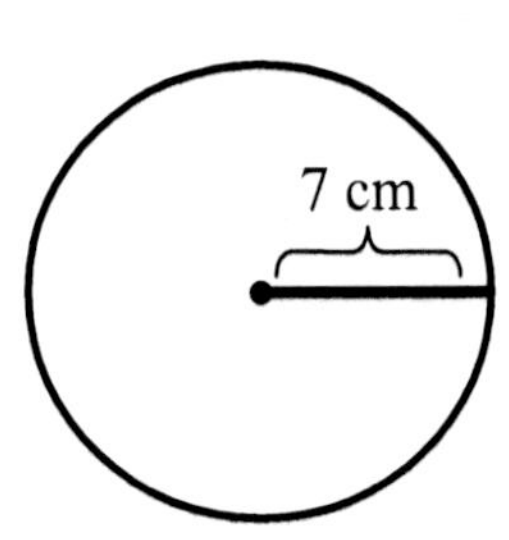

57.

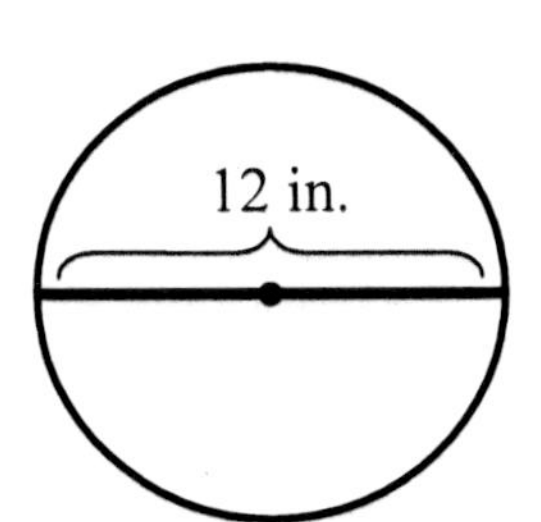

58.

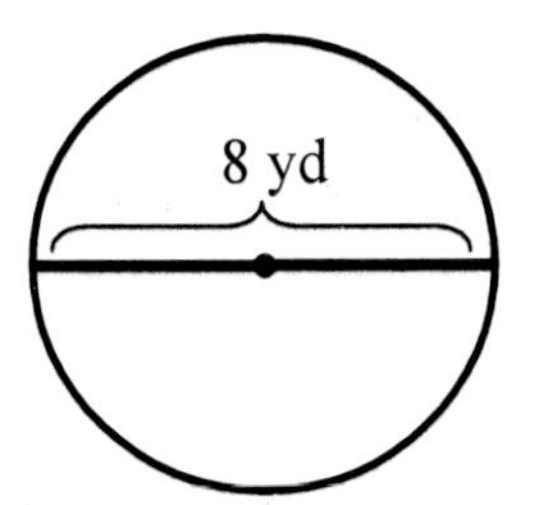

FALL QUARTER 2003

Course	Letter Grade	Credits
CHEM 140	B +	3
CHEM 141	B −	2
ENGL 101	B	5
MATH 124	A	5
HUM 101	B +	3

WINTER QUARTER 2004

Course	Letter Grade	Credits
CHEM 150	B +	3
CHEM 151	B	2
MATH 125	C	5
SOC 101	A −	5

SPRING QUARTER 2004

Course	Letter Grade	Credits
CHEM 160	A −	3
CHEM 161	B +	2
ECON 202	B	5
MATH 126	A	5
ENGR 108	B +	3

FALL QUARTER 2004

Course	Letter Grade	Credits
ENGN 109	B +	3
ENGR 201	A	5
IT 174	B −	5
PSYS 211/221	A	5

WINTER QUARTER 2005

Course	Letter Grade	Credits
ENGN 202	A	5
HUM 102	B +	3
MATH 220	C	5
PSYS 212/222	A −	5

SPRING QUARTER 2005

Course	Letter Grade	Credits
ENGN 203	A	5
MATH 224	A −	3
MATH 264	A	5
PSYS 213/223	A	5

Use John Doe's transcript from above to answer the following questions. Refer to the grade point value chart above example 12. (Give final answers to the nearest hundredth).

59. What was John's G.P.A. for Winter Quarter 2005?

60. What was John's G.P.A. for Spring Quarter 2004?

61. What was John's G.P.A. for the entire school year, starting Fall Quarter 2003 and ending Spring Quarter 2004?

62. What was John's G.P.A. for the entire school year, starting Fall Quarter 2004 and ending Spring Quarter 2005?

DECIMAL NUMBERS

Section 7: Solving Equations with Decimal Numbers

Let's look at possible solutions of equations, using decimal numbers.

Example 1: Is 0.92 a solution of the equation $4.78 - w = 3.96$?

Solution:

$4.78 - w = 3.96$ Substitute 0.92 in the place of w.

$4.78 - 0.92 \stackrel{?}{=} 3.96$ Simplify the left side of the equation.

$$\begin{array}{r} \overset{3}{\not{4}}.\overset{17}{\not{7}}8 \\ -0.92 \\ \hline 3.86 \end{array}$$

$3.86 \stackrel{?}{=} 3.96$ However,

$3.86 \neq 3.96.$ This is a false statement. Consequently, 0.92 is not a solution.

Example 2: Is 8.676 a solution of the equation $\dfrac{k}{3.6} = 2.41$?

Solution: $\dfrac{k}{3.6} = 2.41$ Substitute 8.676 in the place of k.

$\dfrac{8.676}{3.6} \stackrel{?}{=} 2.41$ Simplify the left side of the equation.

$\dfrac{8.676}{3.6}$ becomes $3.6\overline{)8.676}$.

$3.6\overline{)8.676}$ becomes $36\overline{)86.76}$.

$36\overline{)86.76}$ becomes $36\overline{)\dot{8}6.76}$.

$$\begin{array}{r} 2.41 \\ 36\overline{)86.76} \\ -72 \\ \hline 147 \\ -144 \\ \hline 36 \\ -36 \\ \hline 0 \end{array}$$

$2.41 \stackrel{\checkmark}{=} 2.41$ This is a true statement. Consequently, 8.676 is a solution.

In Chapter 1 we established properties that are used to solve equations with whole numbers. In Chapter 2 we used those same properties to solve equations with integers. In Chapter 3 we used those properties to solve equations with fractions. In this chapter we will use those properties to solve equations with decimal numbers. Let's review those properties along with an example of how each property is used with decimal numbers.

THE ADDITION PROPERTY OF EQUALITY:

When a, b, and c are real numbers, the following is true:

If $a = b$ then $a + c = b + c$.

If the same quantity is added to both sides of an equation, the new equation is equivalent to the old equation. That is, both equations have the same solution.

Example 3: Solve the equation: $x - 1.6 = 7.3$

Solution:

$x - 1.6 = 7.3$	Use the addition property of equality by adding 1.6 to both sides of the equation.
$x - 1.6 + 1.6 = 7.3 + 1.6$	Simplify the left side of the equation.
$x = 7.3 + 1.6$	Simplify the right side of the equation.
$\begin{array}{r} 7.3 \\ +1.6 \\ \hline 8.9 \end{array}$	
$x = 8.9$	The solution is $x = 8.9$. To check the solution, substitute it back into the original equation in place of the variable.
$x - 1.6 = 7.3$	becomes
$8.9 - 1.6 \stackrel{?}{=} 7.3$	which simplifies to
$7.3 \stackrel{\checkmark}{=} 7.3.$	The statement is true, therefore the solution is correct.

THE SUBTRACTION PROPERTY OF EQUALITY:

When a, b, and c are real numbers, the following is true:

If $a = b$ then $a - c = b - c$.

If the same quantity is subtracted from both sides of an equation, the new equation is equivalent to the old equation. That is, both equations have the same solution.

Example 4: Solve the equation: $6.2 = y + 8.1$

Solution:

$6.2 = y + 8.1$	Use the subtraction property of equality by subtracting 8.1 from both sides of the equation.
$6.2 - 8.1 = y + 8.1 - 8.1$	Simplify the left side of the equation.
$-1.9 = y + 8.1 - 8.1$	Simplify the right side of the equation.
$-1.9 = y$	The solution is $y = -1.9$. To check the solution, substitute it back into the original equation in place of the variable.
$6.2 = y + 8.1$	becomes
$6.2 \stackrel{?}{=} -1.9 + 8.1$	which simplifies to
$6.2 \stackrel{\checkmark}{=} 6.2.$	The statement is true, therefore the solution is correct.

THE MULTIPLICATION PROPERTY OF EQUALITY:

When a, b, and c are real numbers with $c \neq 0$, the following is true:

$$\text{If} \quad a = b \quad \text{then} \quad a \cdot c = b \cdot c.$$

If the same non-zero quantity is multiplied by both sides of an equation, the new equation is equivalent to the old equation. That is, both equations have the same solution.

Example 5: Solve the equation: $-\dfrac{x}{3.4} = 4$

Solution:

$$-\frac{x}{3.4} = 4$$

Rewrite the left side of the equation with the negative sign attached to the denominator.

Recall that $-\dfrac{x}{3.4} = \dfrac{-x}{3.4} = \dfrac{x}{-3.4}$.

$$\frac{x}{-3.4} = 4$$

Use the multiplication property of equality by multiplying both sides of the equation by -3.4.

$$(-3.4)\left(\frac{x}{-3.4}\right) = 4(-3.4)$$

Simplify the left side of the equation.

$$\overset{1}{\cancel{(-3.4)}}\left(\frac{x}{\underset{1}{\cancel{-3.4}}}\right) = 4(-3.4)$$

Simplify the right side of the equation.

$$\begin{array}{r} \overset{1}{-3.4} \\ \times \quad 4 \\ \hline -13.6 \end{array}$$

$$x = -13.6$$

The solution is $x = -13.6$. To check the solution, substitute it back into the original equation in place of the variable.

$$-\frac{x}{3.4} = 4$$

becomes

$$-\frac{-13.6}{3.4} \overset{?}{=} 4$$

which simplifies to

$$4 \overset{\checkmark}{=} 4.$$

The statement is true, therefore the solution is correct.

THE DIVISION PROPERTY OF EQUALITY:

When a, b, and c are real numbers with $c \neq 0$, the following is true:

$$\text{If} \quad a = b \quad \text{then} \quad \frac{a}{c} = \frac{b}{c}.$$

If both sides of the equation are divided by the same non-zero quantity, the new equation is equivalent to the old equation. That is, both equations have the same solution.

Example 6: Solve the equation: $5x = 6.3$

Solution:

$5x = 6.3$	Use the division property of equality by dividing both sides of the equation by 5.
$\frac{5x}{5} = \frac{6.3}{5}$	Simplify the left side of the equation.
$x = \frac{6.3}{5}$	Simplify the right side of the equation.

$$\begin{array}{r} 1.26 \\ 5\overline{)6.30} \\ -\ 5 \\ \hline 1\,3 \\ -\ 1\,0 \\ \hline 30 \\ -\ 30 \\ \hline 0 \end{array}$$

$x = 1.26$	The solution is $x = 1.26$. To check the solution, substitute it back into the original equation in place of the variable.
$5x = 6.3$	becomes
$5(1.26) \stackrel{?}{=} 6.3$	which simplifies to
$6.3 \stackrel{\checkmark}{=} 6.3.$	The statement is true, therefore the solution is correct.

Applications

Example 7: What is the wholesale cost of an item, if the retail cost is \$57.95 and the amount of mark-up is \$24.50? Use the formula $R = W + M$ (where R is the retail cost, W is the wholesale cost, and M is the amount of mark up).

Solution: Using the formula	$R = W + M$ gives us
$\$57.95 = W + \$24.50$.	Use the subtraction property of equality by subtracting \$24.50 from both sides of the equation.
$\$57.95 - \$24.50 = W + \$24.50 - \$24.50$	Simplify the left side of the equation.
$\$33.45 = W + \$24.50 - \$24.50$	Simplify the right side of the equation.
$\$33.45 = W$ or $W = \$33.45$	The wholesale cost of the item is \$33.45. To check the solution, substitute it back into the original equation in place of the variable.
$\$57.95 = W + \$24.50$	becomes
$\$57.95 \stackrel{?}{=} \$33.45 + \$24.50$	which further simplifies to
$\$57.95 \stackrel{\checkmark}{=} \$57.95$.	The statement is true, therefore the solution is correct.

Example 8: How long should it take a car to travel 186.2 miles if its average rate of speed is 53.2 miles per hour? Use the formula $d = rt$ (where d is distance, r is rate of speed, and t is the time spent traveling).

Solution: Using the formula	$d = rt$ gives us
$186.2 = 53.2t$.	Use the division property of equality by dividing both sides of the equation by 53.2.
$\frac{186.2}{53.2} = \frac{53.2t}{53.2}$	Simplify the left side of the equation.
$3.5 = \frac{53.2t}{53.2}$	Simplify the right side of the equation.
$3.5 = t$ or $t = 3.5$	The time it should take to travel 186.2 miles is 3.5 hours. To check the solution, substitute it back into the original equation in place of the variable.
$186.2 = 53.2t$	becomes
$186.2 \stackrel{?}{=} 53.2(3.5)$	which further simplifies to
$186.2 \stackrel{\checkmark}{=} 186.2$.	The statement is true, therefore the solution is correct.

$$\begin{array}{r} 3.5 \\ 532\overline{)1{,}862.0} \\ -\,1{,}596 \\ \hline 2660 \\ -\,2660 \\ \hline 0 \end{array}$$

Section 7 exercises. Check the solutions.

1. Is 3.14 a solution of the equation $23.07 + x = 26.21$?

2. Is 2.718 a solution of the equation $x + 42.802 = 45.502$?

3. Is 0.37 a solution of the equation $m - 0.05 = 0.032$?

4. Is 0.062 a solution of the equation $6.2 - n = 6.138$?

5. Is -4.2 a solution of the equation $2.3 - k = -6.5$?

6. Is -7.1 a solution of the equation $p - 12.2 = 19.3$?

7. Is -3.3 a solution of the equation $4.7m = -15.51$?

8. Is -5.5 a solution of the equation $2.2m = -6.6$?

9. Is 8.9 a solution of the equation $\frac{12.371}{x} = 1.39$?

10. Is 1.584 a solution of the equation $\frac{y}{17.6} = 0.09$?

Solve each of the following equations.

11. $x + 4.3 = 7.21$

12. $y + 6.9 = 10.34$

13. $a - 4.2 = 6.31$

14. $b - 13.8 = 5.94$

15. $\frac{p}{7} = 8.3$

16. $\frac{w}{3} = 1.96$

17. $4x = 6.3$

18. $5y = 8.2$

19. $m + 7.42 = -0.52$

20. $n + 21.5 = -7.24$

21. $c - 82.5 = -0.84$

22. $d - 2.1 = -0.408$

23. $\frac{x}{-7.1} = -5.2$

24. $\frac{y}{-8.5} = -4.6$

25. $-4.1z = 2.296$

26. $-3.9k = 0.0507$

27. $14.9 + h = 7$

28. $6.83 + k = 3$

29. $-0.61 = h - 4$

30. $-0.75 = k - 8$

31. $\frac{z}{0.08} = -62.5$

32. $\frac{m}{0.07} = -31.6$

33. $7.2p = -9$

34. $3.2n = -8$

35. $-8 = w + 17.5$

36. $-12 = z + 3.18$

37. $m - 0.05 = 0.004$

38. $n - 0.07 = 0.016$

39. $-\frac{n}{3.14} = 7$

40. $-\frac{w}{2.71} = 5$

41. $8.1 = 0.03p$

42. $2.5 = 0.05w$

Answer each question by using the given formula.

43. Use the formula $R = \frac{p}{h}$ (where R is the rate of pay, p is the total amount of pay, and h is the number of hours worked), to find the total amount of pay a person makes if they earn \$12.50 per hour and work for 7.5 hours.

44. Use the formula $R = \frac{p}{h}$ (where R is the rate of pay, p is the total amount of pay, and h is the number of hours worked), to find the total amount of pay a person makes if they earn \$16 per hour and work for 6.25 hours.

45. Find the amount of revenue generated by a hotdog stand in one week if the weekly cost to run the stand is \$1,354.76 and the weekly profit is \$746.83. Use the formula $P = R - C$ (where P is the profit, R is the revenue, and C is the cost).

46. Find the amount of revenue generated by a magazine stand in one week if the weekly cost to run the stand is \$2,876.96 and the weekly profit is \$1,235.58. Use the formula $P = R - C$ (where P is the profit, R is the revenue, and C is the cost).

47. Find the amount of interest earned on a savings account if the principal is \$783.44 and the total amount in the account is \$972.75. Use the formula $A = P + I$ (where A is the total amount in a savings account, P is the principal or amount put into the account, and I is the amount of interest in the account).

48. Find the amount of interest earned on a savings account if the principal is \$346.68 and the total amount in the account is \$409.32. Use the formula $A = P + I$ (where A is the total amount in a savings account, P is the principal or amount put into the account, and I is the amount of interest in the account).

49. Find the width of a rectangle if the area is 598 square feet and the length is 32.5 feet. Use the formula $A = LW$ (where A is the area, L is the length, and W is the width of a rectangle).

50. Find the width of a rectangle if the area is 343.1 square feet and the length is 23.5 feet. Use the formula $A = LW$ (where A is the area, L is the length, and W is the width of a rectangle).

51. Find the length of a rectangle if the area is 357.2 square meters and the width is 15.2 meters. Use the formula $A = LW$ (where A is the area, L is the length, and W is the width of a rectangle).

52. Find the length of a rectangle if the area is 392.7 square meters and the width is 15.4 meters. Use the formula $A = LW$ (where A is the area, L is the length, and W is the width of a rectangle).

53. Using the formula $A = \frac{1}{2}bh$, find the height of a triangle that has a base of 5.6 feet and an area of 33.6 square feet.

54. Using the formula $A = \frac{1}{2}bh$, find the height of a triangle that has a base of 7.4 feet and an area of 55.5 square feet.

55. Using the formula $A = \frac{1}{2}bh$, find the base of a triangle that has a height of 11.2 meters and an area of 44.8 square meters.

56. Using the formula $A = \frac{1}{2}bh$, find the base of a triangle that has a height of 9.6 meters and an area of 67.2 square meters.

DECIMAL NUMBERS

Section 8: Estimating

Earlier in this chapter, we looked at rounding decimal numbers. As with whole numbers, we will use front end rounding to estimate sums, differences, products and quotients of decimal numbers.

Example 1: Estimate the sum of 4.35, 0.891, and 12.07.

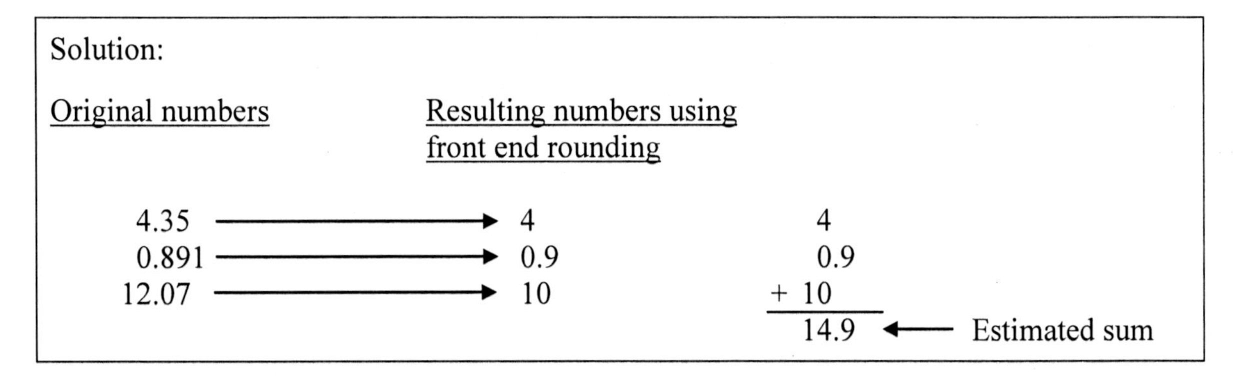

Example 2: Estimate the product of 2.635 and 0.74.

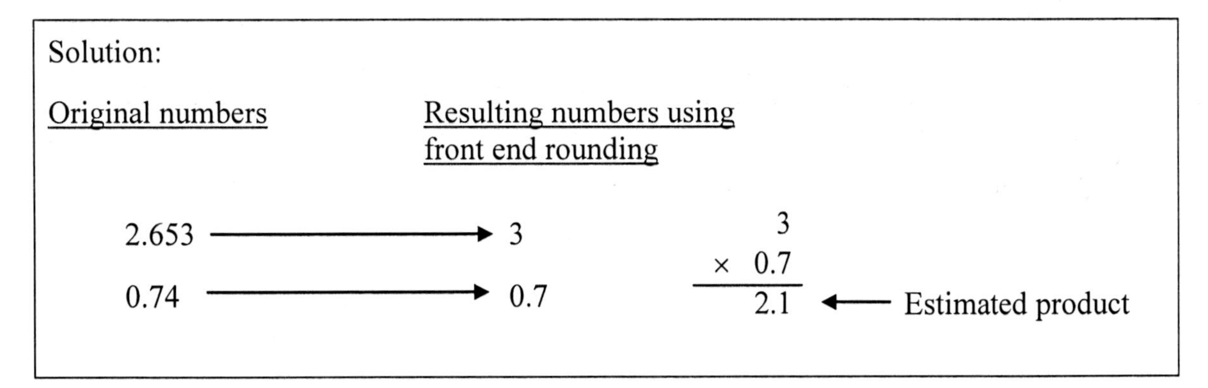

Example 3: Estimate the quotient of 3.705 and 0.784.

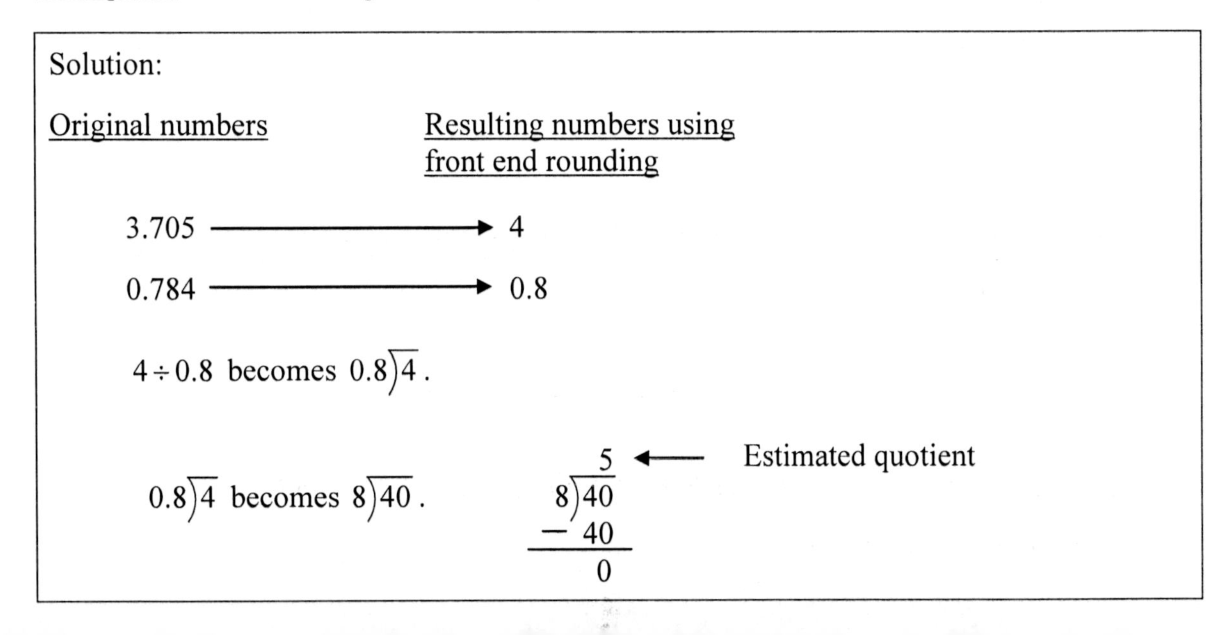

Section 8 exercises. Estimate each sum or difference by using front end rounding.

1.	$0.257 + 0.6409$	**2.**	$14.91 + 0.56$	**3.**	$1.74 + 23.854$
4.	$0.5703 + 0.4308$	**5.**	$31.72 - 26.09$	**6.**	$0.457 - 0.097$
7.	$0.32 - 0.65$	**8.**	$83.47 - 75.77$	**9.**	$48.3 + 50.8$
10.	$38.2 + 60.9$	**11.**	$1.92 - 0.439$	**12.**	$2.63 - 0.254$

Estimate each product by using front end rounding.

13.	$71.3(6.7)$	**14.**	$83.7(9.8)$	**15.**	$(31.8)(0.83)$
16.	$(47.3)(0.24)$	**17.**	$(8.65)(4.49)$	**18.**	$(6.76)(8.55)$

Estimate each quotient by using front end rounding.

19.	$59.87 \div 15.04$	**20.**	$83.92 \div 14.98$	**21.**	$0.95 \div 0.245$
22.	$0.625 \div 0.2533$	**23.**	$6{,}789.74 \div 100$	**24.**	$8{,}546.45 \div 1{,}000$

DECIMAL NUMBERS

Section 9: Roots

Addition and subtraction are sometimes referred to as inverse operations. For example, if you take the number 7 and add 4 to it, you get 11. Then, if you subtract 4 from 11, you get back to the original number 7. Adding and then subtracting the same number brings you back to where you started. Symbolically, the process looks like this:

$$\text{Since } \mathbf{7+4=11}, \text{then } \mathbf{11-4=7}.$$

Multiplication and division are also referred to as inverse operations. For example, if you take the number 5 and multiply it by 3, you get 15. Then, if you divide 15 by 3, you get back to the original number 5. Multiplying and then dividing by the same (non-zero) number brings you back to where you started. Symbolically, the process looks like this:

$$\text{Since } \mathbf{5\cdot 3=15}, \text{then } \mathbf{15\div 3=5}.$$

Another set of inverse operations involves exponents, or raising a number to a power. The inverse operation of this process is called taking the **root** of a number.

What exactly is a root? In a mathematical context, if you take a positive number and square it (that is, raise it to the 2nd power) and then you take the **square root** of the result, you get back to where you started. For example, 5 squared is 25. If you take the square root of 25, you get back to the original number 5. Symbolically, the process looks like this:

$$\text{Since } \mathbf{5^2=25}, \text{then } \mathbf{\sqrt{25}=5}.$$

The symbol $\sqrt{\ }$ is called a **square root symbol**. It is also called a **radical**. The quantity inside of the radical is called the **radicand**. In the example below, we are to take the 2nd or square root of the number 49.

$$\sqrt{49}$$

radical (arrow pointing to the radical sign)
radicand (arrow pointing to 49)

To determine what the square root of 49 or $\sqrt{49}$ equals, ask yourself the following question. What number squared equals 49, or what number times itself equals 49? Since $7^2=49$ or $7\cdot 7=49$ then $\sqrt{49}=7$.

Suppose you want to find the square root of 5, or $\sqrt{5}$. What number squared equals 5? Since $1^2 = 1$, it has to be a number larger than 1. Since $2^2 = 4$, it has to be a number larger than 2. However, since $3^2 = 9$, it has to be a number smaller that 3. In other words, the number we are looking for is between 2 and 3. The square root of 5 doesn't appear to be easy to find. We will talk more about that later, but for now let's talk about the numbers that have square roots which are easy to find. These numbers are called **perfect squares**. A perfect square is a number that has two identical integer factors.

Here is a table of some of the perfect squares.

Integer ↓	Perfect square ↓	Square root of the perfect square ↓
0	$0 \cdot 0$ or $0^2 = 0$	$\sqrt{0} = 0$
1	$1 \cdot 1$ or $1^2 = 1$	$\sqrt{1} = 1$
2	$2 \cdot 2$ or $2^2 = 4$	$\sqrt{4} = 2$
3	$3 \cdot 3$ or $3^2 = 9$	$\sqrt{9} = 3$
4	$4 \cdot 4$ or $4^2 = 16$	$\sqrt{16} = 4$
5	$5 \cdot 5$ or $5^2 = 25$	$\sqrt{25} = 5$
6	$6 \cdot 6$ or $6^2 = 36$	$\sqrt{36} = 6$
7	$7 \cdot 7$ or $7^2 = 49$	$\sqrt{49} = 7$
8	$8 \cdot 8$ or $8^2 = 64$	$\sqrt{64} = 8$
9	$9 \cdot 9$ or $9^2 = 81$	$\sqrt{81} = 9$

Many other perfect squares can be formed by using integers larger than those in the table. In addition, perfect squares can be formed by squaring negative integers. For instance, $(-1)^2 = 1$, $(-2)^2 = 4$, $(-3)^2 = 9$, etc. This creates a small problem, however. If $3^2 = 9$ and $(-3)^2 = 9$, then is $\sqrt{9} = 3$ or $\sqrt{9} = -3$? In some contexts, both solutions are considered correct. However, we will limit our answers to only positive square roots or, **principal square roots** as they are called.

Example 1: Simplify the following radical: $\sqrt{100}$

> Solution: Since $10^2 = 100$ then $\sqrt{100} = 10$.

As with a set of parentheses and a set of absolute value bars, a **radical is a grouping symbol**.

Example 2: Simplify the following expression: $-\sqrt{64}$

Solution: Following order of operations, simplify inside of the radical first.

$-\sqrt{64}$ becomes

$-(8)$. Apply the negative sign to the result of the radical.

-8.

Example 3: Simplify the following radical: $\sqrt{30+6}$

Solution: Following order of operations, simplify inside the grouping symbol first.

$\sqrt{30+6}$ becomes

$\sqrt{36}$. Since $6^2 = 36$ then

$\sqrt{36} = 6$. Or, in a more condensed form,

$\sqrt{30+6} = \sqrt{36} = 6$.

Example 4: Simplify the following expression: $5\sqrt{36+13}$

Solution: Following order of operations, simplify inside the grouping symbol first.

$5\sqrt{36+13}$ becomes

$5\sqrt{49}$. Since $7^2 = 49$ then $\sqrt{49} = 7$. A number next to a radical implies multiplication, just as a number that is next to a set of parentheses implies multiplication.

$5\sqrt{49}$ becomes

$5(7)$ which simplifies further to

35. Or, in a more condensed form,

$5\sqrt{36+13} = 5\sqrt{49} = 5(7) = 35$.

Example 5: Simplify the following expression: $3\sqrt{16}-2\sqrt{25}$

Solution: Following order of operations, simplify the radicals first.

$3\sqrt{16}-2\sqrt{25}$	becomes
$3(4)-2(5)$	which simplifies further to
$12-10$.	Subtracting we get
2.	Or, in a more condensed form,

$3\sqrt{16}-2\sqrt{25}=3(4)-2(5)=12-10=2$..

When a radical contains a single fraction, for example $\sqrt{\frac{4}{9}}$, the expression can be split apart into two separate radicals. One is in the numerator of the fraction and the other is in the denominator. $\sqrt{\frac{4}{9}}$ can be rewritten as $\frac{\sqrt{4}}{\sqrt{9}}$. This allows us to concentrate on simplifying the numerator separately from the denominator. Since $\sqrt{4}=2$ and $\sqrt{9}=3$, $\sqrt{\frac{4}{9}}=\frac{\sqrt{4}}{\sqrt{9}}=\frac{2}{3}$. Of course we could also determine $\sqrt{\frac{4}{9}}$ by asking the question, what number squared equals $\frac{4}{9}$? Since $\left(\frac{2}{3}\right)^2=\frac{4}{9}$, then $\sqrt{\frac{4}{9}}=\frac{2}{3}$. Anyway, a general rule for splitting up a fraction inside of a radical is this: $\sqrt{\frac{\boldsymbol{a}}{\boldsymbol{b}}}=\frac{\sqrt{\boldsymbol{a}}}{\sqrt{\boldsymbol{b}}}$.

Example 6: Simplify the following expression: $-\sqrt{\frac{25}{9}}$

Solution: Rewrite $-\sqrt{\frac{25}{9}}$ as

$-\frac{\sqrt{25}}{\sqrt{9}}$.	Deal with the numerator and denominator separately.
	Since $\sqrt{25}=5$ and $\sqrt{9}=3$
$-\frac{\sqrt{25}}{\sqrt{9}}=-\left(\frac{5}{3}\right)$.	Apply the negative sign to the results.
$-\frac{5}{3}$	The answer could also be written as $-1\frac{2}{3}$.

Variable expressions involving radicals can be evaluated. Here is an example.

Example 7: Evaluate the expression for the given values of the variables: $3\sqrt{ab+c}$, when $a=6$, $b=4$, and $c=1$

Solution: $3\sqrt{ab+c}$	Substitute 6 in the place of a, 4 in the place of b, and 1 in the place of c.
$3\sqrt{(6)(4)+(1)}$	Simplify inside of the radical by following order of operations. Multiplication, followed by addition.
$3\sqrt{24+1}$	which then becomes
$3\sqrt{25}$.	Take the square root of 25.
$\sqrt{25}=5$	
$3\sqrt{25}$	becomes
$3(5)$.	Simplify further.
15	

As we have seen, the square root of a perfect square is an integer. What about the square root of a number that is not a perfect square, for instance, 20? Since $\sqrt{16}=4$ and $\sqrt{25}=5$ then $\sqrt{20}$ must be a number between 4 and 5.

$\sqrt{16}=4$

$\sqrt{20}=?$

$\sqrt{25}=5$

$\sqrt{20}$ is a number that is between 4 and 5. However, writing that number is another matter. $\sqrt{20}$ can be approximated by using a decimal number rounded at a particular place value. However, it can't be written exactly, other than to write it as $\sqrt{20}$.

If we were to use a calculator to find $\sqrt{20}$ we would get 4.5 or 4.47 or 4.472 or 4.4721 or 4.47214 etc. depending at what place value we rounded. We could fill an entire page with digits to the right of the decimal point and still not get the exact value of $\sqrt{20}$. For now, we will limit our calculations to determining which two integers a square root lies between, when that square root is not an integer itself.

Example 8: Between what two whole numbers is $\sqrt{13}$ located?

Solution: The question that needs to be asked is, between what two perfect squares is the number 13? The first perfect square below 13 is 9, and the first perfect square above 13 is 16. From that information we get the following:

$\sqrt{9} = 3$

$\sqrt{13} = ?$

$\sqrt{16} = 4$

Therefore, $\sqrt{13}$ is between the number 3 and the number 4.

We spent a good deal of time discussing square roots, but what about other roots? A square root is undoing a perfect square. What about a cube or a number raised to the fourth power? Can we find the cube root of that number? The answer is yes, and the process is very much like that of finding the square root of a number. Let's start with the number 2.

$2 \cdot 2 \cdot 2 = 2^3 = 8$ Since $2^3 = 8$, then the cube root of 8 is 2.

$5 \cdot 5 \cdot 5 = 5^3 = 125$ Since $5^3 = 125$, then the cube root of 125 is 5.

What about a number raised to the fourth power?

$3 \cdot 3 \cdot 3 \cdot 3 = 3^4 = 81$ Since $3^4 = 81$, then the fourth root of 81 is 3.

We need to know what the notation looks like that allows us to distinguish roots other than square roots. This involves a number outside of the radical that tells what root to take, and is called the **index**. For instance, if we wish to take the cube (or third) root of a number, the index is a 3.

index → $\sqrt[3]{8}$ ← **radical**, ← **radicand**

Since $2^3 = 8$, then $\sqrt[3]{8} = 2$. Since $5^3 = 125$, then $\sqrt[3]{125} = 5$. Since $3^4 = 81$, then $\sqrt[4]{81} = 3$.

Note: Since square roots are the most common roots, instead of using a 2 as the index, we just leave it blank and assume it is a 2.

Example 9: Simplify the following radical: $\sqrt[4]{16}$

> Solution: Since the index is a 4, the question that needs to be asked is, what number, when raised to the fourth power, is 16? Since $2 \cdot 2 \cdot 2 \cdot 2 = 2^4 = 16$, the number is 2.
>
> Since $2^4 = 16$
>
> then $\sqrt[4]{16} = 2$.

Example 10: Simplify the following radical: $\sqrt[5]{1}$

> Solution: Since the index is a 5, the question that needs to be asked is, what number, when raised to the fifth power, is 1? Since $1 \cdot 1 \cdot 1 \cdot 1 \cdot 1 = 1^5 = 1$, the number is 1.
>
> Since $1^5 = 1$
>
> then $\sqrt[5]{1} = 1$.

Applications

The length of a pendulum determines the time required for it to swing through a complete cycle.

Example 11: Find the time required for a pendulum 24 inches long to swing through a complete cycle. Use the formula $T = 1.57\sqrt{6L}$ (where L is the length of the pendulum in inches and T is the time in seconds).

> Solution: Using the formula for the pendulum,
>
> | | |
> |---|---|
> | $T = 1.57\sqrt{6L}$ | gives us |
> | $T = 1.57\sqrt{6 \cdot (24)}$. | Simplify inside of the radical. |
> | $T = 1.57\sqrt{144}$ | Simplify the radical. |
> | $T = 1.57(12)$ | Multiply. |
> | $T = 18.84$ | The time it takes for a pendulum 24 inches in length to swing through a complete cycle is 18.84 seconds. |

The **Pythagorean theorem** states that for any right triangle, (a triangle that contains a 90° angle, which is called a right angle) the following relationship is true: The sum of the squares of the two shorter sides (the legs) of the triangle is equal to the square of the longest side (the hypotenuse) of the triangle. For example, in the triangle below $a^2 + b^2 = c^2$

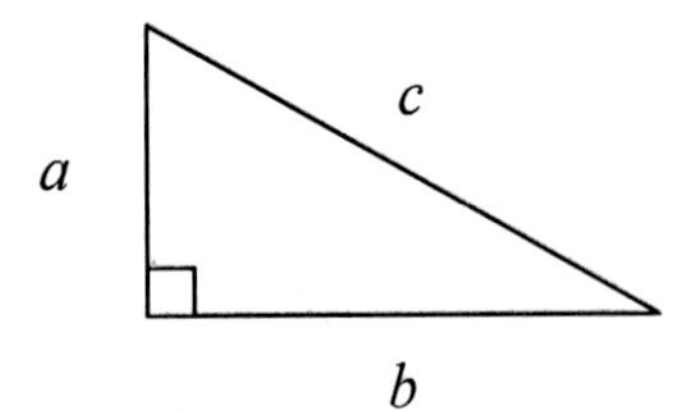

Note: The little box in the lower left corner of the triangle is to indicate a right angle.

By using different variations of the formula $a^2 + b^2 = c^2$, we can determine the length of one side of a right triangle if we know the length of the other two sides. For instance, to find the length of side *a,* we use $a = \sqrt{c^2 - b^2}$. To find the length of side *b*, we use $b = \sqrt{c^2 - a^2}$. Finally, to find the length of side *c* we use $c = \sqrt{a^2 + b^2}$.

Example 12: Use the formula $c = \sqrt{a^2 + b^2}$ to find the length of the longest side of the given triangle.

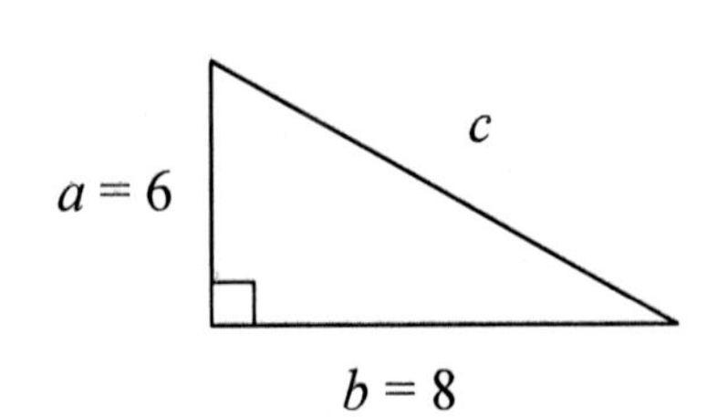

Solution: Using the formula

$c = \sqrt{a^2 + b^2}$ gives us

$c = \sqrt{(6)^2 + (8)^2}$. Simplifying, we get

$c = \sqrt{36 + 64}$ which then becomes

$c = \sqrt{100}$. Finally,

$c = 10$. The length of the longest side is 10.

Section 9 exercises. Simplify each expression.

1. $\sqrt{81}$ **2.** $\sqrt{64}$ **3.** $\sqrt{0}$ **4.** $\sqrt{4}$

5. $-\sqrt{25}$ **6.** $-\sqrt{36}$ **7.** $\sqrt{169}$ **8.** $\sqrt{144}$

9. $\sqrt{121}$ **10.** $\sqrt{196}$ **11.** $-\sqrt{1}$ **12.** $-\sqrt{16}$

13. $\sqrt{71+73}$ **14.** $\sqrt{81+88}$ **15.** $\sqrt{45-9}$ **16.** $\sqrt{49-24}$

17. $\sqrt{64}+\sqrt{36}$ **18.** $\sqrt{144}+\sqrt{81}$ **19.** $\sqrt{64+36}$ **20.** $\sqrt{144+81}$

21. $\sqrt{9^2}$ **22.** $\sqrt{7^2}$ **23.** $3\sqrt{16}$ **24.** $5\sqrt{36}$

25. $-7\sqrt{49}$ **26.** $-8\sqrt{64}$ **27.** $9\sqrt{9}$ **28.** $4\sqrt{4}$

29. $4\sqrt{9}-9\sqrt{4}$ **30.** $9\sqrt{16}-16\sqrt{9}$ **31.** $36+2\sqrt{36}$ **32.** $49+3\sqrt{49}$

33. $3\sqrt{100}-5^2$ **34.** $2\sqrt{121}-4^2$ **35.** $8\sqrt{1}-7\sqrt{0}$ **36.** $6\sqrt{0}-2\sqrt{1}$

37. $\sqrt{\frac{1}{9}}$ **38.** $\sqrt{\frac{1}{4}}$ **39.** $-\sqrt{\frac{4}{49}}$ **40.** $-\sqrt{\frac{9}{64}}$

41. $\sqrt{\frac{64}{16}}$ **42.** $\sqrt{\frac{81}{36}}$ **43.** $\sqrt{\frac{5}{125}}$ **44.** $\sqrt{\frac{7}{175}}$

45. $\sqrt{\frac{121}{4}}+\sqrt{\frac{49}{16}}$ **46.** $\sqrt{\frac{64}{9}}+\sqrt{\frac{1}{36}}$

Evaluate each expression for the given values of the variables.

47. $5\sqrt{x+y}$, where $x=3$ and $y=6$

48. $6\sqrt{h+k}$, where $h=11$ and $k=5$

49. $w\sqrt{x-3}$, where $w=4$ and $x=39$

50. $y\sqrt{z-5}$, where $y=3$ and $z=30$

51. $-3\sqrt{ab}$, where $a=2$ and $b=50$

52. $-7\sqrt{mp}$, where $m=2$ and $p=32$

53. $\sqrt{\frac{a}{b}}$, where $a=49$ and $b=16$

54. $\sqrt{\frac{w}{x}}$, where $w=121$ and $x=81$

55. $\sqrt{x^2+y^2}$, where $x=6$ and $y=8$

56. $\sqrt{w^2-z^2}$, where $w=41$ and $z=40$

57. $\sqrt{c^2}$, where $c=11$

58. $-\sqrt{b^2}$, where $b=13$

Translate each phrase into mathematical symbols. Then determine the result in each case.

59. What is the product of two and the square root of one hundred?

60. What is the difference of the square root of one hundred twenty-one and seven?

61. Find the sum of the square root of forty-nine and two cubed.

62. Find the quotient of twenty-four and the square root of sixty-four.

63. Find the square root of the sum of twenty-three and thirteen.

64. What is the product of negative eight and the square root of nine?

Determine what two whole numbers each radical is located between.

65. $\sqrt{43}$ **66.** $\sqrt{88}$ **67.** $\sqrt{14}$ **68.** $\sqrt{29}$

69. $\sqrt{58}$ **70.** $\sqrt{37}$ **71.** $\sqrt{79}$ **72.** $\sqrt{60}$

73. $\sqrt{125}$ **74.** $\sqrt{150}$

Simplify each of the following radicals.

75. $\sqrt[3]{64}$ **76.** $\sqrt[3]{27}$ **77.** $\sqrt[3]{216}$ **78.** $\sqrt[3]{125}$

79. $\sqrt[3]{1}$ **80.** $\sqrt[3]{8}$ **81.** $\sqrt[4]{81}$ **82.** $\sqrt[4]{625}$

83. $\sqrt[4]{256}$ **84.** $\sqrt[4]{0}$ **85.** $\sqrt[5]{32}$ **86.** $\sqrt[5]{243}$

87. $\sqrt[6]{64}$ **88.** $\sqrt[6]{1}$

Applications

89. Find the time required for a pendulum 1.5 inches long to swing through a complete cycle. Use the formula $T = 1.57\sqrt{6L}$ (where L is the length of the pendulum in inches and T is the time in seconds).

90. Find the time required for a pendulum 13.5 inches long to swing through a complete cycle. Use the formula $T = 1.57\sqrt{6L}$ (where L is the length of the pendulum in inches and T is the time in seconds).

91. The depth, or thickness, of a beam required to hold a given weight varies depending on the material, and its length and width. For a wooden beam to hold 2,000 pounds, use the formula $t = 3\sqrt{\frac{L}{w}}$ (where t is the thickness in inches, w is the width in inches, and L is the length in feet). How thick would a wooden beam need to be if it was supposed to hold 2,000 lbs, when it was only 9 inches wide and 16 feet long?

92. The depth, or thickness, of a beam required to hold a given weight varies depending on the material, and its length and width. For a wooden beam to hold 2,000 pounds, use the formula $t = 3\sqrt{\frac{L}{w}}$ (where t is the thickness in inches, w is the width in inches, and L is the length in feet). How thick would a wooden beam need to be if it was supposed to hold 2,000 lbs, when it was only 4 inches wide and 9 feet long?

93. Find the perimeter of a square with the given area.

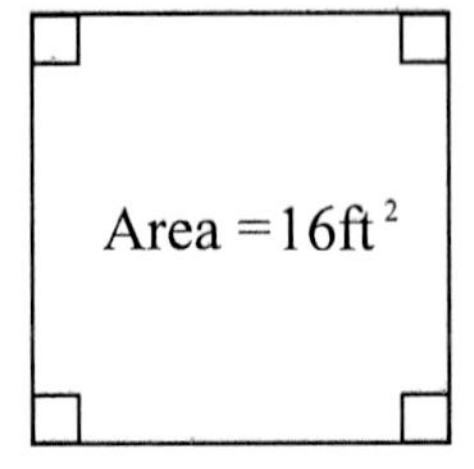

Hint: Use the following formulas: $A = s^2$ and $P = 4s$

94. Find the perimeter of a square with the given area.

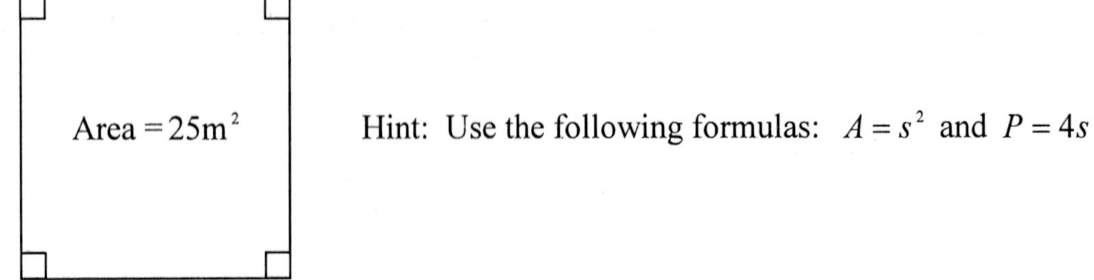

Using the formula given, solve for the unknown length of each right triangle.

95. $a = \sqrt{c^2 - b^2}$

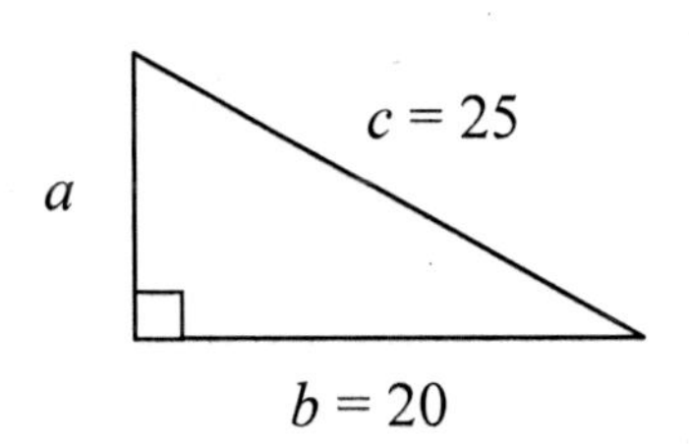

96. $c = \sqrt{a^2 + b^2}$

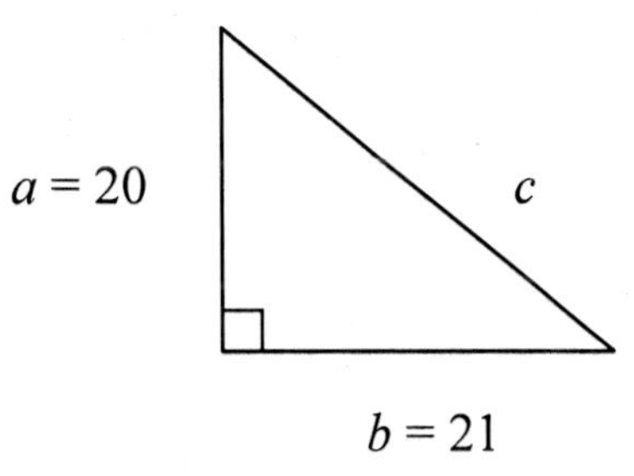

97. $c = \sqrt{a^2 + b^2}$

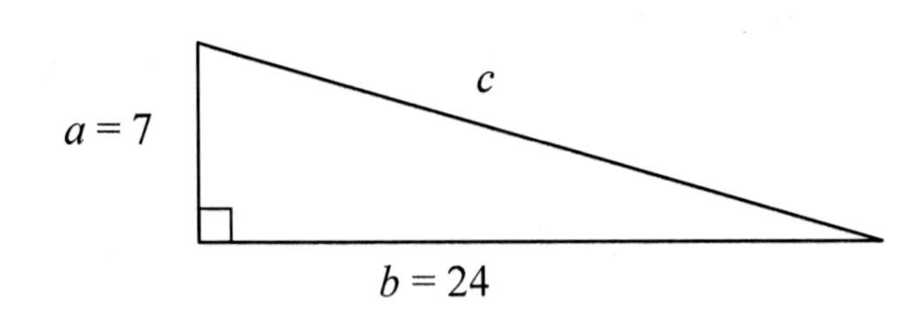

98. $b = \sqrt{c^2 - a^2}$

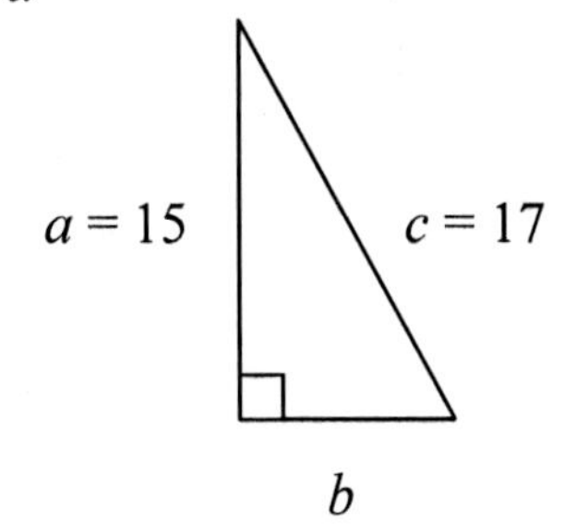

99. How long would a ladder need to be in order for the base to be 5 feet away from a wall, and the top to be leaning against the wall, 12 feet above the ground?

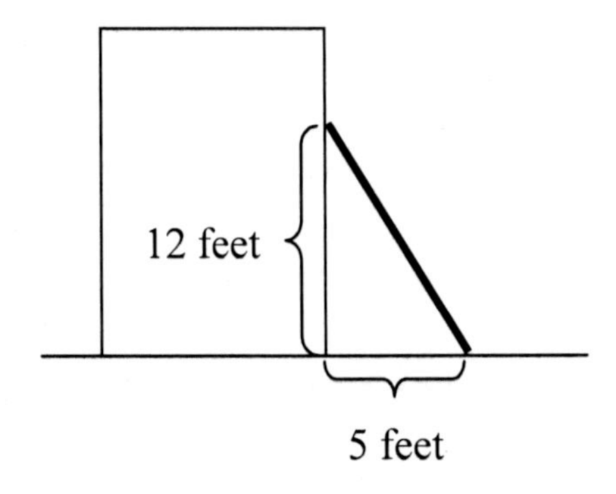

100. The size of a flat screen television set is determined by the length of a diagonal line across its screen. What is the size of the television set pictured below if it is 12 inches wide and 9 inches tall?

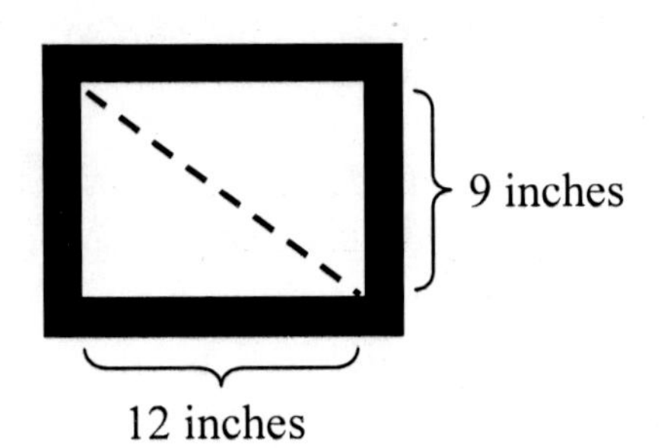

DECIMAL NUMBERS

Section 10: Real Numbers

Let's review the sets of numbers we've looked at so far, and introduce some new ones.

The set of counting numbers, or natural numbers: **1, 2, 3, 4, 5, 6, 7, 8, . . .**

The set of whole numbers: **0, 1, 2, 3, 4, 5, 6, 7, 8, . . .**

The set of integers: **. . . −5, −4, −3, −2, −1, 0, 1, 2, 3, 4, 5, . . .**

After studying fractions and decimals, we're ready to talk about a set of numbers called **rational numbers**.

A rational number is any number that can be written in the form of a fraction $\frac{a}{b}$ where a and b are both integers and $b \neq 0$.

Rational numbers include all natural numbers, whole numbers, and integers. For example, since the integer -3 can be written as the fraction $\frac{-3}{1}$, then -3 is a rational number. Rational numbers also include certain decimal numbers. One way to show this is by the fact that certain types of decimal numbers are equivalent to fractions, which in turn are rational numbers. A **repeating decimal number** is equivalent to a fraction and therefore is a rational number. For instance, $0.\overline{3} = \frac{1}{3}$, $0.\overline{6} = \frac{2}{3}$, $-0.\overline{7} = -\frac{7}{9}$, and $0.\overline{428571} = \frac{3}{7}$. Another type of decimal number is called a **terminating decimal number**. A terminating decimal number is one that doesn't repeat and doesn't just keep going on. In other words, it terminates. A terminating decimal number is equivalent to a fraction and therefore is a rational number. For instance, $0.7 = \frac{7}{10}$, $0.319 = \frac{319}{1{,}000}$, and $-0.23 = -\frac{23}{100}$.

A decimal number that doesn't terminate and doesn't have a digit or block of digits that repeats is called an **irrational number**.

An irrational number is any number that can't be written in the form of a fraction $\frac{a}{b}$ where a and b are both integers and $b \neq 0$.

One example of an irrational number is π, which is used in calculating the area of a circle among other things. To write π as a decimal number isn't possible because it just goes on and on without repeating. Written to 20 decimal places π is 3.14159265358979323846. This, however, is not π. It is just an approximation for π. Typically, we say $\pi \approx 3.14$. The symbol "$\approx$" means "is approximately."

Since the square root of a perfect square is a whole number, the square root of a perfect square is a rational number. For instance, $\sqrt{1} = 1$. So, $\sqrt{1}$ is rational. $\sqrt{4} = 2$. So, $\sqrt{4}$ is rational. $\sqrt{9} = 3$. So, $\sqrt{9}$ is rational.

On the other hand, square roots of numbers that aren't perfect squares are irrational numbers. For example $\sqrt{2}$, $\sqrt{3}$, $\sqrt{5}$, $\sqrt{6}$, $\sqrt{7}$, and $\sqrt{8}$ are irrational numbers.

Approximating to 8 decimal places, $\sqrt{2} \approx 1.41421356$, $\sqrt{3} \approx 1.73205080$, $\sqrt{5} \approx 2.23606797$, $\sqrt{6} \approx 2.44948974$, $\sqrt{7} \approx 2.64575131$, and $\sqrt{8} \approx 2.82842712$.

Finally, there is a set of numbers that includes all of the rational numbers and all of the irrational numbers. This set is called the **real numbers**. The set of real numbers includes all of the other sets of numbers we have discussed in this book. Here is a flow chart of the sets of numbers.

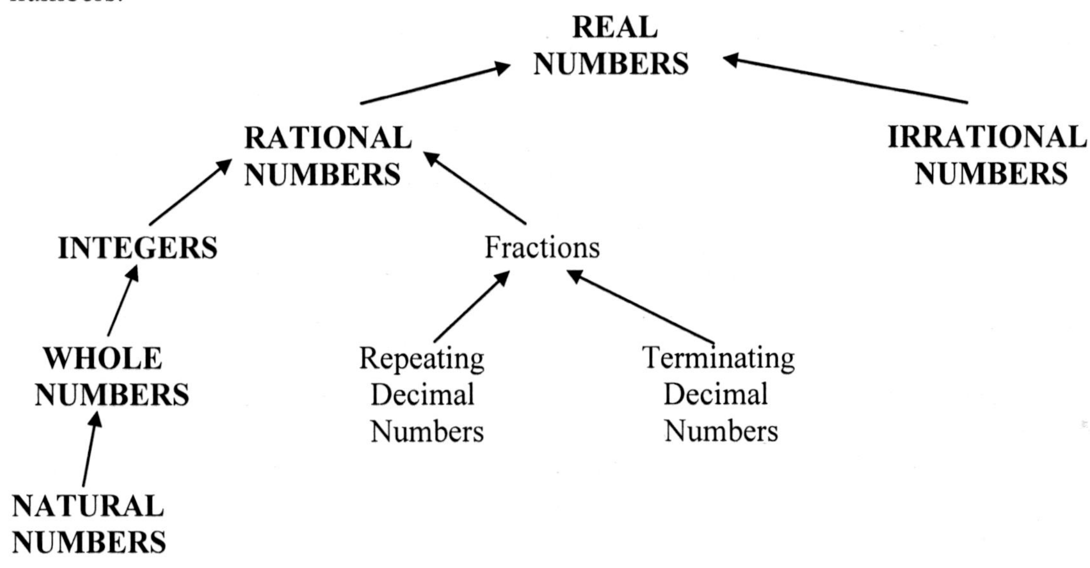

Example 1: To which set, or sets, of numbers do the following numbers belong: 5, 0, $-\frac{2}{7}$, 2.14, -3, $0.\overline{18}$, and $\sqrt{16}$

> Solution: 5 is a natural number, a whole number, an integer, a rational number, and a real number.
>
> 0 is a whole number, an integer, a rational number, and a real number.
>
> $-\frac{2}{7}$ is a rational number and a real number.
>
> 2.14 is a rational number and a real number.
>
> -3 is an integer, a rational number, and a real number.
>
> $0.\overline{18}$ is a rational number and a real number.
>
> $\sqrt{16}$ is a natural number, a whole number, an integer, a rational number, and a real number.

Previously we looked at number line graphs of natural numbers, whole numbers, integers, fractions, and decimal numbers. When we graphed all the integers greater than -2 and less than 3, we plotted only 4 points.

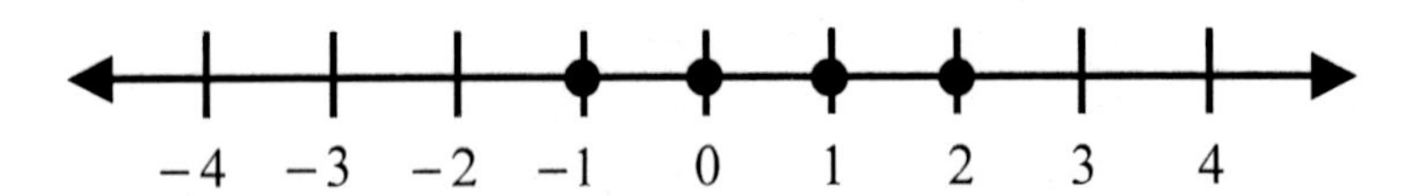

However, if we graph all of the real numbers greater than -2 and less than 3, we get a graph that is continuous, starting just to the right of -2 and ending just to the left of 3.

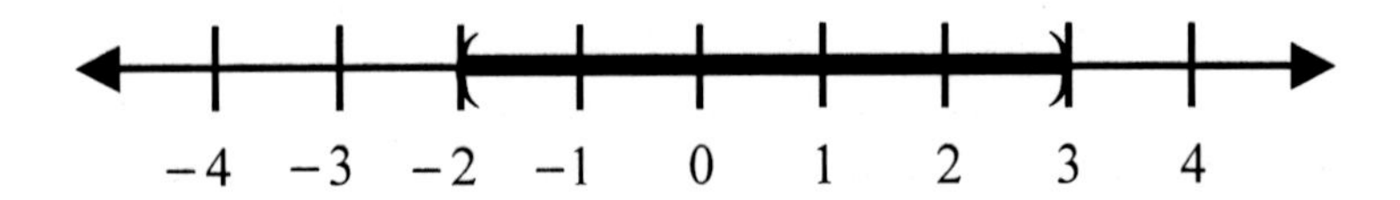

We use **parentheses** on the graph at the numbers -2 and 3 to indicate that the numbers -2 and 3 are not to be included. The reason we get a continuous graph is that if we plot the points that represent all of the real numbers in between -2 and 3, there are an infinite number of points to be represented. Just between the number 1 and the number 2 there are more points than a person could count in their lifetime. What point comes immediately to the right of 1? Is it 1.1, 1.01, or 1.00000000001? We could continue to add zeros to the right of the decimal point forever before we put a 1 at a particular place value.

Example 2: Graph the real numbers between -5 and 2.

Solution: Since -5 is not to be included, we put a left parenthesis at that location on the number line. We then draw a solid line to the right until we get almost to 2. We put a right parenthesis at 2 to indicate that it is also to be excluded from the solution set.

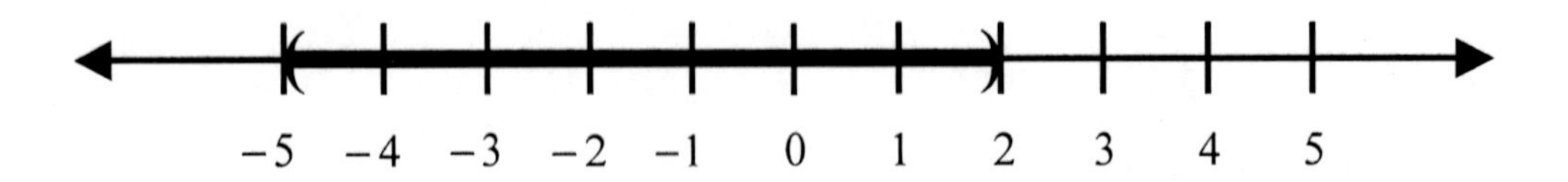

Because the real number line continues to the right forever, we say that it goes to **positive infinity**. And because it continues to the left forever, we say that it goes to **negative infinity**. We use an arrow to show this idea on the number line.

Example 3: Graph the real numbers greater than -3.

Solution: Since -3 is not to be included, we put a left parenthesis at that location on the number line. We then draw a solid line to the right. To indicate all real numbers greater than -3, put an arrowhead pointing in the right direction to imply that the graph goes to positive infinity.

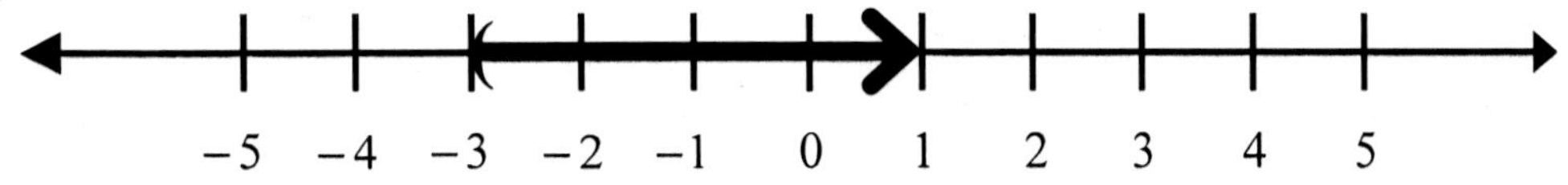

Example 4: Graph the real numbers less than 3.

Solution: Since 3 is not to be included, we put a right parenthesis at that location on the number line. We then draw a solid line to the left. To indicate all real numbers less than 3, put an arrowhead pointing in the left direction to imply that the graph goes to negative infinity.

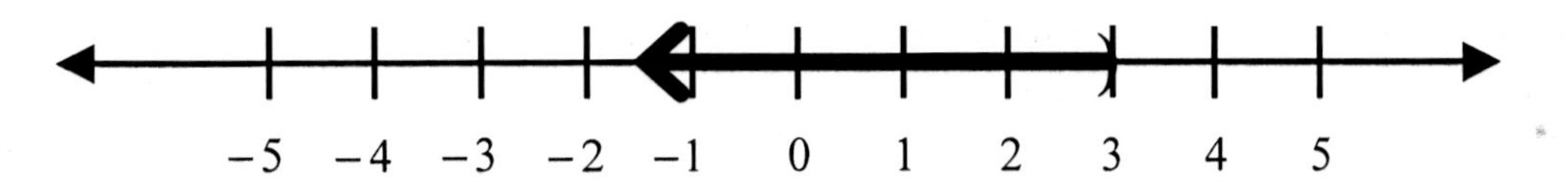

We have used an inequality symbol to compare two numbers. For instance, $-2 < 7$ or $6 > 4$. We can also use inequality symbols in a different way. Suppose we want the set of all real numbers that are greater than 4. If we use a variable such as *x*, we could make the following statement: $x > 4$, that is, "*x* is greater than 4" and create a graph. The graph of $x > 4$ looks like this:

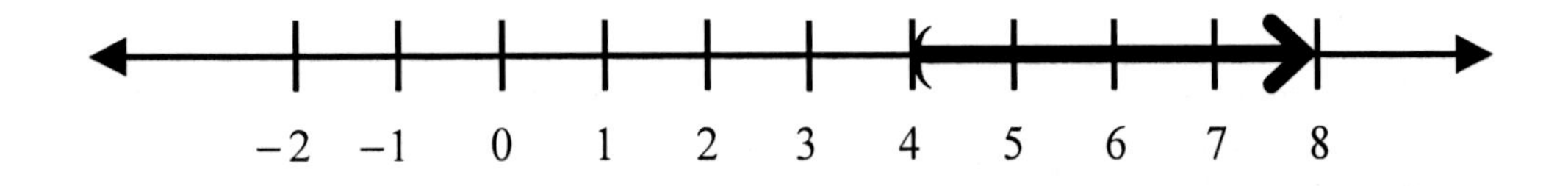

Another example is $x < 1$, that is, "*x* is less than 1." The graph of $x < 1$ looks like this:

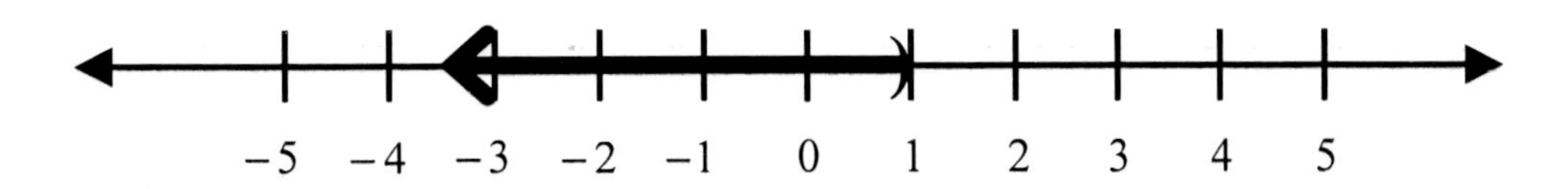

Suppose we want to graph the set of all real numbers that are greater than or equal to 2. By combining a greater than symbol " > " and an equal sign " = " we get a "**greater than or equal to**" symbol that looks like this: " ≥ " The example becomes $x \geq 2$, that is, "x is greater than or equal to 2." This time we want to include the number 2 as part of the graph. Instead of using a parenthesis, we use a bracket like this [. This tells us to include the number where the bracket is located. The graph of $x \geq 2$ looks like this:

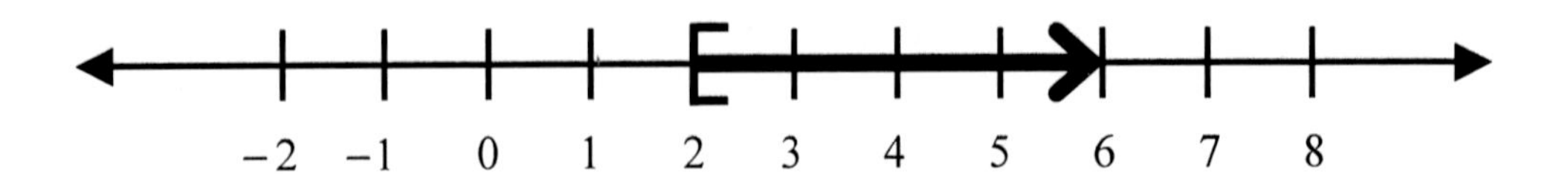

Suppose we want to graph the set of all real numbers that are less than or equal to 6. By combining a less than symbol " < " and an equal sign " = " we get a "**less than or equal to**" symbol that looks like this: " ≤ " The example becomes $x \leq 6$, that is, "x is less than or equal to 6." This time we want to include the number 6 as part of the graph. Instead of using a parenthesis, we use a bracket like this]. This tells us to include the number where the bracket is located. The graph of $x \leq 6$ looks like this:

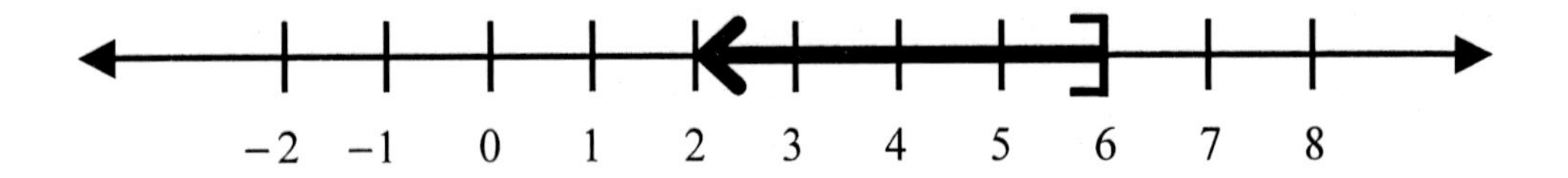

Example 5: Graph $x < 0$ on the real number line.

Solution: Since 0 is not to be included, we put a right parenthesis at that location on the number line. We then draw a solid line to the left. To indicate all real numbers less than 0, put an arrowhead pointing in the left direction to imply that the graph goes to negative infinity.

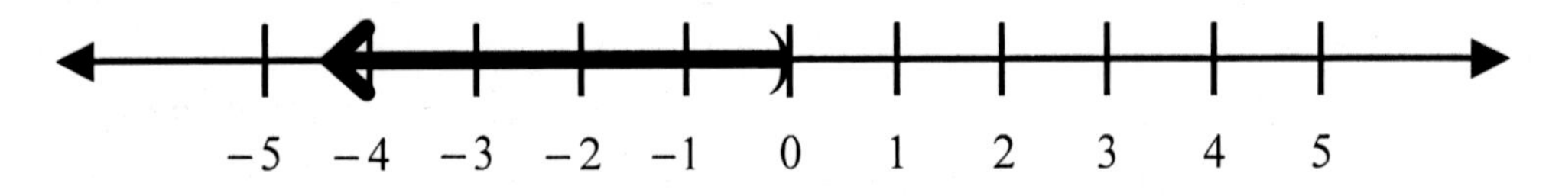

Example 6: Graph $x \leq 0$ on the real number line.

Solution: Since 0 is to be included, we put a right bracket at that location on the number line. We then draw a solid line to the left. To indicate all real numbers less than 0, put an arrowhead pointing in the left direction to imply that the graph goes to negative infinity.

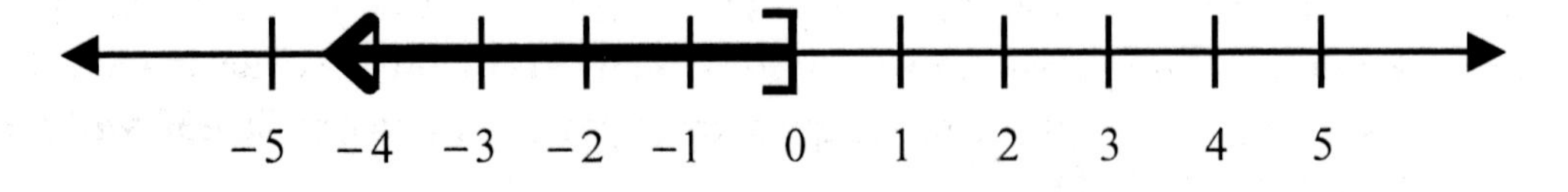

Example 7: Graph $x \geq -2$ on the real number line.

Solution: Since -2 is to be included, we put a left bracket at that location on the number line. We then draw a solid line to the right. To indicate all real numbers greater than -2, put an arrowhead pointing in the right direction to imply that the graph goes to positive infinity.

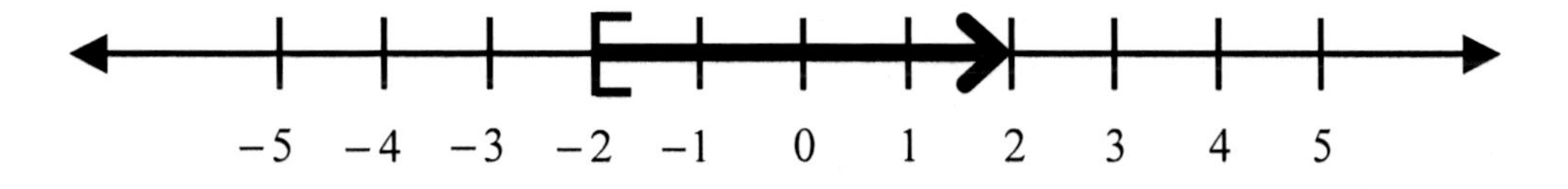

Example 8: Graph $x > -2$ on the real number line.

Solution: Since -2 is not to be included, we put a left parenthesis at that location on the number line. We then draw a solid line to the right. To indicate all real numbers greater than -2, put an arrowhead pointing in the right direction to imply that the graph goes to positive infinity.

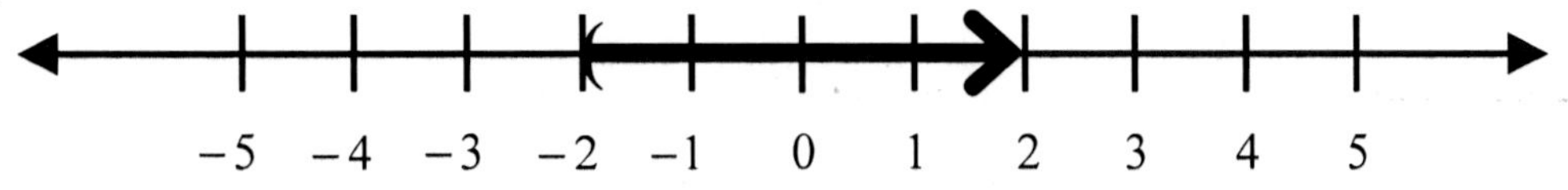

Applications involving inequalities with real numbers

Example 9: Water freezes at a temperature of 32 degrees Fahrenheit or below. Write an inequality statement representing the temperatures at which water will freeze. Will water freeze in a place where the temperature is 34 degrees Fahrenheit?

Solution: We will let the variable T stand for temperature in degrees Fahrenheit. To represent 32 degrees Fahrenheit or below we will use the inequality $T \leq 32$. If we substitute 34 degrees for T in the inequality, we get $34 \leq 32$. Since this is not a true statement, the answer to the question is no. Water will not freeze in a place where the temperature is 34 degrees Fahrenheit.

Example 10: To start a scholarship fund at a local college, a minimum deposit of $5,000 is required. Write an inequality statement representing the amounts of money that could be deposited in order to qualify for starting a scholarship fund. Will a deposit of $6,430 meet the requirement to start a scholarship fund?

Solution: We will let the variable D stand for deposit. To represent $5,000 or more we will use the inequality $D \geq 5{,}000$. If we substitute $6,430 for D in the inequality, we get $6{,}430 \geq 5{,}000$. Since this is a true statement, the answer to the question is yes. A deposit of $6,430 will meet the requirement to start a scholarship fund.

Section 10 exercises. List which set or sets each number belongs to: natural numbers, whole numbers, integers, rational numbers, irrational numbers, and real numbers.

1. $-\sqrt{8}$ **2.** $0.\overline{7}$ **3.** $2\frac{1}{8}$ **4.** -23

5. 14 **6.** $\sqrt{29}$ **7.** $-\frac{2}{7}$ **8.** $-4\frac{2}{3}$

9. 4.55 **10.** 107 **11.** $\sqrt{25}$ **12.** 0.5353

Graph each group of numbers on the real number line.

13. real numbers greater than 3

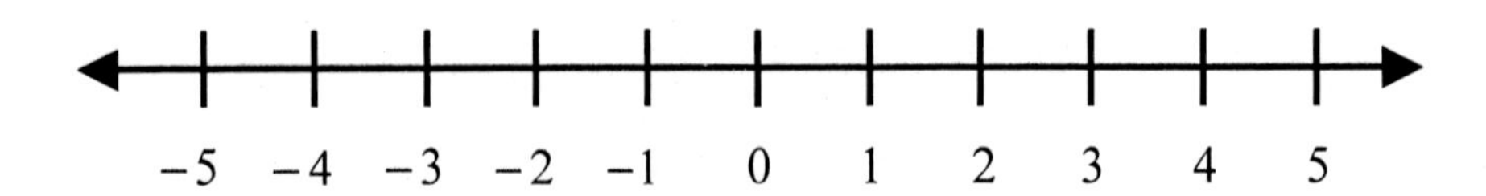

14. real numbers greater than 4

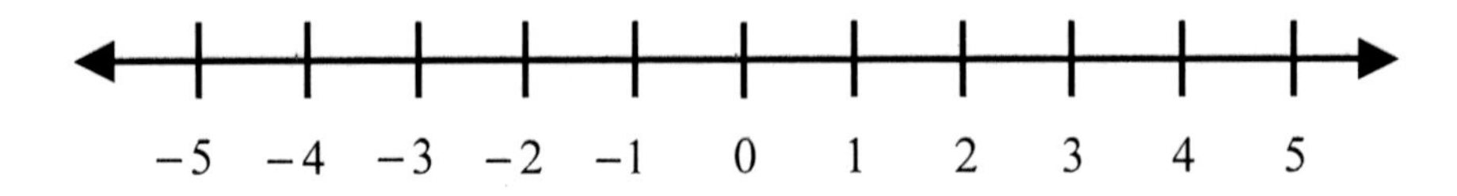

15. real numbers between 0 and 6

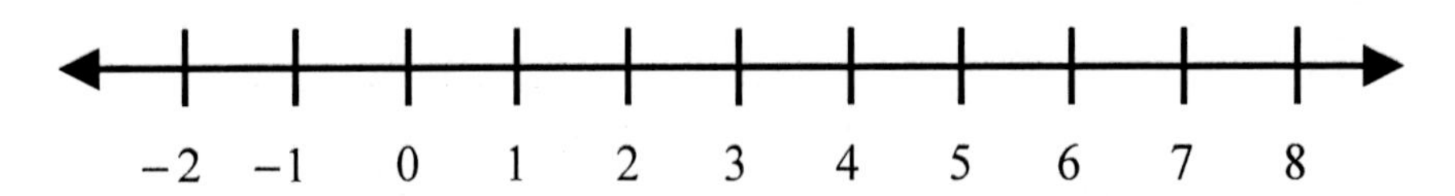

16. real numbers between -6 and 0

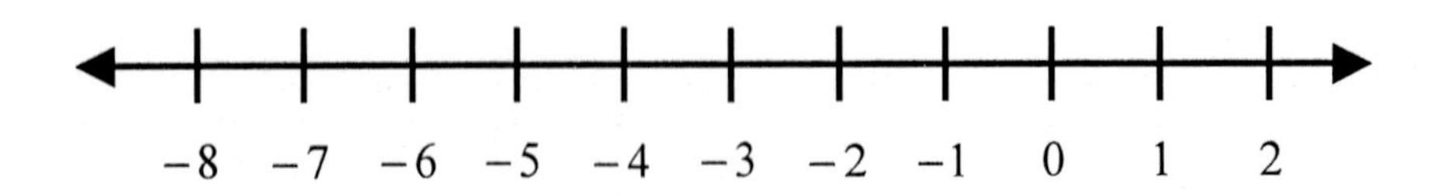

17. real numbers less than -1

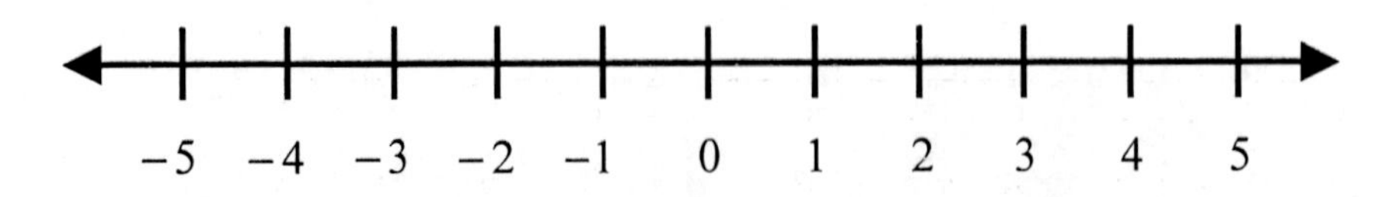

18. real numbers less than 7

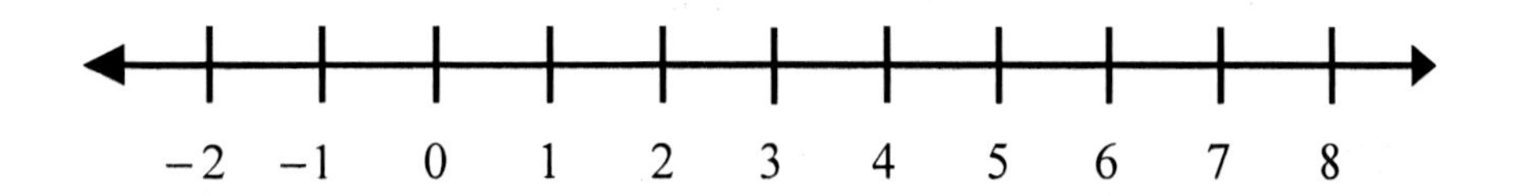

19. real numbers between 4 and 7

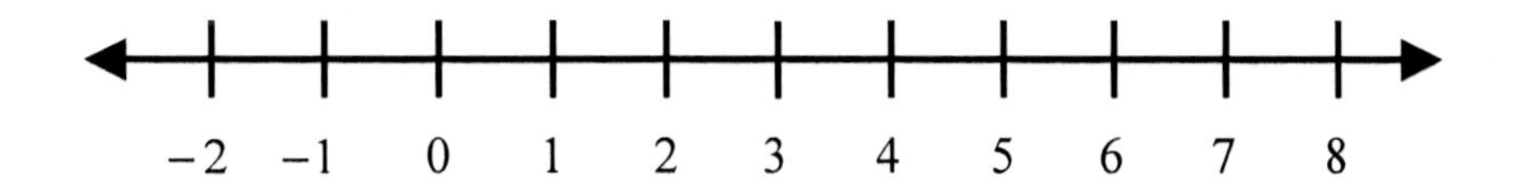

20. real numbers between 2 and 5

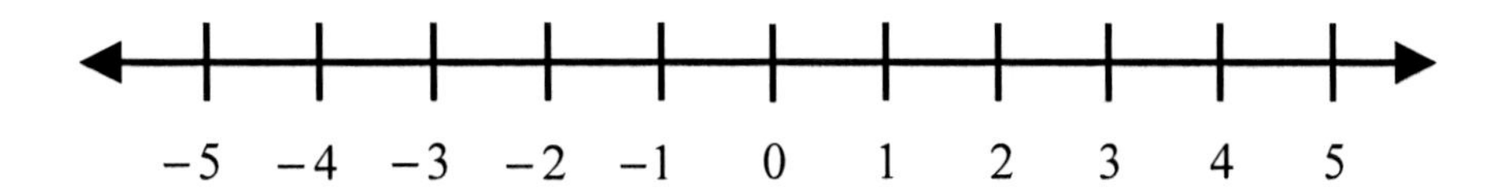

21. real numbers greater than -4

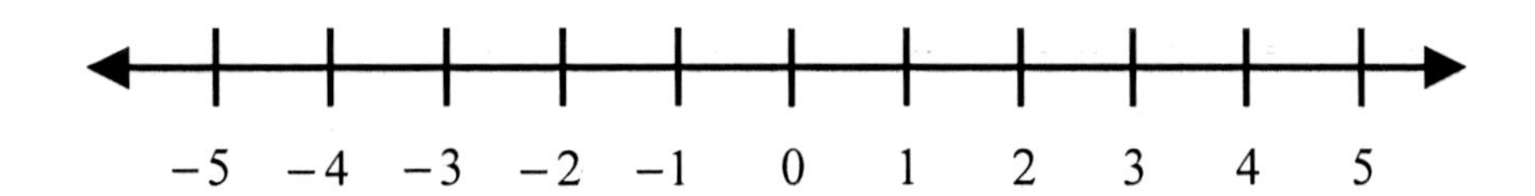

22. real numbers greater than -5

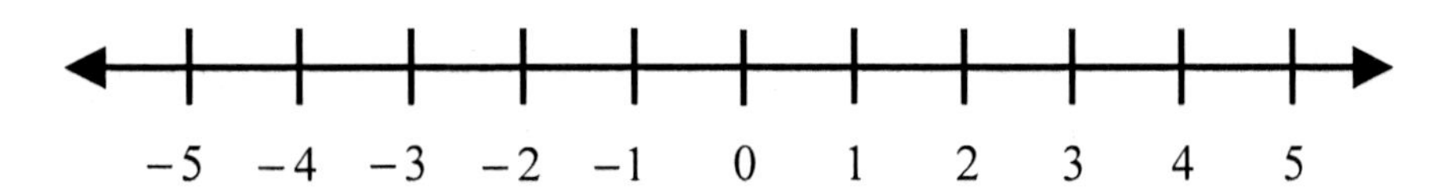

23. real numbers between -3 and -1

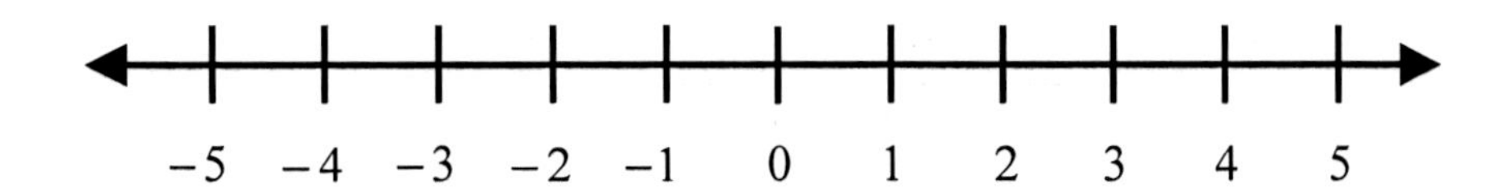

24. real numbers between -5 and -2

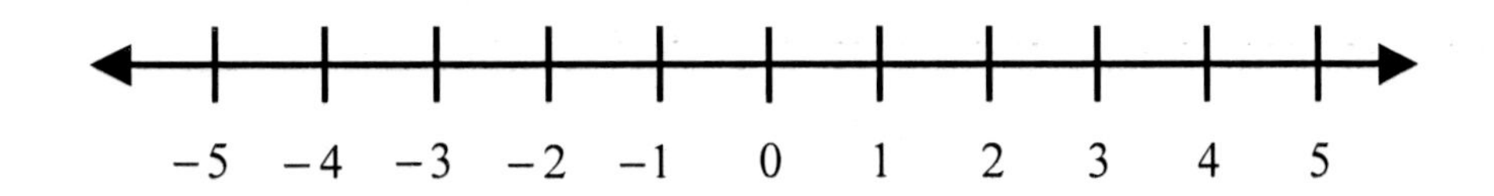

25. real numbers less than 4

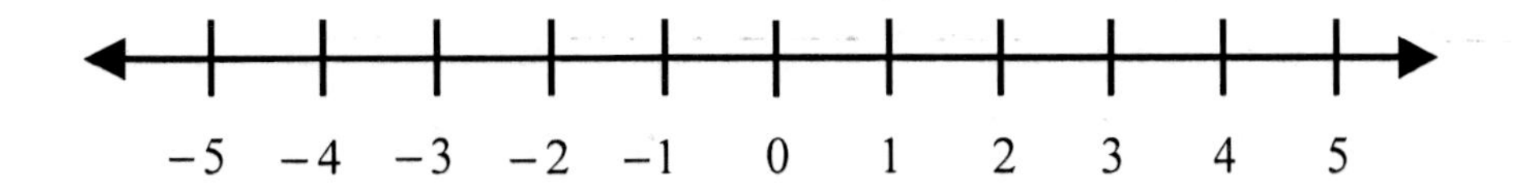

26. real numbers less than -2

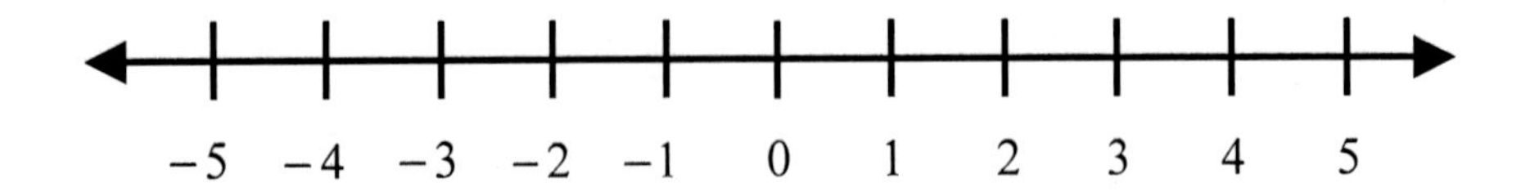

27. real numbers between -4 and 2

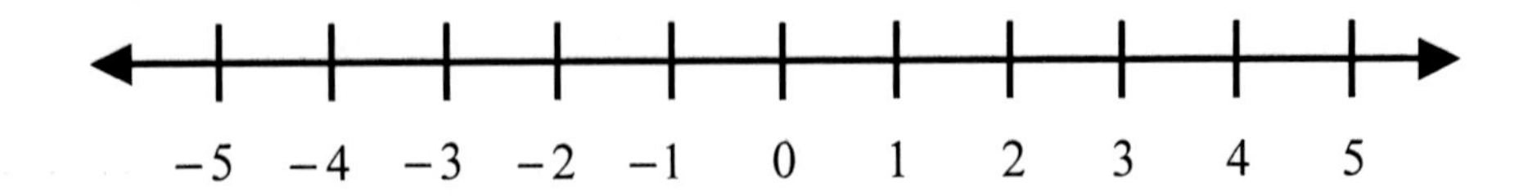

28. real numbers between -1 and 5

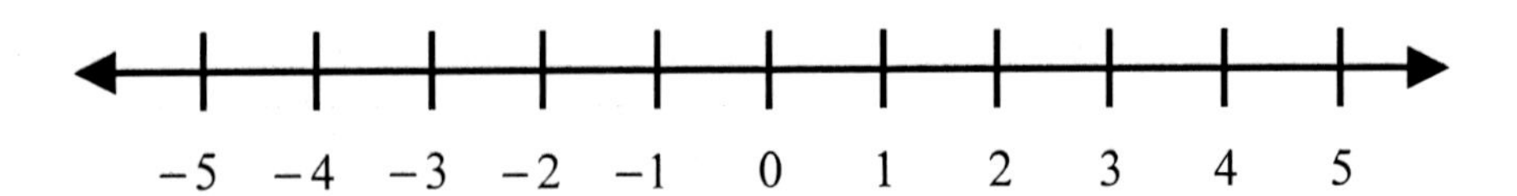

29. List the following real numbers in order from smallest to largest: $-\sqrt{3}$, $\frac{2}{9}$, $0.\overline{3}$, $\sqrt{7}$, 0.8, and -3

30. List the following real numbers in order from smallest to largest: $-\sqrt{5}$, $-\frac{2}{5}$, $0.\overline{2}$, $\sqrt{2}$, 0.5, and -2

Graph each inequality on the real number line.

31. $x < 5$

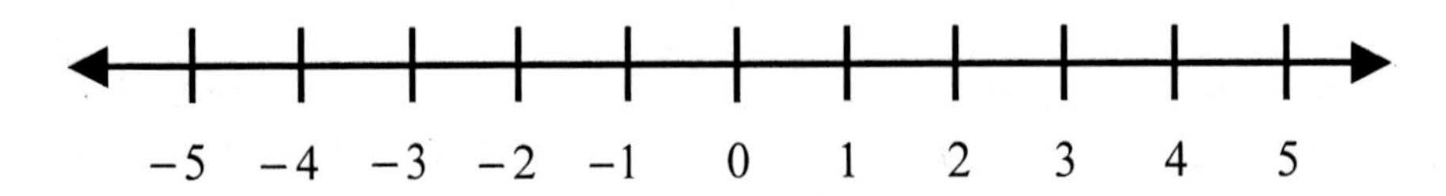

32. $x < -1$

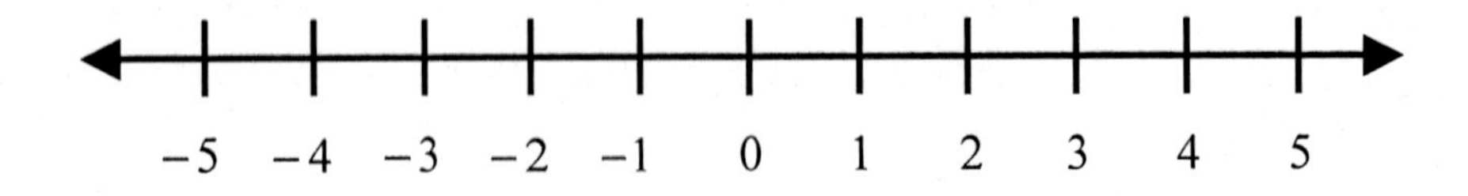

33. $x \geq 0$

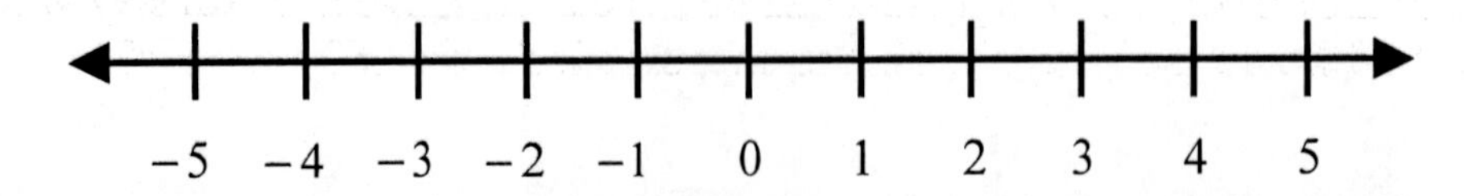

34. $x \geq -3$

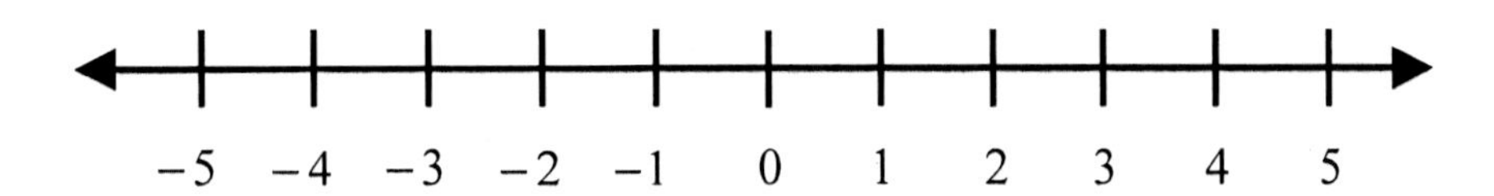

35. $x > -4$

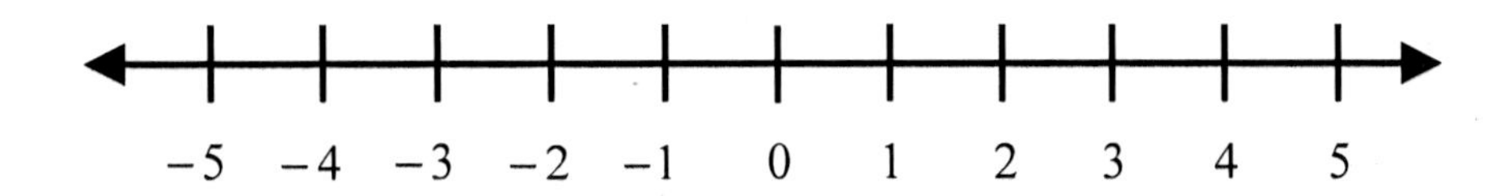

36. $x > 0$

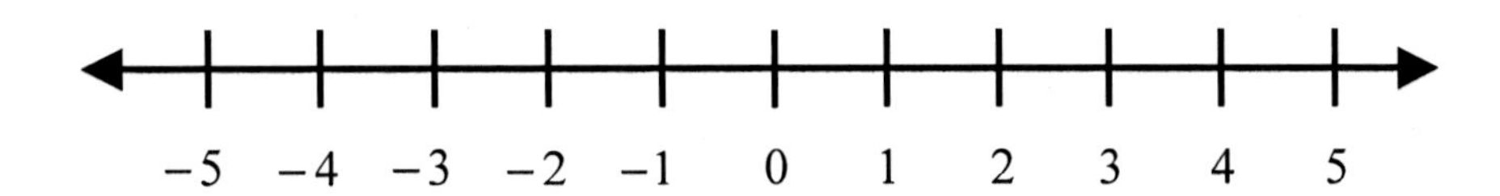

37. $x \leq -2$

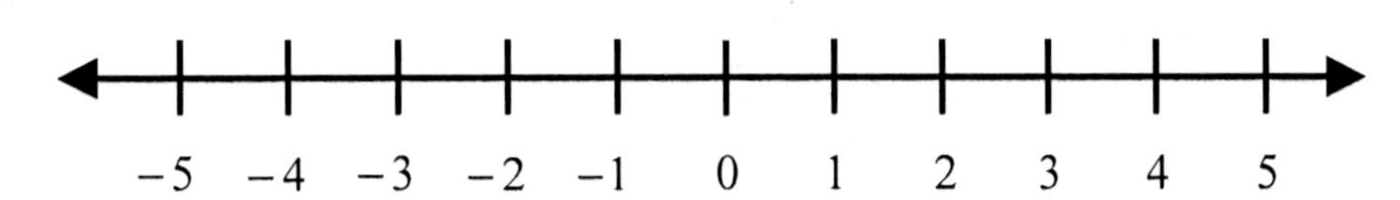

38. $x \leq 4$

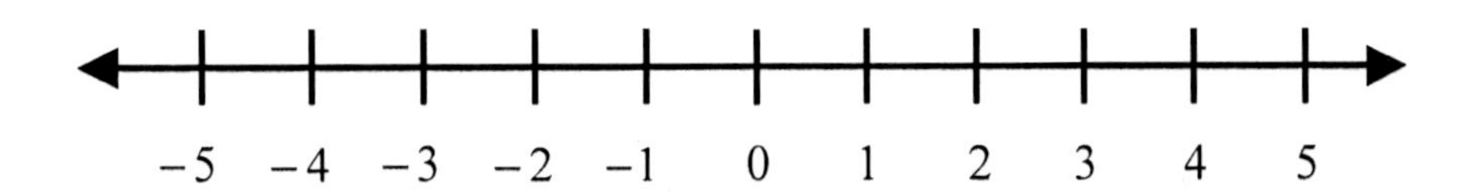

Applications

39. To earn a trip to camp Mike needs to sell at least 150 boxes of thin mints. Write an inequality statement representing the amounts of boxes of mints he can sell and still earn a trip to camp. If Mike sells 167 boxes of thin mints, will he earn a trip to camp?

40. A tank holds a maximum of 75 gallons of water. Write an inequality statement representing the amounts of water that can be put in the tank. Will the tank be able to hold 87 gallons of water?

41. A bridge has a maximum load limit of 12,000 pounds. Write an inequality statement representing the amounts of weight that can be put on the bridge and still stay within the safety limits. Should the bridge be able to support a load of 14,600 pounds?

42. Water boils at a temperature of at least 212 degrees Fahrenheit. Write an inequality statement representing the temperatures at which water will boil. Will water boil in a place where the temperature is 221 degrees Fahrenheit?

43. Joe is on a diet where he is supposed to eat no more than 2,000 calories per day. Write an inequality statement representing the amounts of calories that Joe can eat and stay on his diet. Can Joe eat 1,500 calories in a single day and stay on his diet?

44. To receive an interest rate of 5% on a certificate of deposit, Tom must deposit at least $8,000 at a local bank. Write an inequality statement representing the amounts of money that Tom could deposit and still receive the 5% interest rate on his investment. If Tom deposits $7,500 at the local bank, will he receive the 5% interest rate?

45. Mark is required to sell at least 200 new insurance policies per month in order to keep his job. Write an inequality statement representing the numbers of insurance policies that Mark must sell on a monthly basis. If Mark sells 215 new policies in the month of March, will he still be able to keep his job for April?

46. Ben can eat no more than 12 pounds of chocolate per week without going into a sugar-induced frenzy. Write an inequality statement representing the amounts of chocolate that Ben can eat without slipping into a frenzy. If Ben eats 14 pounds of chocolate in one week's time, will he stay frenzy free?

DECIMAL NUMBERS

Chapter Review

Section 1: An Introduction to Decimal Numbers

Review Exercises: Write the following number in words.

1. 9.63

Write the number as a decimal number in standard form.

2. seven hundred fifteen thousandths

Change the decimal number into a fraction or mixed number.

3. 6.05

Change the fraction into a decimal number.

4. $\frac{57}{1,000}$

Compare the pair of numbers by putting the correct symbol <, >, or = between them.

5. 3.084 3.804

By using the number line, determine the correct inequality symbol > or < to place between the pair of numbers.

6. $-0.5, \quad -0.1$

Round the number to the given place value.

7. 43.329452 Ten-thousandths

8. To get an A in a math class, students must get a 93% or better. If students were allowed to round their grade to the nearest tenth of a percent, would a student with a 92.95% get an A in the class?

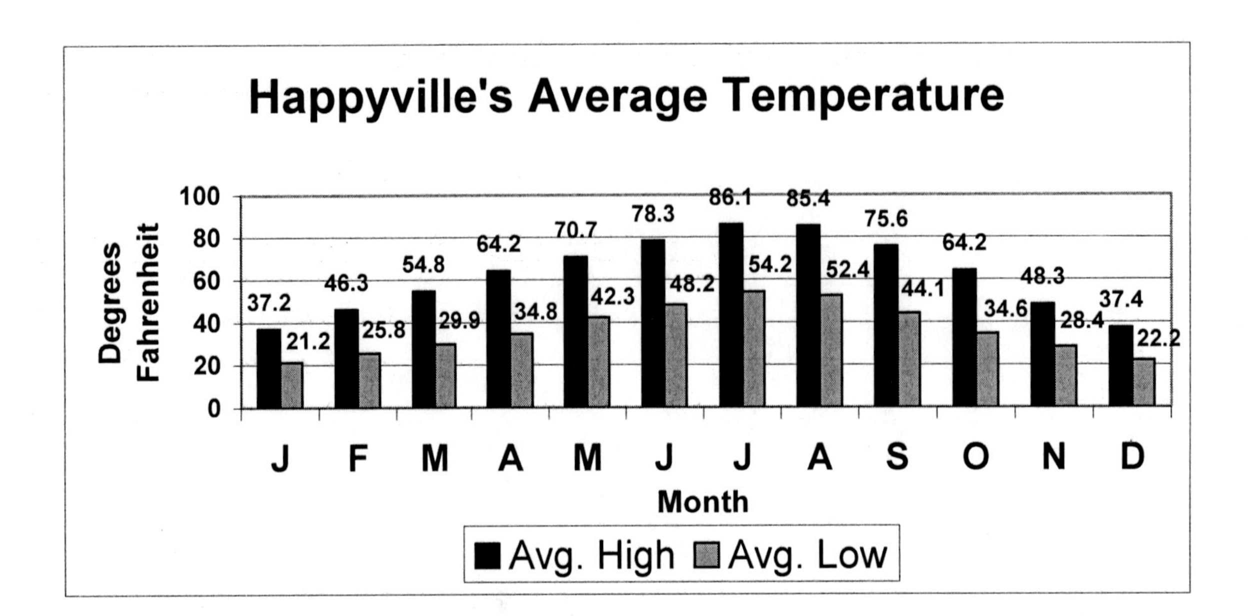

Use the double bar graph above to answer the following question.

9. During which month(s) is Happyville's average low temperature less than 52.4° F and greater than 28.2° F?

Section 2: Adding and Subtracting Decimal Numbers

Review Exercises: Add or subtract.

10. $36.13 - 49.42 + 93.6$

Evaluate the expression.

11. What is 29.4 increased by 18?

Translate the phrase into mathematical symbols using decimal numbers. Then determine the result.

12. How much greater is twenty-eight and two hundredths than negative six and nine tenths?

Evaluate the expression $x + y + z$ for the given values of x, y, and z.

13. $x = 42.6$; $y = 18.43$; $z = -29.17$

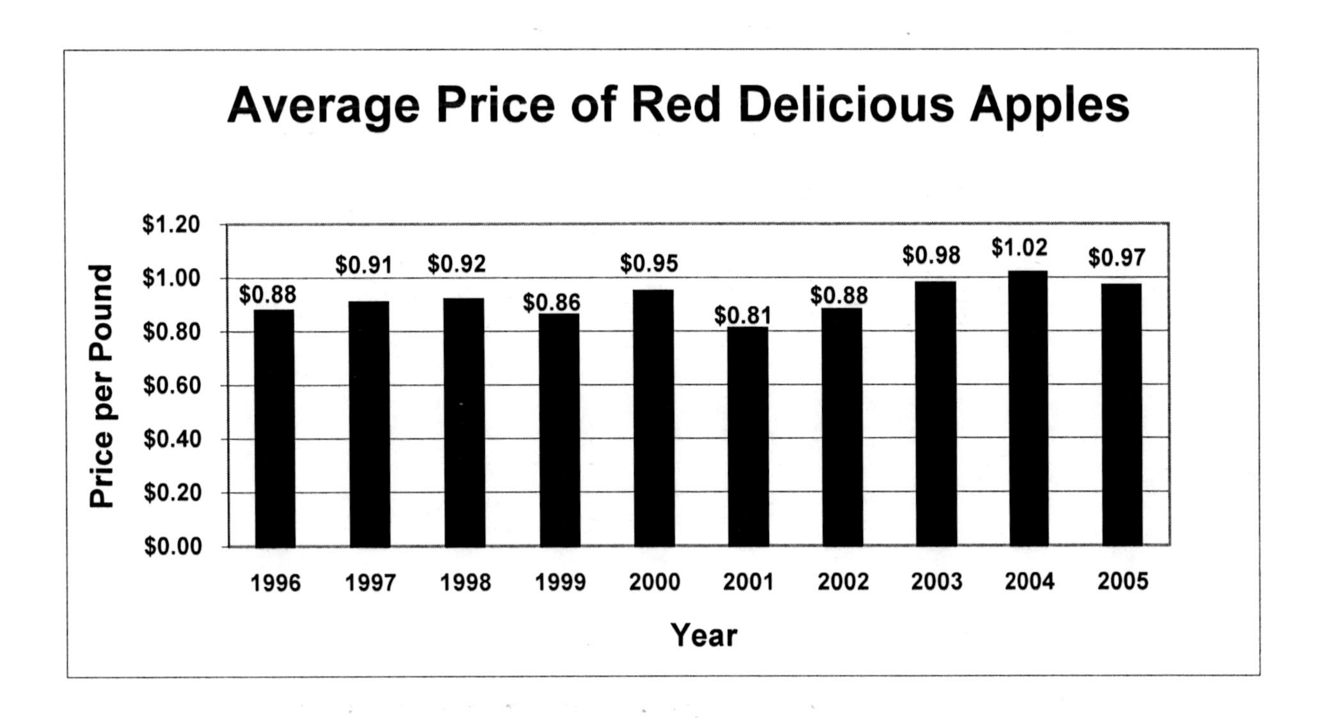

Use the bar graph above to answer the following question.

14. What's the difference between the price per pound of apples in 2004 and the price per pound of apples in 1996?

15. Given that $\angle E = 124.38°$, find $\angle F$ such that $\angle E$ and $\angle F$ are supplementary angles.

Section 3: Multiplying Decimal Numbers

Review Exercises: Multiply.

16. $(-0.81)(-4.07)$

Evaluate the expression.

17. What is -62.31 multiplied by 10^5?

Section 4: Dividing Decimal Numbers

Review Exercises: Divide.

18. $4.2 \div 10^4$

Evaluate the expression $x \div y$ for the given values of x and y.

19. $x = -0.928$; $y = 16$

Using the formula $A = \frac{1}{2}bh$, find the area of the following triangle.

20.

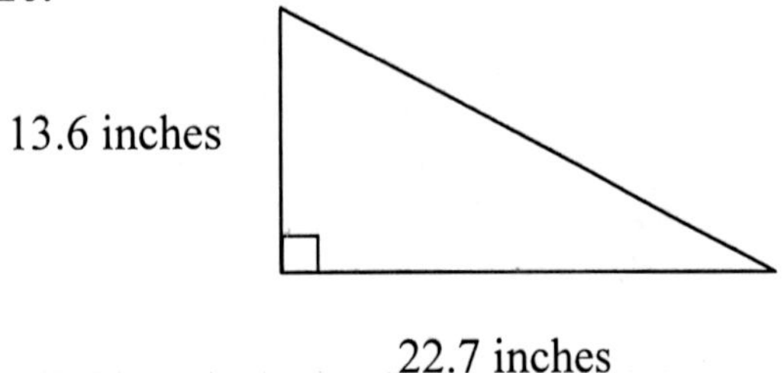

21. If a tank holding 400 gallons of water takes 54 minutes to drain, how many gallons of water would drain from the tank in 1 minute? Give your answer in gallons per minute and round it to the nearest hundredth of a gallon.

Section 5: Converting and Comparing Fractions and Decimal Numbers

Review Exercises: Convert the mixed number into a decimal number. Use a repeating bar in your answer if necessary.

22. $5\frac{2}{11}$

Compare the pair of numbers by placing either < or > between them.

23. $\frac{5}{7}$ 0.715

Use the formula: Batting Average $= \dfrac{\text{Number of Hits}}{\text{Number of Times at Bat}}$ to calculate the baseball player's batting average. (Round answer to the nearest thousandth).

24. Mike "The Chiz" Chrisom had 169 hits in 536 times at bat.

Section 6: Order of Operations with Decimal Numbers

Review Exercises: Simplify the expression.

25. $\dfrac{3^2 - 14.4}{16.6 - 4^2}$

Put the correct symbol <, >, or = in the box between the pair of expressions.

26. $0.034(10)^2 - 43 \div 10^3 \; \square \; 57 \div 10^2 + 0.033(10)^3$

27. Using the formula $F = \frac{9}{5}C + 32$, convert $19°$C into degrees Fahrenheit.

28. If canvas costs $4.69 per square foot, how much would it cost for enough canvas to make a painting 2.5 feet by 3 feet? Round your answer to the nearest cent.

29. Find the approximate circumference and area of the following circle.

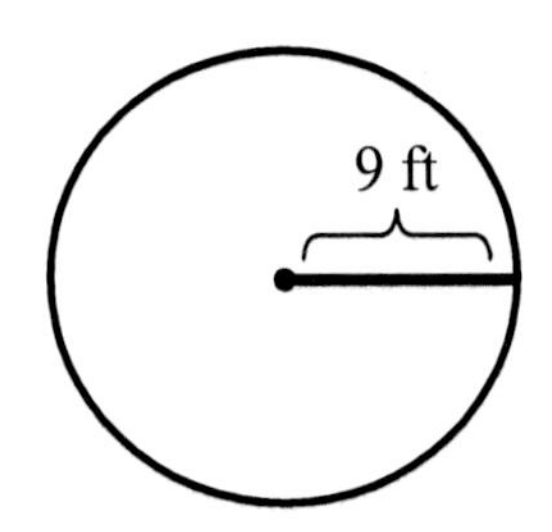

Section 7: Solving Equations With Decimals

Review Exercises: Check the solution.

30. Is 0.057 a solution of the equation $9.4 - n = 9.343$?

Check the solution.

31. Is 1.056 a solution of the equation $\frac{y}{13.2} = 0.08$?

Solve each of the following equations.

32. $d - 3.7 = -0.803$

33. $-3.6k = 0.936$

34. Use the formula $R = \frac{p}{h}$ (where R is the rate of pay, p is the total amount of pay, and h is the number of hours worked), to find the total amount of pay a person makes if they earn \$18 per hour and work for 7.75 hours.

35. Find the amount of interest earned on a savings account if the principal is \$786.03 and the total amount in the account is \$878.26. Use the formula $A = P + I$ (where A is the total amount in a savings account, P is the principal or amount put into the account, and I is the amount of interest in the account).

Section 8: Estimating

Review Exercises: Estimate the difference by using front end rounding.

36. $0.654 - 0.096$

Estimate the product by using front end rounding.

37. $(64.7)(0.25)$

Section 9: Roots

Review Exercises: Simplify each expression.

38. $-\sqrt{36}$

39. $5\sqrt{25}$

40. $4\sqrt{144}-2^3$

Evaluate each expression for the given values of the variables.

41. $\sqrt{\dfrac{w}{x}}$, where $w = 36$ and $x = 81$

42. $-\sqrt{b^2}$, where $b = 15$

Translate the phrase into mathematical symbols. Then determine the result.

43. Find the quotient of twenty-eight and the square root of forty-nine.

Determine what two whole numbers the radical is located between.

44. $\sqrt{50}$

Simplify the following radical.

45. $\sqrt[7]{128}$

Using the formula given, solve for the unknown length of the right triangle.

46. $c = \sqrt{a^2 + b^2}$

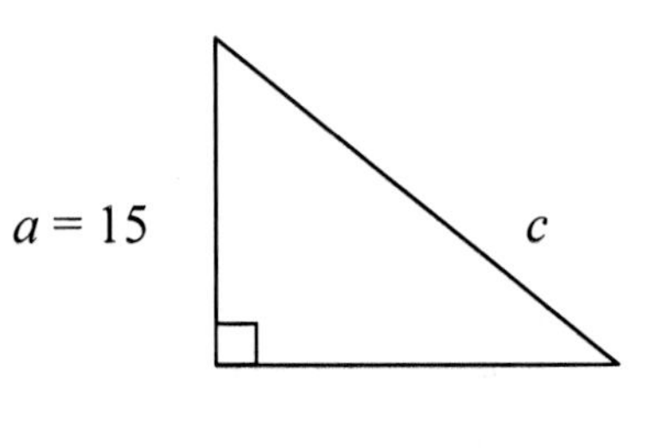

Section 10: Real Numbers

Review Exercises: List which set or sets each number belongs to: natural numbers, whole numbers, integers, rational numbers, irrational numbers, and real numbers.

47. $\sqrt{11}$

48. $-3.\overline{6}$

Graph each group of numbers on the real number line.

49. real numbers between -7 and 2

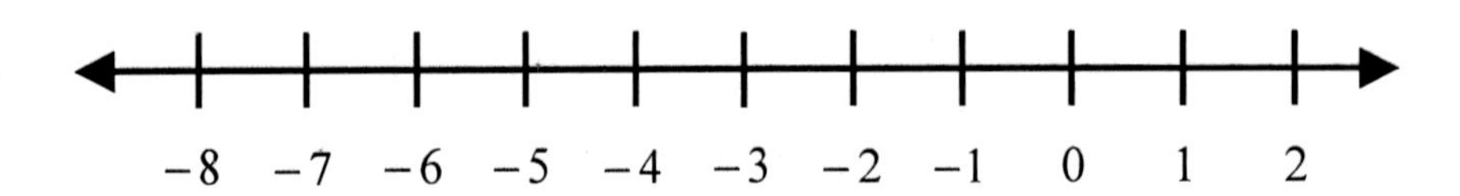

50. real numbers greater than -2

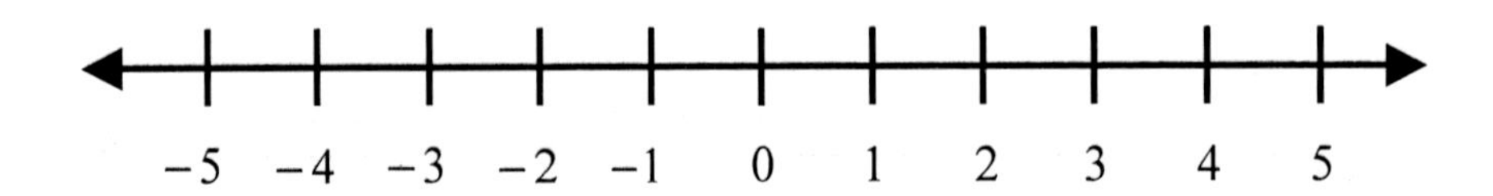

51. List the following real numbers in order from smallest to largest.

$-\sqrt{2}$, $\sqrt{3}$, $-0.\overline{2}$, 0.5, $-\frac{1}{4}$, and 2.

Graph each inequality on the real number line.

52. $x < -2$

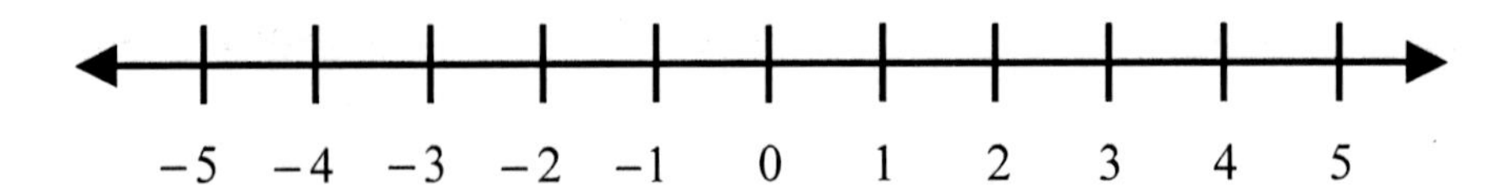

53. $x \leq 2$

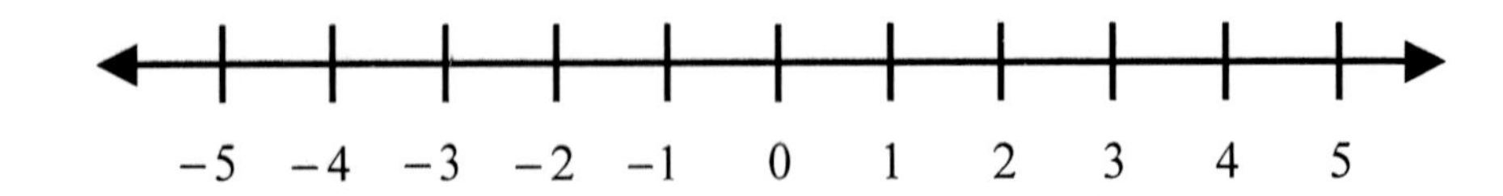

54. To receive an interest rate of 4.6% on a certificate of deposit, Jerry must deposit at least $10,000 at a local bank. Write an inequality statement representing the amounts of money that Jerry could deposit and still receive the 4.6% interest rate on his investment. If Jerry deposits $11,350 at the local bank, will he receive the 4.6% interest rate?

DECIMAL NUMBERS

Chapter Test

Write the following number in words.

1. 17.072

Change the decimal number into a fraction or mixed number.

2. 4.0307

Change the mixed number into a decimal number.

3. $6\frac{97}{1,000}$

Compare the pair of numbers by putting the correct symbol <, >, or = between them.

4. 41.107 41.071

Round the number to the given place value.

5. 0.080808 Thousandth

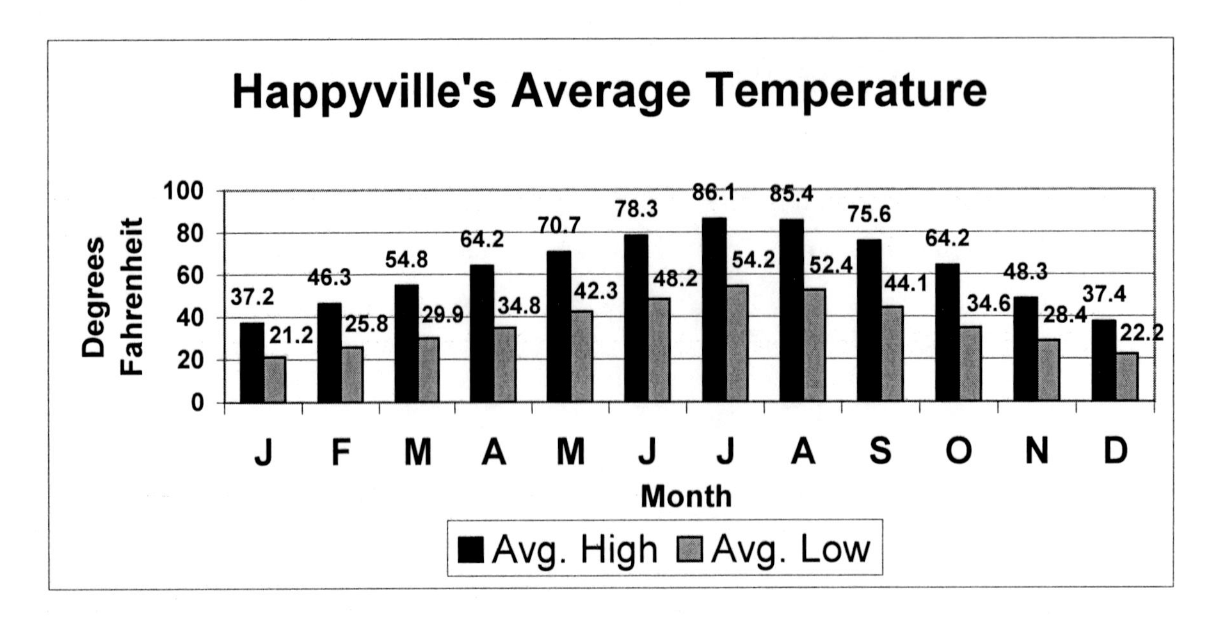

Use the double bar graph above to answer the following question.

6. What is the difference between the highest average high temperature and the lowest average low temperature for Happyville?

Translate the phrase into mathematical symbols using decimal numbers. Then determine the result.

7. What is negative thirteen and eighty-four hundredths subtracted from thirty-five and seven tenths?

Evaluate the expression $a+b+c$ for the given values of a, b, and c.

8. $a=-13.2$; $b=7.24$; $c=-84.71$

Multiply.

9. $0.00036(10^3)$

Evaluate the expression.

10. What is -718.947 divided by 10^5?

Evaluate the expression $x \div y$ for the given values of x and y.

11. $x=50.208$; $y=0.24$

Using the formula $A = \frac{1}{2}bh$, find the area of the following triangle.

12.

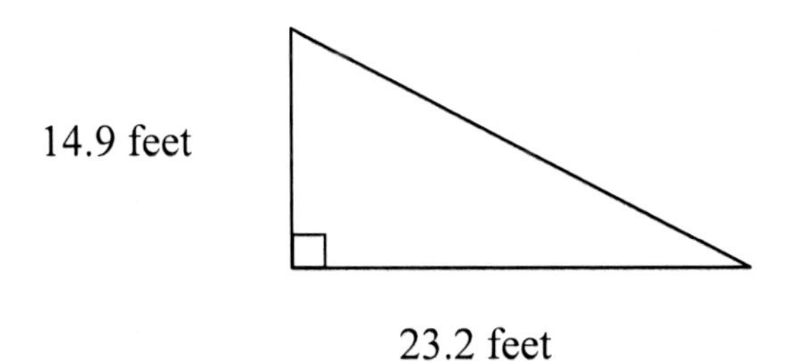

13. If a truck travels 208 miles while using 12.8 gallons of gasoline, how many miles could it travel on 1 gallon of gasoline? Round your answer to the nearest tenth of a mile.

Convert the mixed number into a decimal number. Use a repeating bar in your answer if necessary.

14. $11\frac{1}{9}$

Compare the pair of numbers by placing either < or > between them.

15. $\frac{2}{9}$ $\quad$ 0.222

Simplify the expression.

16. $\dfrac{4.2(10)^2 + 42 \div 10^2}{42 \div 10}$

17. Using the formula $C = \dfrac{5(F-32)}{9}$, convert $48.2°F$ into degrees Celsius.

18. If sod costs \$0.87 per square foot, how much would it cost for enough sod to make a lawn 60 feet by 35.5 feet? Round your answer to the nearest dollar.

19. Find the approximate circumference and area of the following circle.

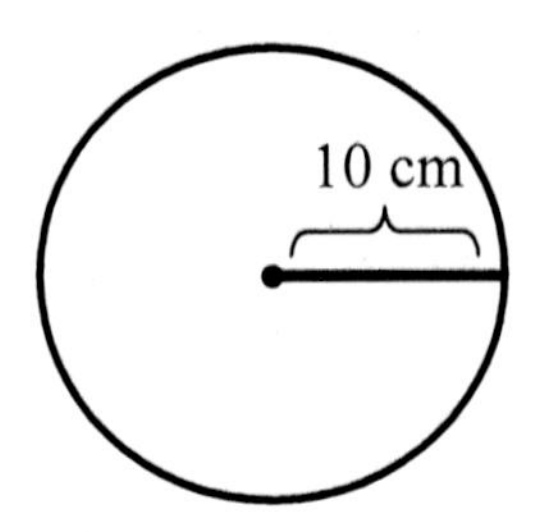

Check the solution.

20. Is 1.288 a solution of the equation $w-3.452=-2.17$?

Solve the following equation.

21. $14.3m=-0.7722$

22. Find the width of a rectangle if the area is 171.6 square feet and the length is 16.5 feet. Use the formula $A=LW$ (where A is the area, L is the length, and W is the width of a rectangle).

23. Find the amount of revenue generated by a shaved ice stand in one week if the weekly cost to run the stand is \$1,746.23 and the weekly profit is \$873.42. Use the formula $P=R-C$ (where P is the profit, R is the revenue, and C is the cost).

Estimate the difference by using front end rounding.

24. $0.754-0.836$

Simplify each expression.

25. $-2\sqrt{81}$

26. $\sqrt{\frac{100}{9}}+\sqrt{\frac{25}{9}}$

Determine what two whole numbers the radical is located between.

27. $\sqrt{41}$

Using the formula given, solve for the unknown length of the right triangle.

28. $a = \sqrt{c^2 - b^2}$

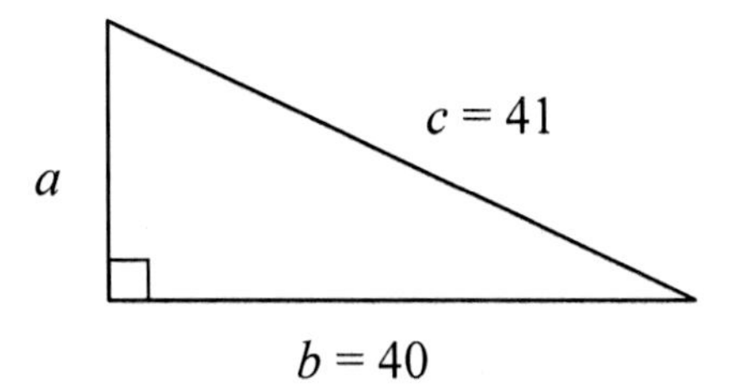

List which set or sets the number belongs to: natural numbers, whole numbers, integers, rational numbers, irrational numbers, and real numbers.

29. 7

Graph the group of numbers on the real number line.

30. real numbers between -6 and -1

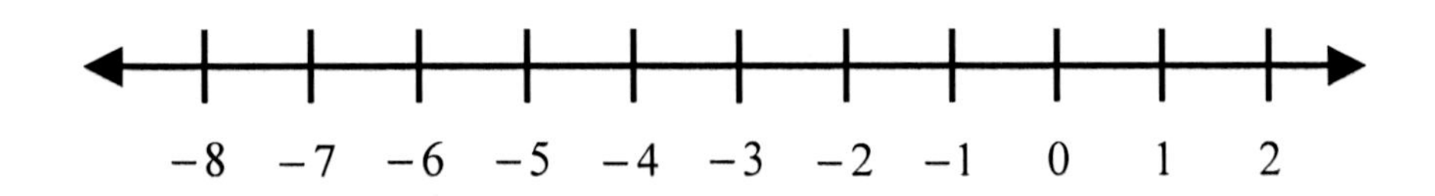

Graph the inequality on the real number line.

31. $x \geq 4$

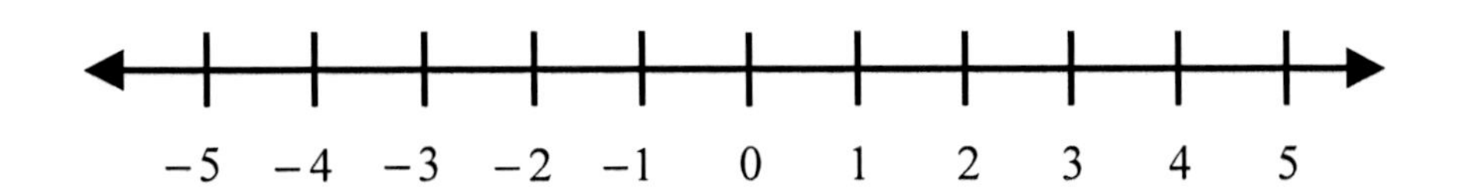

32. A tank holds a maximum of 135 gallons of water. Write an inequality statement representing the amounts of water that can be put in the tank. Will the tank be able to hold 114 gallons of water?

Whole Numbers: Section 1 answers

1. Yes. Whole numbers include all of the natural numbers.

3.

0 1 2 3 4 5 6 7 8 9 10

5.

0 1 2 3 4 5 6 7 8 9 10

7.

0 1 2 3 4 5 6 7 8 9 10

9.

0 1 2 3 4 5 6 7 8 9 10

11.

0 1 2 3 4 5 6 7 8 9 10

13.

0 1 2 3 4 5 6 7 8 9 10

15.

0 1 2 3 4 5 6 7 8 9 10

17.

0 1 2 3 4 5 6 7 8 9 10

19. $81 > 18$ **21.** $415 < 451$ **23.** $4{,}305 > 3{,}450$

25. $0 < 49$ **27.** $48{,}000 > 4{,}800$ **29.** $7 > 4$

Whole Numbers: Section 1 answers continued

31. 118 inches $>$ 39 inches **33.** 206,665 $<$ 206,856

35. 5 **37.** 0 **39.** 3 **41.** 8

43. 2 **45.** forty-nine **47.** six hundred thirty-seven

49. eleven thousand, five hundred sixteen **51.** three million, forty-seven thousand, ten

53. eight hundred six thousand, seven hundred thirteen

55. four thousand, two hundred three

57. ten million, four hundred three thousand, seventeen

59. two hundred sixty-three million, two thousand, one hundred sixty-two

61. thirty-four billion, three hundred nineteen thousand, seven

63. seven hundred forty-six billion, ninety-one million, twenty-eight thousand, eighty

65. 13 **67.** 117 **69.** 4,072 **71.** 86

73. 710 **75.** 6,402 **77.** 654 **79.** 250,026

81. 19,652 **83.** 7,018,014 **85.** 40 + 3 **87.** 100 + 1

89. 1,000 + 80 + 6 **91.** 8,000 + 400 + 7

93. 30,000 + 900 + 7 **95.** 100,000 + 10,000 + 4,000 + 600 + 20

97. 600,000 + 10,000 + 10 + 6 **99.** 500,000 + 7

101. 9,000,000 + 1,000 + 400 + 20 + 7 **103.** 7,000,000 + 100,000 + 70,000 + 700 + 7

Whole Numbers: Section 2 answers

1. 610 **3.** 43,000 **5.** 400

7. 70,000 **9.** 0 **11.** 4,320

13. 100,000 **15.** 1,870,000 **17.** 70,500

19. 2,000 **21.** 1,000,000 **23.** 8,000,000

25. 7,000 **27.** 230,000 **29.** 6,450

31. $200 **33.** Yakima School District #7.

35. The amount paid to the state school levy is greater.

37. December **39.** They usually get the same amount of precipitation.

41. Seattle, Tacoma, Spokane, Vancouver, Bellevue.

43. January and December **45.** From 2001 to 2003

47. $D > C$ **49.** $a < b$ **51.** $c > a$ **53.** $F < B$

55. $K > J$ **57.** $b > a$ **59.** $a < c$

Whole Numbers: Section 3 answers

1. 466 **3.** 678 **5.** 5,361 **7.** 6,469

9. 9,503 **11.** 98,403 **13.** 5,265 **15.** 624,107

Whole Numbers: Section 3 answers continued

17.	24,593	**19.**	4,251	**21.**	732,400	**23.**	1,508,524
25.	231,867	**27.**	21,944	**29.**	The answer may vary.		
31.	11	**33.**	173	**35.**	699	**37.**	384
39.	41,312	**41.**	623	**43.**	3,804	**45.**	21
47.	245	**49.**	750,737	**51.**	3,128	**53.**	999
55.	25,638	**57.**	4,233	**59.**	The answer may vary.		

61.	$7+6$; 13	**63.**	$15-6$; 9	**65.**	$12-8$; 4
67.	$9+15$; 24	**69.**	$78-69$; 9	**71.**	$18-11$; 7
73.	$59+46$; 105	**75.**	17	**77.**	744
79.	255	**81.**	2,914	**83.**	17,221
85.	52,558	**87.**	77	**89.**	586
91.	802	**93.**	1,588	**95.**	29,998
97.	5,628	**99.**	1,008	**101.**	12,850
103.	65,983	**105.**	The commutative property of addition.		
107.	$5+8$; 13	**109.**	$3+9$; 12	**111.**	$0+27$; 27

Whole Numbers: Section 3 answers continued

113. $29 + 62$; 91 **115.** $77 + 216$; 293 **117.** $319 + 412$; 731

119. $6 + (7 + 3)$; 16 **121.** $(9 + 1) + 4$; 14 **123.** $(7 + 13) + 6$; 26

125. $321 + (18 + 12)$; 351 **127.** $12 + (63 + 37)$; 112

129. $(376 + 24) + 419$; 819

Whole Numbers: Section 4 answers

1. \$944 million **3.** \$104 million **5.** 205 therms **7.** 29°F

9. 41°F **11.** 26°F **13.** 22 in. **15.** 30 ft

17. 36 m **19.** 9 ft 8 in. **21.** 15 ft 2 in. **23.** 3 ft 4 in.

25. 66 ft **27.** 1 hr 35 min **29.** 9 lb 4 oz **31.** 2 lb 13 oz

33. Neither one **35.** Supplementary **37.** Complementary

39. Neither one **41.** Complementary **43.** 61°

45. 62° **47.** 141° **49.** 87°

51. 100° **53.** 17° **55.** Complementary

Whole Numbers: Section 5 answers

1. 267 **3.** 12,054 **5.** 20,712 **7.** 0

Whole Numbers: Section 5 answers continued

9.	6,978,048	**11.**	43,890	**13.**	33,948	**15.**	41,328
17.	24,660	**19.**	54,457	**21.**	193,536	**23.**	266,560
25.	5,461,695	**27.**	4,257,368	**29.**	23 R 10	**31.**	2,822
33.	1,488 R 2	**35.**	Undefined	**37.**	84	**39.**	0
41.	136 R 3	**43.**	155	**45.**	1,458 R 2	**47.**	9 R 26
49.	2,804 R 15	**51.**	20 R 44	**53.**	$7 \cdot 12$; 84	**55.**	$27 \cdot 14$; 378
57.	$36 \div 4$; 9	**59.**	$2 \cdot 9$; 18	**61.**	$72 \div 9$; 8		

63. The associative property of multiplication.

65.	$5 \cdot 8$; 40	**67.**	$(3)(9)$; 27	**69.**	$0 \cdot 27$; 0
71.	$(29)62$; 1,798	**73.**	$77 \cdot 216$; 16,632	**75.**	$13 \cdot (5 \cdot 2)$; 130
77.	$(5 \cdot 20) \cdot 16$; 1,600	**79.**	$7 \cdot (2 \cdot 50)$; 700	**81.**	$3 \cdot 0 = 0$

83.	1	**85.**	0	**87.**	$4^3 \cdot 5^2$	**89.**	$x^4 \cdot y^2$
91.	$5 \cdot 6^2 \cdot 10^3$	**93.**	$2^2 \cdot 3^4 \cdot y^2$	**95.**	81	**97.**	216
99.	100,000	**101.**	8	**103.**	1,000	**105.**	7
107.	x^6	**109.**	4^3	**111.**	3^2	**113.**	4^2

Whole Numbers: Section 5 answers continued

115.	76	**117.**	49	**119.**	57	**121.**	2,148
123.	10,000,000	**125.**	Undefined	**127.**	0	**129.**	64
131.	0	**133.**	6,076	**135.**	36	**137.**	232
139.	2,000						

Whole Numbers: Section 6 answers

1.	1, 2, 3, 4, 6, 12	**3.**	1, 5, 7, 35
5.	1, 2, 3, 4, 6, 8, 12, 16, 24, 48	**7.**	1, 2, 3, 6, 9, 18, 27, 54
9.	1, 2, 7, 14, 49, 98	**11.**	1, 19
13.	1, 2, 4, 5, 8, 10, 16, 20, 40, 80	**15.**	1, 5, 17, 85
17.	1, 2, 4, 8, 16, 32, 64	**19.**	1, 3, 11, 33

21.	Prime	**23.**	Composite	**25.**	Prime
27.	Prime	**29.**	Composite; $2^2 \cdot 3^2$	**31.**	Composite; $2^3 \cdot 3$
33.	Composite; 5^3	**35.**	Composite; $2 \cdot 7^2$	**37.**	Composite; $3 \cdot 13$
39.	Prime	**41.**	Composite; $2^2 \cdot 5 \cdot 7$	**43.**	Composite; $3 \cdot 29$
45.	Composite; $2 \cdot 17$	**47.**	Composite; $3 \cdot 31$	**49.**	151, 157
51.	937	**53.**	$1,075	**55.**	875 pounds

Whole Numbers: Section 6 answers continued

57. \$1,800 **59.** \$100 **61.** 15 calories

63. 3 times **65.** P = 24 inches; A = 32 $in.^2$

67. P = 32 feet; A = 64 ft^2 **69.** P = 50 meters; A = 154 m^2

71. 6 feet **73.** 46 feet

75. 48 square feet **77.** 220 miles

79. \$8 per hour **81.** 18 ft^2

83. 7 times

Whole Numbers: Section 7 answers

1. 4 **3.** 40 **5.** 126 **7.** 18

9. 1 **11.** 5 **13.** 4 **15.** 11

17. 16 **19.** 1 **21.** 8 **23.** 8

25. 32 **27.** 144 **29.** 64 **31.** 1

33. 1 **35.** 41 **37.** 47 **39.** 59

41. 49 **43.** 27 **45.** 19 **47.** 1

Whole Numbers: Section 7 answers continued

49.	0	**51.**	5	**53.**	95	**55.**	97
57.	91	**59.**	6	**61.**	37	**63.**	5
65.	88	**67.**	32	**69.**	$32 < 116$	**71.**	$50 > 22$
73.	$25 > 16$	**75.**	20	**77.**	28	**79.**	22
81.	27	**83.**	121	**85.**	178	**87.**	20
89.	$A = 45 \text{ in}^2$	**91.**	15°C	**93.**	68°F	**95.**	$A = 144 \text{ in}^2$

Whole Numbers: Section 8 answers

1.	No	**3.**	Yes	**5.**	Yes	**7.**	No
9.	No	**11.**	Yes	**13.**	Yes	**15.**	$x = 22$
17.	$H = 67$	**19.**	$y = 5$	**21.**	$n = 47$	**23.**	$z = 51$
25.	$w = 16$	**27.**	$m = 6$	**29.**	$W = 11$	**31.**	$x = 14$
33.	$w = 8$	**35.**	$k = 0$	**37.**	$k = 64$	**39.**	$x = 1$
41.	$n = 0$	**43.**	$y = 114$	**45.**	5 hours	**47.**	$22

Whole Numbers: Section 8 answers continued

49.	37 mph	**51.**	\$3,300	**53.**	30 feet	**55.**	\$62

57. $N+8=39$; the number is 31.

59. $9N=45$; the number is 5.

61. $N-19=98$; the number is 117.

63. $N+3=88$; the number is 85.

65. $7N=84$; the number is 12.

67. $N-15=12$; the number is 27.

69. $N+8=14$; the number is 6.

71. $N-60=42$; the number is 102.

73. $J-5=18$; Joe is 23 years old.

75. $3W=24$; the width is 8 in.

77. $S+15=185$; Steve weighs 170 lb.

79. $S-3=58$; Stephanie is 61 in. tall.

81. $W+8=42$; the width is 34 in.

83. $6C=30$; 5 corn dogs were sold.

Whole Numbers: Section 9 answers

1.	10,000	**3.**	10,000	**5.**	700,000	**7.**	0
9.	90,000	**11.**	80,000	**13.**	2,100	**15.**	5,700
17.	1,000	**19.**	54,000	**21.**	28,000	**23.**	20
25.	400	**27.**	450,000	**29.**	2,000	**31.**	1,000,000
33.	3,000	**35.**	800,000	**37.**	2,500	**39.**	300,000

Whole Numbers: Chapter review answers

1.

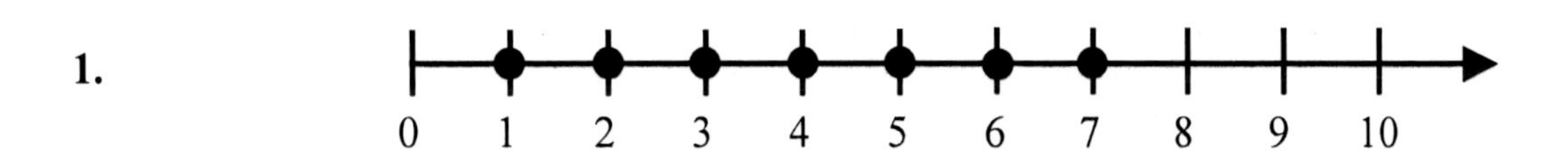

2.

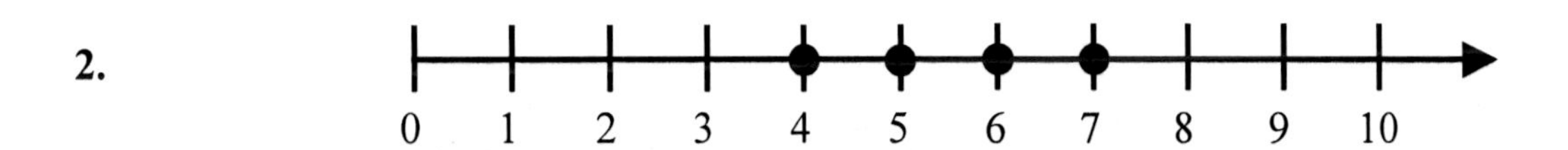

3. $<$

4. 14,409 ft $>$ 11,245 ft

5. 3

6. nine hundred six thousand, five hundred twenty-two

7. 5,027,032

8. 300,000 + 9,000 + 200 + 5

9. 3,900,000

10. City of Widget

11. The amount paid to the Widget School District #5.

12. Hialeah, St. Petersburg, Tampa, Miami, Jacksonville

13. July

14. January

15. $>$

16. 26,934

17. 915

18. 4 + 12; 16

19. $93-10$; 83

20. 7,848

21. 7,890

22. 99 + 416; 515

23. (718 + 82) + 641; 1,441

24. 88 therms

25. 5 ft

26. 1 lb 15 oz

27. $\angle D = 48°$

28. $\angle R = 84°$

29. $\angle W = 51°$

30. 186,420

31. Undefined

32. 9 R 18

33. $72 \cdot 18$; 1,296

Whole Numbers: Chapter review answers continued

34. $69 \div 3$; 23

35. 26(92); 2,392

36. $(25 \cdot 4) \cdot 7$; 700

37. $3^2 \cdot 7^4 \cdot x^2$

38. 343

39. 12^3

40. 10,000

41. 295

42. 1, 2, 5, 7, 10, 14, 35, 70

43. prime

44. composite; $11 \cdot 13$

45. 20 calories

46. P = 28 in.; A = 45 in^2

47. 48 square yards

48. $12 per hour

49. 5 square feet

50. 5 times

51. $13 < 22$

52. 204

53. 30°C

54. No

55. Yes

56. No

57. $w = 37$

58. $y = 13$

59. $p = 86$

60. 48 miles per hour

61. $N - 12 = 13$; the number is 25.

62. $W + 7 = 53$; the width is 46 inches.

63. $8C = 96$; 12 chilidogs were sold.

64. 60,000

65. 5,000

66. 35,000

67. 2,000

Whole Numbers: Chapter test answers

1.

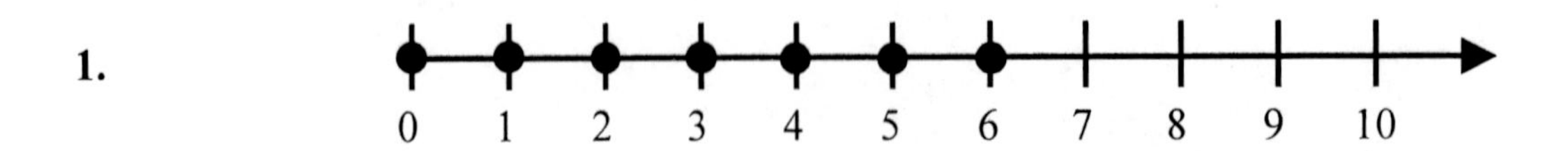

2. $155{,}404 > 153{,}555$

Whole Numbers: Chapter test answers continued

3. three hundred six thousand, eight hundred twenty-three

4.	69,375	**5.**	650,000	**6.**	$>$
7.	August	**8.**	December	**9.**	68,549
10.	27,925	**11.**	$65-29$; 36	**12.**	6,547
13.	(83 + 117) + 312; 512	**14.**	5 ft 10 in.	**15.**	1 lb 14 oz
16.	$\angle R = 31°$	**17.**	0	**18.**	22 R 240
19.	$76 \div 4$; 19	**20.**	3,860(47); 181,420	**21.**	$5^3 \cdot 6 \cdot y^2$
22.	1,331	**23.**	1, 2, 3, 5, 6, 9, 10, 15, 18, 30, 45, 90		
24.	prime	**25.**	$2 \cdot 3^2 \cdot 5$	**26.**	45 square yards
27.	$14 per hour	**28.**	32 times	**29.**	$29 < 30$
30.	277	**31.**	59°F	**32.**	29
33.	6 hours	**34.**	$N - 82 = 19$; the number is 101		
35.	180,000	**36.**	18,000		

Integers: Section 1 answers

1. No. Whole numbers do not include any negative numbers, but integers do.

3.

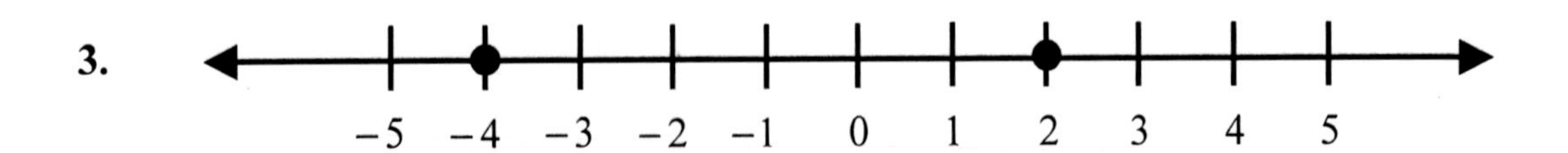

5.

7.

−5 −4 −3 −2 −1 0 1 2 3 4 5

9.

−5 −4 −3 −2 −1 0 1 2 3 4 5

11.	>	**13.**	<	**15.**	<	**17.**	<
19.	>	**21.**	>	**23.**	3	**25.**	9
27.	0	**29.**	14	**31.**	26	**33.**	86
35.	−6	**37.**	12	**39.**	$-k$	**41.**	n
43.	−7	**45.**	0	**47.**	3	**49.**	9
51.	−9	**53.**	7	**55.**	−42	**57.**	−14
59.	$-w$	**61.**	y	**63.**	53	**65.**	69
67.	12	**69.**	13	**71.**	−3	**73.**	>

Integers: Section 1 answers continued

75. $<$ **77.** $=$ **79.** $<$ **81.** $=$

83. $>$ **85.** The Vikings; 92 yards **87.** The Cadets

89. Asia; -408 meters **91.** Asia **93.** 2000, 2002, 2004, 2005

95. 2006 **97.** 2004 **99.** $7 million

Integers: Section 2 answers

1. -16 **3.** -2 **5.** -12 **7.** -36

9. -73 **11.** 24 **13.** 14 **15.** -24

17. -42 **19.** -1 **21.** -3 **23.** -8

25. 3 **27.** -18 **29.** 0 **31.** -6

33. 0 **35.** -22 **37.** -32 **39.** -11

41. $-14+3;\ -11$ **43.** $-12+(-7);\ -19$ **45.** $17+(-23);\ -6$

47. $-42+(-92);\ -134$ **49.** $0+(-9);\ -9$ **51.** $-41+47;\ 6$

53. $4+\left(-3+(-2)\right);\ -1$ **55.** $\left(-8+(-4)\right)+16;\ 4$ **57.** $(65+54)+(-73);\ 46$

59. $-45+(7+63);\ 25$ **61.** 10 **63.** -7

65. 43 **67.** w **69.** $-n$ **71.** 0

Integers: Section 2 answers continued

73. $34 + (-3) + 5 + (-7) + (-1) + 0 + 4$; 32°F

75. $100 + (-26) + 17 + (-62) + 12 + 32$; \$73

77. $3 + (-5) + (-4) + 15$; 9 yards; No

79. -11

81. 11

83. -6

85. -196

87. -45

Integers: Section 3 answers

1. -4

3. -22

5. 38

7. 17

9. 1

11. -31

13. 98

15. -12

17. -2

19. 8

21. the opposite of negative sixty-three

23. six minus negative ten

25. seven minus the absolute value of negative four

27. negative four plus negative thirty-four

29. the absolute value of negative six, plus negative four

31. negative nine minus negative thirty-six

33. four plus negative twenty-eight

35. negative four minus the absolute value of six

Integers: Section 3 answers continued

37. negative five minus six

39. the opposite of the absolute value of negative three, minus fourteen

41.	$-7+9$; 2	**43.**	$2-7$; -5	**45.**	$\lvert -4\rvert -16$; -12
47.	$80+(-73)$; 7	**49.**	$18-\lvert -47\rvert$; -29	**51.**	$-6+(-39)$; -45

53.	-4	**55.**	-48	**57.**	25	**59.**	51
61.	10	**63.**	8	**65.**	11	**67.**	-15
69.	-25	**71.**	-3	**73.**	-23	**75.**	-31
77.	-23	**79.**	-17	**81.**	$30 million		
83.	8,936 meters	**85.**	113 meters	**87.**	9 strokes	**89.**	– $9

91. 687 feet above base camp; -26°F

Integers: Section 4 answers

1.	-48	**3.**	119	**5.**	-54	**7.**	294
9.	387	**11.**	-27	**13.**	1,440	**15.**	0
17.	$-3x$	**19.**	$6y$	**21.**	$-4a$	**23.**	36

Integers: Section 4 answers continued

25. negative; -42 **27.** positive; 60 **29.** negative; -525

31. positive; 120 **33.** negative; -840 **35.** $-14\cdot 3$; -42

37. $-12(-7)$; 84 **39.** $17(-23)$; -391 **41.** $0(-9)$; 0

43. $4(-5\cdot(-2))$; 40 **45.** $(-4\cdot 25)(-27)$; 2,700

47. $15(50\cdot(-2))$; $-1{,}500$ **49.** $(25\cdot 4)(-45)$; $-4{,}500$ **51.** -4

53. -2 **55.** Undefined **57.** -37 **59.** -13

61. 1 **63.** 0 **65.** -24 **67.** -5

69. -13 **71.** Undefined **73.** 13

75. $-6\cdot 18$; -108 **77.** $2(-2)$; -4 **79.** $3(-55)$; -165 **81.** $\frac{-63}{-7}$; 9

83. $\frac{-81}{9}$; -9 **85.** -35 **87.** -4 **89.** -80

91. -7 **93.** 108 **95.** 7 **97.** -7

99. -504 **101.** $-1{,}300$ **103.** $-\$4$ **105.** -2 yards

107. $-\$2$ million **109.** 1st Quarter **111.** $-\$24$ million **113.** 5°F

115. 45°F **117.** -4°F

Integers: Section 5 answers

1. -34 **3.** -59 **5.** -25 **7.** -16

9. 21 **11.** -2 **13.** -40 **15.** 7

17. undefined **19.** 49 **21.** -35 **23.** 5

25. 0 **27.** 16 **29.** -56 **31.** 5

33. 27 **35.** -16 **37.** 6 **39.** 400

41. 29 **43.** $-3=-3$ **45.** $-96<96$ **47.** $-45>-188$

49. 16 **51.** -27 **53.** 16 **55.** -75

57. 27 **59.** -55 **61.** -243 **63.** 12

65. **a)** 3 **b)** 3 **c)** They are the same number. 3 and -3 have the same absolute value since they are the same distance from zero on the number line.

67. 5^2-3^2; 16 square feet **69.** -5°C **71.** 5°F

73. -20°C **75.** -40°F

Integers: Section 6 answers

1. No **3.** No **5.** Yes **7.** No

9. Yes **11.** No **13.** $x=-16$ **15.** $H=-11$

17. $y=-9$ **19.** $n=-127$ **21.** $z=-58$ **23.** $w=8$

Integers: Section 6 answers continued

25. $m = -11$

27. $W = -45$

29. $x = -66$

31. $w = -8$

33. $k = 0$

35. $k = -66$

37. $x = 1$

39. $n = 0$

41. $y = 97$

43. $N - 14 = 3$; the number is 17.

45. $N + 9 = -17$; the number is -26.

47. $2N = -68$; the number is -34.

49. $60 + N = 39$; the number is -21.

51. $N + 95 = 17$; the number is -78.

53. $N - 5 = -5$; the number is 0.

55. $N - 45 = -8$; the number is 37.

57. $-9N = 81$; the number is -9.

59. $N - 3 = -9$; the lowest temp. was $-6°$.

61. $4F = -12$; its earnings for 2005 were $-\$3$ million.

63. $E - 125 = -153$; the lowest elevation in Europe is -28 meters.

65. $2F = -8$; he lost 4 yards during the first play of the game.

Integers: Chapter Review answers

1.

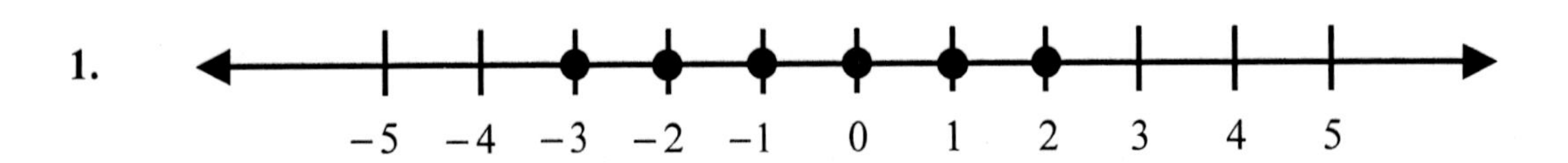

2. >

3. 37

4. y

5. -78

6. >

7. The Tigers; 14 yards

8. The Lions; -25 yards

9. 0

10. -35

11. $77 + (-92)$; -15

Integers: Chapter Review answers continued

12. $(-12+(-8))+35$; 15 **13.** 84

14. $26+(-4)+2+(-9)+(-3)+0+5$; 17°F **15.** -47 **16.** -1

17. $8-(-60)$; 68 **18.** -22 **19.** -82

20. 5,981 meters **21.** 7,368 meters **22.** 814 feet above base camp; 22°F

23. $4h$ **24.** $16(-81)$; $-1{,}296$

25. $(-2\cdot 50)(-7)$; 700 **26.** -6 **27.** $\frac{91}{-7}$; -13

28. -18 **29.** -34 **30.** 1 under par **31.** -5°F

32. 20 **33.** 3 **34.** 9 **35.** -32

36. $-40=-40$ **37.** -23 **38.** -4°F **39.** -35°C

40. Yes **41.** Yes **42.** No **43.** $R=-11$

44. $x=-11$ **45.** $y=-38$ **46.** $p=-59$

47. $5N=-35$; the number is -7. **48.** $N-29=-77$; the number is -48.

49. $4F=-28$; its earnings for 2004 were $-\$7$ million.

50. $E-58=-86$; the lowest elevation in Europe is -28 meters.

Integers: Chapter Test answers

1. 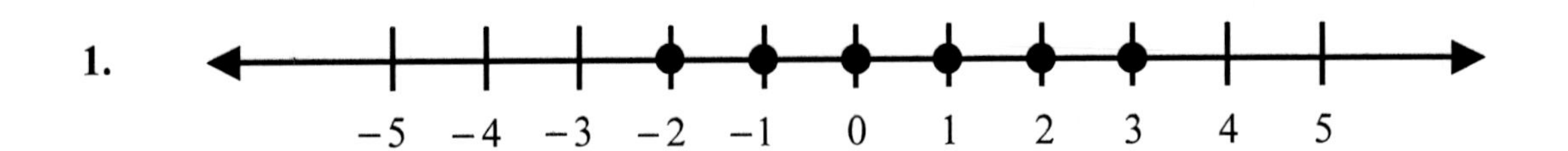

2. $-w$

3. $=$

4. $39+(-47)$; -8

5. a

6. $86+(-12)+8+(-17)+(-6)$; \$59

7. $-85-(-46)$; -39

8. -3

9. 25

10. 125 meters

11. $-3y$

12. $53\cdot(-4\cdot 25)$; $-5{,}300$

13. $\frac{-74}{-37}$; 2

14. 3

15. 1°F

16. 75

17. $=$

18. 16

19. −10°C

20. Yes

21. No

22. $M=-59$

23. -71

24. $-7N=35$; -5

25. -28 meters

Fractions: Section 1 answers

1. 10 **3.** 30 **5.** 12 **7.** 75

9. 54 **11.** 24 **13.** 51 **15.** 96

17. 120 **19.** 200 **21.** 105 **23.** 60

25. 270 **27.** 600 **29.** 840 **31.** 30

33. 2 **35.** 7 **37.** 8 **39.** 1

41. 9 **43.** 3 **45.** 10 **47.** 4

49. 15 **51.** 19 **53.** 1 **55.** 1

57. 6 **59.** 12 **61.** 3 **63.** 7

65. **a)** 40 **b)** 120 **c)** 10 **67.** 12

69. 3 times **71.** 4 strips

Fractions: Section 2 answers

1. proper fraction
3. mixed number
5. improper fraction
7. mixed number
9. proper fraction
11. improper fraction
13. $\frac{3}{4}$
15. $\frac{3}{5}$
17. $\frac{3}{8}$
19. $\frac{5}{8}$
21. $\frac{8}{7}$; $1\frac{1}{7}$
23. $\frac{17}{6}$; $2\frac{5}{6}$
25. 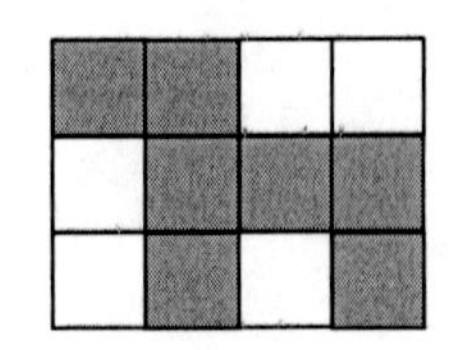

Answers may vary.

27. 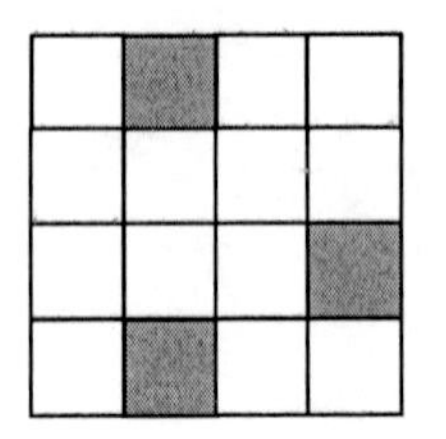

Answers may vary.

29. 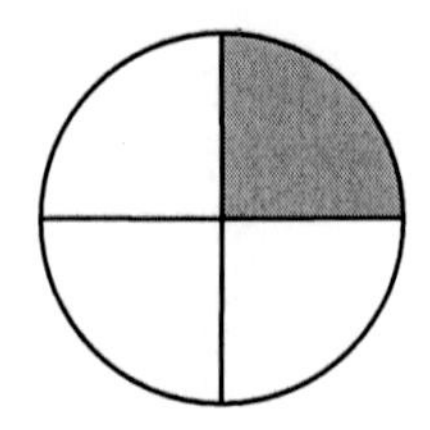

Answers may vary.

31. seven ninths
33. two and three sevenths
35. negative eight elevenths
37. negative six and five sixths
39. fifteen halves
41. nine eighths
43. $7\frac{9}{10}$
45. $-\frac{9}{15}$
47. $\frac{3}{14}$
49. $\frac{36}{5}$
51. $12\frac{1}{2}$
53. $\frac{1}{3}$
55. $5\frac{1}{3}$
57. $2\frac{5}{7}$

Fractions: Section 2 answers continued

59. 6	**61.** $3\frac{7}{10}$	**63.** 3	**65.** $12\frac{3}{4}$
67. 4	**69.** $2\frac{7}{9}$	**71.** $6\frac{1}{8}$	**73.** 1
75. $\frac{31}{4}$	**77.** $\frac{107}{11}$	**79.** $\frac{6}{1}$	**81.** $\frac{50}{9}$
83. $\frac{48}{1}$	**85.** $\frac{87}{8}$	**87.** $\frac{34}{5}$	**89.** $\frac{127}{10}$
91. $\frac{100}{3}$	**93.** $\frac{20}{13}$	**95.** $\frac{28}{42}$	**97.** $\frac{54}{60}$
99. $\frac{21}{49}$	**101.** $\frac{144}{306}$	**103.** $\frac{40}{48}$	**105.** $\frac{364}{91}$
107. $\frac{56}{7}$	**109.** $\frac{35}{56}$	**111.** $\frac{240}{900}$	**113.** $\frac{546}{756}$
115. $\frac{5}{3}$	**117.** $\frac{3}{7}$	**119.** 1	**121.** $\frac{5w}{7}$
123. 0	**125.** $\frac{3}{4}$	**127.** m	**129.** $\frac{7}{10}$
131. $\frac{3}{11}$	**133.** $\frac{p}{3}$		

Fractions: Section 2 answers continued

135. $\frac{7}{18}$; $\frac{17}{45}$ not equivalent

137. $\frac{4}{7}$; $\frac{4}{7}$ equivalent

139. $\frac{8w}{3}$; $\frac{8w}{3}$ equivalent

141. $\frac{2}{3}$; $\frac{2}{3}$ equivalent

143. $\frac{17w}{4}$; $\frac{17x}{4}$ not equivalent

145. $\frac{9}{11}$; $\frac{9}{11}$ equivalent

147. No. A mixed number is always larger than 1 and a proper fraction is always smaller than 1.

Fractions: Section 3 answers

1.

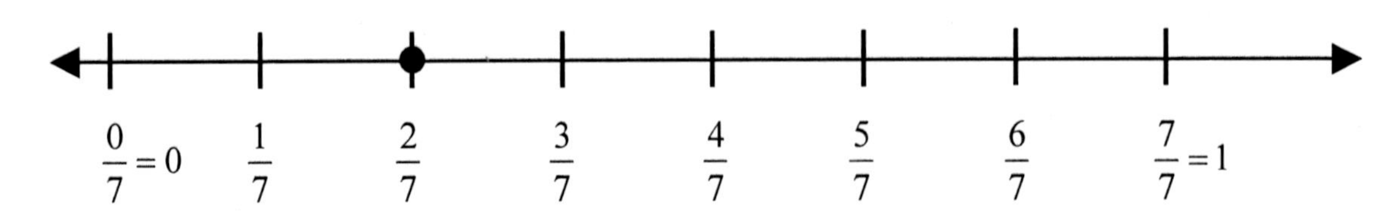

$\frac{0}{7}=0$ $\frac{1}{7}$ $\frac{2}{7}$ $\frac{3}{7}$ $\frac{4}{7}$ $\frac{5}{7}$ $\frac{6}{7}$ $\frac{7}{7}=1$

3.

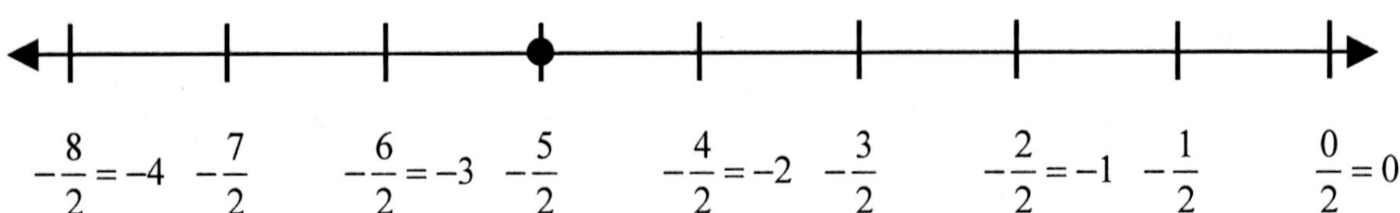

$-\frac{8}{2}=-4$ $-\frac{7}{2}$ $-\frac{6}{2}=-3$ $-\frac{5}{2}$ $-\frac{4}{2}=-2$ $-\frac{3}{2}$ $-\frac{2}{2}=-1$ $-\frac{1}{2}$ $\frac{0}{2}=0$

5.

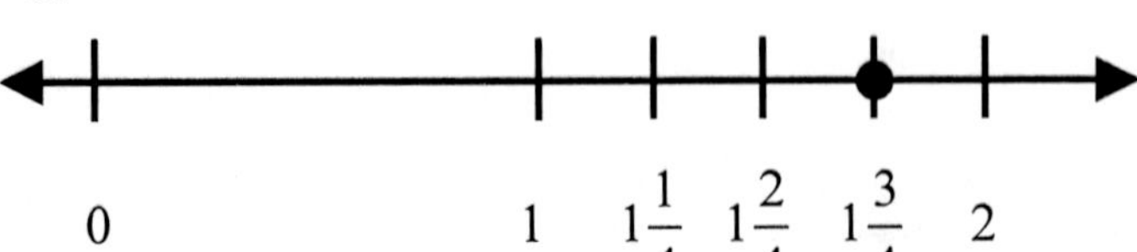

0 1 $1\frac{1}{4}$ $1\frac{2}{4}$ $1\frac{3}{4}$ 2

Fractions: Section 3 answers continued

7.

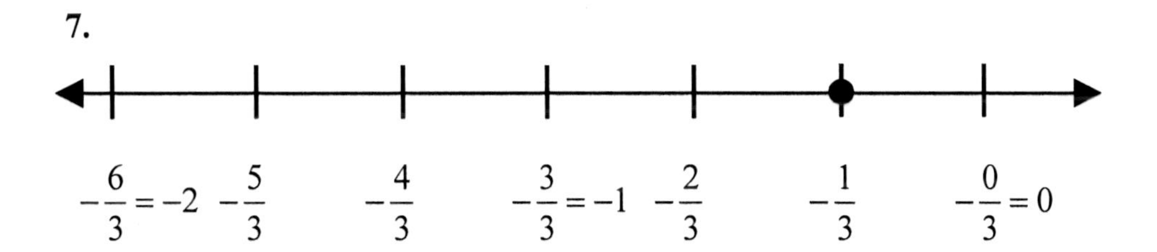

9.

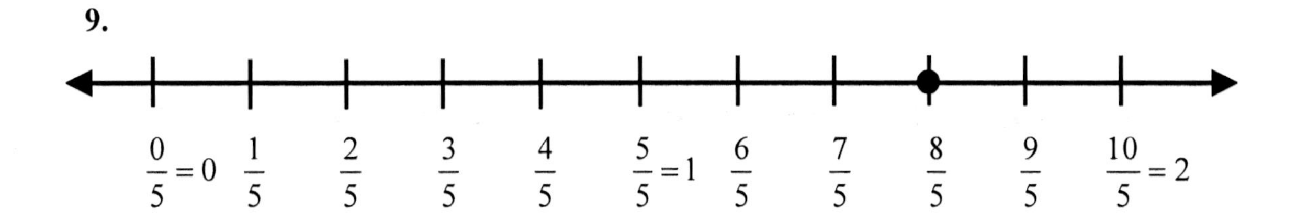

11.

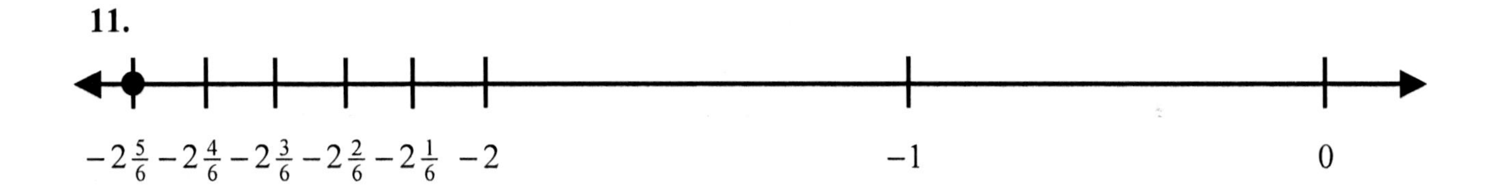

13. LCD = 12 **15.** LCD = 30 **17.** LCD = 8 **19.** LCD = 84

21. LCD = 120 **23.** LCD = 42 **25.** $\frac{5}{12}<\frac{1}{2}$ **27.** $\frac{6}{11}>\frac{1}{2}$

29. $\frac{3}{4}>\frac{2}{5}$ **31.** $\frac{7}{16}<\frac{2}{3}$ **33.** $\frac{6}{13}<\frac{7}{12}$ **35.** $\frac{7}{30}>\frac{3}{70}$

Fractions: Section 3 answers continued

37. $\frac{4}{7} < \frac{3}{5}$

39. $\frac{11}{14} > \frac{3}{4}$

41. $\frac{2}{3} > \frac{7}{11}$

43. $\frac{13}{24} < \frac{9}{16}$

45. $-\frac{2}{3} > -\frac{5}{7}$

47. $\frac{13}{17} < \frac{10}{13}$

49. $\frac{9}{7} > \frac{14}{11}$

51. $-\frac{7}{8} < \frac{3}{4}$

53. $\frac{7}{15} > \frac{11}{25}$

55. $\frac{5}{3} < \frac{9}{5}$

57. $-\frac{4}{9} < -\frac{3}{7}$

59. $\frac{17}{24} > \frac{11}{16}$

61. $\frac{2}{3}$

63. $\frac{5}{12}$

65. $\frac{3}{4}$

67. $\frac{5}{7}$

69. $\frac{2}{7}$

71. $\frac{7}{20}$

73. $\frac{3}{40}$

75. $\frac{3}{50}$

77. $\frac{21}{400}$

79. $\frac{3}{8}$ in., $\frac{7}{16}$ in., $\frac{1}{2}$ in., $\frac{9}{16}$ in., $\frac{5}{8}$ in., $\frac{11}{16}$ in., and $\frac{3}{4}$ in.

81. 2 lattés purchased per week.

Fractions: Section 4 answers

1. $\frac{3}{5}$

3. 1

5. $-\frac{2}{3}$

7. $\frac{3}{11}$

Fractions: Section 4 answers continued

9.	$\frac{11}{x}$	**11.**	$-\frac{1}{w}$	**13.**	$\frac{19}{10}$ or $1\frac{9}{10}$	**15.**	$\frac{18}{m}$
17.	$14\frac{5}{8}$	**19.**	$18\frac{3}{4}$	**21.**	16	**23.**	$8\frac{6}{7}$
25.	$-\frac{29}{21}$ or $-1\frac{8}{21}$	**27.**	$\frac{31}{56}$	**29.**	$\frac{10}{7}$ or $1\frac{3}{7}$	**31.**	$\frac{5}{126}$
33.	$\frac{7}{3}$ or $2\frac{1}{3}$	**35.**	$-\frac{1}{30}$	**37.**	$\frac{7}{24}$	**39.**	$15\frac{7}{24}$
41.	$-16\frac{23}{24}$	**43.**	$12\frac{2}{3}$	**45.**	$-\frac{11}{48}$	**47.**	$21\frac{17}{35}$
49.	$6\frac{1}{24}$	**51.**	$-\frac{2}{3}$	**53.**	$10\frac{9}{40}$		
55.	$-\frac{9}{56}$	**57.**	$9\frac{41}{48}$	**59.**	$\frac{9}{7}$ or $1\frac{2}{7}$	**61.**	$-\frac{17}{42}$
63.	3	**65.**	$8\frac{6}{55}$	**67.**	0	**69.**	$16\frac{1}{2}$
71.	$\frac{59}{60}$; Julie	**73.**	$\frac{17}{50}$	**75.**	$23\frac{1}{2}$ ft		

Fractions: Section 5 answers

1.	$\frac{3}{5}$	**3.**	$\frac{1}{3}$	**5.**	$\frac{2}{7}$	**7.**	$\frac{9}{11}$
9.	$-\frac{4}{m}$	**11.**	$\frac{2}{p}$	**13.**	$2\frac{3}{8}$	**15.**	$\frac{7}{10}$
17.	$6\frac{2}{9}$	**19.**	$1\frac{7}{8}$	**21.**	$5\frac{1}{7}$	**23.**	$2\frac{1}{3}$
25.	$\frac{5}{18}$	**27.**	$\frac{7}{18}$	**29.**	$\frac{1}{45}$	**31.**	$-\frac{6}{7}$
33.	$\frac{2}{15}$	**35.**	$-\frac{21}{20}$ or $-1\frac{1}{20}$	**37.**	$\frac{1}{6}$	**39.**	$2\frac{5}{9}$
41.	$4\frac{179}{210}$	**43.**	$5\frac{4}{5}$	**45.**	$1\frac{17}{24}$	**47.**	-1
49.	$\frac{1}{5}$	**51.**	$-\frac{1}{9}$	**53.**	$\frac{43}{30}$ or $1\frac{13}{30}$	**55.**	6
57.	$6\frac{1}{2}$	**59.**	$\frac{71}{36}$ or $1\frac{35}{36}$	**61.**	$9\frac{1}{7}$	**63.**	$2\frac{41}{45}$
65.	$-\frac{13}{40}$	**67.**	$2\frac{16}{21}$	**69.**	$\frac{9}{16}$ of an acre	**71.**	$16\frac{1}{2}$ yards

Fractions: Section 5 answers continued

73. $2\frac{1}{4}$ in. 75. $3\frac{3}{40}$ miles 77. $9\frac{1}{24}$ pounds 79. $3\frac{11}{24}$ feet

81. $21\frac{1}{2}$ in. 83. $\frac{5}{6}$ cup 85. $\frac{1}{50}$

87. Supplementary 89. Neither 91. $\angle Y = 50\frac{9}{13}°$

93. $\angle D = 73\frac{7}{12}°$ 95. $\angle F = 95\frac{16}{21}°$

Fractions: Section 6 answers

1. $\frac{7}{12}$ 3. $\frac{1}{3}$ 5. $\frac{1}{5}$ 7. 2

9. $\frac{3}{11}$ 11. 0 13. $\frac{gh}{20}$ 15. $\frac{9}{32}$

17. $-\frac{13}{16}$ 19. 3 21. Undefined 23. -1

25. $\frac{11}{6}$ or $1\frac{5}{6}$ 27. $-\frac{2x}{y}$ 29. $\frac{289}{205}$ or $1\frac{84}{205}$ 31. $\frac{1}{2}$

33. $-\frac{5}{2}$ or $-2\frac{1}{2}$ 35. $\frac{1}{2}$ 37. $\frac{4}{3}$ or $1\frac{1}{3}$ 39. 0

Fractions: Section 6 answers continued

41. $\frac{1}{2}$

43. $-\frac{1}{4}$

45. $\frac{40}{3}$ or $13\frac{1}{3}$

47. $\frac{23}{2}$ or $11\frac{1}{2}$

49. $\frac{7}{2}$ or $3\frac{1}{2}$

51. $\frac{115}{2}$ or $57\frac{1}{2}$

53. 5

55. $\frac{12}{7}$ or $1\frac{5}{7}$

57. $-\frac{7}{5}$ or $-1\frac{2}{5}$

59. 1

61. $\frac{26}{9}$ or $2\frac{8}{9}$

63. $\frac{99}{4}$ or $24\frac{3}{4}$

65. $\frac{14}{15}$

67. $\frac{45}{56}$

69. Yes

71. Yes

73. No

75. Yes

77. Yes

79. No

81. No

83. Yes

85. No

87. Yes

89. No

91. Yes

93. $\frac{8}{3}$ or $2\frac{2}{3}$

95. $-\frac{11}{5}$ or $-2\frac{1}{5}$

97. 8

99. 0 has no reciprocal since it would be undefined.

101. $\frac{5}{13}$

103. $\frac{4}{7}$

105. $\frac{1}{x}$

107. $-\frac{1}{4}$

109. $-\frac{4}{3}$ or $-1\frac{1}{3}$

111. $\frac{25}{8}$ or $3\frac{1}{8}$

113. $\frac{35}{54}$

Fractions: Section 6 answers continued

115. $\frac{27}{2}$ or $13\frac{1}{2}$ **117.** -18 **119.** $\frac{9}{2}$ or $4\frac{1}{2}$ **121.** $\frac{3}{4}$

123. -1 **125.** $\frac{7}{2}$ or $3\frac{1}{2}$ **127.** 0 **129.** $8\frac{1}{3}$ cups

131. $\frac{3}{4}$ hour **133.** $30\frac{1}{3}$ hours **135.** $12\frac{1}{4}\text{ ft}^2$ **137.** $28\frac{1}{6}\text{ in.}^2$

139. 22 ft^2

Fractions: Section 7 answers

1. $\frac{3}{2}$ or $1\frac{1}{2}$ **3.** $\frac{25}{2}$ or $12\frac{1}{2}$ **5.** 1 **7.** $\frac{81}{100}$

9. $-\frac{2}{3}$ **11.** 0 **13.** $-\frac{1}{22}$ **15.** $\frac{9}{4}$ or $2\frac{1}{4}$

17. 10 **19.** Undefined **21.** -6 **23.** $\frac{2}{3}$

25. $\frac{32}{15}$ or $2\frac{2}{15}$ **27.** $\frac{2}{7}$ **29.** $\frac{xy}{18}$ **31.** $\frac{3}{4}$

33. 8 **35.** Undefined **37.** $-\frac{4}{3}$ or $-1\frac{1}{3}$ **39.** $\frac{50}{81}$

Fractions: Section 7 answers continued

41. $\frac{2}{5}$ **43.** $-\frac{1}{2}$ **45.** $\frac{15}{28}$ **47.** 16

49. $-\frac{35}{2}$ or $-17\frac{1}{2}$ **51.** $-\frac{3}{2}$ or $-1\frac{1}{2}$ **53.** 0 **55.** $\frac{2}{19}$

57. 9 batches **59.** $\frac{3}{4}$ of an hour **61.** 32 tiles

63. $9\frac{1}{4}$ pounds **65.** \$16 per hour **67.** $6\frac{5}{8}$ ounces

69. $55\frac{1}{5}$ miles per hour

Fractions: Section 8 answers

1. $\frac{16}{49}$ **3.** $\frac{4}{9}$ **5.** $\frac{1}{3}$ **7.** $-\frac{4}{9}$

9. $-\frac{3}{640}$ **11.** $-\frac{1}{125}$ **13.** $\frac{1}{135}$ **15.** $\frac{121}{25}$ or $4\frac{21}{25}$

17. 1 **19.** $\frac{49}{9}$ or $5\frac{4}{9}$ **21.** $\frac{3}{4}$ **23.** $\frac{2}{3}$

25. $\frac{21}{20}$ or $1\frac{1}{20}$ **27.** $-\frac{3}{11}$ **29.** $-\frac{14}{33}$ **31.** $\frac{3}{5}$

Fractions: Section 8 answers continued

33. -18 **35.** $\frac{3}{10}$ **37.** $\frac{3}{28}$ **39.** $\frac{50}{27}$ or $1\frac{23}{27}$

41. $\frac{8}{9}$ **43.** $\frac{17}{33}$ **45.** $-\frac{12}{25}$ **47.** $\frac{5}{4}$ or $1\frac{1}{4}$

49. $-\frac{41}{12}$ or $-3\frac{5}{12}$ **51.** $\frac{1}{3}$ **53.** 0

55. $\frac{137}{54}$ or $2\frac{29}{54}$ **57.** 2 **59.** 1 **61.** $\frac{1}{4}$

63. $\frac{9}{25}$ **65.** $-\frac{1}{27}$ **67.** $\frac{16}{625}$ **69.** $\frac{27}{25}$

71. $-\frac{9}{32}$ **73.** $\frac{25}{4}$ or $6\frac{1}{4}$ **75.** $\frac{1}{7}$ **77.** -21

79. $\frac{171}{80}$ or $2\frac{11}{80}$ **81.** $\frac{1}{36}$ **83.** $\dfrac{3\frac{1}{2}+2\frac{3}{4}+4\frac{1}{6}}{5}$; $2\frac{1}{12}$ cups

85. $\dfrac{1\frac{1}{2}+\frac{3}{4}}{\frac{1}{4}}$; 9 medallions **87.** $\dfrac{26\frac{1}{8}+15\frac{1}{4}+13\frac{3}{4}}{6\frac{1}{8}}$; 9 bottles

Fractions: Section 8 answers continued

89. $\dfrac{8\frac{1}{2}+10\frac{3}{4}+5\frac{1}{8}+7\frac{3}{16}}{5}$; $6\frac{5}{16}$ oz

Fractions: Section 9 answers

1. Yes **3.** No **5.** No **7.** Yes

9. No **11.** No **13.** Yes **15.** Yes

17. No **19.** $x=14$ **21.** $x=-\frac{3}{8}$ **23.** $x=\frac{1}{8}$

25. $x=\frac{1}{3}$ **27.** $m=24$ **29.** $w=-12$ **31.** $k=\frac{4}{13}$

33. $m=\frac{4}{3}$ or $m=1\frac{1}{3}$ **35.** $w=-14$

37. $k=-3$ **39.** $a=-\frac{14}{11}$ or $a=-1\frac{3}{11}$

41. $n=1$ **43.** $x=-\frac{9}{2}$ or $x=-4\frac{1}{2}$

45. $w=\frac{5}{3}$ or $w=1\frac{2}{3}$ **47.** $z=\frac{7}{15}$

49. The solution is correct. **51.** The solution is correct.

53. $\frac{8}{11}n=-\frac{4}{7}$; The number is $-\frac{11}{14}$ **55.** $n-\frac{4}{9}=-\frac{2}{5}$; The number is $\frac{2}{45}$.

Fractions: Section 9 answers continued

57. $n+\frac{7}{9}=8$; The number is $7\frac{2}{9}$.

59. $-\frac{5}{8}n=\frac{3}{4}$; The number is $-\frac{6}{5}$ or $-1\frac{1}{5}$.

61. $n-\frac{1}{6}=\frac{1}{12}$; The number is $\frac{1}{4}$.

63. $n+\frac{1}{2}=\frac{7}{4}$; The number is $\frac{5}{4}$ or $1\frac{1}{4}$.

65. $n-\frac{7}{10}=-\frac{7}{30}$; The number is $\frac{7}{15}$.

67. $n+2\frac{3}{8}=6\frac{1}{8}$; The number is $3\frac{3}{4}$.

69. $\frac{n}{-3}=8$; The number is -24.

71. $\frac{n}{7}=9$; The number is 63.

73. $\frac{1}{5}L=6$; The length is 30 meters.

75. $M-\frac{1}{4}=72\frac{1}{8}$; Monty weighs $72\frac{3}{8}$ kg.

77. $\frac{1}{12}C=23{,}000$; The C.E.O. makes $276,000.

79. $P+\frac{3}{5}=8\frac{1}{2}$; The pine tree is $7\frac{9}{10}$ yards tall.

81. $18=\frac{p}{7}$; The total amount of pay is $126.

Fractions: Chapter Review answers

1. 4,200 **2.** 6 **3.** 32 **4.** Improper fraction

5. $\frac{8}{5}$; $1\frac{3}{5}$ **6.** $3\frac{3}{13}$ **7.** $\frac{44}{7}$ **8.** $4 = \frac{16}{4}$

9. $\frac{5}{8}$ is not equivalent to $\frac{2}{3}$.

10.

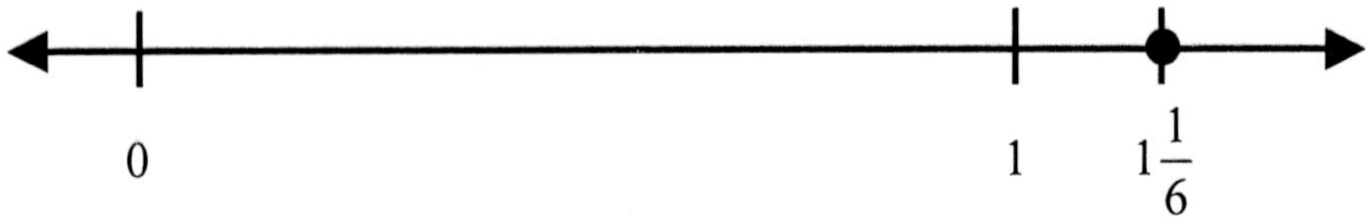

11. $\frac{8}{7} > \frac{9}{8}$ **12.** $\frac{7}{15}$ **13.** $9\frac{7}{36}$ **14.** $-\frac{76}{45}$ or $-1\frac{31}{45}$

15. $\frac{3}{7}$ **16.** $\frac{4}{5}$; Pete **17.** $22\frac{3}{5}$ yards **18.** $\frac{11}{12}$

19. $1\frac{11}{28}$ **20.** $\frac{1}{3}$ **21.** $8\frac{5}{6}$ **22.** $2\frac{31}{40}$ miles

23. $\angle P = 33\frac{1}{2}°$ **24.** $\frac{33}{2}$ or $16\frac{1}{2}$ **25.** 2 **26.** Yes

Fractions: Chapter Review answers continued

27. $-\frac{1}{3}$

28. $-\frac{7}{10}$

29. -33

30. $\frac{13}{16}$ of an hour

31. 32 square feet or $32\ \text{ft}^2$

32. Undefined

33. $-\frac{4}{3}$ or $-1\frac{1}{3}$

34. 16

35. 80

36. $-\frac{20}{81}$

37. $\frac{111}{110}$ or $1\frac{1}{110}$

38. $-\frac{1}{15}$

39. $\frac{27}{35}$

40. $-\frac{9}{8}$ or $-1\frac{1}{8}$

41. $\frac{101}{96}$ or $1\frac{5}{96}$

42. No

43. $y=-\frac{1}{12}$

44. $z=-\frac{1}{2}$

45. $n-\frac{1}{5}=\frac{7}{10}$; $n=\frac{9}{10}$

46. $\frac{1}{16}F=25$; Her food bill is \$400.

47. $15=\frac{p}{12}$; The total amount of pay is \$180.

Fractions: Chapter Test answers

1. 210 **2.** 7 **3.** $4\frac{1}{2}$ **4.** $\frac{40}{11}$

5. $\frac{4}{7}$ is equivalent to $\frac{4}{7}$. **6.** $\frac{11}{13} < \frac{17}{20}$ **7.** $\frac{3}{4}$

8. $8\frac{1}{3}$ **9.** $-\frac{1}{10}$ **10.** $\frac{7}{36}$ **11.** $5\frac{5}{6}$

12. $10\frac{3}{4}$ inches **13.** $4\frac{9}{10}$ miles **14.** 1

15. $-\frac{5}{2}$ or $-2\frac{1}{2}$ **16.** -13 **17.** $1\frac{5}{6}$

18. 82 square inches or 82 in^2 **19.** 0 **20.** $-\frac{9}{14}$

21. 12 **22.** 32 **23.** $-\frac{4}{75}$

24. $\frac{33}{16}$ or $2\frac{1}{16}$ **25.** $\frac{6}{65}$ **26.** $\frac{2}{7}$ **27.** Yes

28. $x = -\frac{2}{5}$ **29.** $n + \frac{2}{7} = \frac{5}{14}$; $n = \frac{1}{14}$ **30.** \$234

Decimal Numbers: Section 1 answers

1. 7 **3.** 0 **5.** 7 **7.** 7

9. 0 **11.** 3 **13.** 9 **15.** 2

17. forty-six and three tenths

19. four hundred seven and thirty-five thousandths

21. twenty-eight thousand, fifteen and seventy-one thousandths

23. three hundred and three hundredths

25. sixty and seven hundred eight ten-thousandths

27. four thousand, three hundred eighty-five ten-thousandths

29. 73.016 **31.** 10,005.0005 **33.** 17.123 **35.** 38.00001

37. 0.2 **39.** 6,004.0017 **41.** $9\frac{7}{10}$ **43.** $\frac{43}{100}$

45. $5\frac{1}{100}$ **47.** $\frac{9}{10{,}000}$ **49.** $\frac{419}{1{,}000}$ **51.** $341\frac{83}{100}$

53. 0.9 **55.** 5.03 **57.** 0.409 **59.** 0.0063

61. 72.73 **63.** 3.081 **65.** $<$ **67.** $=$

Decimal Numbers: Section 1 answers continued

69. < **71.** > **73.** > **75.** <

77. 0.4068; 0.68; 4.68 **79.** 0.0049; 0.049; 0.409; 0.49

81. 0.008; 0.0081; 0.079; 0.08

83.

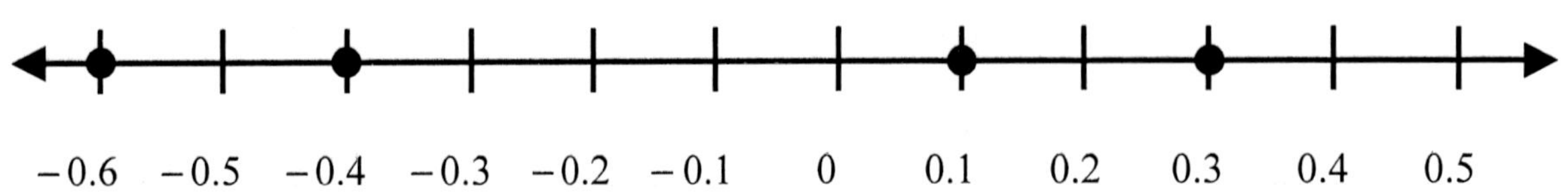

85.

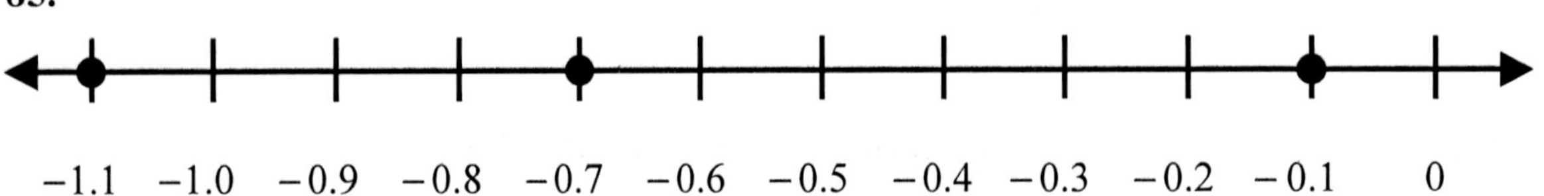

87.

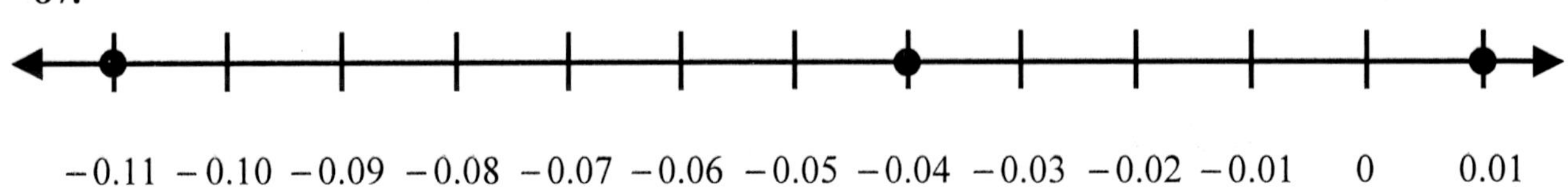

89.

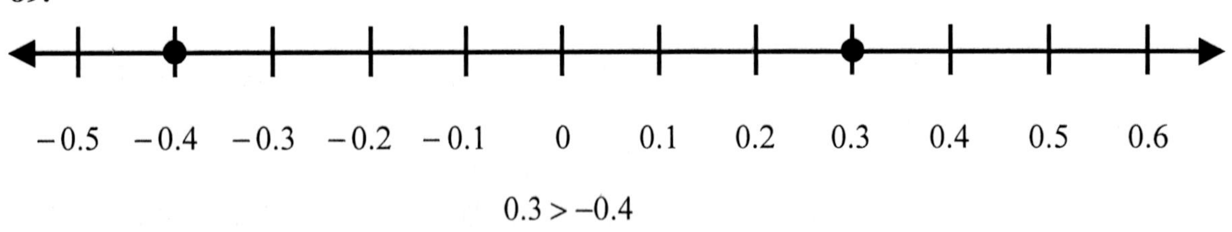

$0.3 > -0.4$

91.

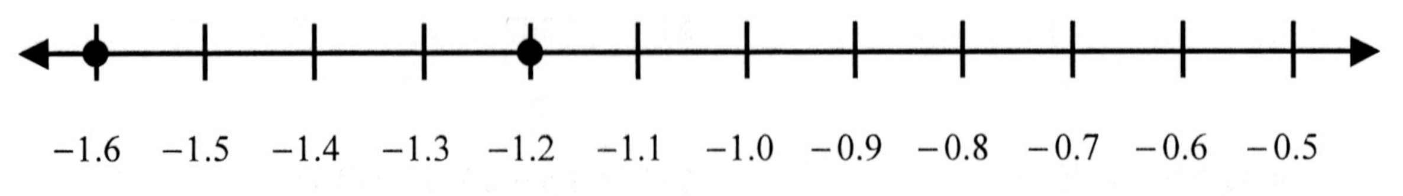

$-1.2 > -1.6$

Decimal Numbers: Section 1 answers continued

93.

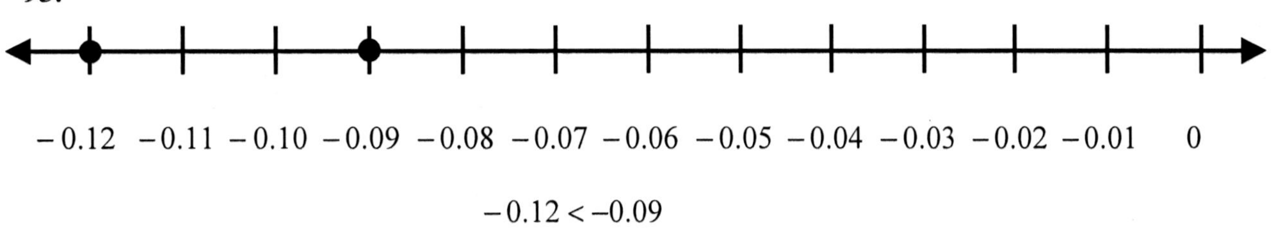

$-0.12 < -0.09$

95.	357.02	**97.**	375,000	**99.**	0.000802	**101.**	843
103.	11.0	**105.**	3,483.012	**107.**	3,480	**109.**	643.8800
111.	2,400	**113.**	0.3 gallon	**115.**	0.47 Liter	**117.**	0 kilogram
119.	Yes	**121.**	March, April, May, October, and November				
123.	decrease						

Decimal Numbers: Section 2 answers

1.	39.75	**3.**	9.1	**5.**	37.39	**7.**	−7.7
9.	−123.67	**11.**	112.1	**13.**	−10.75	**15.**	3.9963
17.	−32.1422	**19.**	55.49	**21.**	8.08	**23.**	8.9
25.	−9.891	**27.**	51.06	**29.**	3.04713	**31.**	72.64
33.	$49.7 + 12.03$; 61.73			**35.**	$3.4 + 0.207$; 3.607		

Decimal Numbers: Section 2 answers continued

37. $-0.18-(-15.72)$; 15.54 **39.** 2.22 **41.** 54.59

43. 1.2005 **45.** -1.84 **47.** -52.88 **49.** 80.16

51. -9.39 **53.** 664.863

55.

NUMBER OR CODE	DATE	TRANSACTION DESCRIPTION	PAYMENT, FEE, WITHDRAWAL (-)		DEPOSIT, CREDIT (+)		BALANCE $112 . 96	
17488	3/04/08	Clothes	$42	18			$42	18
							$70	78
17489	3/07/08	Food	$63	85			$63	85
							$6	93
	3/10/08	Deposit			$378	93	$378	93
							$385	86
17490	3/14/08	Electric bill	$43	78			$43	78
							$342	08
17491	3/26/08	Video rental	$5	41			$5	41
							$336	67
	3/30/08	Deposit			$38	50	$38	50
							$375	17

57. $0.09 **59.** between 2002 and 2003 **61.** 0.043 inch

63. 48.3° **65.** 56.19° **67.** 72.58° **69.** 140.2°

Decimal Numbers: Section 3 answers

1. 0.021 **3.** 7,813 **5.** 2.5564 **7.** 0.17

9. -0.24 **11.** 0.5 **13.** 0.034522 **15.** -685

Decimal Numbers: Section 3 answers continued

17. 1.52080002 **19.** 494,000 **21.** 420 **23.** 689,200

25. 0.2675 **27.** −82,400 **29.** −1.265 **31.** 185.42

33. −0.222 **35.** 3,426.14 **37.** 0.448 **39.** −734.2

41. −15.51 **43.** $447 **45.** $8.68 **47.** $12.45

49. $4.20 **51.** $26.08 **53.** 79¢ **55.** 16.8 feet

57. 23.5 inches **59.** $28.09\,ft^2$ **61.** $26.64\,in^2$

63. 59¢ is fifty-nine cents while 0.59¢ is fifty-nine hundredths of a cent.

Decimal Numbers: Section 4 answers

1. 0.05 **3.** 0.07234 **5.** 9,100 **7.** 7.276

9. 1,200 **11.** 48.2 **13.** 1 **15.** −0.25

17. −5,000 **19.** −0.57003 **21.** 0.00314 **23.** 0.06

25. 0.0271828 **27.** 0.0000004 **29.** 30,200 **31.** 0.0238

Decimal Numbers: Section 4 answers continued

33. 0.0035 **35.** 60.1 **37.** -3.4 **39.** 2.33

41. -0.045 **43.** 62.3 **45.** 8.8 **47.** -0.3

49. 7.9 **51.** -0.99 **53.** 1.29 **55.** 1.77

57. 26.4 meters **59.** 28.615 m^2 **61.** 16.3¢ per egg

63. 28.6 miles per gallon **65.** 38.2 people per square mile

67. $10.94 per acre **69.** $8.98 per pound **71.** 88.75% **73.** 4.63 miles

75. 0.986 **77.** 338.2248191 **79.** 0.0046 **81.** 6,008.05

83. $-9{,}750$ **85.** 137,010 **87.** -0.08403 **89.** 765

91. 0.00000408 **93.** -0.00006 **95.** 0.1 **97.** 310,000

99. 408.63 **101.** 0.00125 **103.** 42

Decimal Numbers: Section 5 answers

1. $\frac{24}{25}$ **3.** $7\frac{19}{50}$ **5.** $9\frac{2}{5}$ **7.** $\frac{129}{250}$

Decimal Numbers: Section 5 answers continued

9. $\frac{19}{40}$ **11.** $\frac{389}{1,000}$ **13.** $87\frac{123}{250}$ **15.** $16\frac{121}{2,000}$

17. 0.4 **19.** $0.\overline{2}$ **21.** $3.8\overline{3}$ **23.** 6.7

25. $0.\overline{36}$ **27.** 2.75 **29.** $2.\overline{3}$ **31.** $5.58\overline{3}$

33. $<$ **35.** $>$ **37.** $<$ **39.** $<$

41. $>$ **43.** $>$ **45.** $<$ **47.** $\frac{17}{20}$

49. 6.375 pounds **51.** $\frac{33}{125}$ **53.** 3.785 Liters **55.** 0.310

57. 0.297 **59.** 0.270 **61.** 3.54 **63.** 6.26

Decimal Numbers: Section 6 answers

1. 9.2 **3.** 9.2 **5.** -1.21 **7.** -0.16

9. 0.16 **11.** 3.48 **13.** 0.008 **15.** -8.2

17. 11.2 **19.** -2 **21.** 1 **23.** 6.728

25. 5 **27.** -0.5 **29.** $9.3 > -9.3$ **31.** $0 = 0$

Decimal Numbers: Section 6 answers continued

33. $-2.39 < 0.475$ **35.** 1.45 **37.** 0.082 **39.** -10.35

41. 48.2° F **43.** -1.12° F **45.** 12.3° C **47.** $53.96

49. $435 **51.** $698 **53.** $C \approx 25.12$ in.; $A \approx 50.24$ in^2

55. $C \approx 31.4$ ft; $A \approx 78.5$ ft^2 **57.** $C \approx 37.68$ in.; $A \approx 113.04$ in^2

59. 3.24 **61.** 3.28

Decimal Numbers: Section 7 answers

1. Yes **3.** No **5.** No **7.** Yes

9. Yes **11.** $x = 2.91$ **13.** $a = 10.51$ **15.** $p = 58.1$

17. $x = 1.575$ **19.** $m = -7.94$ **21.** $c = 81.66$ **23.** $x = 36.92$

25. $z = -0.56$ **27.** $h = -7.9$ **29.** $h = 3.39$ **31.** $z = -5$

33. $p = -1.25$ **35.** $w = -25.5$ **37.** $m = 0.054$

39. $n = -21.98$ **41.** $p = 270$ **43.** $93.75 **45.** $2,101.59

47. $189.31 **49.** 18.4 feet **51.** 23.5 meters **53.** 12 feet

55. 8 meters

Decimal Numbers: Section 8 answers

1.	0.9	**3.**	22	**5.**	0	**7.**	-0.4
9.	100	**11.**	1.6	**13.**	490	**15.**	24
17.	36	**19.**	3	**21.**	5	**23.**	70

Decimal Numbers: Section 9 answers

1.	9	**3.**	0	**5.**	-5	**7.**	13
9.	11	**11.**	-1	**13.**	12	**15.**	6
17.	14	**19.**	10	**21.**	9	**23.**	12
25.	-49	**27.**	27	**29.**	-6	**31.**	48
33.	5	**35.**	8	**37.**	$\frac{1}{3}$	**39.**	$-\frac{2}{7}$
41.	2	**43.**	$\frac{1}{5}$	**45.**	$\frac{29}{4}$	**47.**	15
49.	24	**51.**	-30	**53.**	$\frac{7}{4}$	**55.**	10
57.	11	**59.**	$2\sqrt{100}$; 20	**61.**	$\sqrt{49}+2^3$; 15		

Decimal Numbers: Section 9 answers continued

63. $\sqrt{23+13}$; 6 **65.** 6 and 7 **67.** 3 and 4 **69.** 7 and 8

71. 8 and 9 **73.** 11 and 12 **75.** 4 **77.** 6

79. 1 **81.** 3 **83.** 4 **85.** 2

87. 2 **89.** 4.71 seconds **91.** 4 inches **93.** 16 feet

95. $a = 15$ **97.** $c = 25$ **99.** 13 feet

Decimal Numbers: Section 10 answers

1. an irrational number and a real number **3.** a rational number and a real number

5. a natural number, a whole number, an integer, a rational number, and a real number

7. a rational number and a real number **9.** a rational number and a real number

11. a natural number, a whole number, an integer, a rational number, and a real number

13.

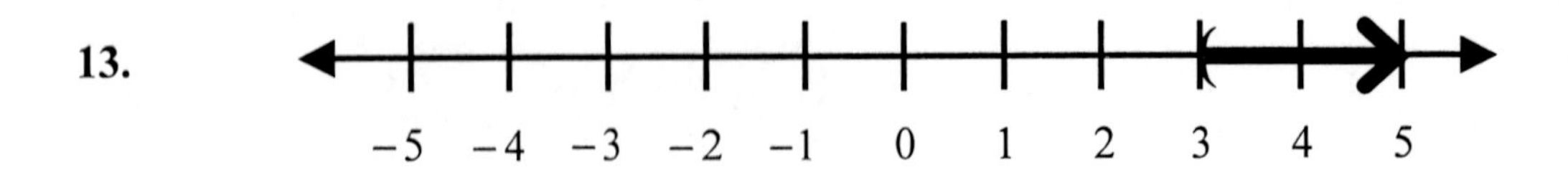

Decimal Numbers: Section 10 answers continued

15.

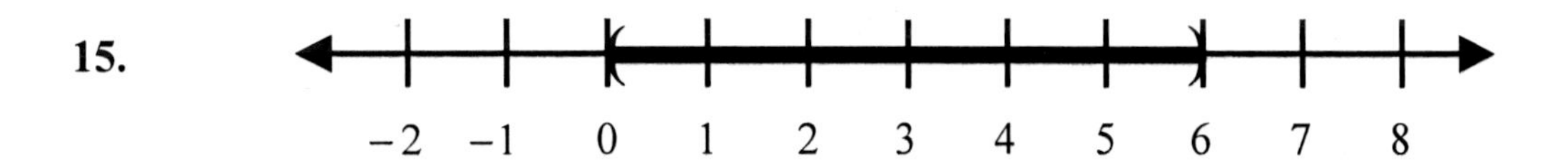

17.

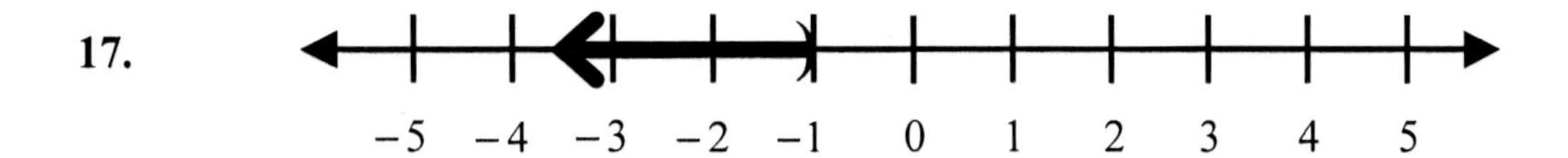

19.

−2 −1 0 1 2 3 4 5 6 7 8

21.

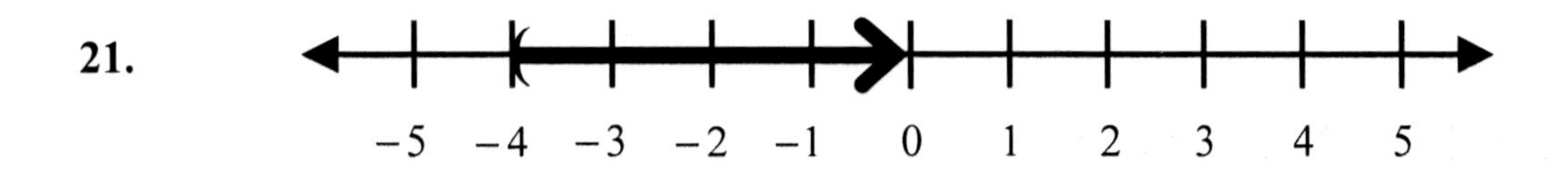

23.

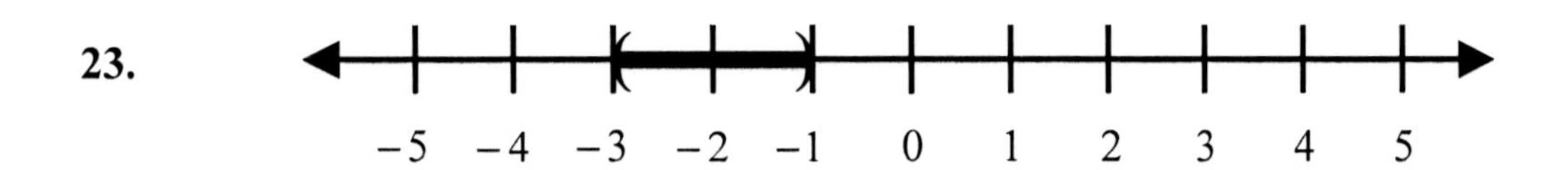

25.

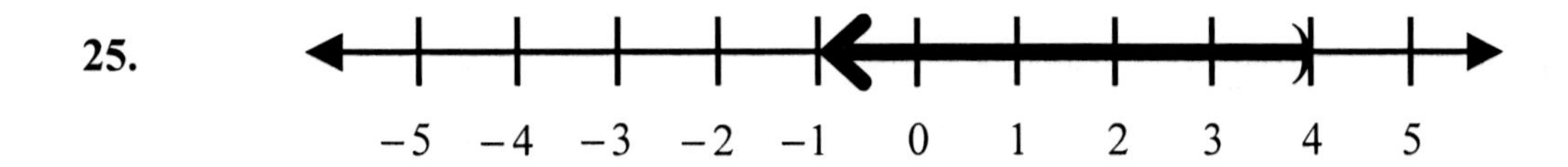

27.

−5 −4 −3 −2 −1 0 1 2 3 4 5

29. $-3, -\sqrt{3}, \frac{2}{9}, 0.\overline{3}, 0.8, \sqrt{7}$

Decimal Numbers: Section 10 answers continued

31.

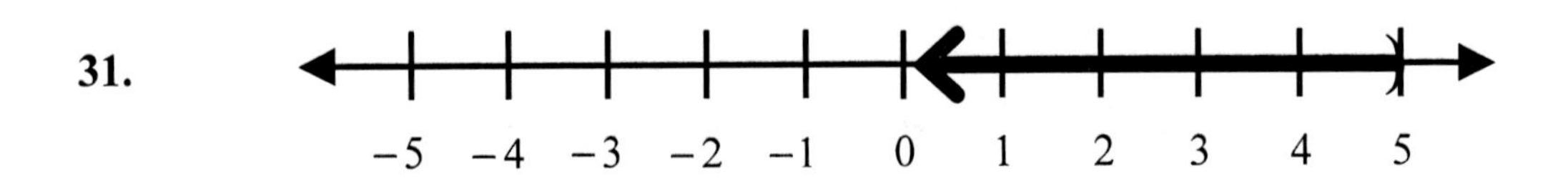

33.

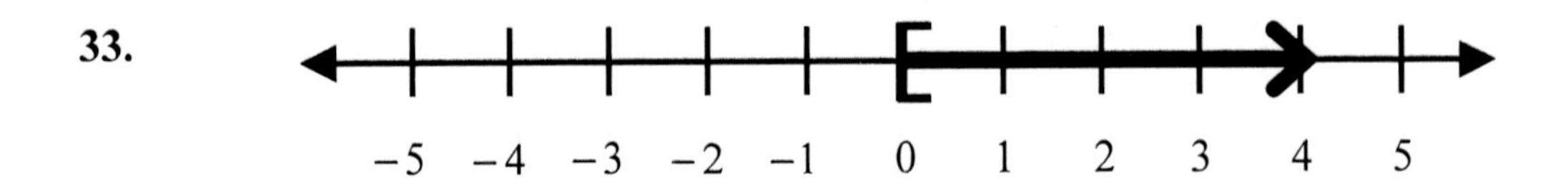

35.

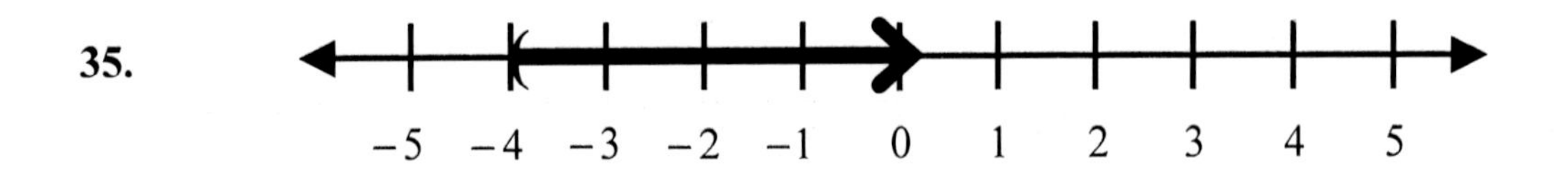

37.

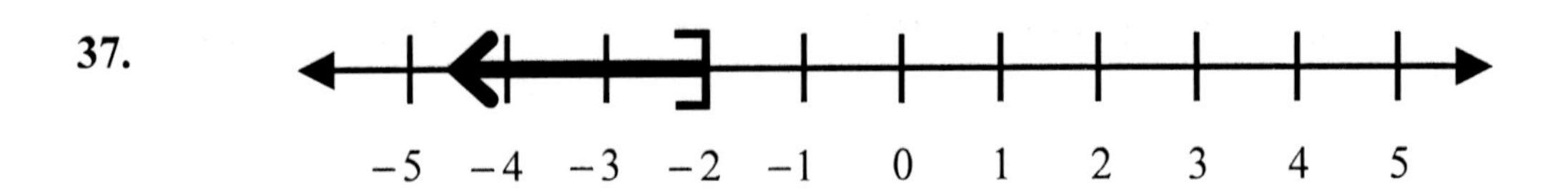

39. $B \geq 150$; Yes

41. $W \leq 12{,}000$; No

43. $C \leq 2{,}000$; Yes

45. $I \geq 200$; Yes

Decimal Numbers: Chapter review answers

1. nine and sixty-three hundredths

2. 0.715

3. $6\frac{1}{20}$

4. 0.057

5. $<$

Decimal Numbers: Chapter review answers continued

6.

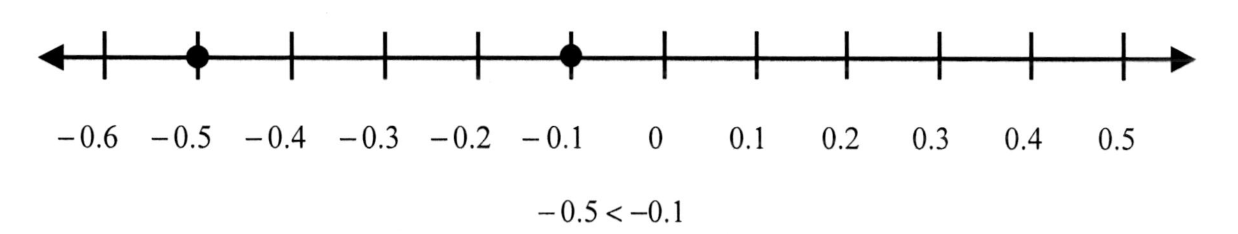

$-0.5 < -0.1$

7. 43.3295 **8.** Yes

9. March, April, May, June, September, October, and November **10.** 80.31

11. 47.4 **12.** $28.02-(-6.9)$; 34.92 **13.** 31.86

14. \$0.14 **15.** 55.62° **16.** 3.2967

17. $-6{,}231{,}000$ **18.** 0.00042 **19.** -0.058 **20.** 154.36 in.^2

21. 7.41 gallons **22.** $5.\overline{18}$ **23.** $<$ **24.** 0.315

25. -9 **26.** $3.357 < 33.57$ **27.** 66.2°F **28.** \$35.18

29. $C \approx 56.52$ ft; $A \approx 254.34\ \text{ft}^2$ **30.** Yes **31.** Yes

32. $d = 2.897$ **33.** $k = -0.26$ **34.** \$139.50 **35.** \$92.23

Decimal Numbers: Chapter review answers continued

36. 0.6 **37.** 18 **38.** -6 **39.** 25

40. 40 **41.** $\frac{2}{3}$ **42.** -15

43. $28 \div \sqrt{49}$; 4 **44.** 7 and 8 **45.** 2 **46.** $c = 25$

47. irrational and real **48.** rational and real

49.

$-8 \quad -7 \quad -6 \quad -5 \quad -4 \quad -3 \quad -2 \quad -1 \quad 0 \quad 1 \quad 2$

50.

$-5 \quad -4 \quad -3 \quad -2 \quad -1 \quad 0 \quad 1 \quad 2 \quad 3 \quad 4 \quad 5$

51. $-\sqrt{2}, -\frac{1}{4}, -0.\overline{2}, 0.5, \sqrt{3}, 2$

52.

$-5 \quad -4 \quad -3 \quad -2 \quad -1 \quad 0 \quad 1 \quad 2 \quad 3 \quad 4 \quad 5$

53.

$-5 \quad -4 \quad -3 \quad -2 \quad -1 \quad 0 \quad 1 \quad 2 \quad 3 \quad 4 \quad 5$

54. $D \geq 10{,}000$; Yes

Decimal Numbers: Chapter test answers

1. seventeen and seventy-two thousandths **2.** $4\frac{307}{10,000}$ **3.** 6.097

4. $>$ **5.** 0.081 **6.** 64.9°F

7. $35.7-(-13.84)$; 49.54 **8.** -90.67 **9.** 0.36

10. -0.00718947 **11.** 209.2 **12.** $172.84\,\text{ft}^2$ **13.** 16.3 miles

14. $11.\overline{1}$ **15.** $>$ **16.** 100.1 **17.** 9° C

18. \$1,853 **19.** $C \approx 62.8$ cm; $A \approx 314\ \text{cm}^2$ **20.** No

21. $m = -0.054$ **22.** 10.4 feet **23.** \$2,619.65 **24.** 0

25. -18 **26.** 5 **27.** 6 and 7 **28.** 9

29. natural numbers, whole numbers, integers, rational numbers, and real numbers

30.

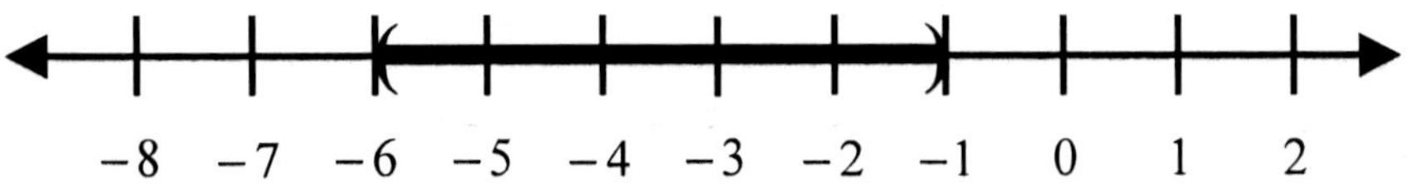

−8 −7 −6 −5 −4 −3 −2 −1 0 1 2

31.

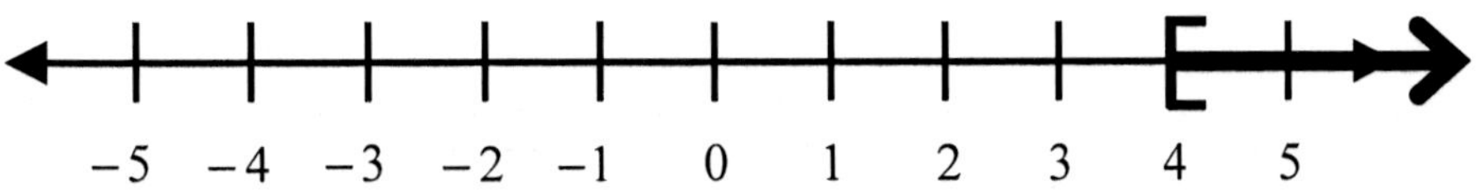

−5 −4 −3 −2 −1 0 1 2 3 4 5

32. $G \le 135$; Yes